NEW PHYSICAL GEOGRAPHY

Fig. 1. — Twin Glacier, Taku River, Alaska. The glaciers were formerly larger and joined to make a miniature piedmont glacier. At that time a moraine was deposited that now forms the dam to the lake. In the foreground, at a lower level, is seen the Taku River, an aggrading glacial stream. Note also the cirque erosion of the mountains. What other glacial features do you identify?

NEW
PHYSICAL GEOGRAPHY

BY

RALPH S. TARR, B.S.

LATE PROFESSOR OF DYNAMIC GEOLOGY AND PHYSICAL GEOGRAPHY
IN CORNELL UNIVERSITY

AND

O. D. von ENGELN, Ph.D.

PROFESSOR OF PHYSICAL GEOGRAPHY IN CORNELL UNIVERSITY

REVISED EDITION

ILLUSTRATIONS BY B. F. WILLIAMSON

New York
THE MACMILLAN COMPANY
1939

FROM THE PREFACE TO THE
ORIGINAL EDITION

The teaching of physical geography is still in its experimental stage, and it is the opinion of many teachers that the ideal method of presentation has not yet been proposed, notwithstanding the several excellent texts which have appeared. The *New Physical Geography* is still another effort to solve the problem of how best to present the subject to beginning students.

In the *New Physical Geography*, treatment of the lands has been placed before that of air and ocean because so many schools commence the study in the fall and take classes into the field. The chapters on atmosphere and ocean have been given less space than in the author's previous books; yet all topics of distinct importance are treated with sufficient fullness to make them clear.

Perhaps the most decided difference between *New Physical Geography* and the author's other books lies in the introduction of a much fuller treatment of life in its relation to the land, air, and ocean, the human interest of each topic being emphasized. This has been done throughout the text, and, at the end of the book, in a series of chapters devoted to that subject exclusively.

Especial pains have been taken to illustrate the book fully. It is believed that an illustration, properly selected, is of the very highest value, — the best substitute for the object itself. Every illustration in the book is introduced for use, and almost every one is referred to at least once in the text.

As aids to the study of the text, a brief Summary is given at the close of each section, and a Topical Outline and a set of Review Questions are placed at the end of each chapter. These summaries, topics, and questions cover the essentials in the text; and their use as a basis for work, with such modifications and additions as may be deemed necessary, will be a far lighter task than the production of an entire series by the teacher. Thus, relieved of a form of drudgery, time will be available for the expenditure of energy in more profitable lines.

In most of the better schools physical geography is fast becoming a laboratory science. With this in mind, a series of Suggestions is appended to nearly every chapter, and one Appendix is devoted to maps and laboratory equipment, another to field work.

A very large number of teachers have given the author the benefit of their experience in the form of suggestive criticism. To all of these teachers the author is greatly indebted for their kindly interest. It goes without saying that the author is profoundly indebted to the host of workers in physiography, from whom he has drawn so much inspiration, suggestion, and fact. From the writings of these physiographers the author has culled whatever seemed to him suited to a scheme of elementary instruction; and so numerous, and often so unconscious, is the influence of these fellow-workers, that specific acknowledgment would be quite impossible. Doubtless the most profound influence upon the author is that of his two teachers, Professors Shaler and Davis, the importance of which to him cannot be overestimated. Together with other physiographers, the author further recognizes in Professor Davis a leader in American physiography, from whom even some of the fundamental principles of the subject have been derived. An examination of the following pages would show the influence of this physiographer in many places, an influence not confined to the pure science, but extending to the pedagogy of the subject as well.

RALPH S. TARR

ITHACA, NEW YORK
    July 21, 1903

PREFACE TO THE REVISED EDITION

When the original edition of *New Physical Geography* was published in 1903 it gained an extraordinarily wide adoption immediately. The presentation of the subject and the make-up of the book, both, were so attractive that students had difficulty in using *New Physical Geography* for home study — their parents wanted to read it. For ten years or more physical geography was a very popular high-school subject.

In the following decade, however, the teaching of physical geography in the secondary schools experienced a decline. Attempts were made to humanize high-school geography and to give the subject a content having an emotional pitch. But these departures have not developed the degree of interest that attached to the study of high-school physical geography in the decade following 1903. Physical geography as presented in *New Physical Geography* was wholesome and informative; its comprehension required thoughtful study. It provided the pupil with an understanding of the varied aspects of the natural environment. And it should be remembered that all out-of-door activities of a lifetime, no matter where spent, involve continuous contact with this natural environment.

It is anticipated that this new issue of *New Physical Geography* will promote a revival of the high-school study of physical geography as the original edition gave the subject its earlier vogue. If no other reason for the extensive re-introduction of physical geography into the high-school curriculum existed, then the single fact of the advent of the automobile should be enough to occasion this return. Never before has the average person had so wide an opportunity of coming into contact with the diverse aspects of nature as is afforded him to-day through the use of the automobile. River valleys, gorges, waterfalls, divides, meandering brooks, cliffs, lake shores, waves, tidal marshes, mountain peaks, and mountain parks, each and every topographic phenomenon has for most people a degree of significance it never had before. For classes in country high schools physical geography has such obvious and direct practical value that it is rather difficult to understand how, on any logical ground, it has in any instance been displaced.

Although the distinctive characteristics of the original edition have been preserved, what appears between these covers is virtually a new book.

But nothing has been changed merely for the sake of making the book different. Old users will be pleased to find that the revision gives them all the features that proved so serviceable in the original. Where there was no necessity for changing the content of sections because of new developments in the science, and except as the language has been altered to make certain statements and exposition more exact and clear, Professor Tarr's easy and convincing style has been retained.

Nevertheless a very great number of changes and additions needed to be made. The content of physical geography has been enriched by many contributions since the time of the original publication. The whole book has been painstakingly revised. It is still an elementary text, but subjects of some difficulty (for example, the tides) generally dismissed with a few vague and sometimes conflicting statements are dealt with completely enough to make understanding possible. Students who have used this text should therefore be able to try with confidence examinations in which questions on these topics are asked. In this connection attention is called especially to the discussion of rotational deflection of winds and ocean currents.

A particular feature of the original *New Physical Geography* was the richness of its illustrative material. Pictures, diagrams, and maps were not only profusely used but each one was inserted for a definite purpose also and had educational significance. But despite the fact that the illustrations were so numerous and so rich in teaching value in the old edition considerable effort has been expended to make those of the new edition even more effective. The best of the old pictures have been kept, diagrams have been redrawn to make them more realistic and more completely and exactly explanatory, and numerous new items have been added. It is felt that many new users will be attracted to the revised book because of the high quality, pertinence, and extensiveness of its pictorial content. Practically every point is illustrated, and the pictures together with the very complete titles directly and consistently supplement and confirm the text.

Credit for photographs and other illustrative material is given wherever possible under the subject. Special acknowledgment is due to the following persons, corporations, and institutions for courtesies in supplying and permitting the use of their material.

The Taku River Co., Juneau, Alaska; Yerkes Observatory, Williams Bay, Wis.; Endless Caverns, New Market, Va.; U. S. Reclamation Service; U. S. National Park Service; U. S. Army, Air Service; U. S. Navy Department, Bureau of Aeronautics; U. S. Fish Commission; New Zealand Tourist and Health Resorts Department; G. E. Kirk; G. F. Morgan;

W. C. Bowen; E. G. Robinson; A. W. Abrams; Benjamin Shaub; R.
Raffius; G. B. Callister; L. C. Read; Dr. John L. Rich; Dr. M. Sauramo;
American Museum of Natural History; New York Zoological Society;
E. B. Shoedsack; Dr. R. W. Miner; Williamson Submarine Tube Corpora-
tion; Professor F. Pack; Professor N. Bengtson; Professor Collier Cobb;
The Lehigh Valley Railroad Company. Indebtedness is also acknowledged
to C. W. Furlong, who made the original drawings for the first edition,
which have in many cases been carefully followed in this edition.

ITHACA, NEW YORK
June 25, 1926

CONTENTS

INTRODUCTORY

MAN is vitally dependent upon air, water, and earth. The air supplies oxygen for breathing and for fire; it supplies carbon dioxide to plants; it brings vapor for rain; and its presence and movements profoundly affect climate.

The ocean is the source of vapor; it furnishes many kinds of food-fish; it is the highway of an ever increasing commerce; and it influences the climate of every land.

The lands furnish a home for man; they are mantled with a soil in which the food plants grow; and from the rocks are obtained mineral fuels, building stones, and metals. Both plant and animal life are greatly influenced by the forms of the land and the distribution of land and water.

The sun is also of vital importance, for its heat and light make life on the globe possible. The heat sets the air in motion, forming winds which bring rain, modify climates, and start waves and currents in the ocean.

The movements of the earth — rotation and revolution — are also important. Rotation brings day and night, which influence the habits of men, animals, and plants. Revolution causes seasons which have a still greater effect on life.

Plants, animals, and mankind have become adapted in a wonderful manner to the soil, climate, and other features of their surroundings. Most animals and plants live either in the water or on the land; but some have adopted the air as their home, while others have taken to life underground, though always near the surface.

Air and water are ever changing; the lands are also changing, though more slowly; and plants and animals are varying in their relation to air, ocean, and land. These changes have a profound effect on man, and it is therefore important to study about them.

Such a study is known as **Physical Geography, which may be defined as the study of the physical features of the earth and their influence on man.**

NEW PHYSICAL GEOGRAPHY

CHAPTER I

THE EARTH AS A PLANET

1. Shape of the earth. The full moon at first glance appears to be a circular disk. But if we look more closely, it is seen to have the roundness of a ball. This roundness shows even more clearly when the moon is viewed through a telescope. It is then perceived that the moon is a sphere in the heavens (Fig. 2). If we stood on the moon, the "full earth" would be a similar sphere in the sky about four times as wide as the full moon looks to us (Fig. 3).

Over two thousand years ago it was known that the earth was a sphere; but this was later forgotten, and for a long time the earth was thought to be flat. Before the time of Columbus, navigators imagined all sorts of

Fig. 2. — The moon.

terrors at the edge of a flat earth; and Columbus had difficulty in finding sailors who were willing to face these imaginary terrors. The successful outcome of Columbus' voyage caused students to give new consideration to the earlier known evidence indicating that the earth is a sphere.

Columbus stated: "I have always read that the world, comprising the land and the water, is spherical, as testified by the investigations of Ptolemy and others, who have proved it by the eclipses of the moon and other observations made from east to west, as well as by the elevation of the pole (pole or north star) from north to south."

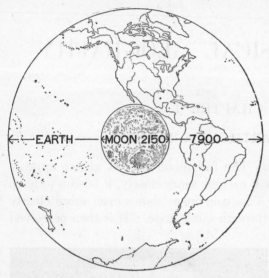

Fig. 3.— Relative size of earth and moon. The figures are the diameters in miles. How many times larger in diameter is the earth than the moon? In circumference? In volume (cubic miles)?

EARTH — MOON 2150 — 7900

Proofs that the earth's surface is curved. (*a*) Standing on the seashore, or on the deck of a vessel at sea, one has visual proof that the earth's surface is curved (Fig. 4). The sails and smoke of distant ships are seen but the hulls of these ships are hidden behind the curvature of the earth (Fig. 5). As a ship comes nearer the observer, more and more of it is seen.

(*b*) This proof of a curved surface is confirmed, further, by the fact that, as the observer climbs from a lower to a higher point of view, the horizon circle continually expands. That is, he can see more of a ship,

Fig. 4. — The curved ocean surface.

or a more distant ship, than he could from the lower elevation (Fig. 6). It would not be possible to see farther from a high place than from a low place over a flat water-surface.

(c) Travelers have gone around the earth in various directions and returned to their starting points without retracing their courses.

(d) Places not on the same meridian have noon at different times.

(e) As we travel north, southern stars sink to lower positions in the sky; northern ones are seen to be higher in the heavens.

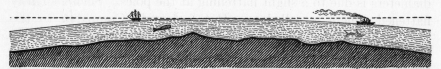

Fig. 5. — To show why part of a distant ship is hidden. The dotted line is the line along which a man on the deck of the sailing vessel would look.

(f) The earth's shadow thrown on the moon at the time of an eclipse is bounded by part of a circle (Fig. 7).

Proofs that the earth is a sphere. These facts do not in themselves also prove that the earth is a sphere. It might have the shape of a cucumber, of an egg, of a cylinder, of a round coin, and the same effects be produced at certain places on its surface. But when it is further noted that:

(a) everywhere on the oceans the hulls of ships disappear at the *same rate;*

(b) the circular horizon also *expands uniformly* everywhere with similar increases in the altitude of the observer;

(c) travelers going around the earth on great circle routes all need to go the *same distance* to return to their starting points;

(d) the difference in noon time *varies uniformly* with angular distance east and west;

(e) the rising and sinking of the stars in altitude *varies uniformly* with distance north and south;

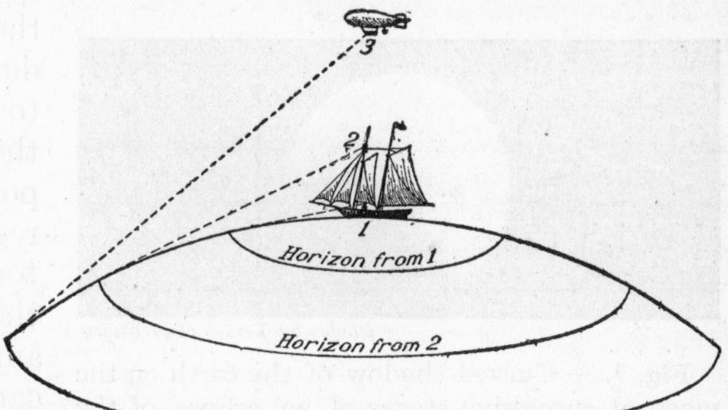

Fig. 6. — The wider horizon gained by elevation shows the earth's surface to be curved. Why is the lookout placed high up on the mast of a ship instead of on deck at the bow?

(f) the earth's shadow on the moon at the times of eclipses *always* has a circular boundary no matter what the position, and with the earth *rotating* during the eclipse; then it is evident that the form of the earth must be that of a sphere, that is, not only curved, but *equally curved* everywhere.

Actual measurement in many different places and in different directions at those places also proves that the curvature is everywhere the same. This curvature must be allowed for in digging canals. It amounts to the number of miles squared, times 8 inches. Thus for a distance of four miles it is 4 squared = 16 x 8 inches = 128 inches or $10\frac{2}{3}$ feet.

The earth is not an exact sphere, for the diameter at the equator is 7926 miles, and at the poles 7899. This difference in the two diameters is due to a slight flattening at the poles. Such a slightly flattened sphere is called an *oblate spheroid.* Compared to the earth as a whole this flattening is so slight that the polar diameter would be only one sixteenth of an inch less than the equatorial diameter on a globe eighteen inches in diameter.

Photos by Yerkes Observatory

Fig. 7. — Curved shadow of the earth on the moon at successive stages of an eclipse of the moon by the earth. As the outline of the shadow is not sharp this evidence of the earth's spherical form is not as convincing to the observer as he may expect it to be.

This flattening was discovered through application of another proof of the earth's generally spherical form. The attraction of surface gravity on a given object as measured by a spring balance, or as shown by the rate of the swing of a pendulum, is sufficiently uniform to prove a globular form. But there is enough variation in polar, as compared to equatorial regions, to show that the equatorial regions are farther from the center of gravity. The amount has been determined by careful and exact measurements of the slight differences.

Eratosthenes (275–194 B.C.) early came to recognize the spherical shape of the earth and he attempted to measure its size. He noticed that the stars rose or sank as one went north or south. He also saw that on June 21, the longest day of the year in the northern hemisphere, the sun's rays at noon went straight down to the bottom of a deep well at Syene, Egypt. At Alexandria, Egypt, 5000 stadia[1] to the north, he found that on the same day of the year the sun's rays made an angle of 7° 12′ with a vertical pillar. As the sun's rays come to the earth in parallel lines, he could show by a

[1] The stadium was a Greek unit of measurement about 607 feet long.

geometrical construction (Fig. 8) (if two parallels are cut by a transversal, the alternate interior angles are equal) that the angle of 7° 12′ (7.2°) was that part of the earth's circumference of 360°. If 7° 12′ = 5000 stadia, then 360° = 250,000 stadia. We do not know how successful he was because we do not know exactly how long the stadium was, nor how accurate his measurement of the 5000 stadia between Syene and Alexandria, Egypt. But he must have come quite near the truth. Had he known and accepted Eratosthenes' measurements, Columbus would

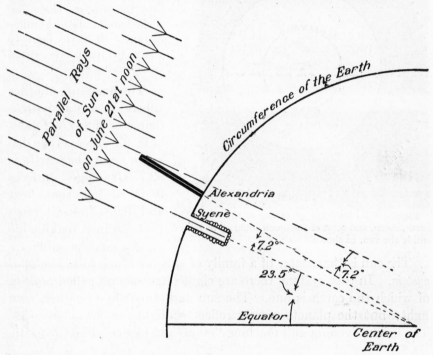

Fig. 8. — Eratosthenes' measurement of the earth's circumference.

probably have hesitated in attempting so long a voyage as these would have shown the westward route to China to be.

Summary. *The earth is a slightly flattened sphere, or oblate spheroid. Its curved surface can be seen on the ocean; actual measurements of a uniform rate of curvature everywhere, and repeated observations of eclipses of the moon, prove that it is a sphere; its size and shape have been exactly determined; and the distance around it in all directions is known.*

2. Other spheres. The earth is only one of a great number of spheres in space. The nearest of these is the moon, whose average distance from the earth is about 240,000 miles.   The stars are also spheres, far larger than the moon, and billions of miles away. These stars are all fiery hot; but the moon is a cold mass of rock.

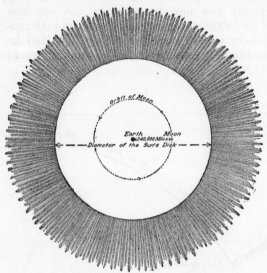

If the earth be represented as a dot and the earth's orbit as a circle two inches in diameter, then the nearest star, except the sun, on the same scale would be $4\frac{1}{3}$ miles distant.   It takes light $4\frac{1}{3}$ years to reach the earth from that star.

The huge sun, another sphere, is a star with a diameter of 864,392 miles (Fig. 9).   Its average distance from the earth is 92,750,000 miles, and yet it is so hot that heat and light from it cross that distance, making life on the earth possible.

Fig. 9. — To show the great size of the sun.   The earth, moon, and orbit of the moon could all be placed inside the sun, as shown.

The sun is the center of a family of spheres which form the *solar system*.   In this system there are eight large spheres called *planets*, of which the earth is one.   The sun and stars shine by their own light; but the planets merely reflect sunlight, as the moon does. The bright evening and morning "stars" are planets, like the earth.

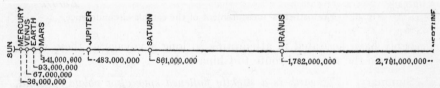

Fig. 10. — The distances from the sun to the different planets.   The figures show distances in miles.

From one of them the earth would be seen to have the same steady, bright light that they show to us.

Some of the planets are far more distant than the sun (Fig. 10), Neptune, the most distant, being nearly 2,800,000,000 miles away.   How distant that is may perhaps be understood by the following illustration. If an express train could have started toward Neptune in the time of Christ, and have traveled steadily onward day and night at the rate of sixty miles an hour, it would not yet be halfway there.

Not only are the planets far away, but some of them are very large (Fig. 11). Jupiter, the largest, is 88,392 miles in diameter. In the space between Mars and Jupiter there are also a number of very small spheres, called *planetoids* or *asteroids*. The largest is about 500 miles in diameter. The smallest planetoid known is probably less than 10 miles in diameter; on it the force of surface gravity is so slight that one could hurl a stone with sufficient force to have the stone go off into space and not return.

Mars is the only one of the planets that has conditions nearly enough like those on the earth to make it possible that it may support beings

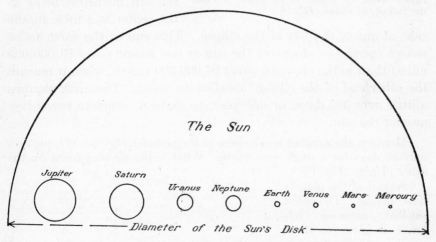

Fig. 11. — To show the relative size of the planets and the sun.

like us. Some astronomers have thought that certain lines on its surface are great irrigation canals bordered by cultivated lands. Mercury would be too hot for human life; Venus lacks water; Jupiter, Saturn, Uranus, and Neptune are too cold, because they are so far away from the sun.

Summary. *Other spheres besides the earth are the stars, sun, moon, planets, and planetoids. The moon and planets shine by reflected light, the stars and sun are fiery hot. In the solar system, which includes the sun, moon, planets, and asteroids, the largest sphere is the sun, the largest planet Jupiter, and the most distant planet Neptune.*

3. Movements of the spheres. It is known that the solar system as a whole and the other suns, the stars, are all moving through space at great speed in various directions. The sun and all the planets whose movements are known have been found to turn, or *rotate*, on an axis. The earth takes 23 hours and 56 minutes for *rotation;* the sun, over 25 days; Jupiter, 9 hours, 55 minutes; the moon, $27\frac{1}{3}$ days.

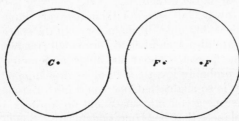

All members of the solar system also travel, or *revolve*, around the sun. This *revolution*[1] is along a nearly circular path, or *orbit*. The orbit is not an exact circle, but an *ellipse* (Fig. 12), and the sun, instead of being at the center, is a little to one

Fig. 12. — A circle (on left) and ellipse (on right). Note the center of the circle (*C*) and the foci of the ellipse (*FF*).

side, at one of the *foci* of the ellipse. This causes the earth to be nearer (*perihelion distance*) the sun at one season (over 91,000,000 miles) than in the opposite (over 94,000,000 miles), when it reaches the other end of the ellipse (*aphelion distance*). The earth requires a little over 365 days, or one year, to make a complete revolution around the sun.

Mercury, the smallest and nearest of the planets (Figs. 10, 11), requires only 88 days for a single revolution. What is the time required by the other planets (Fig. 13)?

Several of the planets have moons. The word *satellite*, meaning follower, is given to these smaller spheres because they follow their planets in their revolution around the sun. The earth has one moon; no moons have been discovered for Mercury or Venus; but Saturn has nine moons with known orbits. It is thought that each satel-

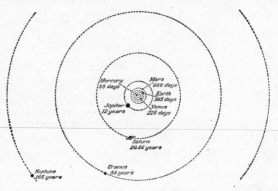

Fig. 13. — Time of revolution of the planets.

lite rotates on an axis and revolves around its planet. The moon makes one revolution around the earth in about $27\frac{1}{3}$ days, that is in exactly the same time as it requires to rotate on its own axis. Hence the moon always presents the same side toward the earth.

[1] For fuller treatment of revolution, see Appendix A, which should be studied carefully by students who plan to enter college.

Summary. *As far as known, all the planets rotate on axes, and all revolve around the sun in elliptical orbits. The periods of rotation and revolution differ. Satellites accompany several of the planets. We see only one side of the moon.*

4. Rotation of the earth. Many uninformed persons believe that the sun rises, passes through the heavens, and sets in the

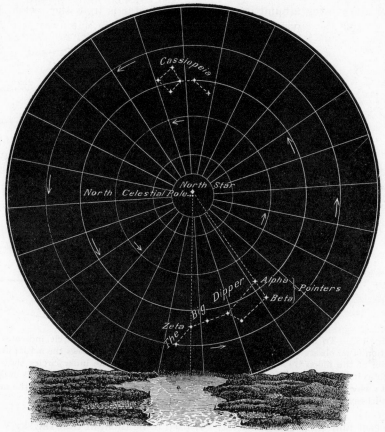

Fig. 14. — The Big Dipper, North Star, and northern heavens. The North Star describes a small circle about the celestial pole. See Suggestion (16) p. 19.

west. Our own ancestors, centuries ago, held the same belief. We still use their terms, *sunrise* and *sunset*, though we well know that it is the turning of the earth on its axis that makes the sun appear to rise and set. In looking from the window of a train it sometimes seems as if objects were passing by, while it is really you yourself that are moving. In the same way, as the earth turns with us toward the east, the sun seems to travel in the opposite direction.

The rising and setting of the moon, and the apparent movements of the stars at night, are also due to the earth's rotation. Find the North Star by following the pointers on the outer side of the Big Dipper (Fig. 14). Notice that it does not move appreciably, but that the Dipper and the other stars swing around it. The farther a star is from the North Star the greater the circle through which it swings, those far away rising in

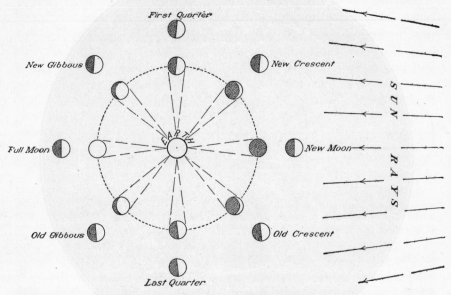

Fig. 15. — To illustrate the phases of the moon. The center circle indicates the position of an observer on the earth. The outer series of circles shows the actual illumination of the moon by the sun, one half always lighted; the inner circles show the moon as it appears from the earth at different times of the lunar month. This diagram shows why a line joining the horns or cusps of the moon is at right angles to the nearly parallel rays of the sun.

the east and setting in the west. It used to be thought that the sky was a great dome with stars set in it, a few miles from the earth, and that it slowly swung around the earth. We now know that the earth's axis points very nearly toward the North Star and that, as the earth turns, it causes the other stars to appear to swing round the North Star.

Summary. *It was formerly thought that the sun and the stars moved; we now know that these apparent movements are caused by the earth's rotation. The axis of the earth points toward the North Star; therefore the other stars seem to circle round the North Star.*

5. Effects of revolution and rotation. Rotation of the earth has given the basis for our computation of time. Thus we reckon a day as the period required for one rotation *with respect to the sun* (24 hours). Each hour of the day is the time required for the sun's rays to advance 15° over the curved surface of the rotating earth. By rotation, also, the day is divided into a period of light and one of darkness. Name some habits of plants, animals, and men that are determined by this effect of rotation.

Revolution of the earth is also a matter of the highest importance. By it another standard of time, the year, is fixed. Revolution, in combination with rotation and the inclination of the earth's axis, also causes an apparent movement of the sun, by which it rises and sets farther north or south at different times. These changes

Fig. 16. — Simplified diagram of lunar and solar eclipses. The day side, white, and the night side, dark, of the earth are shown. "Moon[1]" is the position of the moon at the time of an eclipse of the moon; "Moon[2]" is the position of the moon at the time of an eclipse of the sun.

in the sun's position, which cause the seasons, have determined some of man's most characteristic habits. Name some ways in which revolution affects you,— your home, clothes, foods, and games. Recall from your study of geography how revolution affects the habits of the Eskimo.

Summary. *Rotation determines the length of our day, causes day and night, and influences our habits. Revolution gives us our year, our seasons, and also profoundly affects our manner of living.*

6. Phases of the moon. The moon has no light of its own. Its shine is due to its reflection of sunlight. One half of the moon is always illuminated; but its form as we see it depends on how much of the lighted half is visible from the different positions in the orbit. In Fig. 15 the outer circle of moons shows the actual illumination by the nearly parallel rays of the sun, the inner circle, the forms of the illuminated part as seen from the earth, and the names of the various *phases*.   The night side of the earth is shaded, as is also the dark half of the moon.

It is to be noted that a line connecting the horns, or *cusps*, of the moon

Fig. 17. — Diagram of the eclipse of the sun, January 24, 1925.   The size, distance, and position of the sun are, of necessity, incorrectly pictured, but the diagram should enable the reader to understand the general situation.

is always at right angles to the direction of the nearly parallel rays of the sun.   Also, the horns are always turned away from the sun.

Summary.   *The moon shines by reflected sunlight and one half of it is always lighted.   Its form, as we see it, depends on its position in its orbit around the earth.*

7. Eclipses. If the full moon occurs when the moon is at or near the line of intersection of the planes of the orbits of the earth and moon, that is, if the moon, earth, and sun are in line, or nearly in line, an eclipse of the moon occurs. Then the moon passes into the cone-shaped shadow of the earth and the sun's light is cut off from it (Fig. 16).

An eclipse of the sun (really an eclipse of the earth by the moon) occurs when the same conditions are met, except that the moon is in the new-moon

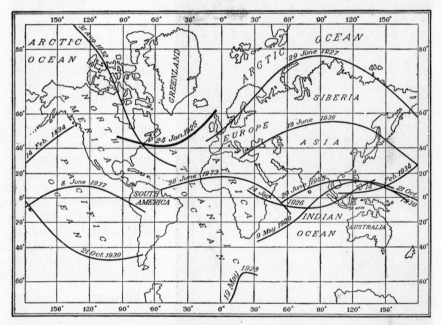

Fig. 18. — Paths of total eclipses of the sun, 1925–1973. Note that two, that of 1925 and that of 1932, pass through the east of North America a comparatively few years apart, giving unusual opportunity for the observation of this phenomenon to generations now living. Where would you plan to go, and when, to see a total eclipse of the sun if you missed these two?

position (Fig. 16). Further, as the earth is larger than the moon, the moon does not need to be so near the line of intersection of the two planes at the time. Also, for the same reason, the cone of the moon's shadow becomes very narrow in the distance between the moon and the earth so that the places on the earth from which a given eclipse of the sun is seen as a total eclipse are in a narrow belt (Fig. 17). Sometimes, indeed, the moon's shadow is not long enough to reach the earth, because the moon's orbit, like that of the earth, is an ellipse. Then the moon's disk is not large enough to cover the sun's disk and the eclipse is annular, that is, a ring of sunlight shows all around the covering moon. At most the diameter of the circular shadow of a total eclipse can be only 167 miles; 90 miles is the average. Outside that belt the eclipse is only partial.

Photo by Kirk

Fig. 19. — Total eclipse of the sun as seen in the center of the band of totality at Cornell University, Ithaca, New York, January 24, 1925.

Figure 18 is a map of the belts, or *paths*, of the total eclipses of the sun for a number of years. From it the reader may calculate his expectancy of seeing a total eclipse. At such a time the moon is invisible until suddenly its black disk cuts the western edge of the sun. Sunlight steadily becomes fainter. Everything looks queer. Animals become nervous. Then the sun is completely covered, and the stars shine brightly. Rose-colored prominences show around the edge of the moon, and beyond these streamers of pearly light appear (Fig. 19). At most the total eclipse lasts about 7 minutes. Then the moon begins to move off the western side of the sun.

Summary. *Eclipses of the moon are due to the shadow of the earth cutting off the light of the sun from the moon; eclipses of the sun result when the moon's shadow cuts off the light of the sun from the earth. At the time of an eclipse the planes of the earth's and the moon's orbits intersect, or nearly intersect, and the three spheres, sun, moon, and earth, must be in line, or nearly in line.*

8. Gravity and gravitation. The earth exerts on all bodies upon it an attraction which we call *gravity*. By gravity men are held to the surface of the earth; a stone thrown into the air is drawn back to the earth; the air is prevented from flying away into space; and the oceans are held in place. It gives to the ocean a curved surface, because each particle of water is attracted toward the center of the sphere. Each part of this curved surface, or *sea level*, is at right angles to a line leading toward the earth's center. All celestial bodies have this *surface gravity*.

The bigger the body and the denser its substance, the greater is its surface gravity. As the mass of the earth is great in comparison to that of objects on its surface, it holds these objects, and the air and water as well, against the force of gravitation (see below) and the centrifugal force of rotation.

Bodies in space also exert an attraction on other spheres. For example, the moon exerts an attraction upon the earth, and the earth upon the moon; but the earth, being larger, has the stronger effect. This attraction of bodies in space is called the *attraction of gravitation*.

Gravitation is the bond that holds the earth and other planets to the orbits along which they travel about the sun. If it were possible for the sun to lose all its attraction of gravitation, the earth would fly off into space, as a stone whirled by a string flies away if the string breaks. Gravitation also holds the moon so firmly that it swings around the earth with such regularity that its position a thousand years from now can be accurately foretold. The law of gravitation was discovered over two centuries ago by Sir Isaac Newton; yet even now no one knows exactly what causes it nor why it operates in the universe, except that it is dependent only on the masses and the relative distances of the attracting bodies.

Held by gravitation, the earth is able to travel along its orbit of 600,000,000 miles each year at a rate of over 1000 miles a minute. At the same time, it is turning on its axis so rapidly that a person on the equator is moving at the rate of 17 miles a minute. We are not aware of these rapid movements, because the land, water, and air go with us. Even when traveling on a noisy railway train, we sometimes forget that we are moving. But the earth moves without jar or noise, and there are no near-by objects for us to pass swiftly; therefore, for many generations men did not even suspect that they were moving at all.

Summary. *Surface gravity is the attraction that holds objects to the earth; it causes the curved surface called sea level. Gravitation, whose law of action was discovered by Newton, is the attraction exerted by bodies in space on one another. Gravitation holds the heavenly spheres to their orbits.*

9. Heat in the solar system. The sun is the only member of the solar system that is hot enough to glow; but in past ages the other members apparently have been hot also. The earth is cold at the surface, but hot within (p. 24); the small moon was apparently

Fig. 20. — Craters on the moon, seeming to indicate former volcanic eruptions due to a heated condition of the interior, but possibly due to the impact of huge meteorites.

once hot within (Fig. 20). It is, however, possible that the interior heat of the planets and the earth's moon was generated after their formation (p. 26).

The heat of the sun is so great that even the materials of stony minerals exist in it in the form of gases. It is hotter than the greatest heat that men have been able to generate in the hottest electrical furnaces. This white-hot sun is slowly cooling by radiating its heat off into space; but a few small points, of which the earth is one (Fig. 21), intercept a minute portion of these rays, on which animal and plant life depend. Let a ball one inch in diameter be the earth; then a ball nine feet in diameter about one thousand feet away would be the sun.

With great speed these rays cross the 93,000,000 miles that separate us
from the sun. They reach the earth in about 8 minutes, while, at the rate

of a fast express train,
175 years would be re-
quired. The sun may
cool down to a red heat,
in some far-distant future
age; then life on the earth
as at present constituted
will no longer be possible.
Evidence now available
indicates that the radia-
tion of the sun and other
stars is produced in large
part by the transforma-
tion of their matter into
radiant energy.

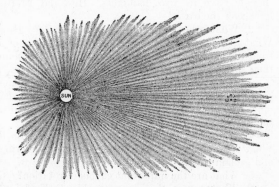

Fig. 21. — To illustrate the very small proportion
of all the rays passing out from the sun that reach
the earth.

Summary. *The members of the solar system show signs of heat,
either past or present. Heat radiated from the white-hot sun passes rapidly
across space; and some of it, reaching the earth, makes life possible.*

TOPICAL OUTLINE, QUESTIONS, AND SUGGESTIONS

TOPICAL OUTLINE. 1. **Shape of earth.** Former belief; proofs of curvature,
of spherical form; exact shape; length of diameters; problem of Eratosthenes.

2. **Other spheres.** The moon; stars; sun; solar system; relative size of planets;
relative distance; planetoids.

3. **Movements of the spheres.** (*a*) Rotation: time required. (*b*) Revolution:
nature of path; effect on distance from sun to earth; time required. (*c*) Satellites:
meaning of name; number; movements.

4. **Rotation of the earth.** Apparent movement of sun, former belief; real
explanation; movements of stars; explanation.

5. **Effects of rotation and revolution.** (*a*) Rotation: effect on divisions of
time; on day and night; on habits of man. (*b*) Revolution: effect on division
of time; on seasons; on habits of man.

6. **Phases of the moon.** Nature of moonlight; part of moon illuminated at
all times (except eclipse); reason for form of moon as seen from earth; position
and direction of horns of moon.

7. **Eclipses.** Position of sun, moon, and earth at moon's eclipse; sun eclipse
really an earth eclipse; narrow path on earth of total sun eclipse; annular eclipse;
conditions during a total eclipse of the sun.

8. **Gravity and gravitation.** (*a*) Surface gravity: nature; effects; nature of
sea level. (*b*) Gravitation: nature; movements of moon and planets; discovery
by Newton. (*c*) Rapid movements of earth.

9. **Heat in the solar system.** (*a*) Evidence of heat in the solar system.
(*b*) Sun's heat: conditions of sun; rate of passage of rays; proportion received by
earth; effect of future cooling of sun.

QUESTIONS. Section 1. What was formerly believed concerning the shape of the earth? What proof is there that the earth is spherical? What is its exact shape? Give its two diameters. How did Eratosthenes measure the circumference of the earth?

2. What other kinds of spheres are there? How do planets and stars differ? What is the solar system? What are planetoids or asteroids? Give the distance from the sun to each of the planets (Fig. 10). Name the planets in the order of their size (Fig. 11).

3. What important movements have the planets? State the difference in time of rotation. Of revolution. What is the distance from earth to sun at opposite seasons? Why this difference? Why does the moon always present the same side toward the earth?

4. What was formerly thought regarding the daily movement of the sun? What is now known to be the cause of it? Describe the movements of the stars, and explain them.

5. What are the important effects of rotation? Of revolution?

6. What causes the moon to shine? Explain the horns of the moon, the shape of the full moon.

7. What conditions of position of the planes of the orbits of the moon and the earth, and the position of the sun, moon, and earth must be met if an eclipse is to occur? Give reasons why a total eclipse of the sun occurs only very seldom at any one place. What are the observations of a person situated in the path of a total eclipse of the sun?

8. What is surface gravity? Give examples of its effects. What is the attraction of gravitation? What effects has this upon revolution? Why are the earth's movements not more noticeable?

9. What is the evidence of heat in the members of the solar system? What change is going on in the sun? What effect has that on the earth? At what rate does sunlight travel?

SUGGESTIONS. *These suggestions are made rather freely, though it is not expected that any school will find it feasible to carry out all, or even a majority. From among them, however, every teacher will find it possible to select some.* (1) Carefully examine the moon and note its roundness. If possible, look for the craters through a telescope or spyglass. (2) If an eclipse of the moon comes during the year, observe it and note the circular outline of the earth's shadow. (3) With a lamp, throw on the wall the shadow of a ball in various positions. Do the same with a cylinder; with a square. Which always shows one kind of outline? (4) Write down briefly all the ideas that occur to you of the conditions different from those that exist which would result if the earth were flat instead of being a sphere. Continue this list as following chapters are studied, adding new consequences as these become clear. (5) A period devoted to the meaning of scale may be combined with a study of the size and distance of the members of the solar system. This can be done with profit by cutting disks out of brown paper to represent the planets (say on a scale of one inch for 5000 miles); and marking off distances in the school yard (say on a scale of one inch for 200,000 miles) to represent distances. (6) Take a string five feet long with a loop in the end. Put the loop over a nail driven in the floor. With a piece of chalk at the other end of the string draw a circle. Now drive another nail two inches from the first. Take a string ten feet long and tie the ends. Put it over the two nails, and with a chalk held in the loop draw a figure as near a circle as you can. It will not be a circle, but an ellipse

If you put the two nails (the foci) farther apart, say six inches, the ellipse will be still less like a circle. (7) Rotate a globe or apple in front of a light to illustrate the cause of day and night. (8) Observe the stars of the Big Dipper and the North Star at 8, 9, and 10 o'clock. What changes do you notice? (9) Choose a night with no moon, clear and dark, and point a camera toward the North Star through a window which has a free exposure to the sky. Let the lens remain wide open for five or six hours, but be sure to close it before dawn. What does the finished picture, made from a film so exposed, show? (10) Compare the movements of a planet in the heavens, say the evening "star," with that of a neighboring star. Why the difference? (11) With a telescope look for the moons of Jupiter and the rings of Saturn. (12) What are shooting stars and comets? (13) Observe the moon each night it is visible throughout a month and make small sketches of its changing form. Keep directions the same in all the sketches. If some nights are cloudy in one month, try to fill in during the following month. Do the days of succeeding calendar months and moon months correspond? (14) In some astronomy, read about the sun and the planets. (15) Point to different cities on the earth allowing for the curvature of the earth as you point. (16) When Zeta of Ursa Major, the star (also called Mizar) at the bend of the handle of the Big Dipper, is in a vertical line with the North Star, the North Star is exactly in the North. See Fig. 14.

Reference Books. *References to a few selected books are placed at the end of each chapter. Other reference books are listed in Appendix L. The following books are given in something of their order of difficulty. All deserve a place in a good school library. Encyclopedias may often also be consulted to advantage if the special books are not at hand.*

JOHNSON, *Mathematical Geography*, American Book Company, New York, 1907; TODD, *New Astronomy*, American Book Company, New York, 1897 (good diagrams); McKREADY, *A Beginner's Star Book*, G. P. Putnam's Sons, New York, 1912; GRONDAL, *The Music of the Spheres*, The Macmillan Company, New York, 1926; MOULTON, *Introduction to Astronomy*, The Macmillan Company, New York, 1923; McCABE, *Wonders of the Stars*, G. P. Putnam's Sons, New York, 1923; JONES, *General Astronomy*, Longmans, Green & Company, New York, 1922.

Laboratory Exercise. Exercise I in TARR AND VON ENGELN'S *Laboratory Manual of Physical and Commercial Geography*, The Macmillan Company, New York, should be performed in connection with the study of this chapter.

CHAPTER II

GENERAL FEATURES OF THE EARTH[1]

There are three quite different parts of the earth: (1) the solid rock crust of the earth, or *lithosphere;* (2) the liquid ocean, or *hydrosphere,* which partially covers the solid earth; and (3) the gaseous envelope, or *atmosphere.*

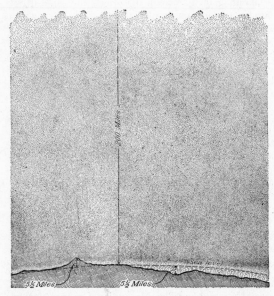

Fig. 22. — A diagram suggestive of the relative depths of air and water on the earth. Fifty per cent of the weight of the air is in the lower 3.6 miles of its depth. Five and one half miles is about the greatest height of mountains above the sea; the greatest ocean depth is about the same. "Man is a deep-sea inhabitant of the ocean of air."

10. The atmosphere.[2] There is some air at a height of 200 or 300 miles from the earth, and a few molecules of its gases may exist as far out as two thirds the distance to the moon; but most of it is within a few miles of the earth's surface (Fig. 22). The air is a mixture of transparent gases, mainly oxygen and nitrogen, whose presence on every hand we hardly realize. Yet our every breath draws it in for the purpose of supplying life-giving oxygen. Though it cannot be seen, we feel its presence when the wind blows, or when we move rapidly through it.

[1] For latitude and longitude, see Appendix B; for maps, see Appendix I. College preparatory students should study the matter in Appendix B, Latitude, Longitude, and Time, carefully to gain a competent understanding of these subjects. Appendix I, Maps, should be conned to secure an equally thorough appreciation of its content and particularly of the nature and interpretation of contoured maps. These studies should in both cases be supplemented by practical exercises as there suggested.

[2] See also Chapter XII.

There are many ways in which the air is of high importance. All plants and animals depend upon its gases for life. Its oxygen causes fire to burn, and, by a slow combustion, causes decay of animal and plant tissues. It diffuses light and heat from the sun, and transmits the waves which we perceive as sound. Water vapor, or water in the gaseous state, is part of the air. Winds, which bear this vapor, and warm and cold air, from place to place, are a result of the movement of air. For many centuries the wind has been used for driving ships over the waters and for turning windmills on the land.

The surface of the earth itself is profoundly modified by the influence of the air. Winds move loose fragments about and wear the rocks away, especially in desert regions. Rains, made possible by vapor in the air, give rise to streams, which carve channels in the land and bear rock fragments to the sea. Waves, which winds form in the ocean, batter at the rocky seacoast. Even quiet air, by the action of its water vapor and oxygen, is causing the solid rock slowly to decay and to crumble. Thus soil is formed from which most plants draw their mineral food.

Summary. *The air, composed chiefly of oxygen and nitrogen, extends 200 or 300 miles above the earth, but its denser and main mass is within a few miles of the surface. Breathing, fire, decay, diffusion of light and heat, sound waves, winds, rain, waves, and many changes of the land, including the formation of soil, are dependent on the atmosphere.*

11. The oceans.[1] If the earth were a perfect sphere, it would be entirely covered by water to a depth of several thousand feet; but the surface is so irregular that the ocean is not able to cover it completely, as the air does. It has been drawn by gravity into the depressions and rises high enough to cover only the continental margins (Figs. 104, 317).

Nearly three fourths of the solid earth is hidden from view by this water mantle, the area of the oceans being about 145,000,000 square miles, of the lands about 52,000,000 square miles. Near their contact with the continents the oceans are shallow; but far from land the water is deep. One may sail, with no land in sight, for thousands of miles in water whose average depth is 10,000 to 15,000 feet. In its deepest parts the ocean has a depth of over five and a half miles.

This vast expanse of water is of great importance in many ways. It is the seat of abundant life, many forms of which are of such value that ships are sent out to secure them. Cod, halibut, haddock, bluefish, salmon, shad, lobsters, oysters, clams, seals,

[1] See also Chapter X.

whales, sponges, pearl oysters, and precious corals are among the ocean animals of importance to man.

For a long time the ocean was an almost impassable barrier to the spread of man; but as men learned to navigate and to build strong ships, it became a highway instead of a barrier. To-day the Atlantic is crossed with safety and comfort in five or six days; less than a century ago this journey required weeks and was one of peril. Transportation between America and Europe is far easier now than it was between Rome and Athens at the time of the Roman Empire. Ships cross the oceans in all directions, carrying merchandise and passengers to every quarter of the globe. The harbors from which these ships go forth are the sites of great cities, prospering by commerce and by the industries to which this gives rise. By means of the ocean highway, too, civilization has spread rapidly to all quarters of the globe.

The ocean supplies the vapor for rain, upon which all land animals and plants depend. The ocean, by the agency of the winds that blow over it, also profoundly influences the temperature of neighboring lands, moderating the heat of summer and the cold of winter. Therefore, lands reached by ocean winds, like the northwestern coast of United States and Europe, have far less extreme climates than lands in the same latitude, like central and eastern United States, where ocean winds are less common.

Summary. *The ocean occupies depressions on the earth's surface, covering three fourths of the globe to an average depth of* 10,000 *to* 15,000 *feet. The ocean is of importance: as a source of food-fishes and other valuable animals; as the route and highway of navigation and overseas commerce; as the source of water vapor; and in modifying climate.*

12. The solid earth. Near the continents the sea floor is covered with sediment washed from the land by rain, rivers, and waves. Farther out, it is mantled with the remains of animals that, on dying, have settled from the water above. On the dry land there is almost everywhere a layer of loose rock fragments, the *mantle rock*, the surface part of which is called *soil*. Thus nearly the entire earth is covered by loose materials.

In some places the soil has been brought by glaciers, in others by rivers; but much of it has been formed by the decay and crumbling of the rocks. Were it not for this soil most of the plants, which are of such use in supplying materials for food, clothing, and shelter, could not grow. The loose soil permits the roots of plants to penetrate it, hence to secure water and plant food, and it also serves to hold the plants upright.

Wherever the soil mantle is penetrated to sufficiently great depth, solid rock, or *bed rock*, is found beneath it (Fig. 23). Sometimes the bed rock is several hundred feet beneath the surface; but it is usually found at a depth of a few feet or a score or two of feet. In places, especially among mountains or on other steep slopes, there is no soil cover at all. As the rock crumbles in such situations, the fragments fall away so quickly that soil cannot accumulate.

The bed rock that is everywhere found beneath the soil varies greatly from place to place, often consisting of materials that are of great use to man. In some places the bed rock is sandstone or granite, useful for building purposes; in other places it is limestone, valuable for building, for making lime, or for use in blast furnaces. In various parts of the world, layers of coal are found bedded with the rocks; and there are deposits of iron ore, salt, and other substances; also veins of lead, zinc, silver, gold, and other metals.

Fig. 23. — Bed rock beneath the soil.

Summary. *The solid earth, like the air and ocean, is of great importance to man. It furnishes him with a home. It is almost everywhere covered with a soil mantle, in which food-plants and other vegetation grow. Everywhere beneath the soil mantle is found solid bed rock, from which many valuable mineral substances are obtained.*

13. The earth's interior. From river valleys, tunnels, quarries, mines, and well borings, many facts have been learned about the outer, or *lithosphere*, part of the solid earth. But this knowledge tells little about the great interior. However, astronomers have shown that, while the outer part of the earth is from two to three times as heavy as water, the interior is five or more times as heavy, and is perhaps composed of metal. The interior is more rigid than steel (Fig. 24).

Several facts indicate that the interior is highly heated: there are hot springs; volcanoes erupt melted rock; and mines show an increase in temperature of about 1° F. for every 50 or 60 feet of descent. If this increase continues, the temperature of the interior of the earth must be very high.

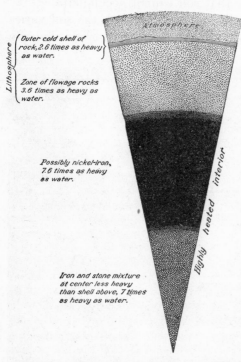

It was formerly believed that beneath a thin outer crust the interior was molten; but it is now considered certain that, though very hot, the interior is solid. We still use the term *earth's crust*, however, for the cold outer portion of the earth. There are a number of reasons for the conclusion that the interior is solid: (1) if it were liquid, there would be tides in it; (2) the behavior of the earth toward other spheres is that of a solid body; (3) earthquake shocks in Japan have been measured by delicate instruments in England, and the time of passage and nature of the record received indicate a solid interior.

Fig. 24. — One conception of the structure of the earth's interior. Study of earthquakes, the magnetism of the earth, and the known fact of the greater density below the surface shell of rocky material, are the evidence on which such a diagram as this is based.

It is a well-known fact that greater heat is required to melt most substances under pressure than without pressure. It is believed, therefore, that the interior of the earth is prevented from melting by the tremendous weight, or pressure, of the rocks that rest upon it. At a depth of six to fifteen miles the pressure is great enough to crush rocks; and, therefore, deep in the earth, below this upper portion, or *zone of fracture,* is a zone where cavities cannot exist, the *zone of flowage.*

Summary. *Several facts indicate that the interior of the earth is highly heated, and it was formerly thought to be molten; but, for a number of reasons, its matter is now believed to be solid, though hot, and to be prevented from melting by the pressure upon it.*

14. Hypotheses of the earth's origin. The orderly arrangement of the solar system and the fact that the earth is only one of a number of planets, all of which have similar characteristics and are made up of the same elements, have led to the assumption that the present condition of the earth is the result of systematic development from an earlier different state. Astronomers and geologists have tried to unravel this most ancient history of the earth. In general their arguments are founded on evidence gathered by study of the solar system, and comparison of it and its members to other celestial bodies. On that basis various schemes accounting for the origin of the solar system have been set forth. None is free from faults; all fail to fit in every particular our present understanding of things. Two, however, are sufficiently complete and satisfactory to have merited consideration as hypotheses, that is, first attempts at explanation

The Nebular Hypothesis proposes that all the matter of the solar system was once a slowly rotating, unit, spheroidal mass of hot gas, a *nebula,* extending beyond the orbit of the farthest out of the existing planets. This hot nebula cooled, and on cooling shrank. The result of such shrinking was that it rotated faster. The same energy used to make a large wheel rotate slowly, if applied to a small wheel, will cause it to spin rapidly. The greater speed of rotation caused the equatorial belt of the nebula to bulge out. When the speed of rotation grew sufficiently great, some of the equatorial matter refused to contract further because its centrifugal force exactly balanced gravity. As the rest of the nebula continued to contract, this equatorial matter became a ring revolving about the central mass. In time the ring parted and the material in it was attracted by gravitation to its largest and thickest part. Thus a ball was formed, the outermost planet. In time other planets were similarly formed. Some of the planets themselves gave off rings; in this way the earth got its moon. The present remainder of the original hot nebula is the central sun, still white-hot, of the solar system. The earth, once a hot gas, first cooled to form the atmosphere with a molten globe under it. Further cooling gave rise to a solid crust on the molten globe, and to the condensation of the water vapor in the atmosphere to form water, which, falling as rain, made the oceans. The interior of the earth is still hot; the moon has cooled to its core.

The Nebular Hypothesis accounts particularly for a molten, liquid earth-interior, and the evidence now at hand indicates a solid, rigid earth instead. One difficulty of a molten earth is that it could not spin, or rotate, freely. A solid, hard-boiled egg can be spun on its end; a fresh egg with a fluid interior cannot be started spinning readily on account of the internal friction between successive layers of the liquid stuff moving at different rates. The moons of some planets revolve in an opposite direction to that of the larger body to which they belong. The sum of the energy of movement now possessed by the planets and the sun should be the same as that of the original nebula; and if that is true there was not enough centrifugal force to throw off matter at the distances that the planets are removed from the sun. These are objections to the Nebular Hypothesis.

The Planetesimal Hypothesis assumes the original existence of a nebula, spiral in form instead of spheroidal; cold instead of hot, made up of solid particles instead of gaseous ones. The idea is got from the discovery that numerous spiral nebulae (Fig. 25) now exist in the universe. The spiral nebula has a central nucleus about which opposite curved arms revolve. In these arms are other dense spots like that of the nucleus, but smaller. Around such dense spots still smaller masses, the *planetesimals*, minute planets, revolve. By collision and gravitative attraction the planetesimals of the earlier, solar-system, spiral nebula were, in time, gathered into the various dense spots and so became planets. The earth was one such nucleus; a smaller one gave rise to the moon. At first the planets were cold, but the interiors became hot by the effects of pressure as more and more stuff was built up on the original mass. This heat is now again being lost. The atmospheric gases and water vapor were present in the original minute planetesimals and were released as these became heated. At first these gases escaped into space; but as the earth became larger they were held to the central mass by surface gravity.

One objection to the Planetesimal Hypothesis is that the spiral nebulae observed in the heavens, to which the original spiral nebula assumed for the solar system is compared, are of vastly greater dimensions than the solar system as we know it.

Summary. *The Nebular Hypothesis of the evolution of the solar system assumes that a great, globular mass of hot gas, a nebula, cooled gradually; the Planetesimal Hypothesis that a spiral nebula composed of cold particles was in time collected by collision and gravitation to make up the sun and the planets. Many facts remain unexplained by or are contradictory to both hypotheses.*

15. Air, water, and rock. At ordinary temperatures the air is a mixture of gases; but with great cold and pressure these gases may be changed to a liquid and even to a solid state. Water, ordinarily a liquid, changes at 32° F. to a solid, and at 212° F. to a gas; in fact, some water-vapor gas rises from water at ordinary temperatures. Rock, as we know it, is a solid; but volcanoes show that under higher temperatures it becomes a liquid; and in the mass of the very hot sun, some of the rock elements are so highly heated that they are in the state of gases. From this it is seen that *the terms gas, liquid, and solid apply merely to states of*

Photo by Ritchey, Yerkes Observatory

Fig. 25. — Spiral nebula in Ursa Major. What points in the planetesimal hypothesis does this photograph of an actual nebula illustrate?

matter. When the conditions change, any one of these states of matter may be altered to one of the other states.

The three earth materials — air, water, and rock — have been described as if they were quite separate; but really they are closely related and mingled. There is not much rock material in the atmosphere, though volcanic and desert dust is often borne long distances in it; and the haziness of the air is partly due to dust blown up from the ground. Water vapor is mixed with all air, even that of the driest deserts.

Water also pervades the earth's crust, entering even the densest rocks. Wells reach it and supply drinking water; it slowly trickles out of the ground in springs; miners find it far below the surface; and volcanic eruptions bring vast quantities of it to the surface. In cold climates the water in the earth is frozen, changing the soil to a solid, rocklike mass. In the Arctic lands the ground below the surface layer is permanently frozen to a depth of several hundred feet. Accordingly the term *hydrosphere* is quite as appropriate as atmosphere or lithosphere.

That air also enters the ground is proved by the fact that land plants die if the pores of the soil are kept filled with water. But some air is mixed with water. If a fish is placed in water from which all the air has been expelled, the fish will die because there is no free oxygen for it to breathe. Water bears mineral substances in solution; and rock particles in suspension are also mingled in water.

Summary. *Air (gas), water (liquid), and rock (solid) may each be changed to one of the other states of matter. They are mingled: there is earth material and water vapor in the air; air and water in the earth; and air and rock material in the water.*

16. Irregularities of the earth's crust. While the earth regarded as a whole is a huge sphere flattened at the poles, its outline considered in detail is far from regular. The surface is roughened by a series of continental elevations, between which are broad depressions, occupied by the oceans. The ocean depressions, or basins, average 10,000 to 15,000 feet in depth;

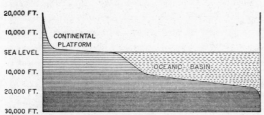

Fig. 26. — To show, approximately, the proportion of continents and ocean basins between different levels.

but the average height of the lands above sea level is only 2000 to 3000 feet. Fully three fourths of the ocean bottoms are broad expanses of plain; and far more than half the land is either plain or low plateau (Figs. 26, 27).

Mountain chains and volcanoes rise high above the general level of both sea bottom and land. The Hawaiian Islands are volcanic cones on a submarine mountain fold fully 1500 miles in length; and the Japanese Islands, Philippines, and West Indies are also mountain chains rising from the sea floor.

It is among the mountain chains of the land that the greatest elevations on the globe are found. In the Andes there are peaks over 40,000 feet higher than the sea bottom 75 miles to the west. The highest mountain in the world, Mount Everest, is about 5½ miles high; and the greatest ocean depth known is over 6 miles beneath the level of the sea. Eleven miles is a great difference in elevation as we consider heights and depths; but it is a very small amount compared to 7900 miles, the diameter of the earth.

Fig. 27. — The main mountain axes of North America.

These irregularities of the earth's surface are generally thought to result from the loss of interior heat (p. 16). As the interior of the earth cools and shrinks, the outer crust wrinkles, causing some parts to rise, others to settle (p. 50). Such changes of level are even now in progress (p. 52), and there is much evidence that there have been great changes in the past. One of the most important facts in physical geography is that the earth's crust is in slow movement; for by reason of it, the outlines of the lands and oceans are ever varying.

Summary. *The earth's surface has been roughened by the effects of shrinking of the heated interior. This has caused continental elevations and oceanic basins, and, on both of these, mountain chains and volcanoes. The average depth of the ocean is about five times the average height of the land; but the loftiest mountains are about as high as the greatest ocean depths, making a total difference in level of about eleven miles.*

17. Conflict of erosion and elevation. Wherever the solid matter of the earth is exposed to the air, it is being attacked and slowly worn away.   The weather causes the rocks slowly to crumble (p. 54); rivers carve valleys and carry the rock fragments off toward the sea (p. 76); glaciers scour the land over which they pass (p. 294); waves batter the shore, cutting cliffs, building beaches, and supplying rock fragments for removal by the currents (p. 367).

Fig. 28. — Relief map of North America.

The result of the action of these *agencies of erosion* is that the land surface is at first made very irregular.   But after a time the erosive processes are concentrated on a reduction of the higher places. Because of this the level of the land is gradually lowered and its surface eventually made regular by such action.

The sea floor, on the other hand, is from the beginning made more regular. Beyond the reach of the waves there is practically no erosion; and the deposit of rock fragments from the land, levels up the near-shore portions of the sea bottom (Fig. 29).

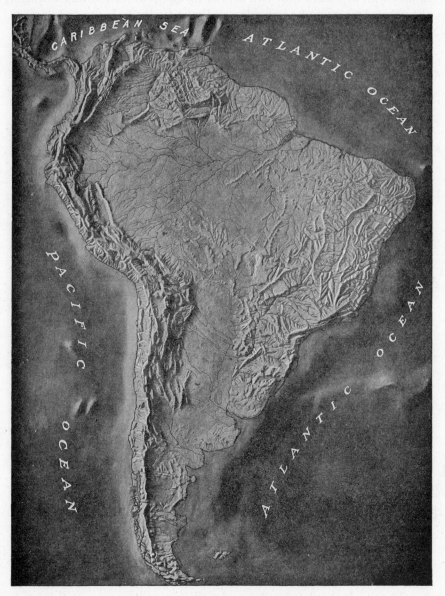

Fig. 29. — Relief map of South America.

Thus, on the one hand, movements of the crust are raising the land; on the other, the agencies of erosion are cutting into it, lowering it, and removing its fragments toward the sea. There is an opposition, or conflict, of two sets of forces, one set tending to raise, the other first to make irregular and eventually to lower the surface of the land. In recent geologic time (See Appendix D) the forces of elevation have been more powerful; but the agencies of erosion have already deeply sculptured the lands.

This conflict has been in progress for many ages, and the present land surface, which we are about to study, is the result of it. The valleys, which our railways and canals follow; the mountains, which act as barriers to winds and to the spread of plants, animals, and men; the smooth coastal plains; the interior plateaus; the harbors in which our shipping gathers; the sites of our leading cities; and many other land features are a result of the conflict between the forces of elevation and the agencies of erosion.

Summary. *Agencies of erosion — weather, rivers, glaciers, waves, etc. — are cutting into the land and strewing the waste over the sea floor. On the other hand, forces of elevation are raising the land. This causes a conflict, in which the forces of elevation have in recent geologic ages been more potent. The forms of the present land surface, which so greatly influence man, are the result of this conflict.*

18. The continents. A continent is a large elevated platform of the earth's crust surrounded by ocean. Usually the continental margin is submerged beneath the sea (Fig. 30), sometimes, as off eastern North America, for a distance of 50 to 100 miles from the coast. The submerged portion of the continental platform is known as the *continental shelf*. At its outer edge the continental shelf is faced by an abrupt slope, called the *continental slope* (Fig. 104), which descends steeply to the deep sea bottom. Although the average elevation of the continents is but 2000 to 3000 feet above sea level, when measured from the base of the continental slope their average height is 10,000 to 15,000 feet. Some portions of the continental surfaces, for example the Dead Sea, are below sea level.

Continents have a framework of mountain ranges with connecting plains and plateaus (Figs. 29, 30, 31, 32, 33). They are crossed by rivers, which, developing and utilizing valleys, drain the land;

but over one fourth of the land has no drainage to the sea. In these cases the water runs into *interior basins* or basins without outlet.

The outline of a continent follows closely the structural lines determined by its mountain ranges; indeed, mountains have been called the skeletons

Fig. 30. — Relief map of Africa.

of continents. From this standpoint the plains and plateaus may be called their tissues. In fact, many of the plains and plateaus have been built of rock fragments worn from the mountain skeleton.

To illustrate, off eastern Asia, from the Kurile Islands to the Philippines, there is a mountain chain now rising. A large part of the rock waste worn from these mountains, and from the mainland, is being deposited in the sea that separates the islands from the mainland. These deposits may in time fill the enclosed sea, and a slight uplift of the land may raise the smooth sea bottom plain, forming dry land, and thus joining the mountain islands to the coast of the mainland. It is by similar changes that continents have acquired the forms and extent they now show.

Summary. *Continents are elevated blocks of the earth's crust whose real margin is beneath sea level. They consist of plains, plateaus, and mountains, partly drained into interior basins. They owe their outline to mountain skeletons connected by plains and plateaus, largely built up of rock waste from the mountains.*

Fig. 31. — The island continent of Australia; also New Zealand, New Guinea, and several chains of islands that are parts of mountain chains in the sea.

19. Relation of continent forms to man. The separation of the continents has interfered with the spread of man. Their low elevation has been very favorable to mankind. Had the average elevation (2000 to 3000 feet) been as great as the average depression of the oceans (12,000 to 15,000 feet), the greater part of each continent would be too high and cold to support a dense population. The development of men and nations has been affected

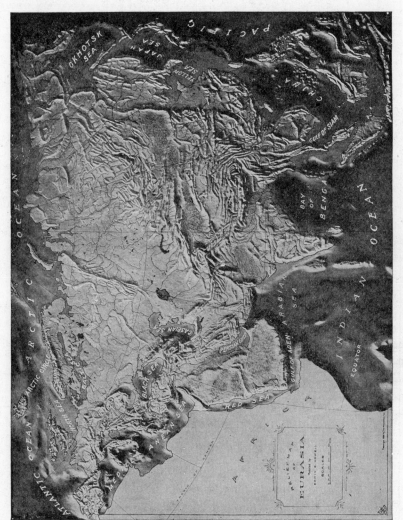

Fig. 32. — The great continent of Eurasia.

Fig. 33. — Europe.

in many ways by the continent form, the outline of its coast, the enclosed bays and seas, the islands, and the distribution of mountains and plains.

An irregular coast line favors navigation; and it is an interesting fact that the inhabitants of continents that have regular outlines have advanced far less rapidly than those whose coast has many harbors and bays (Fig. 33).

Summary. *The elevation, surface features, and coast line of continents have greatly affected men, animals, and plants.*

20. Form of the oceans. The continents are clustered around the north polar region, with tongues projecting southward; the

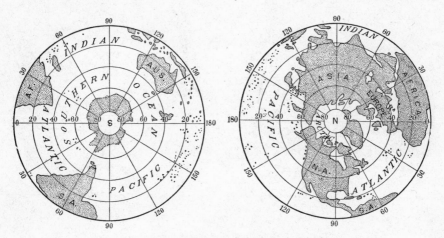

Fig. 34. — The southern and northern hemispheres.

ocean water is centered around the south polar region, with triangular tongues projecting northward between the continents (Fig. 34). In outline the oceans are very irregular, because the irregular continents form their boundaries.

We commonly recognize five oceans. It is customary to choose an arbitrary boundary — the Antarctic circle — for the ice-laden *Antarctic Ocean;* but it is far better to consider as a great *Southern Ocean* (Fig. 34) all the water south of Australia, Africa, and South America. Three great ocean tongues extend northward from this Southern Ocean: (1) the *Indian Ocean,* which reaches up to Asia between Australia and Africa; (2) the immense *Pacific,* which extends up between America, Australia, and Asia, to the point where America and Asia almost meet; and (3) the *Atlantic* tongue, bounded by the Americas on one side and Africa and Europe on the other. The Atlantic is given an hour-glass shape by the narrowing where the projection of South America reaches eastward toward that of Africa. The *Arctic Ocean* is an ice-covered, deep-sea basin, partly cut off from the Atlantic by Greenland and Iceland.

The northern hemisphere contains the greater part of the land, while the southern hemisphere is essentially a water hemisphere (Fig. 34). By choosing the proper circle, it is possible so to divide the earth as to have one hemisphere in which most of the land ($\frac{6}{7}$) is placed, and the other with little land ($\frac{1}{7}$) (Fig. 35). London is very near the center of the land hemisphere.

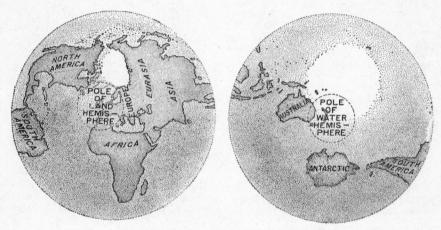

Fig. 35. — The land and water hemispheres.

Now that men no longer timidly skirt the coasts in small boats but steer boldly out to sea in great ships that visit every ocean, the needs of ocean navigation have led to the making of canals for short cuts across land barriers. Formerly, vessels sailing from Europe to India went all the way around Africa; now they take a short cut across the Isthmus of Suez (Fig. 509). Similarly, ships from the eastern United States and Europe, bound for western South America, western North America, and the northeast of Asia make a short cut by way of the Panama Canal (Fig. 376).

Summary. *Most of the ocean water is in the southern hemisphere, three triangular tongues extending from the great Southern Ocean northward between the continents.*

21. Plan of the earth. Study of a globe, and of diagrams and models of the continents (Figs. 28–32, 34–36), which show the position and relationship of highlands and lowlands, brings to light much evidence that the larger features of the earth are not distributed in a haphazard way. As with the solar system, so also there seems to have been a progressive development of the continents and the ocean basins as they now exist.

Thus continental platforms and ocean basins, occurring at opposite ends of diameters of the earth, are *antipodal* (Fig. 36) in position. Most striking is the occurrence of the Arctic Ocean, a true, deep-sea basin, at one pole of the earth and the Antarctic Continent at the other. North

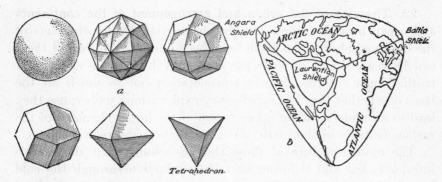

Tetrahedron.

Fig. 36. — The series of solid figures in *a* shows that the cubic content decreases as the number of faces or sides decreases, the surface area remaining the same. In *b* the effect of this decrease in cubic content, with unchanged surface area, is indicated as applied to the earth.

America lies opposite the Indian Ocean. The great continental mass of Eurasia and that of Africa are matched on the other side of the globe by the vast expanse of the southern Pacific Ocean. Australia lies squarely opposite the widest part of the north Atlantic Ocean. Only South America does not fit completely into the scheme; its southern extension lies opposite part of eastern Asia.

In general the continental platforms have their widest expansion in the northern hemisphere, the ocean basins in the southern hemisphere; it is due to this that a land and a water hemisphere may be indicated (Fig. 35). Again the continental platforms are characteristically triangular in shape, tapering southward. The fact that the lines of mountain structure (Figs. 27 and 29) repeat this triangular pattern is evidence that the form is not due to a chance arrangement of coast lines brought about by a particular level of ocean waters.

There is a correspondence also between particular features of different continents. North America and South America show such resemblances

most conspicuously.   In both of these continents very old rocks and mountain roots are found in the northeast; in Labrador in North America, in
eastern Brazil in South America.   The western border of each continent is
made up of a continuous belt of newer, higher mountains, with basins
between the ranges, recent volcanoes, and great lava plateaus.   Wide low
plains occupy the central areas.   These plains are drained by great rivers
flowing in corresponding directions.

Summary.   *The continental platforms and oceanic basins occupy antipodal positions; most of the continental land is in the northern hemisphere.
The continents are characteristically triangular in shape, and taper southward.
There are also resemblances and repetitions of particular features in the
different continents.*

**22. Theories of the origin and arrangement of the continents
and ocean basins.**   Numerous theories accounting for the facts of
the observed plan of the earth have been offered.   No one of these
can be regarded as proved; yet each may have some element of
truth.   Such theories deserve consideration not so much on the
basis of whether they are satisfactory explanations, as because they
lead to an understanding appreciation of the larger elements of the
surface features of the earth, their distribution and relationships.

The more complete of these theories assume that the earth's
interior is hot and is losing heat by conduction through the cold
outer shell of rock, the lithosphere crust.   It has been calculated
that the interior earth gives off enough heat each year to melt
a coating of ice ¼ inch thick spread over the whole of the outer
surface of the earth.   Due to such loss of heat the interior core is
further assumed to be shrinking in mass, while the cool outer shell
remains unchanged in dimensions.   Accordingly the outer shell is
progressively left unsupported and tends to collapse, or fall in,
toward the interior.   As movement downward, that is, toward the
center of the earth, must therefore be the greater effect, this explains immediately *why the ocean basins are so much more extensive
and deeper than the continental platforms.*

The simplest theory of the triangular forms of the continents points out
that the continental platforms are only remainders of a former higher-
level surface, parts of the cover of the earth when it had a larger diameter.
Such remnants will be small, and will be bounded by the fewest possible
number of sides that will enclose an area, hence a triangle.   The oceans,
on the other hand, will be large and be many sided.   By drawing on
paper two, many-sided, straight-line figures, irregular in form, then cutting

these out and attempting to match the edges the student may see how this works out.

In what is known as the Tetrahedral Theory the same idea is carried further. It can be shown by geometry that a sphere contains the greatest volume of material with a given size of cover; and, on the other hand, that a tetrahedron is the solid which will contain the least amount of material with the same size of cover (Fig. 36). It is therefore argued that, starting with a spherical earth, interior contraction with an unshrinkable outer shell will tend to produce a tetrahedral surface form. The student is to be cautioned against thinking that this theory says that the earth's shape is tetrahedral. Such is not the case. It merely proposes that the outermost shell, a tiny fraction of the whole mass, is warping toward the tetrahedral shape.

Study of Fig. 36 brings appreciation of the remarkable number of ways in which this theory fits the facts. It explains the opposite positions of the Arctic Ocean and the Antarctic Continent, and the antipodal positions of the continents and oceanic basins generally. The continents, it is seen, occur at the edges and corners of the tetrahedron, the oceanic basins at the flat faces. Further, the continents taper southward, and most land is in the northern hemisphere. At the northern-hemisphere corners, where the sides of the tetrahedral figure meet, are found the most ancient rocks of these lands at the appropriate 120° points. Gravity observations show that, on the whole, the southern hemisphere has less mass than the northern hemisphere.

Two other theories assume that the effects of a contracting interior will be taken up by adjustments in the zone of flowage (p. 25) of the lithosphere shell, and that the outer rigid part of this shell floats on this deeper rock stuff made mobile by pressure.

According to the *isostatic* (equal stand) theory the continental platforms are merely islands of lighter stuff which float at a higher level than the heavier stuff of the bottoms of the oceanic basins. (Water is so much lighter than rock that the volume of the ocean waters has little significance in this connection.) Two blocks of wood, the one of oak, the other of pine, of the same size and shape, floating in water will illustrate this. The pine block, like the continents, floats higher because it is less dense. Gravity observations indicate that these relations actually obtain between the continental and oceanic areas, the ocean-bottom stuff is uniformly heavier, that is, denser. Further, mountains on the continents are found to be lighter than the surrounding areas of plains.

The isostatic theory does not explain the forms of the continents. Another theory, the *displacement hypothesis*, has recently been proposed to account for the continental outlines in accord with isostatic conditions. It suggests that not only do the continental masses float higher, but also that they are parts of a once larger mass. This mass fractured and parts drifted away from it forming separate continental islands floating on the zone-of-flowage sea. The evidence of this is to be found in the fact that the shores of opposite continents can be fitted into each other, as with the pieces of a picture puzzle. Thus if the outline of the western coast of Africa and the eastern coast of South America be traced from a globe, the two tracings will be found to fit together very neatly. Other similar correspondences will be noted on a mere inspection of a globe. If such drifting about of the continents has occurred, a solution is also available for many geographical facts otherwise difficult of explanation.

Summary. *Certain theories of the origin of the plan of the earth are based on the assumption that the earth is contracting due to loss of heat; others that the material of the surface shell of the earth floats high or low, according to its density, in the mobile, underlying rock formations comprising a zone of flowage.*

TOPICAL OUTLINE, QUESTIONS, AND SUGGESTIONS

TOPICAL OUTLINE. 10. **The atmosphere.** Extent; composition; proof of its existence; importance, — life, fire, decay, diffusion of light and heat, sound waves, winds, vapor, wind power; effects on land; soil.

11. **The oceans.** Distribution of water; area covered; depth; importance, — animal products, navigation, vapor supply, effect on climate.

12. **The solid earth.** Covering of sea floor; of land; origin of soil; importance; depth; absence on steep slopes; condition beneath the soil mantle; valuable mineral substances.

13. **The earth's interior.** Weight of material of outer part and of interior; proofs of interior heat; former belief; earth's crust; reasons for present theory; effects of pressure.

14. **Hypotheses of the earth's origin.** Order and unity of solar system; progressive development. Outline of Nebular Hypothesis, difficulties of. Planetesimal Hypothesis.

15. **Air, water, and rock.** (*a*) States of matter: air, water, and rock illustrate the three states; changes of each of these to the other two states. (*b*) Intermingling: rock and water in air; water and air in earth; air and rock material in water.

16. **Irregularities of the earth's crust.** Average depth of ocean basins; average height of continents; proportion of plains; distribution of mountains and volcanoes; amount of irregularity of earth's surface; cause of irregularities; changes in level.

17. **Conflict of erosion and elevation.** Nature of agencies of erosion; effect on land, on sea floor; conflict between erosion and elevation; importance of result upon man.

18. **The continents.** Definition; real boundaries; elevation; surface features; drainage; relation of mountains to continent form — illustration.

19. **Relation of continent forms to man.** Effect of separation; of low elevation; of coast line.

20. **Form of the oceans.** General form and outline; subdivisions of the ocean waters; boundaries of each; land and water hemispheres; value of oceans for navigation; isthmian canals.

21. **Plan of the earth.** Regularity of. Antipodal position of continents and oceanic basins; land and water hemisphere; triangular shape of continents; ancient

rocks. Resemblances between North America and South America: old rocks, mountains, plains, rivers.

22. **Theories of the origin and arrangement of the continents and ocean basins.** Reasons for consideration of; basis of theories; cooling, contraction, and collapse; extensive areas of oceanic basin. Theory of triangular remnants; Tetrahedral Theory; limitation of, facts in accordance with Tetrahedral Theory. Theory of Isostasy; confirmation of by observation. The displacement hypothesis.

QUESTIONS. Section 10. What is the extent of the atmosphere? Name some important effects of the air.

11. What influence has gravity on the oceans? What are the area and depth of the oceans? Of what importance is the ocean for its animal products; for navigation; for its influence on climate?

12. What covers the sea floor? The land? What is the origin of soil? Of what value is it? What is beneath it? Why is it sometimes absent? What valuable materials come from the solid earth?

13. What reasons are there for believing the earth's interior to be highly heated? Why is it no longer believed to be molten? What prevents it from melting? What is the earth's crust?

14. What facts indicate an orderly development of the solar system? How does the Nebular Hypothesis differ from the Planetesimal Hypothesis? Give some objections to the Nebular Hypothesis.

15. How do the states of air, water, and rock vary? What are the three states of matter? How are air, water, and rock mingled?

16. Compare the ocean depths and continent elevations. What is the general condition of ocean bottoms and continents? Where are mountains found? How many times greater is the earth's diameter than the height of Mt. Everest? What is the cause of these irregularities?

17. What agencies are attacking the land? What effect has this attack on the land? On the sea floor? What conflict is there between opposing forces? How has this conflict been of importance to man?

18. What are the characteristics of a continent? What relation do the mountains have to the continent form? Give an illustration.

19. How has the continent form affected man?

20. State the distribution of the ocean water: its general distribution; the subdivisions, starting from the Southern Ocean; the meaning of land and water hemispheres. What obstacles have been overcome?

21. Recite the antipodal positions of continents and oceanic basins. What other similarities in form and structure suggest orderly development in the plan of the earth? Compare the features of North America and South America; rocks, mountains, rivers, etc.

22. What conditions are assumed as the basis of one set of theories of the plan of the earth? What large relationship is directly explained by such assumptions and how? What is the simplest theory of continental form? What is the geometrical basis of the Tetrahedral Theory? Recite evidence in favor of the Tetrahedral Theory. What is the basis of the Theory of Isostasy? How is it confirmed by observation? What theory was suggested by correspondences in the opposite shore lines of continents?

SUGGESTIONS. (1) In a small jar seal a plant, being careful to have it well watered, and see whether it grows after the oxygen is exhausted. (2) Place a candle in a fruit jar, light it and see if it burns after the oxygen is used up. (3) Why are there holes beneath the flame of a lamp? (4) Have some oxygen generated in the chemical laboratory, and place in it a smouldering piece of cloth. Explain the change that occurs. (5) How deep is the soil in your vicinity? Find some cut — a cellar, railway cut, or stream valley, — where bed rock is seen beneath the soil. How thick is the soil? Of what is it composed? What kind of rock underlies it? Is the line between rock and soil a sharp line? (6) To illustrate the three states of matter: freeze some water; melt the ice; then evaporate the water over the fire. Where does the water go? Place some water in a shallow pan in a room and watch it from day to day. Where does it go? What becomes of the water that you pour on plants? Of that sprinkled on the city pavements? (7) Stir mud and water together. Have you ever seen a stream resembling the muddy water? Where did the mud come from? Where was it being carried? (8) Carefully weigh a piece of chalk. Soak it in water and weigh it again. Why the difference? Most rock will illustrate the same thing, but, being less porous, not in the same degree as chalk. (9) Place some salt in water and stir it once in a while. Where has the salt gone? After twenty-four hours pour the water off and evaporate it. Do you find the salt? Chalk, marble, and many mineral substances will dissolve as the salt did, but in smaller quantities. (10) See whether there are fossils in the rocks of your neighborhood. If so, find out whether they once lived in the sea. What do they prove? (11) Try to spin a fresh egg, a hard-boiled egg. What does this experiment show? (12) On a globe locate the point exactly antipodal to your home. (13) Search for continental correspondences other than those given in the text. (14) Try sucking the air from the inside of a hollow rubber ball. What form does the ball take?

Reference Books. See references at end of Chapters III, X, and XII; MILL, *International Geography*, D. Appleton & Company, New York, 1907; HOBBS, *Earth Evolution and its Facial Expression*, The Macmillan Company, New York, 1921, will be found an interesting and suggestive book for the teacher; WEGENER, *Origin of Continents and Oceans*, E. P. Dutton & Company, New York, 1924.

CHAPTER III

CHANGES IN THE EARTH'S CRUST

23. Relation of man to the land. In a railway journey from Atlantic City, east of Philadelphia, to Chicago a great variety of land forms may be seen. First the seashore; then a lowland plain; then a hilly country; then a wild mountain region, with long ridges separated by broad valleys; then a rugged plateau, with rivers deeply set between steeply rising, wooded banks; then the open plains. Besides these large features many smaller ones are noticeable — rivers, creeks, brooks, rapids, waterfalls, flood plains, lakes, narrow gorges, broad valleys; in fact, all the great variety of land forms to be found in a large area of diversified country.

The careful observer will note also the following facts regarding settlement and industry. The steeper hill and mountain sides are still forested (Fig. 81), and lumbering is the only industry on their rocky slopes. Few houses are seen in the narrow valleys, though here and there a waterfall has given the site for a mill, or even a town; and, in a few places, there is some industry connected with the production of valuable minerals from the mountain rocks. On the other hand, the open plains and low hills, both to the east and west of the mountains, are everywhere inhabited; houses are almost always in sight, woods are scattered, farms are seen on every side, and the land is dotted with villages, towns, and cities.

This route passes three of the ten largest cities in the United States, — Chicago the second in size, Philadelphia the third, and Pittsburgh the ninth. One is a lake port, one a sea port, and one a river port.

These few facts indicate that there is a relation between the form of the land and the industries of the people. Every educated person should know the causes which operate so to modify the form of the land as to adapt it to different industries. This inquiry belongs to physical geography, or, as it is often called, *physiography*.

45

To appreciate truly this subject it is necessary to carry our inquiry back far enough to understand some geological facts and principles; and to this purpose the present chapter is largely devoted.

Summary. *There are great differences in the land surface from place to place, and consequently in the industries of man. Physical Geography, or Physiography, studies the causes for these differences and their relation to one another.*

Photo by von E.

Fig. 37. — A shale cliff in a gorge. The layers of the cliff are made of clay, but some, one especially, are more sandy and hence stronger than the others. How does this show?

24. Rocks of the crust.[1] The many different kinds of rocks in the earth's crust are included in three large classes — *sedimentary, igneous,* and *metamorphic*.

(A) *Sedimentary rocks.* Rock fragments — pebbles, sand, and clay — are washed into seas and lakes by rain, rivers, and waves. They settle in the quiet water, the coarser fragments sinking to the bottom first. The motion of the water, agitated by waves and currents, keeps the finer fragments suspended for a longer time, and they therefore sink to the bottom farther from shore. Thus the water assorts the rock fragments according to size.

On some days the waves and currents are weak, on others strong; sometimes the rivers bring little sediment, at other times much. These differences in currents, and in materials supplied, cause the

[1] Appendix C contains a description of common minerals and rocks.

deposit of layers of different kinds, one on another. Each layer is of the kind that waves and currents are able to bring (Fig. 41).

Such layers are called *strata* (singular, *stratum*), and the rock is said to be *stratified*. Some strata are thin, others thick. Sometimes only one stratum is seen in a cliff, while in other cliffs there are strata of different kinds (Fig. 37), possibly conglomerate, sandstone, shale, and limestone.

When the sediment is deposited, it is loose and unconsolidated, like a gravel bank. The pressure of other layers, deposited above, and the

Photo by Williston

Fig. 38. — A gravel and clay bank with some layers partly consolidated by cementation and therefore standing out slightly from the face of the bank. Why?

action of percolating water slowly bind the fragments together, forming solid rock. The percolating water dissolves mineral substances in one place, carries them on, and deposits some around the sediment grains. This binds, or cements, the rock fragments together. The most common rock cements are the common soluble minerals, carbonate of lime, oxide of iron, and silica. One may often see the process of cementing in a gravel bank where a white coating of carbonate of lime has been deposited on some of the pebbles.

Summary. *Sedimentary rocks are in layers, or strata, formed by the assorting power of waves and currents, which vary in strength and carry* *finer particles farther from shore than the coarser particles. By pressure and the deposit of mineral cements, the loose rock fragments are bound together, forming solid rock.*

(B) *Igneous rocks.*[1] These rocks have risen from within the earth in a melted state. In some cases the eruption produces a lava flow, which cools to form a thick, massive layer of solid rock. Such beds are usually less regular and more massive than sedi-

Fig. 39. — Granite, lower left figure; pumice, upper left; gneiss, right. What differences in make-up of these three rock types may be distinguished in the picture?

mentary strata. In other cases the violence of the eruption blows the lava into bits of volcanic ash or porous pumice (Fig. 39). Lava and ash usually build a cone around the volcanic vent or neck (Fig. 40).

Much molten rock fails to reach the surface. Such *intruded* igneous rock is found in various positions, cutting across the sedimentary and other

[1] See also Chapter VII.

rocks. A narrow crack filled with lava forms a *dike* (Figs. 40 and 49); a mass of lava thrust between strata forms an intruded *sheet* or *sill* (Fig. 40); large, irregular masses, rising into the cores of mountains, form *bosses*

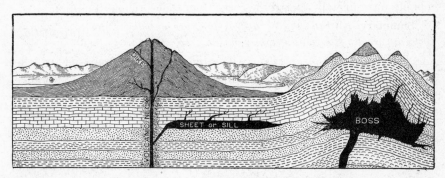

Fig. 40. — To illustrate the origin of igneous rocks. The cone on the left is a volcano, made of lava and volcanic ash. When uncovered by denudation a large boss is known as a batholith.

(Fig. 40). Pikes Peak and many other peaks are *batholiths* of hard granite rock (Fig. 39), brought to light by the wearing away of the layers into or under which they were intruded.

Summary. *Igneous rocks are formed by the cooling of molten rock, some at the surface, in the form of lava flows and volcanic ash, some as intruded dikes, sheets, bosses, and batholiths.*

(C) *Metamorphic rocks.* When subjected to great pressure, or heat, or both, rocks are changed, or *metamorphosed.* By metamorphism lime

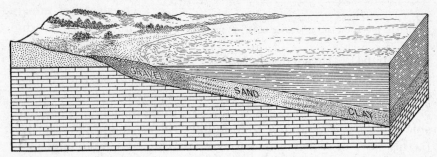

Fig. 41. — To illustrate the deposit and distribution in coarseness of sedimentary rocks. On the extreme left are coarse pebbles; on the extreme right, clay; in the middle, sand. Some layers of pebbles were dragged out to the sand area when the currents and waves were strong; and some sand layers were stratified with the clay strata.

stone is altered to marble; shale, to slate; and sandstone, to quartzite. The change may go so far that, as in the case of *gneiss* (Fig. 39) and *schist,* it is often impossible to tell the nature of the original rock. Metamorphic rocks are especially common among mountains where, during the mountain formation, the strata have been subjected to great pressure and heat. These changes have bent, folded, broken, and twisted the layers (Fig. 50), and often completely altered the rocks from their original condition.

Summary. *When subjected to heat, pressure, or both, as among mountains, rocks are greatly altered or metamorphosed.*

(D) *Resistance of rocks.* All minerals, when exposed to the weather, are attacked by the elements; but there is much difference in the rate at which different ones wear away. Quartz, for example (Appendix C), is hard, only slightly soluble, and does not decay; feldspar is hard and does not dissolve, but decays without great difficulty; calcite is both soft and easily soluble.

The rate of disintegration of rocks depends in large part on the kind of minerals of which they are composed. Sandstone and quartzite (Appendix C), made mainly of quartz, are usually very durable rocks; and so is granite, which is mostly quartz and feldspar. On the other hand, limestone and marble, made of calcite, are easily dissolved.

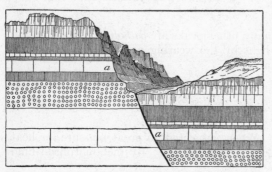

Fig. 42. — A fault.   The same layer (*a a*) stands at different levels on the two sides of the fault plane.

The decay of minerals and rocks is due partly to the action of water (p. 54). Hence dense, massive rocks, like many gneisses and granite, are not so easily disintegrated as porous or friable ones, like sandstone and schist, into which water enters easily.   Because of these facts weak rocks are worn away, forming valleys, while durable rocks are left standing to form hills, ridges, and peaks (Fig. 44). If this law, or rule, is understood, remembered, and applied, a very great part of all the science of the physiography of the lands will be quickly grasped.

Summary. *Some minerals and rocks are durable, others weak. Therefore as the land wears down, valleys are formed where the rocks are weak; hills, ridges, and peaks where they are more durable.*

25. Changes in level of the land. The old ideas, that the hills are everlasting and that the land is firm and stable, are now known to be incorrect. On the contrary, the land is ever changing. Hills are slowly wearing away, valleys are being deepened here and filled there, and the waste is being carried by stages to the sea.

In addition to this, the crust of the earth is slowly rising in some places and sinking in others. By these movements former

Fig. 43. — The columns of Jupiter Serapis at Puzzoli, on the Bay of Naples, Italy. These ruins of an old temple, built on dry land, were lowered beneath the sea, then raised to their present position. Notice the rough surface in the marble columns, reaching about to the height of the wall. This is due to a salt-water shellfish (Lithodomus) which bores into the rocks along the Mediterranean coast. These borings prove that the columns have stood beneath sea level up to that point.

sea bottoms have been raised to become parts of continents; mountains have been formed; and lands have been lowered beneath the sea. A generally accepted explanation of these changes is the slow cooling and contraction of the heated interior (pp. 24 and 40). They may also be due to the shifting of loads (pp. 41 and 176).

Evidence of notable changes in level during past ages is abundantly preserved in the rocks. Beaches and coral reefs are found many feet above the sea (Figs. 105, 368); and fossil remains of ocean animals are entombed in the strata, even of high mountains. There is also full proof that changes of level are now in progress. For example: a part of the Scandinavian peninsula, north of Stock-

Photo by U. S. G. S.

Fig. 44. — A ridge in the foothills of the Rocky Mountains. These rock strata were deposited in the sea in a horizontal position, then tilted during the growth of the mountains. They prove change in level as a result of mountain growth. The upper layer is stronger than the others, because of hardness and composition, and hence resists the weather better. This is why it stands up so sharply while the weaker layers below are more rapidly crumbling away.

holm, has risen seven feet in 150 years; Eskimo houses in Greenland have been lowered into the sea; the land around the Great Lakes is slowly rising; and in 1822, and again in 1835, the coast of Chile was raised two to four feet. In September, 1899, part of the coast of Alaska near Mount St. Elias was uplifted forty-seven feet. These are a few only of many known instances (Fig. 43).

These changes of level are of two kinds: (1) rapid and local, where mountains are now growing, as in Alaska and western South America; and (2) slow and widespread, where large areas slowly swing up or down, as in northeastern North America (p. 363). While in some places the lands are sinking, as a general rule they are rising. This has been true for long periods of the past, and, as a result, the continents are very largely made of sedimentary strata that were deposited in shallow ancient seas.

Summary. *The surface of the land is slowly wearing away; it is also being raised here and lowered there. There are both local rapid movements and a slow swinging up or down of large areas. On the whole, the continents have been rising, and this is why their surface rocks are so largely sedimentary strata.*

26. Disturbance of the strata. The sedimentary strata are deposited in nearly horizontal layers parallel to the sea floor (Figs. 37, 48). When made dry land, the emergence of the strata is usually by slow, broadly extended movements which disturb not at all, or only slightly, the original horizontal position (Fig. 106). The plains of the Atlantic coast and the Mississippi valley, and the plateaus of the West, have such horizontal strata.

In mountain-making, on the other hand, the strata are folded and broken by the great

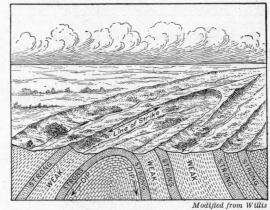

Modified from Willis

Fig. 45.—An anticline, top partly worn away. Which rocks stand up as ridges? Why?

pressure. Accordingly the layers in mountain regions are not usually horizontal, but are tilted at all angles (Figs. 44, 301). Lava and metamorphic rocks (p. 49) also are common in mountain regions. For these reasons mountain rocks are far more complex in kind and position than those of plains (Fig. 180).

Various names have been given to the forms assumed by the disturbed mountain strata. A break in the rocks, accompanied by movement on one or both sides, is known as a *fault* (Figs. 42, 49). An arched upfold of the strata is known as an *anticline* (Figs. 45, 50); a downfold is a *syncline* (Fig. 46). In an anticline the rocks incline, or *dip* (Figs. 45, 50, 80), both ways from the axis of the fold; in a syncline they dip *toward* the axis (Fig. 46). Where a fold has a dip in only a single direction, it is called a *monocline* (Fig. 47). Some folds are very regular or *symmetrical* (Fig. 50); others are quite *unsymmetrical;* and in some, the folding has gone so far that the folds are actually *overturned.* In very intense folding the strata are sometimes *crumpled.*

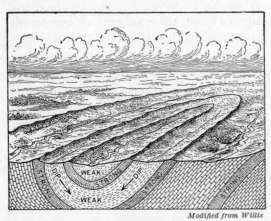

During their movement, rocks are often cracked by the strains. These cracks are called *joint planes* (Figs. 51, 67). The joint planes usually extend vertically into the rocks, and in stratified rocks consist of two sets, commonly meeting almost at right angles. Water readily enters along these natural planes of splitting (Fig. 54), which therefore

Modified from Willis

Fig. 46. — A syncline modified by erosion. How do the valley and ridge forms differ from those in Fig. 45?

promote the disintegration of the rocks. Joint planes are of great importance in quarrying, for they make natural breaks which facilitate the splitting out of blocks of stone.

Summary. *In plains and plateaus the uplifted stratified rocks are commonly left in nearly their original horizontal position; but in mountains they are folded and faulted. Joint planes, or natural planes of breakage, are also produced by the strains.*

27. Agents of weathering. When exposed to the air, rocks crumble and fall apart in the same manner that wood rots and nails rust.

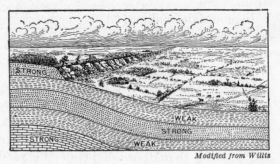

Modified from Willis

Fig. 47. — A monocline

This decay and disintegration, or *weathering,* is due to the action of various agencies, the most important of which are percolating water, air, and the action of animals and plants. These agencies bring about changes in part by dissolving and decaying minerals, in part by mechanical means, as when rocks are ruptured by frost.

Living organisms, animals and plants, do not decay and disintegrate as rocks do because they are covered and protected by a skin or bark. When wounded or cut, this protective covering heals over and prevents decay and further damage. But rock stuff has no protective covering, and the agencies of decay are continually acting on it.

Summary. *Rocks decompose, and crumble, or weather, by the chemical and mechanical action of percolating water, air, and animals and plants.*

Photo by Lee

Fig. 48. — Horizontal strata in the West. The strong layers make vertical cliffs.

28. Action of underground water. A portion of each rain sinks into the soil, and part of it percolates into the rocks, for underground water is able to enter even the densest of rocks. Some of this water enters along joint planes (Fig. 54); some between the rock grains; and some along the cleavage planes of the minerals (Fig. 52).

In moist climates, shallow wells may be fed by underground water even in rock; and upon it farms, entire villages, and towns depend for drinking water. It is underground water, too, that the roots of plants seek in the soil. Without it they die. Its presence is further shown by springs, which are places where underground water comes to the surface in some quantity (p. 96).

Underground water finds many mineral substances which it is able to dissolve. Its power of solution is greatly increased by carbon dioxide and other substances, which it obtains from the air and from decaying vegetation.

Aided by oxygen, carbon dioxide, and other substances, the underground water also causes changes in composition of many minerals. These changes are not very unlike that which causes a shiny nail, when exposed to dampness, to decay to a yellow, powdery iron rust. By such changes more substances are produced which the percolating water can carry off in solution. The roots of plants seek and obtain some of these soluble mineral products, which are mineral *plant foods*. This decay, together with removal of portions, causes minerals and rocks to crumble.

Photo by Martin

Fig. 49. — A fault. Notice that the white layer, once continuous, does not match on the two sides of the fault plane. The fault plane itself has been invaded by a dike of molten volcanic rock.

In cold climates the mechanical action of water is of importance in disintegrating rocks. The water in the soil, in the joint planes, and in the microscopic rock crevices freezes in winter. When water freezes it must expand; and, as a bottle breaks when water freezes in it, so in winter the rocks are often broken by frost action. This frost action is an important agent of rock disintegration, for the pressure developed by expansion on freezing may be as great as 1000 pounds on a square inch of surface (Fig. 54).

Summary. *Water percolates into soil and even into the most minute pores of solid rock. It dissolves some minerals, changes others, and thus causes the rocks to disintegrate. In cold climates frost also aids in disintegration.*

29. Influence of air in weathering. Warming causes the outside layers of rocks to expand, and cooling causes them to contract. A fire

Photo by U. S. G. S.

Fig. 50. — A nearly symmetrical anticline.

built against a rock, for example, causes its surface parts to expand and crack. In hot deserts the warming of rocks by day, and cooling by night are important means of disintegrating them. This is the weathering process known as *exfoliation*, a word that means peeling off of thin layers. Because of it the corners, especially, of projecting rock masses in desert areas are broken off and the tops take on a rounded form. When of large size these rounded-top rock masses are known as *exfoliation domes* (Fig. 454).

Recent careful investigation has shown that processes of weathering other than heating and cooling contribute greatly to the rounding of rock masses by exfoliation, and may be solely responsible for this effect.

The oxygen and carbon dioxide of the air, taken underground by water, help in the processes of disintegration; they also cause changes in damp soil and rock at the surface.

Summary. *Air helps in rock disintegration by its changes in temperature and by supplying oxygen and carbon dioxide.*

Fig. 51. — Joint planes on the shores of Lake Cayuga, New York. The two sets, almost vertical, meet at nearly right angles. The smooth faces of the cliff are due to the fact that the rock has been broken out from it along the joint planes.

30. Organisms as agents of weathering. The roots of plants help to pry rock materials apart. In their search for water and plant food, the roots and tiny rootlets enter any crevice to be found (Fig. 55). On growing larger they exert such pressure on the walls of the crevices as often to rupture them. In this way rocks are broken apart and soils pulverized.

The ash left when wood is burned is largely mineral matter that the roots have taken as plant food. This proves that plants remove mineral substances from the soil and rock, and therefore that they help in disintegration. They aid also by supplying carbon dioxide and organic acids to water which, on soaking into the soil, passes through decaying vegetation.

Animals are likewise effective agents of weathering. This is especially true of burrowing animals, such as earthworms, moles, ants, woodchucks, and prairie dogs. They stir up the soil, thus making it more open to the entrance of water; they bring soil to the surface, thus exposing it to the weather; and some, like the earthworms, take soil into their stomachs, grinding it a little as it passes through. Earthworms are among the most important of agents in soil preparation. Darwin estimated that earthworms bring to the surface every year ten or more tons of rock stuff per acre and that they add over eleven tons of fertility-making organic matter to each acre of soil in the same period.

Summary. *Weathering is aided by plant roots, which pry off fragments and remove mineral substances; by carbon dioxide and organic acids, supplied from decaying vegetation; and by the action of burrowing animals, especially earthworms.*

Fig. 52. — A microscopic view of a thin section of granite rock. This shows that even the small mineral grains of the rock have fine cracks and pores.

31. Rate of weathering. Because the weather had completely destroyed their form, it was found necessary to replace certain stone ornaments (gargoyles) that were placed on the Lincoln Cathedral, in England, about seven centuries ago. On the other hand, delicate scratches on rocks, made by glaciers not less than 10,000 years ago, are still perfectly preserved wherever they have been covered by a foot or two of soil (Fig. 276). These facts show that the rate of weathering is slow, but that it varies with circumstances.

The *nature of the rock* is one cause for difference in the rate of weathering. Some rocks disintegrate quickly, others slowly.

Another cause for variation is *climate*. Where there is little moisture, as in deserts, there can be little change due to frost, solution, or decay; and weathering is, therefore, very slow. An obelisk (Fig. 53), which had stood for over 3000 years in the desert climate of Egypt, began to decay so rapidly when removed to the damp climate of New York that it was necessary to protect it with a glaze. In cold climates, frost action is very active; in hot, damp climates the abundant vegetation supplies organic substances to the warm percolating water, greatly aiding it in its action of changing and dissolving the minerals.

Exposure is also of importance in determining the rate of weathering. Even a thin soil cover protects the rock from the weather. Rock fragments, loosened by weathering, remain on level surfaces and gentle slopes, forming a protecting soil blanket. But on steep slopes, from which the fragments fall away as fast as they are loosened, the rock is kept constantly exposed to the elements (Figs. 37, 66). Therefore, cliffs, precipices, and mountain slopes are places of relatively rapid weathering. That the rocks are crumbling is proved by the fact that every now and then a fragment falls from the cliffs (Fig. 66); but, even in the most favorable places, weathering is so slow that one might see no marked change in a lifetime. Centuries are required for great changes.

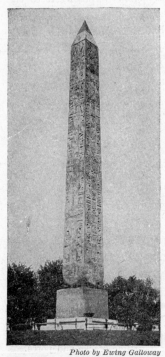

Photo by Ewing Galloway

Fig. 53. — The Obelisk in Central Park.

Summary. *Even under the most favorable conditions, weathering is very slow as time is measured by the length of human life. Its rate varies with the rock, climate, exposure, and steepness of slope. Steep slopes are especially favorable to relatively rapid disintegration because the falling away of loosened fragments leaves the rocks exposed.*

32. Results of weathering. Without question, the most important result of weathering is the formation of soil. While some

Photo by von E.

Fig. 54. — Percolating water seeping out of the rock and freezing.

Fig. 55. — The roots of a tree prying open the rock of a ledge.

of the crumbling rock is removed in solution, there is a remnant, or *residue*, which cannot be dissolved. This remnant forms *residual soil* (Figs. 56, 57), which sometimes mantles the rock to a depth of over a hundred feet. For every foot in thickness of residual soil as much as ten feet in thickness of the original rock may have been removed by solution. A large part of the land is covered by residual soil, resting on the rock whose decay produced it. Other

Photo by Russell

Fig. 56. — Residual soil. A few rounded pieces of solid rock remain, not yet completely disintegrated.

kinds of soil are those brought by wind, by rivers, and by glaciers, or raised from the shallow sea bottom adjoining coasts. Such soils are not residual, but *transported*.

Weathering supplies mineral substances for underground water to remove in solution. It is this that gives "hardness" to water, and the valuable properties to many mineral springs. One of the most common of these dissolved mineral substances is carbonate of lime, which supplies corals and shell-bearing animals with the lime from which beds of lime-stone are made in the sea.

Rock fragments, loosened from cliffs by weathering, gather at the base, forming *talus slopes* (Figs. 66, 159, 161). Occasionally great masses are loosened, failing as *landslides* and in *avalanches* (Figs. 58, 160, 440). There is also a very slow, almost imperceptible movement of rock fragments down even gentle slopes, known as *soil creep*. It is this that makes some streams muddy even during periods of dry weather.

Soil creep, although so slow, is on the whole probably more important than the fall of larger pieces of rock from cliffs and the rushing down of

Fig. 57. — A diagram to illustrate the formation of residual soil. Notice that the soil is finer near the surface, where roots and earthworms penetrate, and that it grades downward into solid rock.

great masses in landslides. That is because soil creep is going on always and on even the gentlest of slopes. In dry weather when the sun's heat causes the soil to crack, because moisture is evaporated from between the particles, the crack opens downhill. At the time of the next rain the soil fills up again with water and the crack is closed, again downhill. That means that the block of soil material up-slope has moved down a fraction of an inch. The same effect is produced, as frost and heat and cold cause expansion and contraction. As a result, the whole sheet of loose mantle-rock material overlying the bed rock is slowly, but surely and continually, moving downhill to the streams and to the sea. In places the motion of the soil creep is so strong that it causes the edges of the solid rock to be bent over (Fig. 59).

The loosened rock fragments, large and small, are used by the rivers as tools (Fig. 66) in cutting their valleys; and, on reaching the sea, they are deposited as beds of sedimentary rock (p. 46). By this removal of rock fragments and dissolved mineral substances, supplied by weathering, valleys are being slowly broadened.

Finally, weathering is a delicate tool of rock sculpturing. It easily discovers which rocks are weak, and which durable; and, by removing the weaker rocks faster, it etches the durable strata into relief (Figs. 38, 44). The importance of this fact is more fully shown in later chapters.

Photo by Hamlin

Fig. 58. — Landslide on south side of San Jacinto River, California.

Summary. *Among the important results of weathering not described in previous paragraphs are:* (1) *the formation of residual soil, or soil of rock decay;* (2) *the supply of soluble mineral substances to water;* (3) *the formation of talus and landslides;* (4) *the supply of cutting tools to rivers;* (5) *the supply of materials for the formation of sedimentary strata;* (6) *valley broadening; and* (7) *rock sculpturing.*

33. The agents of erosion. Besides weathering, which decomposes and disintegrates the rock, thus preparing it for removal, there are several agents of *erosion* which remove and deposit rock fragments. The action of these agents is fully stated in other chapters and requires merely to be mentioned here.

These agents are: (1) *wind*, especially active along the coast (p. 377) and in deserts (p. 146), where there is little vegetation to protect the soil; (2) *rivers* (Chapter IV), everywhere engaged in removing materials produced by weathering, and at the same time often deepening their own valleys with the rock fragments that they carry; (3) the *oceans*, whose waves, tides, and currents attack the land along the coasts (Chapter XI), and in which sediment

Photo by Walcott

Fig. 59. — Edge of rock bent and broken at surface by downhill creep.

washed from the land is deposited (pp. 46, 327); (4) *lakes*, which resemble oceans (p. 386); and (5) *glaciers* (Chapter VIII), at present important only in high mountains and in the polar latitudes.

Summary. *The agents of erosion — wind, rivers, oceans, lakes, and glaciers — remove and deposit rock fragments.*

34. Denudation. The combined effect of the agents of weathering and erosion may be called *denudation*. By denudation the lands are being sculptured (Figs. 78, 79a, 79b) and their general level lowered. (Some writers use the word erosion in the sense that denudation is here defined.) If the material removed by the Mississippi River were taken equally from every part of its drainage area, the surface of the valley would be lowered one foot in 6000 years (Fig. 64).

Opposed to this tendency to wear the land away is the constant change in level of the land (p. 50), by which plains are being raised above the sea, plateaus made higher, and mountains uplifted (p. 29). These uplifts are continually giving denudation new tasks to perform. Were it not for this elevation of the land, it is probable that the continents would long since have been reduced nearly to sea level; for the age of the earth is very great.

Summary. *Denudation is the combined action of weathering and erosion. It tends to lower the land; but, though the age of the earth is great, frequent uplift has prevented denudation from lowering the continents in entirety to the condition of a level plain.*

35. Age of the earth.[1] No one knows how old the earth is. But all who have studied the question are agreed that it cannot be less than many millions of years, and most geologists hold that it must be at least five hundred million years old.

So slow is the action of denudation that a person living by a river side, or on the seashore, may see no notable change, even in a lifetime; yet careful study will show that slow changes are in progress. Geological study has proved that slow changes have accomplished great results in the past; and this could not have happened unless there had been a great length of time involved.

Among these evidences of great changes are the following. The Colorado River has slowly cut a canyon over a mile in depth. Lofty mountain ranges once existed where New York and Philadelphia now stand; but these mountain ranges were later quite completely worn away. Volcanoes also have been worn down to their very roots. To have accomplished slowly these great results demands vast periods of time. Sedimentary rocks furnish evidence leading to the same conclusion. Commonly years are required for a layer of sediment a foot thick to be deposited; yet some sections reveal 40,000 feet of strata that were deposited in ancient seas.

The sodium in the salt of the oceans may all be assumed to have been removed by solution from rocks by weathering and carried down to the sea by rivers. Once in the sea the salt does not get back to the land. Sea water evaporates to give moisture to the air and fall as rain. The salt remains. The total quantity of salt in the oceans is quite accurately known, as is also the total amount of salt brought to the ocean each year

---

[1] For a list of the geological periods, see Appendix D.

by rivers. Accordingly, by dividing the figure representing the amount of salt in the oceans by that of the annual addition through rivers a quotient is obtained that expresses the probable age of the oceans. This quotient varies between seventy million and one hundred million years accordingly as different corrections are used. But in any case the age of the oceans is shown to be very great. (See also p. 332.)

From these geological facts the conclusion that the earth is vastly old seems unescapable; and the conclusion is supported by evidence furnished by physicists and biologists. Consequently, all geologists and physical geographers are now as convinced on this point as astronomers are that the sun and stars are millions of miles away. To appreciate fully the conclusions reached in the following pages, the student must start out with the same conviction.

Summary. *Evidence furnished by geologists, physicists, and biologists proves that the earth is many millions of years old.*

TOPICAL OUTLINE, QUESTIONS, AND SUGGESTIONS

TOPICAL OUTLINE. 23. **Relation of man to the land.** Changes noted on a railway journey: larger features; smaller features; industries; cities; relation between land form and industries.

24. **Rocks of the crust.** Three divisions. (A) *Sedimentary rocks:* manner of deposit; terms used; consolidation. (B) *Igneous rocks:* on the surface; intruded into the crust. (C) *Metamorphic rocks:* cause; results; metamorphism in mountains. (D) *Resistance of rocks:* differences in minerals; in rocks; effect on land form, the law of weathering.

25. **Changes in level of the land.** Slow wearing away; movements of the crust; cause; proofs, — from rocks, from present changes; instances; two classes of movements; effect on continents.

26. **Disturbance of the strata.** Original position; position in plains; in mountains; fault; anticline; syncline; dip; monocline; unsymmetrical fold; overturned fold; crumpling; joint planes; importance.

27. **Agents of weathering.** Agents effective; results; protective cover.

28. **Action of underground water.** Entrance of water; proof of its presence, — wells, plant roots, springs; solution; substances aiding solution; changes in minerals; result; plant food; frost action.

29. **Influence of air in weathering.** Heat and cold; exfoliation; effect of oxygen and carbon dioxide.

30. **Organisms as agents of weathering.** (*a*) Plants: mechanical action of roots; removal of mineral substances; aid to underground water. (*b*) Animals: kinds; effects; earthworms.

31. **Rate of weathering.** Illustrations of differences in rate; effect of rock; of climate, — arid, damp, cold, warm and damp; of exposure, — gentle slopes, steep slopes; slowness of weathering.

32. **Results of weathering.** Residual soil; transported soils; dissolved mineral substances; talus; landslides; soil creep; supply of tools to streams; formation of sedimentary strata; valley broadening; rock sculpturing.

33. **The agents of erosion.** Winds; rivers; oceans; lakes; glaciers.

34. **Denudation.** Definition; tendency; effect of uplift.

35. **Age of the earth.** Probable age; reasons for conviction; evidence of great age; importance of grasping the conception.

QUESTIONS. Section 23. What land forms are seen on a journey from Philadelphia to Chicago? What relation between land forms and industries?

24. What are the three divisions of rocks? (A) How are rock fragments assorted by water? What is the meaning of the terms strata, stratum, and stratified? How are stratified rocks consolidated? (B) In what conditions are igneous rocks accumulated on the surface? Describe three kinds of igneous intrusions. (C) What is the nature of metamorphism, and its results? Why is it so common in mountains? (D) How do minerals vary in durability? What two conditions influence the rate of rock disintegration? What effect has this on the form of the land? What is the general law of weathering?

25. What changes are in progress on the earth's surface? What evidences are there of past and present changes of level? What is the nature of these movements? What effect has this on the continents?

26. Why are the strata of plains commonly horizontal? What is the condition in mountains? Define fault; anticline; syncline; dip; monocline. Draw diagrams to illustrate symmetrical, unsymmetrical, and overturned folds. What are joint planes? Of what importance are they?

27. What are the agents of weathering and how do they act?

28. How does underground water enter the rocks? What proofs are there of its presence? In what two ways does it act chemically in disintegrating the rocks? How does it act mechanically?

29. In what ways is the air effective as an agent of weathering? Describe exfoliation and its effects.

30. In what ways do plants aid in weathering? Animals?

31. Give illustrations of differences in rate of weathering. State the three chief causes for differences. What effect has exposure?

32. How is residual soil formed? How else are soils accumulated? Describe soil creep. State the other effects of weathering.

33. What effects are caused by the agents of erosion?

34. What is denudation? How is it opposed?

35. What evidence is there that the age of the earth is great?

SUGGESTIONS. (1) Imitate sedimentation in a glass dish. Place sand, fine pebbles, and clay in the dish with water. Stir vigorously and let it settle. (This experiment may be made even more effective if a mixture of sand, pebbles, and clay is made to represent land, then washed with a sprinkling pot into a glass aquarium partly filled with water.) Where does the finest material settle? Are the layers horizontal? Vary the rate of washing and observe what happens. (2) Even if the rocks and minerals in Appendix C are not studied, specimens of quartz, feldspar, calcite, sandstone, limestone, granite, and marble should be studied. The last four can be obtained readily, probably in a stone yard. The three minerals may be purchased from a mineral dealer for a very small sum. Do not get valuable specimens, but buy by the pound and break up for class use. Study the characteristics mentioned in the Appendix. (3) Are the rocks of your neighborhood horizontal or tilted? If the latter, can you find folds or faults? Describe what you find. Look for joint planes and study them; does water escape from them? Are there any quarries in which they are of use?

(4) Find specimens of rock in the fields, or elsewhere, showing weathering. What signs of weathering do you find? Are there red or yellow stains? What causes them? (5) To prove that water expands on freezing, fill a bottle with water and freeze it. (6) Heat a large piece of stone on one side, then cool it quickly by putting cold water on it. These experiments illustrate the expansion with heat and contraction with cold, though of course in nature the changes are not so great as this. (7) Look for illustrations of roots prying rocks apart. This may best be seen on cliffs where trees are growing. Make a photograph of an especially good example. Tell what you see. (8) Watch the earthworms. The "casts" left when they are driven out of the swollen ground after a heavy rain are made of earth from their stomachs. What evidence do you find that earthworms help in weathering? Darwin considered them of enough importance to write a book on them. (9) If you live in a glaciated country (Fig. 272), look for glacial scratches recently uncovered. Are they fresh? Why? Look for others uncovered for a longer time. Are they fresh? Why? (10) Study the soil of your vicinity carefully and tell its characteristics. (11) If you can find a cliff, look for a talus slope. Of what is it made? Are the fragments angular or round? Are they all of the same kind of rock as the cliff? Have any fragments been removed by water? Have any fallen recently? Go there in spring, when the frost is coming out of the ground, and see if there have been recent falls. (12) If the water of your vicinity is hard, find out if mineral is deposited in tea kettles or in engine boilers. Perhaps the teacher of chemistry may suggest a way of proving that there is mineral in the water. (13) Are any of the streams that you know receiving rock waste from the valley sides? When does most come? Watch the streams to see. Does this sediment prove that denudation is now in progress? Would much change take place in a year? In a century? In a million years? Think of this carefully.

Reference Books. SCOTT, *Introduction to Geology*, The Macmillan Company, New York, 1902; PIRSSON and SCHUCHERT, *Textbook of Geology*, 2 vols., John Wiley & Sons, Inc., New York, 1924; CHAMBERLIN and SALISBURY, *Introductory Geology*, Henry Holt & Company, New York, 1914; MERRILL, *Rocks, Rock Weathering, and Soils*, The Macmillan Company, New York, 1897; PIRSSON and KNOPF, *Rocks and Rock Minerals*, John Wiley & Sons, Inc., 1926; LOOMIS, *Field Book of Common Rocks and Minerals*, G. P. Putnam's Sons, New York, 1924; CLARKE, *The Data of Geo-Chemistry*, Bull. 695 U. S. Geological Survey, 1920; LYON and BUCKMAN, *Nature and Properties of Soils*, The Macmillan Company, New York, 1922.

Laboratory Exercises. Exercises VIII to XIV inclusive in TARR and VON ENGELN's *Laboratory Manual for Physical and Commercial Geography*, The Macmillan Company, New York, should be done in connection with the study of this chapter. See also Appendix C.

CHAPTER IV

RIVERS AND RIVER VALLEYS

36. Supply of water. Part of the rain water returns to the air by evaporation, part sinks into the ground, and part goes over the surface of the ground and is called the *immediate run-off.* That

Fig. 60. — Stream and waterfall at high water, Ithaca Falls, Ithaca, New York. This stream was moving pebbles as large as those in the gravel bar in the foreground. What would be the effect of these while pounding down the face of the falls? Time of snow melting; note remnant of snow patch to left of falls.

portion which passes back to the air need not be considered here. Most of that which sinks into the ground (p. 55) eventually returns to the surface by slow seepage and from springs; it is the *delayed run-off.* The delayed run-off may continue for months on its slow

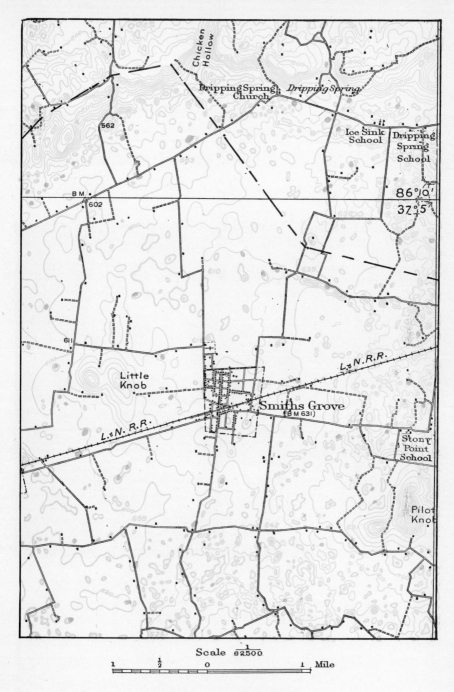

Scale $\frac{1}{62500}$

1   ½   0   1   Mile

Contour interval 20 feet

Plate I. — Part of Mammoth Cave, Kentucky, sheet; Topographic Atlas of the
United States; U. S. Geol. Sur.

Sink holes and sink-hole topography in a region underlain by limestone, see Figs. 86, 87. Account
for the absence of streams in this area.

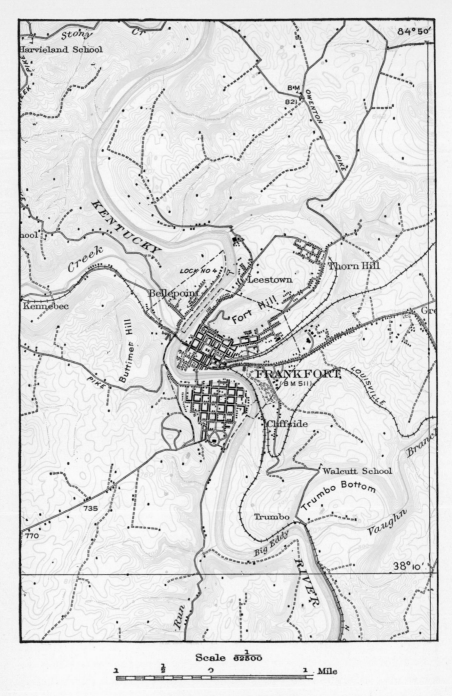

Scale $\frac{1}{62500}$

Contour interval 20 feet.

Plate II. — Part of Frankfort, Kentucky, sheet; Topographic Atlas of the United States; U. S. Geol. Sur.

Entrenched meanders of a rejuvenated stream, see p. 94 and Fig. 129. The northern bend illustrates the cut bank and slip-off slope relation, p. 103. At Trumbo Bottom and at Thorn Hill abandoned meander curves of a higher level occur.

underground journey before finding conditions that favor its return to the surface to give rise to the *perennial flow* of streams. In the long, underground course the irregularities in time and amount of rainfall are averaged into a uniform flow. Were it not for this steady source of supply, rivers would quickly dry up after each rain. Then river navigation would be stopped, river water power would

Fig. 61. — Bellows Falls, Vermont. A stream at the height of a flood. Such a stream is capable of moving bowlders weighing many pounds. Doubling the rate of a stream's flow increases its carrying power sixty-four times. Transporting power increases as the sixth power of the velocity. Suppose that the velocity of a stream capable of moving a bowlder weighing one pound is increased three times. How heavy a bowlder could it then move?

frequently fail, and the water supply of many cities would be cut off for a large part of the time.

From a fourth to a third of the rain water enters streams as immediate run-off. Therefore each rain swells for a time the volume of a stream, by adding much or little to the steady supply from underground. When the snow melts or the rains are heavy, rivers may be quickly transformed to raging torrents (Figs. 61, 95, a, b, c) and floods result.

The presence of the forest tends to reduce floods. Its dense undergrowth, the mat of decaying vegetation, and the tangle of roots very effectively slow up the immediate run-off of the water. There is a faster and a greater run-off (1) during heavy rains than during long, slow drizzles; (2) on clay soils than on sandy soils; (3) on frozen soils than on those with no frost. Disastrous floods usually result from exceptionally heavy rains, the Dayton, Ohio, flood of 1913 for example (Fig. 95 a, b, c).

Some rivers have their water supply quite completely regulated. This is true in large degree of those whose supply comes chiefly from large and copious springs (p. 96). Lakes act almost perfectly as regulating reservoirs (Fig. 62); out of them streams flow with little change in volume; thus the volume of Niagara shows only slight variation. Swamps also help to regulate the water supply. Glaciers regulate the flow of many mountain streams; but the melting of ice and snow in summer on the summits greatly increases the volume of streams that rise in mountains which are snow-covered throughout the year.

Photo by von E.

Fig. 62. — Lake Cayuga, New York. The broad expanses of lake waters serve as regulating reservoirs to stream flow, keeping the volume of outlet streams steady and uniform.

Summary. *Underground water gives to streams a steady supply; the rains and melting snows increase their volume. The forest, nature of the rain, soils, and frost influence the rate and nature of the run-off. Disastrous floods are usually the result of exceptionally heavy rains. Springs, lakes, swamps, and glaciers tend to regulate the volume of rivers.*

37. Rain sculpturing. The surface of a road or a plowed field is often gullied by the washing action of rains and rain-born rills (Fig. 176). The material removed is carried on toward the larger streams. In moist countries (Fig. 63) this rain sculpturing is not usually very effective. In arid regions where there is little vegetation to protect the surface, the loose clayey soils are deeply gullied by the occasional torrential rains characteristic of arid regions; and there is so little weathering that the steep slopes are not greatly rounded. Such rain-sculptured lands are known as *Bad Lands*, one of the largest sections being in South Dakota (Fig. 38). The rain-sculptured areas are unfit for agriculture, and even for cattle raising.

Where the forest has been cleared for centuries, as in parts of China, Greece, and Italy, and in parts of the south of the United States where the cleared land has not been properly cared for, rain sculpturing has destroyed much farm land.

Summary. *In arid lands, and where the forest has been removed, the land is sometimes so gullied by rain sculpturing as to unfit it for agriculture. In the West such regions are known as Bad Lands.*

38. Divides and valleys. In a large view the surface of the land is made up of hills and hollows only, that is of *divides* and *valleys.* Each divide and each valley has its own peculiarities of form, and they differ greatly in size. Parts of a large divide or valley may be subdivided into lesser divides and valleys both. But whether a divide is broad or narrow, it is the area from which the rain water drains off, and the valley is the depression in which the flow collects, and down which it proceeds as a current.

The distinction between valleys and divides exists because the valleys have been eroded into the land by the collected flow of the rain water. With but few exceptions *streams have carved the depressions along which they flow.* The gulleys due to rain sculpture that are so conspicuous in the

Fig. 63.—A rain-sculptured earth column in the Tyrol of Austria. The bowlder which caps it helps to protect the clay beneath.

Bad Lands are the smallest expression of this fact. The valleys of brooks, creeks, rivers, and finally of great streams like the Mississippi are progressively larger.

There are three important lines of evidence that streams carve their valleys. One is that the valleys vary in form according to the kind of mantle-rock and bed-rock material, the *structure*, into which they have been cut. This point is considered more fully in other parts of this book. A second is that quite uniformly there is a correspondence between the size of a stream and the size of its valley. A small stream flows down a small valley, a larger stream down a greater valley. The third is that all streams transport mineral and rock matter in solution, and also as fragments. Many streams are always muddy, others are sediment-laden at times of high water, but all streams carry some rock stuff all the time. This material must come from somewhere. The natural source is from the sides and bottom of the course along which the stream flows. Hence it follows that the streams must be enlarging their

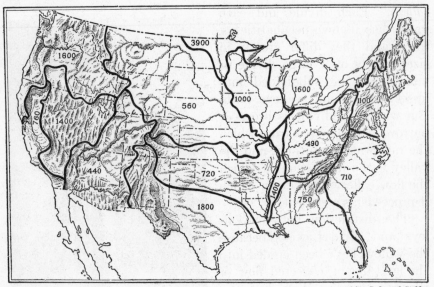

After Dole and Stabler

Fig. 64. — Map to show estimated rate at which level of land is being reduced by denudation processes. The figures in the different areas are the number of years required for the land to be lowered one inch. The figures are approximate and comparative, not exact.

valleys, and if they are doing so now, they must have done so in the past (Fig. 65).

Summary. *Most broadly considered the surface of the land is made up of divides and valleys only. Various lines of evidence make it clear that the valleys exist because streams have carved them into the mantle- and bed-rock structure.*

39. The rock load of rivers. To the mineral load which is brought in solution by underground water (p. 55) is added some which the river water dissolves from its bed. This dissolved load is sometimes very noticeable, as when river water is "hard," or, as in southwestern United States, even salt or alkaline.

Fragments of rock, loosened by weathering (Figs. 66, 81, 128), or washed in by the rain, are also carried by rivers. Water buoys up these suspended rock fragments so that they lose about one third of their weight. A current moving at the rate of one and a half or two miles an hour, that is about half as fast as a man walks, will transport small pebbles; one moving a quarter of a mile an hour carries only clay. In mountain torrents and during times

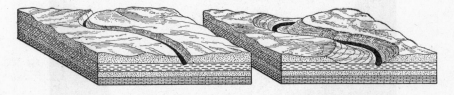

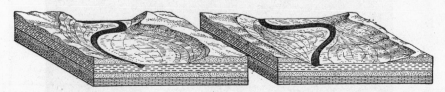

Fig. 65. — Four diagrams to illustrate valley broadening by lateral swinging.

of flood (Fig. 61) bowlders weighing hundreds of pounds are swept along; but only sand and clay can be moved over level lowlands.

These rock fragments are used as tools of erosion. The grinding of pebbles together rounds them and gradually wears them down to sand and clay; and the river bed is also worn away, or eroded, by the grinding of these fragments against it.

The load which rivers bear may be judged from the following. The Mississippi River annually carries to the sea 7,500,000,000 cubic feet of sediment. This would make a prism one mile square at the base and 268 feet high. It also carries 2,850,000,000 cubic feet of mineral matter in solution. Other rivers are bearing similar loads. From this it is evident that rivers are performing a great task in removing rock waste from the lands (p. 72, Figs. 64, 99).

Summary. *Rivers bear great loads of minerals in solution; also rock fragments, whose size varies with the velocity of the currents. These are used as tools of erosion.*

40. Erosive action of rivers. Rivers aid in lowering the general

Fig. 66. — The Gunnison River, Colorado. Rock fragments from the cliffs have made a talus, which, sliding into the river, supplies it with tools for erosion. A railway follows this narrow valley, one of its bridges being seen in the distance. To pass along this gorge it has to wind about, crossing the stream by bridges and tunneling the rocks.

level of the land by removing the materials supplied by weathering and by rain wash. At certain periods in their history most of them

Fig. 67. — A narrow gorge (Enfield) in central New York. The stream course is here guided by two joint planes which cause the smooth, straight walls between which the water is flowing in the middle distance. Note the dislodged, rectangular block of rock in the course, also the right angle turn of the stream in the distance. What is the significance of these features?

are also engaged in a vigorous attack on their channels. This action is both chemical (*corrosion*) and mechanical (*corrasion*), and it results in the formation of river valleys.

The rate of valley deepening varies greatly according to the rock, the slope, and the volume. A stream naturally cuts faster in weak than in durable rock; on steep slopes than on gentle slopes; with great volume than with small volume. The effect of difference in volume may be seen in many streams, which at ordinary times

Photo by von E.

Fig. 68. — A stream swinging against and undercutting a shale cliff, showing lateral erosion in a gorge. Note that the rock cliff remains vertical or slightly overhanging. See Fig. 65.

erode only little, but when in flood become very effective erosive agents (Figs. 61, 67).

Since sediment supplies rivers with cutting tools, this also has an important effect on river erosion. When there is little sediment, erosion is greatly reduced. For example, Niagara River emerges from Lake Erie as clear water, the sediment having been deposited in the lake. Therefore, down to the Falls, the river has been able to do very little toward cutting a valley (Fig. 461). The Colorado River, on the other hand, with a heavy load of sediment, has cut an enormous canyon (Figs. 128, 458), which it is still rapidly deepening.

Other rivers, like the lower Mississippi, have more sediment than they can carry, and must deposit some of it, building up their beds. Rivers that are deepening their valleys are said to be *degrading* (Fig. 67), those that are building up their beds are *aggrading* their valleys (Figs. 96, 103).

Joint planes also influence the rate of erosion, and sometimes direct the course of a stream (Fig. 67). Ice is likewise of importance. In winter it diminishes the supply of water; but in spring its melting adds to the floods; and it breaks off fragments of the rock and carries them along.

Photo by Martin

Fig. 69. — Lateral swinging of a stream against an unconsolidated clay bank, which is caused to slump and slide into the stream continually. In this way the valley is being broadened. Compare with Fig. 68 where the same process is acting on consolidated rock.

Summary. *As rivers cut vertically on their beds, the rate varies with the rock, slope, volume, and sediment supply. Some rivers are degrading, others aggrading, their valleys. Joint planes and ice also influence the rate and direction of river erosion.*

41. Potholes. Much of the first narrow down-cutting of the valley of a stream that flows over a steep slope is wrought by *pothole* grinding (Fig. 70). As the current rushes along its course, it encounters some variation in the structure of the bed rock in its

channel. This may be the place where two joint planes intersect
and form a minute depression. A grain of sand or a pebble lodges
there and is swirled around and around by the water passing over.
Thus the lodged fragment is itself reduced in size by grinding
against the bottom, but meanwhile it, in turn, makes the original
hollow deeper. Other pebbles lodge, the current itself is set to
swirling at that point, and shortly a considerable depression, a
pothole, is excavated. Once started a pothole is maintained even

Photo by von E.

Fig. 70. — A single pothole in Watkins Glen, New York. Account for the fluting of
the rocks on the side of the pothole.

after the general level of the bed of the stream has been lowered
beyond the depth of the original irregularity in the bed-rock
structure.

The bottom of the pothole becomes gradually wider as it develops. Larger and larger grinders become lodged and more and
more of the current of the stream is involved. The name comes
from the resemblance to an old-fashioned, round-bellied pot. Other
potholes are started and grow large. Eventually two potholes
intersect at the bottom. Ordinarily the current at flood time then
breaks down the narrow ridge of rock remaining between them at

the top, but occasionally this persists as a miniature *natural bridge* (Fig. 71). As the processes of pothole boring and intersection continue, the whole channel of the stream is sunk in the rock. The operation is very like an easy way of making a deep groove in a board — by first making a series of auger holes in a line and close beside each other and then whittling out the ridges between with a pen knife.

Summary. *Pothole grinding plays a very important part in the down-*

Photo by Libbey

Fig. 71. — Series of intersecting potholes with remnant natural bridges above, in lava rock, Hawaii. Note the potholes above the waterfalls. What will happen when the bottom of the pothole just above the falls has been worn slightly larger in diameter? What has happened to the level of the tops of the natural bridges below the falls?

ward erosion of swift-flowing streams. The process of pothole grinding makes a very interesting study and may readily be observed in many regions.

42. Waterfalls. When a stream is degrading its bed, conditions are often discovered which cause the formation of rapids and falls. Most commonly a difference in the durability of the strata is responsible. Weak rocks are cut more rapidly than strong, massive, or durable rocks, therefore rapids and falls occur where a degrading stream flows from a strong to a weak layer. Such falls are very common in regions of horizontal strata, where strong layers (Fig. 72) retard erosion upstream while weaker layers beneath and downstream are removed. This undermines the strong layer, and when a piece breaks off, the fall retreats upstream (Fig. 73a, b), its crest always being located on the steep edge of the durable stratum (Fig. 72). There are thousands of illustrations of this, of

Photo by Harris

Fig. 72. — Vicksburg, Mississippi. A durable layer of rock in a stream bed. When the water is higher there is a fairly large fall, and the falling water removes the less resistant layer from beneath and undermines the strong formation at the crest.

which Niagara, located on a massive and durable layer of dolomitic (see Appendix C) limestone (Fig. 461), is the largest and best known.

Falls and rapids show that streams concentrate their energy at points where the declivity of the stream course is greatest. This is well illustrated by Niagara, where the falling water has excavated a deep hole, called a *plunge pool,* at the base of the fall. A plunge pool is a large scale example and special kind of pothole (Fig. 462). Because of the plunge-pool action at the bottom, aided by weathering above, the valley below a falls over horizontal strata commonly takes an amphitheater form. The concentration of degradation at the points where the stream-bed slope is greatest means also that such places are being most rapidly reduced to the average slope of the stream's channel.

Not all waterfalls are over horizontal strata (Figs. 74, 457). If the strata dip upstream, the falls tend to disappear very rapidly by intersecting with the general slope of the stream. If the durable rocks extend vertically across the stream bed, the falls (*e.g.* Yellowstone Falls) do not recede but are gradually lowered by the wearing down of the top of the strong layer. If the durable rock dips down stream, a *rapids* is formed over its dipping top surface. *Joint-plane falls* are a special type where a strong layer is so much cut by joints that the crest of the falls is irregularly broken by the joint blocks falling away. In horizontal strata if the vertical distance between one strong layer and the next below is not great in proportion to the depth of the stream current, rapids are formed. The Lachine Rapids of the St. Lawrence are of such origin. A special type of waterfall (*e.g.* Yosemite Falls) called a hanging valley fall (p. 270) is found in glaciated regions.

Waterfalls and rapids are of great importance in supplying power, the water being led through canals or pipes and allowed to fall upon a wheel or against a turbine which turns machinery. Of course the natural waterfall is then diminished in size or caused to disappear completely. Niagara Falls power, transmitted by electricity, lights and runs the cars of Buffalo and supplies energy for great chemical industries; falls in the Alps and Sierra Nevada supply electric power for places many miles away.

Summary. *Falls and rapids, of use for water power, are common where a degrading stream flows from strong to weak rocks as at Niagara. There are many special types and famous examples of these phenomena.*

43. Valley widening. The greater part of the widening of stream valleys is directly due to weathering (Figs. 66 and 128), but the stream promotes both the weathering and the widening by removing the loosened fragments as they are brought to its channel by gravity. As the top of the valley side is the earliest cut through by the stream and continues to be the steepest and most exposed part for a long time, the attack of the weathering processes acts there first and continues there to be most rapid and effective for a long period. Accordingly valleys very quickly become broader at the top than the width of the stream current.

Streams also broaden their valleys directly by lateral cutting (Figs. 65 and 68). This is especially true where the river is cutting into mantle rock (Fig. 69) or very slightly consolidated bed rock,

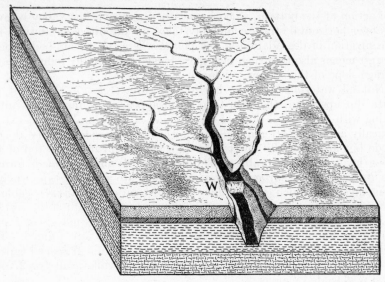

73a

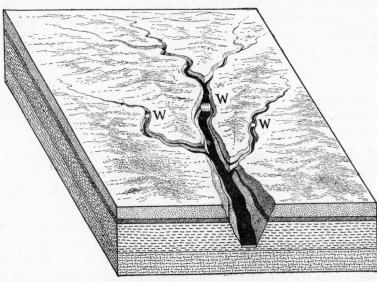

73b

Figs. 73a and 73b. — Two diagrams to illustrate the history of a waterfall. In 73a a strong layer (the darkest) has a waterfall (W) over its edge. As the falling water undermines this strong layer the fall retreats upstream, always being located on the strong layer. At a later stage, therefore (73b), the fall is farther upstream; and falls are also present on the same layer in two tributaries. The stream erosion, largely due to waterfall recession, has formed a deep gorge below the fall, as in the case of Niagara.

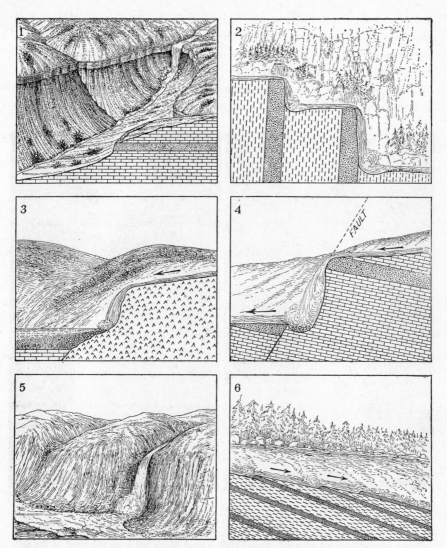

Fig. 74. — Diagrams to illustrate various causes for waterfalls and rapids. No. 1 shows the most common type: a strong layer, horizontal or dipping upstream, underlain by weak formations. Niagara is this type. In No. 2 vertical masses of stronger rocks cause the falls. These falls do not retreat upstream. Why? Yellowstone Falls are of this type. In No. 3 the stream leaves a wide area of resistant rocks to flow over a similar wide stretch of weak rocks. The falls along the Fall Line (p. 123) originated in this way. No. 4 is uncommon and does not persist long after the break occurs unless the nature and arrangement of the rock formation favor falls development. Explain why this is so. No. 5 is a type of falls found in glacial and glaciated regions (see p. **70**). Yosemite Falls are of this type. No. 6 shows that rapids develop instead of falls if the resistant layers dip downstream.

and flows in a curved course swinging first against one bank and then against the other.   Thus the bottom of the valley as well as the top is widened.   This explains a feature that students often have difficulty in understanding; why valleys are commonly wider at the bottom than is the stream channel.   On observing this fact a first conclusion is that the stream was once larger than in the

Photos by Howe and von E.

75a   75b

Figs. 75a and 75b. — Taughannock Falls near Ithaca, New York, 220 ft. high.   The angles and smooth rock faces near the upper part, and the angle in the crest of the fall, are caused by joint planes.   About 1900 a huge block fell from the crest of the fall, giving it its present shape (75b).   Before that, the crest of the fall projected down-stream, as is shown in 75a, the left figure.   Examine the rock walls below the crest of the falls in both pictures.   What evidence, if any, of changes do you note?

present.   This is not necessarily the case, and not even normally true, although the flood-flow of streams does greatly aid in the bottom-widening process.

Summary.   *Valleys are widened at the top by weathering and at the bottom by the lateral cutting of the current.   A valley considerably wider* *than the stream current does not necessarily, or even ordinarily, mean that the stream once had a greater volume.*

44. Headwater erosion. Streams also lengthen their valleys. This takes place through the process of *headwater erosion* (p. 187). Where the flow of the rain wash first becomes concentrated in a current, a gully in the soil is formed. At the head of such a gully the soil gradually crumbles away (Fig. 176) in much the same manner that the crest of a waterfall recedes. Thus a channel depression is gradually extended headwards into the divide, is deepened and widened, and the length of the valley increased.

Summary. *Streams lengthen their valleys by the extension of rain gullies into the divide areas. This process is called headwater erosion.*

LIFE HISTORY OF A RIVER VALLEY

A river valley, like an animal or plant, changes as it grows older. To understand these changes, or the life history of a river, it seems best to start with simple conditions — a plain of moderate elevation, with nearly horizontal strata, and a moist climate. This might be an old sea bottom (Figs. 41, 112) recently uplifted to form dry land. Later study will show that there are many departures from such ideally simple conditions; but

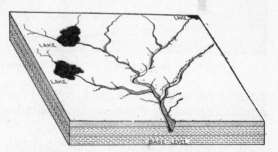

Fig. 76. — A young drainage system on a plain. The valley bottoms are still well above base level; the divides are flat-topped; there are few tributaries in the main streams; and lakes still exist.

these variations will be better understood if we first study a simple case. Such a study will reveal some important laws of valley formation.

45. Young stream valleys. On such a plain as that just described the drainage is at first somewhat indefinite. Rain water fills depressions due to original inequalities in the level of the surface of the plain, forming shallow lakes; and large expanses of the level plain form flat-topped divides, often swampy, because tributaries to drain them have not developed. Wherever water runs off, it flows downhill in consequence of the original slope, or has a consequent course.

The *consequent streams* quickly cut into the plain, forming narrow, steep-sided valleys (Figs. 76, 109). As they degrade along their beds, they discover differences in resistance of the strata, and therefore develop falls (Fig. 73a, b) and rapids. At the same time weathering and lateral swinging slightly widen the valley.

There is a limit below which no part of a stream may deepen its bed, and this is called its *base level* (Fig. 77). The level of the sea is the permanent base level, and the down-cutting of every stream that enters the sea is arrested by it. Lakes act as temporary base levels; but their effect does not last long, because the sediment that the streams bring, fills and destroys them (p. 311).

While the lakes are being filled or drained and the valleys deepened, tributaries are developing. Little by little the tributary

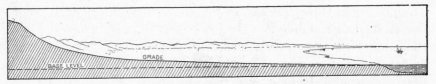

Fig. 77. — Diagram to illustrate the meaning of grade and base level.

streams gnaw their way back from the main stream by headwater erosion, narrowing the flat-topped divides and in time draining the level, swampy areas.

A stream with these characteristics — a steep-sided valley, waterfalls, lakes, ill-defined divides, and tributaries only partly developed — is a *young stream* and its valley is a *young valley*. It has not acted long; consequently its valley is in the first stages of development; it is still undergoing rapid change in form. A young stream valley is better developed in its lower portion than above, as a young tree has a thick, strong trunk and delicate, growing branches. The Niagara Gorge (Fig. 460) and Colorado Canyon (Fig. 128) are good examples of young stream valleys (see also Figs. 166, 443); but no lakes remain in the whole course of the Colorado.

Although such valleys are termed young, the time required to develop them even so far, is long, measured in years. A river may have been eroding for 5000 or even 50,000 years, and yet have a valley with the characteristics of youth. As in the case of plants, some of which grow old in a few weeks while others require months or even years, so in river valleys there is a great difference, under different circumstances, in the time required to pass the stage of youth. Yet in all cases the features of youth are so distinctive that a young valley is hardly more difficult to distinguish than a young plant.

Summary. *A young river is one that has not advanced far in the development of its valley. It, therefore, has a steep-sided valley, a bottom as wide only as the current, few tributaries, indefinite divides, and, if conditions favor, waterfalls and lakes. The term "youth" does not refer to years, but to the stage of development.*

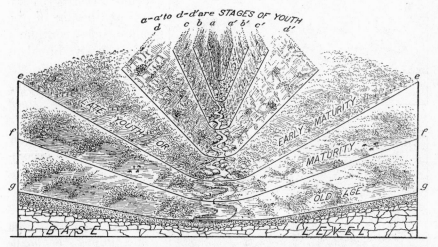

Fig. 78. — To illustrate the broadening of valleys from youth to old age. Note that in youth stream valleys have first a gorge and later a "V" form. This V is widened at the top as maturity is attained.

46. The grade of a stream. The lowest gradient to which a stream can cut its channel is one down which it is just able to carry its sediment load. This lowest slope, specifically called the *grade*, is a curved line, reaching base level at the river mouth and rising rapidly near the divide (Fig. 77). All streams that have not reached grade are eroding toward it, and young streams, which have a steeper slope than necessary, are actively degrading their beds toward grade. It often happens, however, that a stream has slopes so gentle in some sections that it cannot move its sediment load over them. Deposit is made in those parts and this steepens the slope. Most streams on broad flood plains are thus aggrading their valleys.

Summary. *The grade of a stream is the lowest slope over which the current can move its sediment load. Young streams are degrading their valleys toward this grade; but many streams are engaged in aggrading portions of their courses and such deposit develops a steeper slope.*

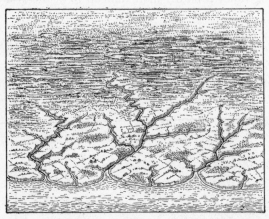

79a

47. Mature valleys.
When grade is reached by a river, further down-cutting ceases; but weathering of the valley sides continues. This slowly broadens the valley, wearing the sides back and making the slopes less steep (Figs. 78, 79a, 79b). The broadening of the valley is first accomplished near the mouth; but it slowly extends upstream. Young streams exist for a long time among the headwaters of a river system, as young twigs appear on the outer branches of even an old tree.

79b

Figs. 79a and 79b. — To illustrate increase in the area and length of the slopes subject to weathering and erosion as the valleys broaden and lengthen. In 79a the slopes leading down to the valleys are short and few; in 79b they are present on nearly the whole surface. 79a is the stage of youth; 79b that of maturity.

In a *mature* stream valley, grade has been reached throughout most of the course, and any lakes that may have originally existed have long since been filled. Nor can there be waterfalls, because the graded stream is no longer cutting downward into the rock.

Tributaries to the mature stream valley have been developed

in such numbers that the divides have become dissected, hence well defined, and all water that falls on the land finds slopes ready for it to flow down (Plate V). Again the comparison may be made to a tree, which at first has a trunk and few branches, but, as it grows older, develops an increasing number of minor branches and twigs.

By the development of so many tributaries the number of slopes and the amount of surface exposed to weathering are greatly

After Powell

Fig. 80. — A superimposed stream; Green River, the Uinta Mountains, Utah-Colorado. The stream first cut its valley in horizontal strata (background of drawing) that formerly extended unbroken across the top of the folded mountain ridge. As the river degraded its valley it was let down, *superimposed,* on the anticlinal structure, across which it has eroded a narrow gorge. This is one origin of *water-gaps.*

increased (Fig. 79a, b). These increasing slopes may supply so much sediment to the main streams that they cannot carry it all to the sea. They then begin to aggrade their courses to establish a steeper grade down which to carry the sediment. In doing this they build flood plains (p. 100).

Summary.   *A valley with moderately sloping sides, a fairly well-established grade, no lakes, waterfalls or rapids, well-defined divides, numerous tributaries, and flood plains in its lower portion is mature.*

Photo by Hillers-Walcott

Fig. 81.— Doe River, Tennessee, cutting across the Appalachian highlands in a narrow, winding valley with sides so steep that the forest has not been removed.   This valley has the typical V form of late youth.   Notice that the spurs alternate on the two sides of the valley.   Compare with Figs. **82, 83.**

48. Old valleys. As valleys grow older, the slopes become more and more gentle (Fig. 82) and the divides lower until the whole surface of the land is reduced almost to sea level. A once high, rugged area, reduced in old age to a low, rolling surface, is called a *peneplain* (almost a plain) (Figs. 217, 441). At intervals an eminence of considerable height may rise above the level of a peneplain; this is a *monadnock*, named after Mt. Monadnock, N. H. (Fig. 292), and remains high because of the very superior resistance of its rock structure or because it was a divide area, hence originally higher than the surrounding region (p. 73 and Fig. 439).

Photo by B. & M. R.R.

Fig. 82. — **The Connecticut River at Northampton, Massachusetts.** A valley in beginning old age, or very late maturity. Note the very extensive flood plain and the low valley slopes in the far distance. A city and a wide countryside both find ample room on the valley floor.

Many parts of the continents are ancient enough to have become peneplains; but there are numerous accidents which commonly interfere with this result. Of these accidents the most important are uplifts of the land, which continually give to streams new tasks to perform. Therefore, few valleys have passed the stage of maturity.

Summary. *Old valleys are so broad and old divides so low that the surface is reduced almost to a plain, or to a peneplain; but uplift of the land is so frequent that few regions remain in this condition.*

49. Special conditions. In cutting into the strata of plains and plateaus, rivers may wear down through the horizontal layers to buried mountains (Fig. 128). Such rivers are said to be *superimposed* on the buried structure (Fig. 127). The Snake River, for example, has discovered an old, buried mountain mass in one part of its canyon.

An uplift of the land gives a river new life, or revives it. The stream then cuts a narrow gorge in the bottom of its previously developed valley (Figs. 129, 448). Such a valley is *rejuvenated*, or made young again. Sometimes a river is effective enough as an eroding agency to cut

Fig. 83. — Passumpic Valley, St. Johnsbury, Vermont, fully mature, opened broadly by weathering. The stream has ceased down-cutting and is bordered by a broad flood plain, the site of a village, farms, a railroad, and roads. The forest has been partially cleared from the gentle valley slopes which have been made to furnish plow and pasture lands. The valley is partly filled with glacial deposits, see p. 296.

through mountain folds as they rise across its path and so to maintain its course. Such a stream is held to be *antecedent* to the present topography; the Columbia River crossing the Cascade Mountains is an example of this (Fig. 166).

Where a stream has a wandering flow over a rock structure that shows no differences in resistance to direct and guide its course, it is said to be an *insequent* stream.

Summary. *Superimposed rivers are those which cut through one rock structure to another of different position. A rejuvenated river is one made young again by any cause, as by uplift. An antecedent river maintains its course across obstructions raised by changes in level of the land. An insequent river has a course not guided by rock structure.*

50. Importance of valley form. Young valleys encourage some of man's activities and interfere with others. The waterfalls furnish power; and the lakes are valuable for navigation, for their influence on the climate of neighboring land, and as sources of food-fish. But land cut by young valleys is difficult to cross, the valley bottoms furnish only steep and difficult sites for roads and railways (Figs. 66, 78, 81), and are altogether unsuited for agriculture. On the other hand, where the drainage is so young that

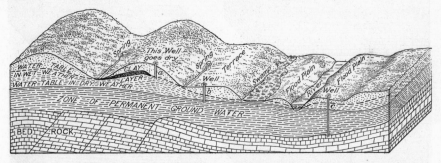

Fig. 84. — Diagram to show the relation of the water table to the surface in dry and wet weather, and its relation to springs, wells, swamps, and streams. Why do some springs and wells go dry?

the flat divides are only little if at all dissected by tributaries, wide level stretches of desirable land may be had on the uplands.

As contrasted with a region of young valleys, in one with mature or old valleys the valley bottoms are the seats of agriculture; their fertile flood plains are among the best farm lands of the world. Travel across country is easy, and the river valleys are important highways (Figs. 82, 83). The rivers, if large, have so gentle a flow that they are navigable. Thus, flourishing farms and thriving towns and cities line the river banks and dot the slopes of mature and old valleys.

Summary. *Young valleys are unfavorable for occupation; but mature and old valleys are adapted to agriculture and dense settlement.*

51. The water table, springs, and underground channels. All the pores and fissures of the mantle rock and bed rock are filled with water at varying depths below the surface, according to the place and the time. Under hills the level of the *ground water* is generally deeper than in valleys; during a dry period it is deeper than after a rain. The undulating and varying top surface of the level of the underground water at any time is known as the *water table* (Fig. 84). Because the water-table surface is not level, underground water, like surface water, flows by pull of gravity from higher to lower levels. On account of the friction resulting

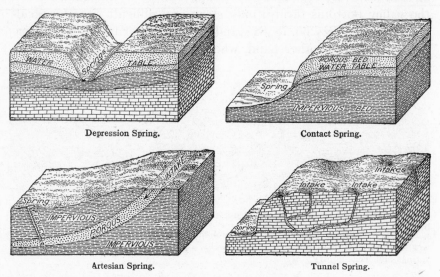

Depression Spring.   Contact Spring.

Artesian Spring.   Tunnel Spring.

Fig. 85. — Four diagrams illustrating different types of springs. The general conditions that give rise to springs are· outcrop of the water table (see also Fig. 84), an impervious bed below a porous bed, and fissures, larger than average, leading to the surface. The source of the water must be higher than the level of the spring.

from the narrowness of the fissures the underground flow is a slow percolation rather than a current. However, the supply is fast enough ordinarily to keep wells full if they are sunk below the level of the *permanent water table,* the lowest level to which the water table sinks in a given locality. Also the level of the surface of any permanent, flowing stream or permanent lake or swamp must coincide with the level of the water table at the shore line. Why?

Where conditions are especially favorable, underground water

(p. 55) is led back to the surface, appearing as a spring. Sometimes it comes out along a porous, sandy layer, sometimes along a joint plane. There are many springs along rivers even below normal stream level; but they occur also on hillsides and, in fact, wherever favorable conditions direct underground water to the surface (Figs. 84, 85).

Some large and permanent springs rise from deep in the ground through fault planes, often bringing heated water to the surface. Such springs commonly have so much mineral in solution that they are known as mineral springs, and have important medicinal properties; in some instances radio-activity also. The Hot Springs of Arkansas, and the mineral springs of Saratoga, Carlsbad, and Vichy are examples of medicinal springs.

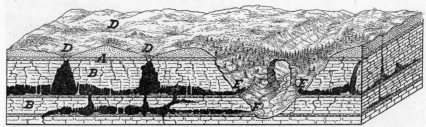

Modified from Shaler

Fig. 86. — To illustrate the formation of limestone caves, sink holes, and natural bridges. The layers *B*, are limestone; *A*, are clay-shale beds, very slightly soluble; *D, D,* are sink holes; *E, E,* cavern entrances; *F,* the place of emergence of a cavern stream. The natural bridge is probably due to partial collapse of a cavern roof or is a remnant of a short underground course of the stream at an earlier time when the lower valley had not been eroded so deeply. Account for the fact that the horizontal passages of the cavern are on the upper surface of the clay-shale layers. What effect has the level of the main drainage of a cavern region on the depth to which the cavern may be dissolved out? Why would there be no solution below the level of the permanent water table?

Water percolating through soluble rock, like limestone, dissolves the rock along joint planes and bedding planes. This often results in the formation of long, irregular underground valleys, or caverns, like that of Mammoth Cave, Kentucky. In such a country much of the drainage is underground (Fig. 86). There may be some large surface streams, but these have few tributaries, the chief water supply coming from the springs (Plate I) that bring the cavern water to the surface. Caverns cannot be dissolved out deeper than the level of the main surface drainage stream of the

region; which, in the Kentucky area, is the Ohio River. Why?
Hence stories of bottomless pits in caves cannot be true.

Entering such a cavern, one passes through a maze of dark, irregular
passages, in which it is easy to lose oneself. From the roof hang *stalactites*
(Fig. 88) of carbonate of lime, which the water dissolved in its passage
through the limestone rock and deposited on emerging into the cavern. In
form they resemble icicles. *Stalagmites* (Fig. 88) are built up from the
cavern floor by the dripping water, as ice columns are formed under a

Photo by Darton

Fig. 87. — A sink hole, near Cambria, Wyoming. The surface drainage flows into
the sink hole and follows cavern passages underground. This sink hole is unusually
large and open at the top. At some distance below the surface it, like others, probably
becomes funnel shaped and clogged by the débris that has fallen in from above.

spout. Often the stalactites and stalagmites unite to form columns
(Fig. 88), and sometimes, as in the Luray Cave, they assume weird and
even beautiful forms.

The surface of a limestone country is pitted with saucer-shaped depressions, known as *sink holes* (Fig. 87 and Plate I). Through these the
water drains into the ground, though commonly the entrance into the
ground is clogged, changing the sink hole to a pond. These sink holes
are caused by settling of the ground, due to solution of the rock beneath.

Fig. 88. — The weird scenery of caverns developed by the irregular formation of stalactites and stalagmites is well shown in this photograph of the "Oriental Palace" in the Endless Caverns of New Market, Virginia.

If there is a cavern below the sink hole the fragments resulting from the collapse and the wash of waste from the slopes tend to clog up the passage to the underground channel.

Weathering, lowering the surface, slowly wears away the cavern roofs. Sometimes only a small part of the roof is left, spanning the valley as a *natural bridge* (Fig. 89). Natural bridges may, however, result from other processes (Figs. 71, 86).

Summary. *The water table is the underground surface below which the pores of the rock are filled with water. Springs occur where conditions direct underground water to the surface, for example: a porous layer, a joint plane, a fault plane (many hot or mineral springs), or a cavern outlet. Caverns occur where underground water dissolves passageways through soluble rock like limestone. The water enters the ground through sink holes, passes along an underground course, and emerges as a spring. It deposits stalactites, stalagmites, and columns in the caverns. A natural bridge may result from the collapse of part of a cavern roof.*

Fig. 89. — Natural Bridge, Virginia. This bridge is probably either part of an old cavern roof, left when the rest was destroyed by weathering; or a remnant of the stream's earlier, higher bed, left when the rest of the valley was deepened by corrosion (erosion by solution).

52. River flood plains. Streams in mature valleys are generally bordered by level plains, built of sediment which the streams have brought. Even a mountain torrent that is degrading its bed may have narrow patches of such deposits on one or both sides. Rivers that are aggrading their courses are always bordered by such alluvial plains, or *flood plains.*

Broad flood plains are due to the fact that there is more sediment than can be carried down the river gradient. Therefore some must be deposited. When such streams rise and overflow their banks, they submerge the neighboring lowland (Figs. 90a, 90b), and, with each flood, deposit a layer of sediment, as mud is deposited

90a

90b   *Photo by Towne*

Figs. 90a and 90b. — Two views of the same stream at different stages in time of flood. In (a) at top, the current is already above low water level; in (b) it has overflowed its banks and is spreading across the flood plain. A further rise develops a complete overflow of the plain and deposit of sediment on its surface. Sand and clay layers remain to raise the level of the plain slightly when the flood subsides.

on a sidewalk when the gutter overflows. This slowly raises the level of the flood plain; and, since it is being built by a broad sheet of water, its surface is made fairly level.

Many broad flood plains, like that of the Nile and the Mississippi (p. 516), are very fertile; and frequent overflow, by bringing new, fine-textured soil, helps to keep them so.   Their levelness and the depth and moistness of their soils further fit them for agriculture. In many arid regions the river water is led out over the flood plains for the purpose of irrigation, and in some arid regions, as along the Nile, the overflows themselves take the place of rainfall.

Photo by Towne

Fig. 91a. — A small ox-bow curve in a meadow brook. A cut-off has been started, but brush was put in to stop it from continuing.

A flood plain is usually highest near the river, because this is the part where the high waters of a flood rising out of the regular channel are first checked, hence deposit most sediment.   This higher portion is known as the *natural levee* (Fig. 96).   On it where a big river has a wide flood plain are farms, towns, and cities; for example, New Orleans (Fig. 94); but behind the natural levee is a much broader, low, swampy tract, too wet for habitation.   At New Orleans, the natural levee was only a few feet above the river level and the swamp.   To protect the towns and farms from overflow, men build still higher embankments, *artificial levees*, which serve to confine many of the floods to the regular channel.   When, however, a great flood breaks through the levee, vast areas are inundated, property is destroyed, and lives lost (Fig. 95a, b, c). Along the Mississippi, such a break is known as a *crevasse*.

No river flows in a perfectly straight line. On the contrary, irregularities in the bed, a slumping down of one bank, and other causes, turn the current toward one side, and cause the stream to cut first at one bank, then at the other (Figs. 92, 93). This starts a curving or swinging of the river, known as a *meander* (Fig. 96), named after a river

Photo by Towne

Fig. 91b. — The same as Fig. 91a with the cut-off completed in spite of the brush. Note the curved river-bar. Why has it formed there?

in Asia Minor whose lower course is very meandering. Flood plains are peculiarly favorable to the development of meander bends because of the low, level land and the loose sediment, which is readily undercut by the current. Although the stream cuts on one bank, the *cut bank*, it deposits sediment on the other, the *slip-off slope* (Figs. 92, 93), and thus in time forms a broad, sweeping curve known as the *ox-bow curve* (Fig. 96). The curves vary in size with the volume of the river, being in the Mississippi fully five miles in diameter. As the meandering continues, it often happens that the stream in time of high water cuts across the neck of a curve and thereafter abandons it (Figs. 91a, 91b) in favor of the new course which is shorter, hence steeper. The lake thus formed is called an *ox-bow lake* (Fig. 296). The ends of such lakes are then sealed off by the deposit of sediment by the river. Flood plains have many such abandoned meanders. On the Mississippi flood plain there are places where the river course has been shortened fifteen miles by a single cut-off.

Summary. *Large flood plains are level tracts of fertile river-built, that is alluvial, land bordering mature and old rivers. They are built up during floods by the deposit of sediment. They are highest near the river, at the natural levee, on which artificial levees are built. The river swings over the flood plain in meander curves, that when later abandoned form ox-bow lakes.*

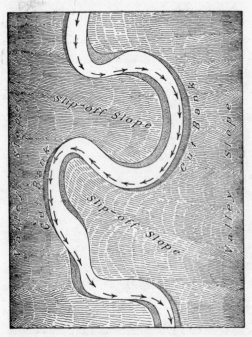

Fig. 92. — To show by arrows how, in meanders, a river current cuts on one bank and deposits on the other.

53. River terraces. The swinging of a river causes it to be first on one side of its valley, then on the other. If it is a degrading instead of an aggrading stream, it cuts downward, as well as laterally, first on one side then on the other. This action may leave *terraces*, or narrow, flat-topped strips, each faced by a steep slope on the side toward the stream (Figs. 97, 98). These are to be distinguished from valley side terraces due to the variation in rate of weathering of horizontal strata of different resistance, as illustrated in the Colorado Canyon (Fig. 128).

If an uplift elevates a flood plain so that the river cuts down into it, a series of perfect terraces is carved in the unconsolidated flood plain deposits previously made. During the removal of any other kind of loose deposits, such as glacial and lake deposits, rivers also carve perfect terraces.

River terraces are commonly excellent farm land. Their soil is normally good; they are well drained; their surfaces are level; and, in arid countries, irrigation ditches are easily led over their tops. Some of the best farm land in the Connecticut valley is terrace land.

Summary. *River terraces are flat-topped strips of land with steep fronts, bordering rivers. They are formed during the removal of unconsolidated*

Fig. 93. — Meanders of Trout Creek, Yellowstone National Park. Here the cut bank and the slip-off slope are both developed to an exaggerated degree.

materials, by a stream that has been revived through uplift, decrease in sediment load, or increase in volume.

54. Deltas. On entering the sea or a lake, a river finds its current suddenly checked. Some of the sediment the river brings is removed by waves and currents, but much is deposited in the quiet water near its mouth, building up land. To this land the

© *Detroit Publishing Co.*

Fig 94. — The Mississippi River, near New Orleans, Louisiana, flowing at a level higher than the flood plain and held in its channel by the artificial levee.

Fig. 95a, b, c. — The Dayton, Ohio, flood of March, 1913. In (a) at top, the first overflowing of the artificial levee into the streets of the city is shown; in (b) the violence of the current as it rushed through the business section. The horses were cut loose by their drivers. The water rose to the top of the lamp-posts. In (c) people are being rescued from houses where they were imprisoned in the upper stories until the flood had in part subsided.

name *delta* is applied, because of the resemblance to the Greek letter delta (Δ), as seen in the delta of the Orinoco (Fig. 100).

Deltas have the triangular shape because on them the river current divides into numerous channels, or *distributaries* (Figs. 99, 100), which spread apart and enter the sea by separate mouths.

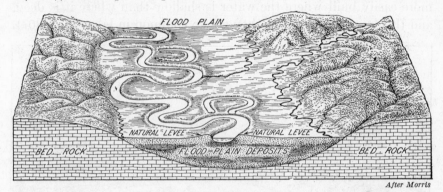

After Morris

Fig. 96. — Diagram of a flood plain in its relation to the bed rock of the valley floor and valley slopes; this shows also meanders, ox-bow lakes, and natural levees.

The river divides because as the current is checked on entering the body of quiet water, its sediment load is dropped right in the channel. The bed of the stream is thus built up higher than the land on either side. Accordingly the current divides into two courses passing on either side of the obstruction. This happens again and again. Thus a gentle gradient is developed by deposition.

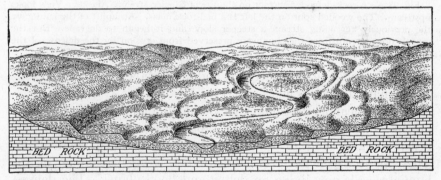

Fig. 97. — Diagram to show the formation of alluvial river terraces by a degrading, meandering river. Account for the fact that the terraces are widest at the points. (See Fig. 98.) Why do the flat tops of the terraces slope gently back toward the valley sides; the tops of the flats at the river level toward the river? This problem will be a test of the degree of understanding attained by able students. (See Fig. 92.)

Deltas are absent from many coasts; for example, northeastern America and northwestern Europe. This is because there has been so recent sinking of the land that there has not yet been time enough to build deltas. It is where the sea bottom is remaining at one level, or slowly rising, that deltas are most common. They are more easily built where the water is shallow than where it is deep, and this is one reason why they are so common in lakes (Fig. 307).

Drawn from a photo

Fig. 98. — A rock-defended terrace on the Lucia Glacier stream, Alaska. View looks upstream. The wooded spur on the left is a bed-rock mass. An uplift of the land gave the previously aggrading stream a steeper slope and it began to degrade. But the gravels downstream from the spur were preserved from erosion by the defense of the consolidated rock.

Absence of tides, strong currents, and large waves are other reasons for so many deltas in lakes.

Rivers meander on deltas, as on flood plains. Indeed, deltas are like flood plains for, as they grow outward, their upper parts become higher and drier and are commonly called flood plains. They make excellent farm land, and a large percentage of the human race is now living on deltas and flood plains. The densest population of China (Fig. 143) and India is centered on the deltas and flood plains of the great rivers, and a large part of Holland is on the delta of the Rhine. The low ground and the danger of floods from sea and river make living in such situations dangerous. Millions of people in India and China have been drowned during floods; but the other attractions are so great that these river-made plains are densely settled.

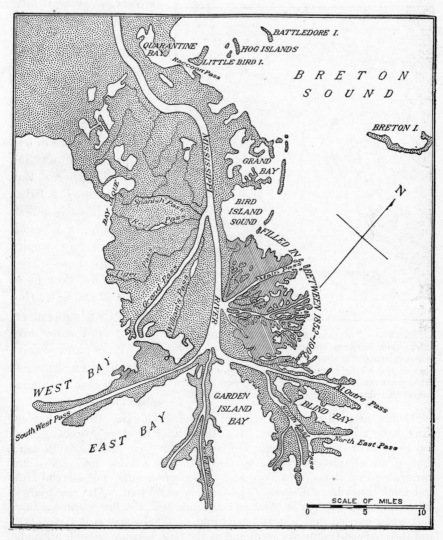

Fig. 99. — The Mississippi delta. Note the area on the right that was filled in between 1852 and 1905. This illustrates how deltas are built out, first on one side, then the other. The area on the left had been filled in before 1852. The U. S. Coast and Geodetic Survey, Washington, D. C., sells charts that will show where filling has taken place since 1905.

Summary. *Deltas are level plains, built up by the deposit of sediment at river mouths; they are commonly triangular in shape because crossed by branching distributaries. They are especially well developed in lakes and other places where the water is shallow, the bottom not sinking, and waves and currents not strong. Like flood plains, they form excellent farm land, and are densely settled.*

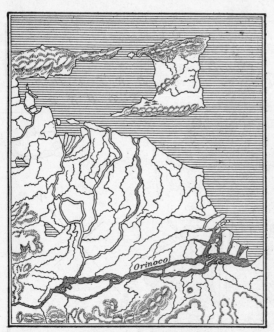

Fig. 100. — The Orinoco delta. Notice its triangular form between the outer distributaries. This is the typical delta shape but many deltas have the apex of the triangle at the lake or sea end because the deposit tends to concentrate at the mouth of the largest distributary or distributaries. See Fig. 99.

55. Alluvial fans. A stream flowing from a steep to a more gentle slope has its velocity checked. If it has much sediment, some may be deposited where the slope changes (Fig. 101). Such a deposit is called a *cone delta*, or *alluvial fan*. Some are small, with steep slopes (Fig. 167); in fact, they may be seen forming at the base of clay banks after a rain; and some are very large and fairly level, covering areas of hundreds of square miles (Plate IV).

Deltas, alluvial fans, and talus cones resemble each other in that all three have triangular outlines. But they differ in other respects. The top slope of a delta is usually less steep than that of an alluvial fan; that of an alluvial fan less steep than that of a talus cone. A delta terminates in a steep front slope at its open water edge, but alluvial fans and talus cones have a single slope from head to foot. The material of deltas and alluvial fans is stratified and finest at the lower end because it is water-carried and water-sorted; that of talus cones is not stratified and the coarsest fragments are found at the base because friction prevents the finer fragments from sliding so readily as the large ones do. Deltas are built up in water, alluvial fans and talus cones on land. However, there are all intergradations of the three forms. Study Figs. 101, 161, and 307 to note the resemblances and differences.

As in a delta, the water flows over an alluvial fan in numerous shifting distributaries (Figs. 100, 101, 307). As soon as one channel

Fig. 101. — Alluvial fans at the base of the Himalaya Mountains, Kashmir, India. Note how the stream in building up the upper fan, on the left, subdivides into many distributaries; also that the one over the fan in the foreground shows the same tendency. On which side, left or right, will the main stream on this fan probably flow next? Why?

becomes too high, it is abandoned and a lower portion of the fan
is built up.   Thus the fan is built up regularly, because all parts
of it are reached by the water.

Mountainous arid lands are especially favorable to the formation
of alluvial fans, because there are many steep slopes, much sediment,
and usually a small amount of water.   At times there are heavy floods,
bringing much sediment; but at other periods the water disappears by
evaporation or by sinking into the gravel.

The lower slopes of large alluvial fans are excellent farming land.   In arid
regions, like the western United States, they are often irrigated because (1)

Fig. 102. — An oasis on an alluvial fan; **El Kantara**, near the Suez Canal, Africa.
The date palms get their moisture from water which has its source in the mountains
and seeps underground through the soil of the alluvial fan.

the soil is good; (2) there is a supply of water at the upper part of the fan;
and (3) there is a good slope down which to lead the water (Plate IV).

Summary.   *Alluvial fans are triangular in outline like deltas and are
built up where streams descend from steep to gentle slopes, as at the base of
mountains.   The lower slopes of large alluvial fans are important agricultural lands.*

56. The filling of valleys.   Many valleys are having their
bottoms raised by the wash of sediment from their sides (Figs.

138, 167). This is especially true in arid regions where there is much sediment and too little rain to carry it off to the sea (Fig. 185).

The valley of California, 400 miles long and 50 to 80 miles wide, furnishes a good illustration (Figs. 222, 344). From the Coast Ranges and the Sierra Nevada the rain wash and the streams are dragging sediment down the mountain slopes. This action builds broad, flat, alluvial fans near the mountains (Plate IV), and still more level deposits farther out in the valley.

A similar case is that of the Po valley in northern Italy. It was once an arm of the sea between the Alps and the Apennines, but it has been filled

Photo by Darton

Fig. 103. — The aggrading North Platte River looking downstream at the Wyoming-Nebraska boundary line. The Platte is like the Rio Grande in its transport and deposit of sediment. In periods of flood part of the sediment previously deposited is moved farther downstream.

by wash from these mountains, and is still being built out into the Adriatic. The many mountain streams are forming low alluvial fans of coarse gravel near the mountains; but near the Po the sediment is finer and the river is bordered by fertile farm land, which is readily irrigated by water from the mountain streams and the Po. It is necessary to build levees along many of the streams to prevent their overflowing the plain. Thus confined to their channels, the rivers are obliged to deposit sediment in their beds. In consequence of this, the water surface of the Po is now well above the level of the surrounding country.

Summary. *The wash of rock fragments from enclosing mountains sometimes deeply fills valleys, especially in arid lands.*

TOPICAL OUTLINE, QUESTIONS, AND SUGGESTIONS

TOPICAL OUTLINE. **36. Supply of water.** Underground supply; run-off; variation in run-off; perennial flow; regulation of river volume; floods.

37. Rain sculpturing. Conditions favoring; results; Bad Lands.

38. Divides and valleys. Make-up of landscape, divides and valleys. Origin of valleys; proof.

39. The rock load of rivers. Dissolved mineral; rock fragments; variation in size; tools of erosion; great load carried.

40. Erosive action of rivers. Nature of action; corrosion; corrasion; lateral cutting; causes for variation in rate; influence of sediment; degrading; aggrading; influence of joint planes; of ice.

41. Potholes. Origin of; nature of; significance of in down-cutting of a stream valley.

42. Waterfalls. Relation to rock; plunge-pool action; types of falls; water power.

43. Valley widening. Weathering; lateral cutting.

44. Headwater erosion. Effect of rain gulleys.

45. Young stream valleys. (*a*) Initial drainage on a plain: lakes; divides; tributaries; consequent course. (*b*) Early stages of development: steep-sided valley; waterfalls; broadening of valley; base level; removal of lakes; narrowing of divides. (*c*) Meaning of youth: characteristics; illustration; age in years; comparison with plants.

46. The grade of a stream. Nature of grade; degrading streams; aggrading streams.

47. Mature valleys. Broadening of valleys; absence of lakes, of waterfalls; development of tributaries, of divides, of flood plains.

48. Old valleys. Peneplains; reasons for absence in existing topography.

49. Special conditions. Streams: superimposed, revived, antecedent, insequent. Rejuvenated valleys.

50. Importance of valley form. Young valleys; mature valleys.

51. The water table, springs, and underground channels. Meaning of ground water; of water table. Flow of underground water. Hot springs. Caves; stalactites; stalagmites; sink holes; natural bridges.

52. River flood plains. Where found; cause of flood plains; fitness for agriculture; natural levees; levees; meanders; cut bank; slip-off slope; ox-bow lake.

53. River terraces. Cause; form; frequency in unconsolidated deposits; utility.

54. Deltas. Cause; name; origin of form; distributaries; surface slope; favoring and opposing conditions; settlement; dangers.

55. Alluvial fans. Cause; size; form; building of the fan; location; formation of lakes; agriculture; shifting of stream.

56. The filling of valleys. Favoring conditions; valley of California; valley of the Po, — filling, farm land, effect of levees.

QUESTIONS. Section 36. In what ways are rivers supplied with water? Define immediate run-off, delayed run-off. What causes variation in run-off? What conditions serve to regulate the volume?

37. What are Bad Lands? Where are they most common? Why?

38. Give the evidence that streams carve the valleys in which they flow.

39. In what two forms is river load carried? How is each supplied? What is the effect of differences in current? What effect have the rock fragments on erosion? Give an illustration of river load.

40. By what two means are rivers wearing at their channels? State the several causes which influence the rate of river erosion. Define degrading and aggrading rivers.

41. How are potholes formed? How does their development affect the degrading of valleys?

42. What is the most common cause for waterfalls? Give an illustration. What are plunge pools? Show by diagram other types of waterfalls and give examples. Of what use are falls and rapids?

43. What is the most important process of valley widening? How and where does it act? How is the valley bottom widened?

44. Describe headwater erosion and tell why it is significant.

45. What are the characteristics of new drainage on a plain? What changes occur in valley form, lakes, tributaries, and divides? What is a consequent stream? Base level? State the characteristics of young valleys. What does the term *youth* mean?

46. What is grade, and what causes it to vary?

47. What changes in valley form occur after a stream has reached grade? What about lakes and falls? What changes occur in tributaries? What influence does this have on sediment?

48. What is a peneplain? A monadnock? Why are they so uncommon?

49. Define superimposed, revived, antecedent, and insequent streams.

50. What influence have young valleys on man? Mature valleys?

51. Define the water table. What is its relation to wells, springs, lakes? State the causes for springs. What causes caverns? What deposits are made in them? What are sink holes? Natural bridges?

52. What causes flood plains? Why are they level? Of what importance are flood plains? What is the natural levee? What causes meanders? Ox-bow lakes?

53. What is the cause of terraces? Why are they desirable for agriculture?

54. What is the cause of deltas? Why so named? What gives the delta form? What conditions favor and what oppose their formation? What about the population of deltas and flood plains?

55. What are the characteristics and causes of alluvial fans? Where do they occur? State the resemblances and differences between deltas, alluvial fans, and talus cones. Of what importance are alluvial fans?

56. In what manner is the valley of California being filled? The Po valley? Of what importance is this valley filling?

SUGGESTIONS. (1) What is the source of the water of a small stream near your home? Does the volume of this stream vary? Why? If there were no underground supply would it in any way affect you? (2) Where does the water run off most rapidly, on a road, a grass-covered lawn, or in the woods? Answer from your own observations. From which place is most sediment washed to the streams? (3) Make a little channel in the ground and pour water into it, varying the amount from a small flow to a flood. Now make a small pond, say, five feet long, with the little channel for its outlet. Pour the same amount of water into the pond that you did into the channel. Does the outflow channel show the same variation in volume? (4) Weigh a stone in the air with a spring balance. Weigh the same stone submerged in water on the end of a string. What does the result show? (5) Make a little trough of rough wood and let water run through it from a faucet. On the bottom of the trough place small pebbles, sand, and clay. Vary the velocity of the water to see what happens. Record your results. (6) Has the stream nearest you a rapid or slow flow? What is the size of the rock fragments that it carries at ordinary times? At times of flood? Why the difference? Is the material at the bottom coarser than that suspended in the current? Where do the rock fragments come from? (7) Are the streams near your home aggrading or degrading? If degrading, are they aggrading in some parts? Why? What differences in activity do you see from time to time? Does rock structure influence the action? Observe the stream in winter and spring to see whether ice helps. Do you know of any places where streams are cutting into their banks? (8) Are there any falls or rapids? What causes them? Are there any potholes? Find what is in the bottom. What does this show? (9) Look for evidences of rain sculpturing on roads, in plowed fields, or under gutters. (10) Has the stream nearest you reached grade? Is the valley young or mature? Study and describe the valley, — its form, tributaries, divides, and falls and lakes (if present). What influence has the valley on roads, railways, and industries? (11) Has your river a flood plain? Is the plain ever flooded? If so, after the next flood go to see whether deposits of sediment have been made. Does the river meander? Have there been any changes in the meanders? (12) Terraces are common in sections where streams are cutting away glacial deposits. Are there any near your home? If so, study and describe them. (13) If there is a pond or lake near by, see whether there are not deltas opposite the mouths of both the large and small streams. If so, report on what you observe concerning their form and the material of which they are made. (14) Are there any alluvial fans? Look for them after a rain at the base of a clay cliff, for example in a railway cut.

General Suggestions. *Scientific expression.* Attention is called to the fact that in this and other chapters the use of the words *hard* and *soft* is avoided in referring to the comparative resistance of rocks to weathering and erosion. Strong and weak, durable and yielding, are pairs to be preferred. Physical hardness is only one of many qualities that affect the rate at which rocks decay and disintegrate. *Work* in the allied science of physics expresses a particular concept; *action* or *effect* are better terms for use in physical geography where in many instances work has ordinarily been employed. Similarly, in science one should not *believe*, for belief implies faith. Rather one should become convinced, or, at least, consider, a thing to be true or false. Again, streams and other inorganic agencies cannot exercise a conscious choice or have a purpose; accordingly it is incorrect to speak of a stream choosing its course, etc.; the stream, rather, is guided, directed, etc., by various factors. Personification of inorganic agencies may make for vividness of presentation; it may also lead to wrong concepts.

These may seem small things and it is easy to slip. Perhaps readers will detect such slips in this book; other writers on the subject may regularly employ the terms here discredited. Nevertheless teachers and students will do well to cultivate preciseness of language, since this, as much perhaps as any little habit, will *develop the scientific attitude* and so lead to that exact and satisfying comprehension of the subject matter that otherwise would not be acquired.

Contour maps. If Appendix I, Maps, has not already been studied, it should be used in connection with this chapter; especially those paragraphs relating to contour maps. The writer is convinced from nearly twenty years of experience in teaching secondary-school, college, and teachers' classes that ability to read and to interpret contour maps competently may be gained only by actual experience in using them. Performance of the laboratory exercises suggested below will serve the purpose well; for college-preparatory students the experience gained from completing these is a minimum essential. In any event Plates I–VIII of this book should be studied and the school should have a number of representative sheets chosen from those listed in Appendix I. Students should learn to recognize the different physiographic items the available plates and sheets illustrate. One way to do this is to refer to the pictures and diagrams in the text that show the same phenomena.

Reference Books. Students should be encouraged to look up in encyclopedias articles on the various topics covered in this and other chapters, especially such items as meanders, terraces, springs, caves. The larger encyclopedias have space for much more extended discussion than is possible in this text, together with many illustrations. This research should be done especially on phenomena that are of particular local interest.

The interested student will gain much pleasure and profit greatly from the study of a *Panorama of Physiographic Types* by A. K. Lobeck, 1926, which can be had by sending 35 cents to the Wisconsin Geographical Press, Madison, Wisconsin.

HOBBS, W. H., *Earth Features and their Meaning*, The Macmillan Company, New York, 1911; GEIKIE, J., *Earth Sculpture*, G. P. Putnam's Sons, New York, 1908; SALISBURY, BARROWS, and TOWER, *Elements of Geography*, Henry Holt & Company, New York, 1912; MARR, J. E., *Scientific Study of Scenery*, Methuen, London, 1900. See also Chapter XVI of this book.

Laboratory Exercises. Exercises XVI, XVII, XVIII, on Contour Maps; XIX and XX on Processes; and XXI on the Mississippi Flood Plain and Delta in TARR and VON ENGELN's *Laboratory Manual of Physical and Commercial Geography*, The Macmillan Company, should be performed in connection with the study of Chapter 1V, Rivers.

CHAPTER V

PLAINS, PLATEAUS, AND DESERTS

PLAINS

57. Continental-shelf plains. Off the coast of eastern North America there is a sea-bottom plain sloping out into deep water (Fig. 104). It attains a width of 50 or 100 miles. Its surface is a

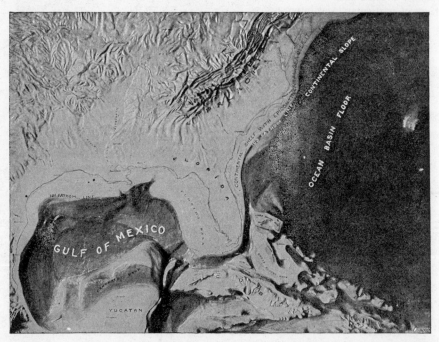

Fig. 104. — Continental shelf, coastal plain, coast line, epicontinental sea, continental slope, ocean-basin floor, as found off the eastern coast of the United States. (Vertical scale is greatly exaggerated, but the mental concept of the comparative relief that the figure gives quite fairly represents the conditions.)

level expanse of sand near the coast, and of mud farther out. This plain is made of layer upon layer of sediment washed from the land; sediment which the waves and currents are constantly

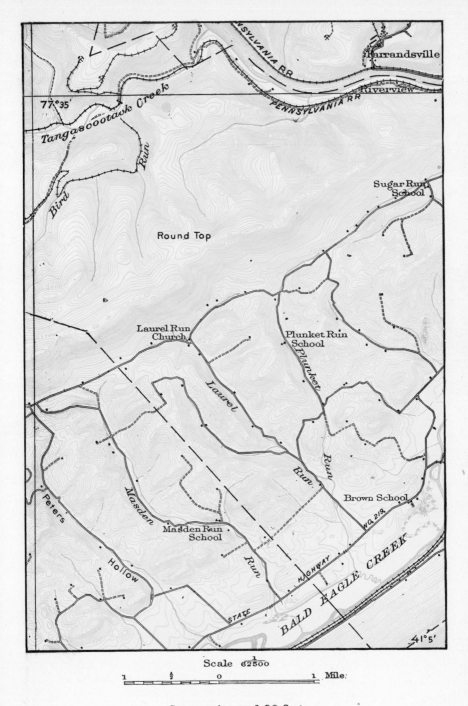

Scale $\frac{1}{62500}$

Contour interval 20 feet

Plate III. — Part of Howard, Pennsylvania, sheet; Topographic Atlas of the United States; U. S. Geol. Sur.

The Allegheny Escarpment. This is one of the new shaded relief maps which show clearly the relation between contour lines and the actual form of the country.

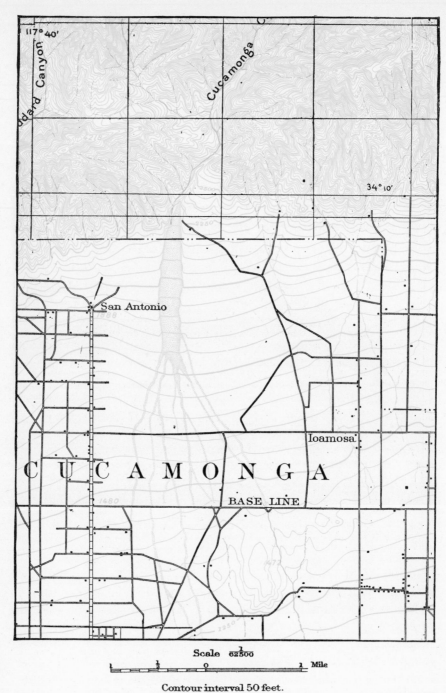

Scale $\frac{1}{62500}$

Contour interval 50 feet.

Plate IV. — Part of Cucamonga, California, sheet; Topographic Atlas of the United States; U. S. Geol. Sur.

Alluvial fan development at the base of a mountain range. Determine the slope of the alluvial fan to the base of the mountains in feet per mile. How does this compare to the slope of the valley of the Cucamonga stream within the mountains?

spreading out. Other continents are bordered by similar sea-bottom plains, or *continental shelves* (Figs. 29, 32).

At the outer, undersea edge of the continental-shelf plains is encountered the abrupt descent to the ocean-basin floor over the continental slope (p. 32). The shallow ocean waters that rest on the continental shelf are called *epicontinental* (on the continent) seas.

Should the sea bottom be raised a few hundred feet, a broad strip of plain would be added to the American continent. This new

Photo by Tarr

Fig. 105. — Uplift of the sea bottom in Alaska, Russell Fiord. The beach in the foreground is now high above the waves and land plants have begun to grow upon it. All this uplift took place in one month, September, 1899.

plain would slope seaward at the rate of a few feet a mile only. The rain that fell upon the plain would find it so level that run-off would be very sluggish. Consequently much of the surface would be swampy.

Summary. *Continents are normally bordered by undersea plains, or continental shelves, having a surface covering of sediment from the land carried to the limit of depth to which waves stir the sea sufficiently to buoy up the finest clay particles.*

58. Coastal plains. Uplifts have actually added such plains to the land (Figs. 109, 110). Some are narrow strips at the base of mountains, as in western South America and Alaska (pp. 50, 359 and Fig. 105), where the land is still rising; others are many miles wide, like the plain that skirts the coast south of New York. Because they border the coast they are called *coastal plains*.

The coastal plain of the Atlantic and Gulf coasts extends from New Jersey to the Rio Grande, and includes the peninsula of Florida, although this has a slightly different bed-rock structure. Wells bored into the coastal plain pass through hundreds of feet of gravel, sand, and clay, often finding water in the porous, sandy layers. Where the water rises to the surface, it is called an *artesian well* (Fig. 106). There are hundreds of such wells along the Atlantic coast, and many cities, such as Atlantic City and Galveston, obtain drinking water from them. Artesian water, in general, is organically

Fig. 106. — Diagram to illustrate the cause for artesian wells on a coastal plain. Water passes down the porous layer P, and is prevented from rising or sinking deeper by the impervious layers, I, I. When a well is bored down to the porous layer the water rises to the surface because it has entered higher than the outlet of the well, and is under pressure of the water in the porous layer, which, therefore, forces it out. Such wells may even be bored on a sand bar in the sea, as at X, finding fresh water beneath the impervious layer (Atlantic City, New Jersey).

pure. It has been freed from the germs that abound in surface drainage by the very complete underground filtration to which it is subjected in percolating through the porous layers.

Much of the North American coastal plain south of New York City is so sandy that it is poorly adapted to agriculture. Such parts are still occupied by an open pine forest. The forest supplies valuable timber, hard pine, and is the site of a great lumber industry. This hard pine also yields turpentine, tar, and wood alcohol. The higher and less sandy tracts of the coastal plain are favorable to agriculture (Fig. 108), producing especially fruit and vegetables for canning in Maryland, Delaware, Florida, and other states; and cotton, corn, tobacco, peanuts, and other products in the South. Along the coast and near the rivers the land is swampy, and was formerly used for rice culture (Fig. 112). Rice is now grown on dryer parts of the southern coastal plain.

After the first uplift of the Atlantic coastal plain south of New York City had been accomplished, the plain stood for a time at a certain level. During that period it was partially dissected by river erosion. Streams, large and small, cut valleys into it. Then

Fig. 107. — The Florida plain along the St. Johns River.

there followed a slight submergence and the sea water was re-admitted to the areas of the lower courses of the streams. All this happened long before the coming of the white man.

The slight sinking of the coastal plain has admitted the sea into the valleys, transforming their mouths to shallow bays (Fig. 111 and Plate VIII), the seats of oyster and fishing industries. Some of the bays have good harbors, though a fringe of sand bars partly cuts

off the entrance to many. The shallower bays and tide-water
rivers are navigable by small craft, thus opening up large areas of
country to water transportation. This was formerly of great
importance in carrying cotton and other products to the seaports
for shipment. Chesapeake Bay (Fig. 111), with its many branches,
is the largest of the coastal plain bays.

Partly because of the low slope, partly because of the later sinking of
the land, the rivers of the coastal plain are in general sluggish. In some

Photo by Callister

Fig. 108. — The Atlantic Coastal Plain at Spring Grove, Virginia. Note the very
level land, the light color of the sandy soil, and the forest area; these are all features
typical of the outer lower lands of the coastal plain.

places, the slope of the plain is so gentle that water does not run off. This
causes swamps, as in parts of Florida and the Dismal Swamp. The surface
of the Florida plain is so young (Fig. 107), and the streams have so little
sediment, that the shallow lakes in depressions of the old sea bottom have
not yet been filled. Farther inland, on its higher levels, streams have
cut into the coastal plain forming shallow, steep-sided valleys, with broad,
flat-topped divides between; on the level surfaces of these the roads run.

Where streams pass from the older land to the coastal plain (Fig. 109), their slopes increase and their courses are interrupted by rapids and falls. The explanation of this fact is that the rivers

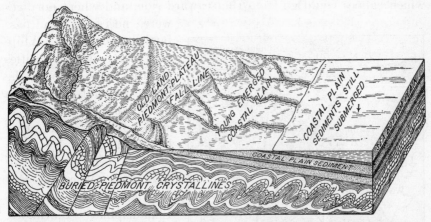

Fig. 109. — Old land, fall line, coastal plain partly dissected, and a sea-bottom plain being formed by the deposit of more sediment on a submerged old land.

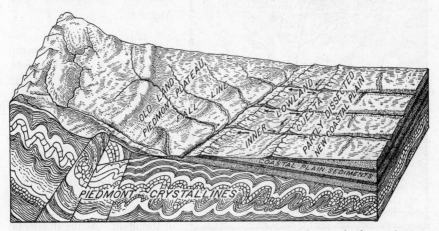

Fig. 110. — Same as Fig. 109 except that a further uplift has made the sea-bottom plain of Fig. 109 a newer part of the coastal plain. Meanwhile the older part of the coastal plain has been dissected into a belted coastal plain with a trellis drainage system. The newer coastal plain shows consequent streams not guided by structure, hence insequent in pattern. This is the condition of the outer belt of the Atlantic coastal plain southward from New York.

have cut faster in the weaker, here softer, clays and sands of the plain than in the harder rocks of the old land. For this reason the boundary between the old land and the plain is called the *Fall*

Line (Fig. 113).   The Fall Line has had a very important influence on settlement.   Even in the days of the Indians, village sites on the rivers were located along this line, — the highest points to which canoes could go from the seaward side, and where portages were necessary to pass farther upstream.   White men have located cities at the same spots, the farthest points to which boats from the sea formerly sailed inland; sites now benefited more by their location near water-power resources.   Along the Fall Line are located Trenton, Philadelphia, Baltimore, Washington, Richmond, Raleigh, Columbia, and Augusta.

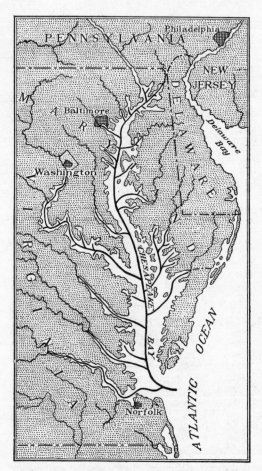

Fig. 111. — Chesapeake Bay.   The lines show the probable position of the rivers that formed this branching, submerged valley.

The rock layers of a coastal plain usually lie in sheets, gently inclined in the direction given them by uplift of the land (Fig. 109).   As the surface of the plain is slowly worn down, durable layers, since they resist denudation better than weak ones, are left as uplands, possibly only a few feet, perhaps scores of feet, above the lower portions of the plain.   Being in sheets, the durable layers form belts of hilly land, *cuestas*, terminating on either side in belts of lower land, where the weaker strata lie (Fig. 110).   The plain is, therefore, sculptured into bands, or belts, of different level, corresponding to the differences in resistance. Such a land surface, found both on recent coastal plains, as in eastern United States, and on older plains, as in interior New York, and in the Paris Basin, France (Fig. 114), is known as a *belted plain* (Fig. 115).

Fig. 112. — The level, low-lying, swampy coastal plain lands of South Carolina seen from Savannah, Georgia. These lands were formerly devoted extensively to rice culture.

The development of a belted coastal plain is an orderly process. The valleys of the consequent streams that flow in parallel lines (Fig. 109) down the original slope of the plain are opened far more widely by weathering in the areas of the weak rocks than in the zones underlain by strong rocks. Accordingly the first small tributaries to the consequent streams have much larger areas to collect drainage in the zones of the weak rocks than on the steeper, short slopes of the sides of a consequent valley in the strong rocks. Also the tributaries in the weak rocks can cut down and enlarge their own valleys faster than can those which start on the strong rocks. The result is that the tributaries on the weak rocks rapidly develop broad valleys which, further, are constantly being lengthened by headwater erosion, whereas the tributaries on the strong layers continue to be small or disappear entirely. Thus lowlands between successive durable layers are opened up (Fig. 110). These are *subsequent valleys* and the streams that erode them are *subsequent streams*, because their development "follows after"

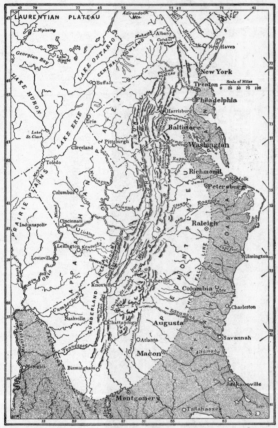

After Bowman

Fig. 113. — The Fall Line. Coastal plain dotted; cities printed in heavy type are located along the Fall Line.

that of the consequent streams. With reference to the form of the divides the belted coastal plain is made up of a succession of *cuestas*, hills that have a steep *inface*, or *escarpment* slope on the landward side and a gentle *dip* slope seaward (Fig. 115). (See pp. 88, 133 and 492.)

Summary.   *Upraised sea bottoms form coastal plains skirting the coasts of continents. There is a well-defined one from New Jersey to Mexico, much* *of whose level surface is too sandy or swampy for agriculture, while in Florida there are many lakes still occupying the original depressions.   A recent slight sinking has readmitted the sea into the river mouths, transforming*

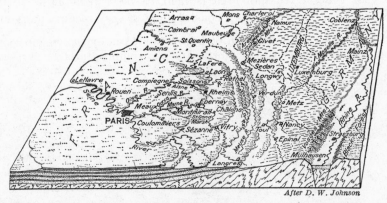

After D. W. Johnson

Fig. 114. — The Paris Basin, France.   An ancient belted coastal plain on and about which much of the fighting of the World War took place.

them into shallow bays.   Where streams descend from the old land to the plain, there is a line of rapids and falls, called the Fall Line.   Dissection of a coastal plain develops wide subsequent valleys, belted plains, and cuestas.

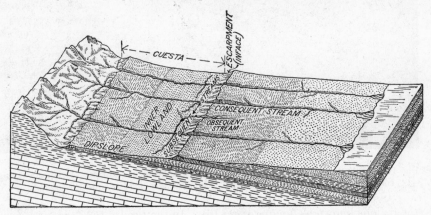

Fig. 115. — A belted coastal plain.   The different symbols in the rocks indicate layers of varying resistance gently inclined.   The topographic features formed by the development of drainage valleys on such structure are named in the diagram.   Explain each one.

59. The Russian and Siberian plains. This, the greatest expanse of plains on any continent (Fig. 33), covers an area far greater than the entire United States.   These plains extend from the Caspian region to the Arctic, including a large part of northern Asia and much of Russia, with a western branch reaching to Holland. In part this great plain is alluvial flood plain, in part delta, and the vast central Russian area is held to be a peneplain (p. 93). The northern border part is a coastal plain of very recent emergence.

This northern coastal plain of Europe and Asia and a similar coastal plain on the Arctic coast of North America comprise a large portion of

Photo by Schrader

Fig. 116.—The tundra plain of the Arctic coast of Alaska in summer. It is a low-lying coastal plain with a cover of mosses, lichens, sedges, grasses, and low bushes.

the regions known as *tundra* (Fig. 116). In the tundra the soil is frozen to a great depth. In summer it thaws at the surface only, making the land a vast swamp; in winter the tundra is a bleak, frozen, snow-covered desert.

Toward the south the Eurasian plain grades into the forest region, which has in part been cleared and opened to agriculture as a result of the building of the Siberian railway. This forest section is perhaps destined to become one of the great farming regions of the world. On its southern side the forest belt grades into the open, grass-covered *steppes* (p. 466), a region too arid for farming, and, therefore, occupied by a nomadic, pastoral people.

The vast tundra lands of North America in Alaska and Canada are being used to an ever greater extent as grazing lands for domesticated reindeer. Meat from these animals already has some importance in southern markets. Thus man is learning to utilize even the most difficult and remote lands of the earth.

Summary. *Vast plains, caused by recent uplift of an ancient sea bottom, extend over a large part of northern Asia, Europe, and North America. There*

Photo by U. S. Reclamation Service

Fig. 117. — The Great Plains, Newell, South Dakota.

is in Eurasia barren, frozen tundra in the north; barren, arid steppe land in the south; and forest and farm land between. In North America the tundra lands are being used for reindeer pasturage.

60. Plains and prairies of Central United States. In ancient geological times the bottom of a sea formerly existing between the mountains of eastern and western North America was raised above sea level. From time to time it has been reëlevated, and numerous additions have been made to its southern margin. Denudation has also been at work, lowering and sculpturing its surface, so that in places it is hilly. Elsewhere it has more recently received vast deposits of glacial débris and so been smoothed over again (p. 292). It forms one of the largest areas of plains in the world (Fig. 28).

Near the Appalachian Mountains the plains reach an elevation of 2000 to 3000 feet; near the Rocky Mountains they rise from 5000 to 6000 feet above sea level. From these higher portions, really

Photo by Morgan

Fig. 118. — The Great Plains in Colorado. A modern picture showing the meeting and passing of east and west bound passenger trains.

plateaus, the surface slopes toward the Mississippi, making a broad valley which that river follows, receiving long tributaries down the slopes from either side.

The plains west of the Mississippi are called, in part, the *Great Plains* (Figs. 117, 118). In the east there is rainfall enough for agriculture; but west of the 100th meridian these plains are best suited to grazing, although in places rivers and artesian wells supply water for irrigation. Where the rainfall is light, there is timber only along the streams. In early days these vast plains were occupied by great buffalo herds.

East of the Mississippi are large areas of plain, called *prairies,* which, when discovered, were also free from forest except along the streams (Fig. 119). The treeless condition was due in part to fires, set by Indians in their buffalo hunts. The main reason, however, for the lack of trees seems to have been local droughts. The summer rainfall of these areas comes mostly in thundershowers. In most years these showers supply water plentifully. But in some years one area, in others another, is completely skipped by the showers. Then all vegetation dries up and crops are ruined. Young trees die, but the roots of grasses simply become dormant until the drought is over and then send up new blades of green. So in primitive days the grass was able to survive the local droughts but the young trees could not; hence the prairies.

These fertile, treeless prairies greatly facilitated the settlement of the Middle West. A crop could be raised the first year, for there was no laborious work of clearing land for farming; and, when this was found out, settlers came rapidly and prospered.

After Gerhard

Fig. 119. — Original distribution of prairie and woodlands in Illinois. The white areas were the flat unbroken grass lands that gave rise to the name prairie. Note that the forest growth was along the stream courses where moisture was more continuously available.

Each of the continents has plains similar to those already described. The great plains of the Amazon, of Argentina, and of Venezuela are examples. A very large part of the land surface consists of plains that at one period or another have been raised from the sea. Accordingly, also, large parts of the surface of the lands are underlain by sedimentary rocks.

Summary. *The ancient, much worn, and in part rebuilt plains of central United States slope from the mountains on each side, forming the great Mississippi Valley. In the West the Great Plains are treeless, because arid; in the East, though the climate is moist, large areas, called prairies, were treeless because of the effect of fires and of occasional local droughts. These plains are adapted to agriculture where humid and to grazing where arid. But certain areas of the arid sections are utilized by practising irrigation.*

61. Lake plains. Sediment deposited in a lake levels its bottom. If the Caspian Sea and Lake Erie could be drained, their bottoms would

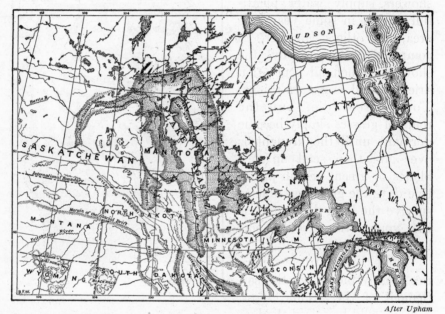

After Upham

Fig. 120. — Extent of the extinct glacial Lake Agassiz, which occupied the valley of the Red River of the North.

appear as broad plains. There are places from which lakes have disappeared. Extinct lakes of this sort were formed by a great ice dam across north-flowing streams when the glacier was melting from North America (p. 289).

An enormous lake of this kind, glacial Lake Agassiz (Fig. 120), larger than all the Great Lakes combined, existed in the valley of the Red River of the North. The fine-grained sediment that was deposited on the bottom of this extinct lake has made a fertile plain (Figs. 121, 122), one of the most famous wheat regions of the world. Its surface is so level that, after a rain, water stands on the ground in sheets. One also gets the same evidence here of the curved surface of the earth that one does when looking across the level surface of the sea (p. 2).

A large lake also once existed in the Great Basin, round Great Salt Lake. When the climate became arid this lake was diminished by evaporation, leaving only small remnants, of which Great Salt Lake is the largest. These remnants occupy shallow depressions in the level lake-bottom plain (Figs. 304, 305, 351a).

There are a number of other classes of plains. Some of these are described in the chapters on Glaciers (p. 286), and Lakes (p. 311). Others, formed by rivers, have already been described,—flood plains (p. 100), delta plains (p. 105), alluvial fan plains (p. 110), and filled valley plains (p. 112).

Photo by Haynes

Fig. 121. — On the Red River valley plains in North Dakota. An old picture showing half-breed Indian collectors of buffalo bones and other bones formerly scattered over the surface of the plains. Compare with Fig. 122.

Summary. *On lake bottoms sediment makes plains which may become dry land by the disappearance of the lakes, as in the valley of the Red River of the North, and the Great Basin.*

62. The erosion cycle on a plain. A *young plain* (p. 87) has a level surface, poorly defined, and perhaps swampy divides, and shallow lakes. The consequent streams flowing down the original slopes at first cut steep-sided valleys, with falls where differences in rock resistance are encountered (Figs. 73a, b, 74 No. 1).

In time the lakes are filled, grade is established, falls disappear, and the valleys widen (pp. 83, 90). Meanwhile tributaries increase in number and divides narrow up. First come the subsequent streams and these in turn develop *obsequent* tributaries, so-called because they flow down the steep face of the escarpments of the cuestas in a direction "opposite" to that of the consequent streams. Thus more and more of the areas of the originally flat-topped divides is furrowed by valleys. The drainage then also has a *trellis* pattern. Such a *mature plain* has an undulating surface, and, if high, it may be so dissected as to become a hilly land (Figs.

Fig. 122. — The Red River valley plains in northwestern Minnesota. A modern picture showing a vast field of young grain. The buildings in the distance are grain elevators. These plains are almost as level as the sea. The horizon line suggests the curvature of the earth.

79b, 123). In an *old plain* the valleys are so broadened that the surface again becomes nearly level.

These changes are also referred to as the *Normal* or *Humid Geographic Cycle* and as the *Life History of a Plain*.

If the strata in the plains do not incline or do not differ in resistance, there is no regular succession of development of consequent, subsequent, and obsequent streams. The pattern of the stream system is not then guided by structure, hence is called *insequent*, following no structure. In pattern such a drainage system is treelike, hence *dendritic*. Nevertheless tributaries develop and the divides are gradually dissected. The Lake Agassiz plain has such an insequent stream system. The successive stages of such development are shown in Fig. 123.

Summary. *A young plain has a level surface and a young drainage system; a mature plain has broad valleys and a hilly surface; an old plain has a level surface again. If the rocks composing the plain incline and vary in resistance, the development of valleys is in a regular order; if not, it is insequent.*

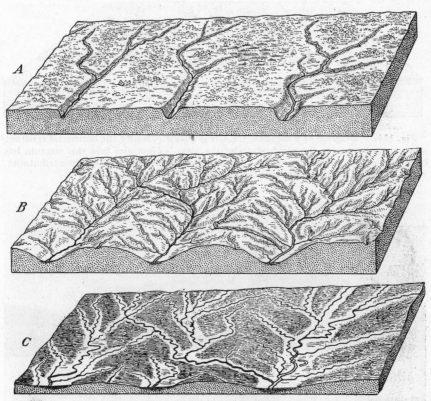

Fig. 123. — To illustrate the erosion cycle on a plain made up of uniform rock and situated in a humid climate some distance from the sea. *A* is early youth, *B* maturity, *C* old age. Note that because the rock is uniform the drainage pattern is insequent and dendritic. Also note that the upper drainage is in old age all connected to the stream on the right — why? The bottom edge of the diagrams represents sea level. If the rock were not uniform what other features would develop? See Figs. 110, 115.

PLATEAUS

63. Nature of plateaus. When mountains are uplifted, the country on either side is also raised, often without much folding of the strata. As the mountains rise higher, the adjoining plains become more elevated, especially near the mountains and between the ranges. They may rise so high that they deserve the name plateaus, for a plateau is only an elevated plain. The plateau along the western base of the Appalachians (Figs. 175, 310, 448) is 2000 to 3000 feet above sea level; that at the eastern base of the Rocky

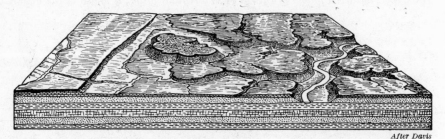

After Davis

Fig. 124. — Diagram of a *mesa* on the Great Plains. Notice the horizontal resistant stratum that protects the material under the mesa. Note also how this stratum has been cut through on all sides by the erosion of the different streams and their tributaries, with the result that the mesa has been completely isolated. See Section 66.

Photo by Russell

Fig. 125. — Mesa in Cook County, Oregon. The durable capping layer is the remnant of a sheet of lava.

Mountains (Fig. 118), from 5000 to 6000 feet; between the Rockies and the Sierra Nevada, often 7000 to 8000 feet; and that north of the Himalayas (Fig. 32), attains 15,000 feet.

Owing to the close relation between plateaus and mountains (Fig. 32), the strata of plateaus, though mostly horizontal, are sometimes broken and tilted; in fact, there is every gradation from slightly tilted plateau blocks (Fig. 150) to true mountains. Lava has often welled from the fissures, flooding large areas of country, as in the Columbia and Snake River valleys (Fig. 212).

Summary. *Plateaus are elevated plains, raised during mountain uplift, with strata usually horizontal, though sometimes tilted.*

64. Sculpturing of plateaus. Rivers upon plateaus have much the same history as upon plains (p. 87); and the erosion cycle of

Photo by Calvin

Fig. 126. — Mt. Hope, Iowa.   A pyramidal hill, the equivalent in structure of a mesa as developed by weathering in a humid region.

a plateau is much the same as that of a plain (p. 133). But, being higher above base level, the streams have more material to erode, and this takes a longer time, though the stages are the same. Also the rock formations in plateaus are usually better consolidated and more durable than in plains. Accordingly in youth streams sculpture plateaus into extremely rugged form, with flat-topped divides, and deep, steep-sided valleys, with falls and rapids. In early maturity the valleys grow broader and develop the characteristic sharp V shape of this stage (Fig. 81). Then the surface is made lower, the valleys widen out, and finally, in old age, the land is level again.

The sculpturing of plateaus is frequently retarded by the fact that the climate is arid and denudation therefore slow (p. 60). For this reason many arid land plateaus are still in the rugged stage of youth, even though they may be far older in years than maturely dissected plateaus of humid regions. For the same reason arid plateaus have an angular topography (Figs. 128, 132), whereas in moist climates denudation more commonly rounds the edges of the strata.

Summary. *Plateaus, like plains, pass through stages of youth, maturity, and old age. But, since they are higher, the time required to lower them is longer, and the land forms produced are more rugged. The arid climate of many plateaus retards denudation and therefore prolongs youth.*

65. Gorges and canyons.

A gorge or a canyon is the deep, steep-sided valley of a young plateau stream (Figs. 67, 443). Gorges and canyons are found on most plateaus, being a characteristic result of the early stages of river erosion in high plateaus. By far the best example is the Grand Canyon of the Colorado (Figs. 128, 458; see also p. 514).

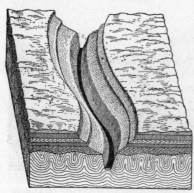

Fig. 127. — A superimposed river, reaching folded rock beneath the horizontal strata of a plateau. See Fig. 128.

For about 200 miles the Colorado River flows in a canyon — in one place 6000 feet in depth — the deepest canyon in the world. Some of the grandest scenes in nature are the views looking down into this river-made valley from the canyon edge, or looking upward from its bottom. The internal structure of the earth's crust is here revealed — thousands of feet of strata, layer on layer, appearing one beneath the other. One cannot look into this enormous cut in the earth without realizing the vast erosion that a river can accomplish when time enough is allowed. Yet all this has resulted from the action of a young stream still cutting down toward grade.

Fig. 128. — The superimposed Colorado River. See Fig. 127. The upper section of the canyon is eroded in horizontally bedded strata, and from these the course of the river was let down, superimposed, on the ancient crystalline rocks of an old mountain mass. In these ancient rocks it has cut the narrow inner canyon.

Summary. *Deep, steep-sided valleys of young plateau streams are called canyons. The greatest of these is the Grand Canyon of the Colorado, over 200 miles long and, in one place, 6000 feet deep.*

66. Mesas and buttes. In plateaus that have an arid climate there are many flat, table-like surfaces (Fig. 124) faced on three or more sides by steep slopes, often cliffs. These are *mesas*, a Spanish word meaning table. An examination of such a mesa shows that the rock on the top is resistant, often lava (Fig. 125). These table-top surfaces are due to the fact that the more durable rock layers have resisted denudation; and, since they are nearly horizontal, have held the surface up to a general level, parallel to the stratification. The steep edges are then typical escarpment slopes (p. 126).

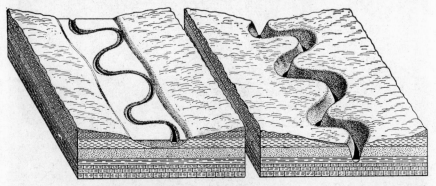

Fig. 129. — A rejuvenated river. In the left figure the stream has reached grade and is swinging over a flood plain in a gently sloping, mature valley. In the right figure the land has been uplifted and a young valley is sunk in the bottom of the mature valley, preserving the meanders that the stream had before the uplift. These may be called *entrenched meanders*. See p. 103. At a later stage the spurs will be much sharpened by weathering.

Small mesas, reduced by denudation, are called *buttes* (Fig. 139). They, too, are capped by durable layers which have preserved them from being worn down. (Another type of butte results from the bringing into relief by denudation of the resistant rocks of volcanic intrusions or vents. See p. 230.) The presence of these flat-topped butte and mesa areas accounts for the name *table-land*, often given to plateaus in arid regions. In humid regions weathering waste accumulates so much more rapidly and is removed so much more slowly, because bound together by moisture and vegetation, that, instead of mesa forms, the same structure gives rise to characteristic pyramidal hills (Fig. 126).

Summary. *Flat-topped areas, called mesas if large, buttes if small, due to the resistance of horizontal beds of strong rock, are common among plateaus and account for the name table-land.*

67. Climate of plateaus. High plateaus are cold because they reach into cool upper layers of the atmosphere. On the plateau of Mexico, for instance, the climate is tropical at the base; coffee is grown on the lower slopes; but grains are the chief crops on top. In the lower Colorado valley, in Arizona, the summer climate is

Photo by Bowen

Fig. 130. — An escarpment in a humid region. The Helderberg Mountains, near Albany, New York. Here the very strong and massive Helderberg limestone overlies the weak Hudson shales. The wide Mohawk Valley occupying the center of the picture is an inner lowland.

almost unbearably hot, while on the plateau it is pleasantly cool. The plateau of Tibet is so high that it has a cold, disagreeable climate, even in summer.

Plateaus are often associated with mountains, which shut out the rain-bearing winds. Many plateaus are therefore arid, and some, like central Asia and parts of western United States, are true deserts.

Summary. *Plateaus have a cooler climate than neighboring lowlands; they are often arid.*

68. Inhabitants of moist plateaus. The plateau at the western base of the Appalachians (p. 136) includes the Catskill, Allegheny, and Cumberland mountains. It is dissected by valleys often 1000 feet deep (Plate III), with sides too steep for cultivation, but, owing to the moist climate, clothed with forest (Fig. 81). There are no true buttes and mesas, and no real canyons. The absence of these is due largely to the fact that in this moist climate weathering is so rapid that talus and alluvial fan slopes accumulate more

Fig. 131. — Sand dunes invading an oasis in Tunis. Note that the slopes of the ripple marks repeat the larger slopes of the dune and show the direction from which the wind blows.

rapidly than the transporting agencies are capable of removing the waste. Also vegetation tends to bind the loose fragments together with its roots and so delays removal. However, escarpments do develop where a particularly strong layer is underlain by a considerable thickness of weaker formations (Fig. 130). The surface is, on the whole, very rugged.

Much of this plateau is a wild region, with a sparse population. It is an important source of timber. South of Pennsylvania the scattered farms are poor. The rugged, timber-covered surface interferes with communication with the outer world, and there are sections in which the people are very backward. Many cannot read or write; small patches of Indian corn on steep slopes or isolated summits are the chief crop production; and, in some parts, the log-cabin home of pioneer times is still in use.

The discovery of coal, oil, and gas has led to the use of parts of this plateau for occupations other than lumbering and the crude farming of the backwoodsmen. Even so, because of better transportation facilities, the plateau of western Pennsylvania has advanced far beyond that of West Virginia, Tennessee, and Kentucky. In western New York (Fig. 294) the plateau is less rugged: in part because it was originally less high, in part because it is made up of less resistant rocks (hence is further advanced in age in the erosion cycle), in part because it has been subject to glaciation (p. 294). It has, in large part, been cleared of forest, and farm lands have been developed

Photo by Raffius

Fig. 132. — Hopi Indian pueblo on the edge of a mesa in Arizona.

wherever possible. Yet even here the upland farms are poor in quality unless deeply covered with glacial soils.

Summary. *Rugged, dissected plateaus in moist countries, like that west of the Appalachians, are largely forest-covered, poorly adapted to farming, and, unless influenced by the development of mineral wealth, are apt to be occupied by a sparse population, backward because out of contact with the outside world and having poor natural resources.*

69. Inhabitants of arid plateaus. Because of their ruggedness, cold-ness, and dryness, arid plateaus are sparsely settled. In the West, large areas of plateau are almost uninhabited except by ranchmen, whose cattle and sheep feed on the sparse growth of grass (Fig. 139).

Because of the dryness there is little farming, except near the mountains where alluvial fans and level portions of the plateau are irrigated by water from the mountain streams. The bottoms of the canyons are now being used for reservoirs by building great dams across them, and the water so impounded is led out on the level tracts of lower elevation (Fig. 299).

The Indians who occupied the arid plateau of southwestern United States farmed by means of irrigation. For protection from roaming bands

Photo by U. S. Reclamation Service

Fig. 133. — Arizona desert land before irrigation. Salt River, Arizona, with Camel Back Mountain in background.

of more savage Indians, they often built their homes, or *pueblos*, on the buttes and mesas. From them they could look out over the country, and be partly protected from enemies by the steepness of the bordering cliffs. Some Indians (Figs. 132, 507) still live in these situations.

Summary. *Arid plateaus are usually sparsely settled, the leading occupation being ranching, with farming by irrigation where possible.*

DESERTS

70. Nature of deserts. A desert is a region in which few forms of life can find sustenance. Thus, by reason of cold, the vast expanse of ice in Greenland is a desert; indeed, it is so inhospitable a desert that, in a large part of its area, *no* animal or plant can live. The term *desert* is, however, commonly applied to those lands on which there is so little rainfall that only a few especially adapted animals and plants can live. About one fifth of the land has an annual rainfall of less than ten inches and is, therefore, desert; and fully as much more is arid, having too little rain for agriculture.[1] Certain areas have desert conditions also because they are underlain by porous sands, sandstones, or soluble limestones, which permit rain to percolate underground so freely that the surface is

Photo by U. S. Reclamation Service

Fig. 134. — Arizona desert land after irrigation; Camel Back Mountain in the distance. Compare with Fig. 133. This is part of a four hundred acre field of sugar beets.

persistently dry. Thus the growth of vegetation is hampered or prevented, although the climate is humid. The central section of Long Island, New York, for instance, shows such characteristics.

It is a mistake to suppose that *no* rain falls in climatically dry regions, for there is no land on the earth so desert that it does not have some rainfall. One of the driest deserts is in southern Peru, where, close by the Pacific, a period of seven years has elapsed between rains. Nor is it correct to imagine deserts as dreary

[1] For explanation of desert climates, see page 462.

wastes of sand and monotonous expanses of plains. It is true that there is much drifting sand (Figs. 131, 501, 509), and that most deserts are either plains or plateaus; but deserts also have many bare, rocky slopes, and even mountains (Figs. 133, 137). But where in the middle of desert regions mountains rise high enough, rain falls on their slopes, and streams flow down their valleys.

Summary. *Deserts are regions of little or no life and are due to cold, and to lack of rain, though even the driest have some rainfall. Deserts are plains or plateaus, with much sand, though there are also bare, rocky slopes.*

71. Drainage of deserts. With so little rain there is naturally little drainage. Most of the rainfall either quickly evaporates from the surface or sinks into the soil; but a heavy rain is followed by a rapid run-off, because there is little vegetation to check the flow of the water. Heavy rains, known as *cloud-bursts*, sometimes occur (Fig. 138), especially in the mountains; and the water, running out upon more level land, causes floods, which, however, quickly subside.

Because of these sudden floods, it is dangerous to camp in a dried-up stream bed, or *arroyo* (Fig. 38). These floods wash down vast quantities of sediment. This forms alluvial fans, often very stony near the mountains.

It may be months or even years between rains, so that desert streams are typically *intermittent*. Those from the mountains have a more regular flow, and some have so large and steady a water supply that they are able to maintain their courses entirely across a desert. Thus the Colorado River and the Nile, fed from distant mountains, flow across deserts to the sea.

Most desert streams carry so little water that they lose themselves, or waste away, a few hundred yards, or a few miles, from the base of the mountains in which they are born. Sometimes they terminate in a salt marsh, or *saline;* sometimes in an *alkali flat* (p. 318); sometimes, when there is enough water, in salt lakes. The alkali and salt are brought in small quantities, dissolved in the water, and left when it evaporates. Where salt lakes formerly existed, and on the salines and alkali flats, there are barren and desolate areas of glistening salt or alkali.

Summary. *Most desert streams are intermittent and subject to occasional floods; but some large rivers, fed from the mountains, maintain their courses across deserts. Many streams waste away on the desert and end in salt lakes, salines, or alkali flats.*

72. Wind action on deserts. On deserts the action of the wind (Fig. 139) is more important than that of water. Small dust whirlwinds are common on hot summer days, and even moderate winds drift the sand and dust along the surface.   Violent winds raise the sand in the air, causing fierce dust storms which obscure the sky and land and even endanger life.   During such a wind the movement of the sand may entirely change the details of the land surface.   The finer dust is often drifted far away, *exported*—dust from the Sahara having settled in central Europe and on ships west of Africa.

It is wind action that piles up the sand which every one associates with deserts.   The sand is made of small rock fragments weathered from

Fig. 135. — Desert of Egypt at the Pyramids.

the cliffs (Figs. 137, 145) and brought down by the streams.   It is drifted about, and, in places, gathered into vast areas of *sand dunes*.   The sand-dune hills may reach a height of several hundred feet, though usually they are much lower.   Sand-dune hills slowly change form and position, and cities in central Asia have been buried by their advance.   Smaller areas of sand dunes also develop along sea and lake coasts (p. 377) and bordering certain river valleys where streams are aggrading their courses.

Sand dunes in deserts start where some obstruction, a projecting rock perhaps, interrupts the steady movement of the wind.   Such a check to its flow causes the wind current to drop some of the sand it has been drifting along. As more and more sand piles up about the obstruction, a dune is gradually formed.   Once it has built the dune, the wind may move it away. A moving dune has a gentle slope toward the wind, a steep side away from the wind.   This is because the wind moves the dune particle by particle. It drifts the sand up the gentle slope and drops it, beyond the crest, to build up as steep a slope as the sand can stand at rest.   By such movement of the dune the obstruction that started it may be uncovered and opportunity be given for a new dune to form there.   As the wind shifts in direction, the drift of the dune also shifts.   The sand on the gentle, windward slope of the dune is commonly rippled with sand waves.   These repeat

Photo by Pack

Fig. 136. — Along the Columbia River in Oregon. Moving sand dunes of perfect form.   Where wind movement is not too strong and sand not too plentiful sand dunes develop this horned form.   Study out the direction from which the wind comes and why the horns develop.

the form of the dune in miniature and are developed in the same way (Fig. 131).   The layers of sand in the dune lie at all angles, for every slight change in wind direction brings about also a change in the position of deposit of the sand.   This gives rise to *wind-drift structure.*   Many of the features of dune formation are duplicated in the drifting of snow and may be studied there by those who do not have the opportunity of observing the sand dunes of the desert or seacoast.

Summary. *Winds move the small rock fragments about, accumulating the sand in favorable positions, thus forming belts of sand dunes which are ever changing in form and position.*

73. The erosion cycle in desert lands. This is also known as the geographic cycle in arid lands (p. 134) for, as in humid regions, the plains, plateaus, and mountains of desert regions are being worn down to a uniform level surface, a *desert plain*.

Assume that a region with desert climate has been given a considerable elevation and much irregularity of surface through uplifting forces acting from within the earth. Such a region may show ridges and hollows of varying size and form, and be made up of many different kinds of rock resting at all angles. The structure, then, may be as complicated as possible.

Fig. 137. — A view in the Sahara. In the foreground is a rocky hill. The weathering and erosion waste of these masses supplies the sand of the desert lowlands. It is washed down by the occasional torrential downpours of rain.

Deserts do have occasional tremendous rainfalls (p. 146), but it is a characteristic of the desert streams that result from such rains that they are intermittent and do not flow out to the sea. The water dries up within the desert, first collecting in the salines or alkali flats. These desert streams and lakes are of the consequent kind. During this stage of youth the consequent streams are engaged in filling the original depressions with the sand and the dissolved stuff washed down from the higher lands. Thus in youth the desert surface is made *less* rugged than it was originally; for the hills are lowered by the weathering and wash, and the depressions are filled with the deposit of this waste, raising their levels. This is quite the opposite from the stage of youth in the humid geographic cycle (p. 133). The deserts of the Great Basin region of the United States have been developed to a stage of late youth by these processes.

Maturity is reached when all the little basins have been filled to overflowing and the waste accumulations slope in great, unbroken sheets (Figs. 133, 145, 473) toward the lowest depression

Photo by Rich

Fig. 138. — The stage of maturity in the arid cycle. Note that the desert basins are waste-filled. A more recent cloud-burst has washed some of the waste from a higher to a lower level across the foreground of the picture. Colorado Desert, California.

within the desert area. This is the stage when sand and sand dunes are the typical features of the desert landscape. At this time too a new agent of erosion, the wind, becomes especially effective. The wind can sweep freely over the level sand wastes. It picks up great quantities of the dry sand particles, carries them along, and hurls them against all projecting rock masses. At some places sand dunes are produced. At other places the wind is strong enough to keep the sand moving and to develop a continuous sandblast action that rapidly wears away the rock (Fig. 139). As the greatest quantity of sand is carried along near the surface, the most active wear is at the low levels, so the rock hills tend to be undercut. The wind, further, is not confined to a channel as is a stream current; instead it blows first from one direction, then from another. Accordingly the rock is undercut from all sides. The weak rocks are eroded more rapidly than the strong ones and

Photo by Hayden

Fig. 139. — Sierra La Sal, Utah. Sand-blast action of wind in eroding desert rocks. This process searches out every irregularity in resistance of the rocks and acts most effectively near the surface of the general level of the desert. Find evidence of these conditions in the picture.

the result of this commonly is to produce very fantastic forms in the desert rock areas (Fig. 140). Such conditions are seen in various parts of the Sahara.

The undercutting takes away the support of the rocks at the higher levels, causing them to crash down. The fallen fragments are then wind-eroded to sand and borne away. Thus the path is cleared for more undercutting. In time all the projecting rock masses are thus beveled off to the levels of the waste-built plains.

After Walther

Fig. 140. — Odd forms produced by wind erosion in the Libyan Desert of Africa.

Photo by Bengtson

Fig. 141. — A blow-out in the sand hills of northwestern Nebraska. When the sparse grass cover of these sandy areas at the border of the arid lands is removed, the wind "blows out" the underlying sand. This may be the source of some of the wind-carried dust that on deposit builds up the loess formations.

Then the desert region is entering upon the stage of old age. The desert of central Asia is being developed from maturity to old age.

Meanwhile the sand used by the wind as a grinding tool is itself reduced to fine powder. Much of the dust so formed is carried out of the deserts by the winds and settles in adjoining lands to form *loess* deposits. Vast areas in China are covered with loess (Fig. 143). If provided with enough rainfall, loess regions make excellent agricultural land because the loess deposits are composed of thick masses of uniformly fine particles, coarser than clay and finer than sand. The loess, also, is very fertile because coming from a desert country the soluble mineral plant foods have been little if at all leached from this rock waste, as they have from much of the weathering material of the humid lands. Another characteristic of the loess is that, although unconsolidated, it stands up in steep cliffs like

Fig. 142. — A deposit of loess on glacial till at Omaha, Nebraska. Note that the loess is all fine-grained, shows no stratification and although unconsolidated stands up in a steep cliff.

solid bed rock where cut through by streams. There are extensive loess deposits along the middle course of the Mississippi and the lower course of the Missouri River in the United States, and along the Rhine River in Europe. These may in part be a record of a more arid climate at one time in those places; probably, however, they are made up of dust picked up by the wind on the flood plains of the streams which carried away the water from the melting of the great ice sheets of the Glacial Period (p. 286, Fig. 142).

Through wind-erosion and wind-export of the dust waste the desert areas are lowered in level, *deflated*. Removal of part of the waste sheet exposes the solid rock in places where the cover

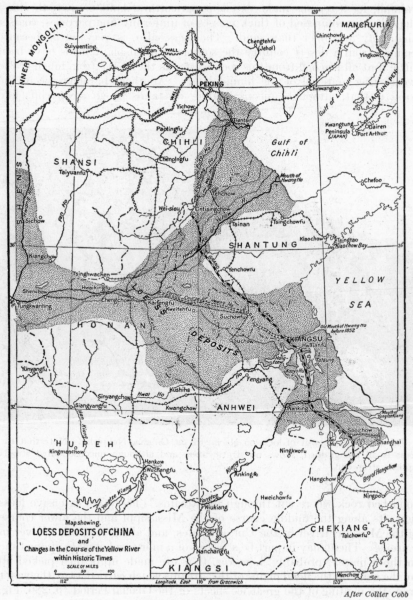

After Collier Cobb

Fig. 143. — Map of the loess deposits of China.

was not deep. Where this occurs, the wind promptly sandblasts the rock area down to the general level of the waste plains. The wind erosion may even dig a hollow in the bed rock if the exposed part happens to be of little resistant material. The next rain, however, washes waste from the surrounding higher areas into the hollow and thus prevents it from becoming indefinitely deep. Thus other rock areas are exposed and worn down in turn. The strong rocks as well as the weak rocks are reduced in height. By these

Fig. 144. — Oasis of Biskra in the Sahara.

processes a *desert plain* of level and fresh bed rock extending across strong and weak rocks alike is finally developed. Its surface may be quite bare or perhaps thinly strewn with bowlders of flinty rock, the last remainder of the rock masses that have been ground away. The Kalahari Desert of South Africa has this aspect.

The arid cycle is not begun or rejuvenated by uplift of the land, neither is it ended by wearing down to sea level. It starts and goes through its different stages solely because of desert climatic conditions and the processes of water action and wind action developed under such a climate. The desert plain at the end of the cycle may be high or low above the level of the sea which is base level for streams. Hence in the desert we have *leveling without base-leveling*. Instead of being covered with residual soil the desert plain is characteristically a bare, fresh rock surface.

Summary. *Desert areas, like humid regions, are reduced to level plains by denudation processes. But the stages of youth, maturity, and old age have different characteristics and are due to different processes from those of the*

Photo by Stewart

Fig. 145. — A mining town in the desert, Silver Bell, Arizona. Note the filling of desert waste between the rock hills.

erosion cycle in humid lands. Export of the desert waste as dust results in loess deposits in adjacent lands.

74. Life on deserts. Deserts offer comparatively little incentive to human occupation. It is true that the barrenness of the country (Fig. 139) is favorable to the discovery of mineral deposits and the arid conditions promote the accumulation of certain ores and valuable non-metallic substances, such as nitrate, and these deposits are much worked despite the difficult conditions (Fig. 145). But there is little opportunity for other industries. The rainfall is too light for agriculture without irrigation, and only a few parts have a water supply for irrigation. Areas which have water are called *oases* (Figs. 102, 144); these are usually either scattered springs in the desert, or else places where streams descend from mountain canyons and flow out upon and percolate under and through alluvial fans. In the hottest of such oases dates are a main food supply (Fig. 474). The date palm is said to thrive best "with its head in the sun and its feet in water." A large stream, like the Nile or Euphrates, causes a large oasis which may support an enormous agricultural population.

A few scattered people find life possible in all the desert, or nearly desert lands. In the Old World some of the desert people (Figs. 137, 501) are *nomads*, or wanderers, who move with their herds from oasis to oasis, to give the animals a chance to feed on the sparse desert vegetation. Such a life of danger and privation develops a hardy, warlike people, with love of freedom and a contempt for the monotonous settled life of the farmer. These people, having learned how to use the camel (Fig. 135), "the ship of the desert," for carrying their burdens, have long been traders and caravan leaders across the deserts. For centuries the chief means of communication between the east and west of the Old World was by caravan. Many of the Bible descriptions refer to desert life, for Palestine is surrounded by desert and is on caravan routes.

Summary. *Except on the oases, deserts are unfavorable to agricultural settlement, being occupied, in the Old World, by a scattered nomadic population engaged in herding and in caravan trade by use of the camel. Much mineral production, however, is developed in desert lands.*

TOPICAL OUTLINE, QUESTIONS, AND LABORATORY EXERCISES

63. **Nature of plateaus.** Association with mountains; relationship to plains· elevation of certain plateaus; tilted plateau blocks; lava floods.

64. **Sculpturing of plateaus.** Life history; effect of arid climates.

65. **Gorges and canyons.** Definition; occurrence; Colorado Canyon.

66. **Mesas and buttes.** Mesas; buttes; table-lands.

67. **Climate of plateaus.** Coolness; illustrations; arid climate.

68. **Inhabitants of moist plateaus.** Surface features of plateau west of the Appalachians; inhabitants; occupations; coal mining; New York.

69. **Inhabitants of arid plateaus.** Climate; ranching; irrigation; Indian pueblos.

70. **Nature of deserts.** Two causes; extent; rainfall; surface features.

71. **Drainage of deserts.** Rainfall; run-off; "cloud-bursts"; arroyos; effects of floods; intermittent streams; large streams fed from mountains; withered streams, Salines, alkali flats, salt lakes; their cause.

72. **Wind action on deserts.** Importance; sand storms; source of sand; sand dunes; change in position.

73. **The erosion cycle in desert lands.** Youth; maturity; fantastic forms; loess; deflation; desert plain; leveling without base-leveling.

74. **Life on deserts.** Mineral; farming; oases; nomads; camel.

QUESTIONS. Section 57. What are the conditions on the sea bottom off the North American coast? What would result if it were elevated?

58. Where are coastal plains found? Why? Why is artesian water found in them? What industries are developed on the Atlantic coastal plain? What has been its history as a land form? What is the nature of the coast line? What are the evidences of youth? What are the cause and effects of the Fall Line? What is a belted plain and how is it formed? How do subsequent valleys develop? What is a cuesta? Its inface? Its dip slope?

59. What is the extent of the Russian and Siberian plains? What is their origin? What are the conditions in the northern, central, and southern portions? Describe the tundra. How may it be utilized?

60. What is the general condition of the plains of central United States? What are the conditions on the Great Plains? Why are the prairies treeless? What effect has this condition had? Account for the development of the central plains region. Where else are similar plains found?

61. What has caused the plains of the valley of the Red River of the North? Those near Great Salt Lake? What other kinds of plains are there?

62. State the life history of a plain. What effect has structure on the development of the drainage system? Define obsequent streams, trellis, insequent and dendritic drainage.

63. How are plateaus related to mountains? How do they differ from plains? What is the condition of the rock strata?

64. How does the life history of plateaus resemble and differ from that of plains? What effect has an arid climate on sculpturing?

65. What is a canyon? Describe the Colorado Canyon.

66. Explain mesas. Buttes. Account for the name table-land. Why are there no conspicuous mesas in plateaus with a humid climate?

67. How do plateaus affect temperature? Give illustrations. Why are plateaus often arid?

68. What is the condition of the plateau west of the Appalachians? What effect has this on the people? What differences are there from Tennessee to New York? Why?

69. Why are arid plateaus sparsely inhabited? What are the industries? How is irrigation agriculture developed? How did the Indians of the Southwest formerly live?

70. State the causes for deserts. What about the rainfall? The surface features?

71. Describe the conditions of drainage in deserts. Define intermittent stream, arroyo. What is the cause of salt and alkali deposits?

72. Describe wind action in deserts. Describe and explain desert sand dunes.

73. Describe the stages of youth, maturity, and old age in the desert cycle of erosion. How does each differ from the similar stage in the humid cycle? How does wind erosion differ from stream erosion? Account for and give the characteristics of loess deposits. What is meant by deflation? What is the nature of a desert plain? Explain leveling without base-leveling.

74. What are the industries of deserts? What are nomads? How do they live? Of what importance is the camel?

Reference Books. JOHNSON, *Shore Processes and Shoreline Development*, John Wiley & Sons, New York, 1919; VON ENGELN, *Inheriting the Earth*, The Macmillan Company, New York, 1922; HUNTINGTON, *Pulse of Asia*, Houghton, Mifflin Company, Boston, 1907; COLBY, *Source Book for the Economic Geography of North America*, University of Chicago Press, Chicago, 1921; FAIRGRIEVE, *Geography and World Power*, E. P. Dutton & Company, New York, 1917; ABBE, *Physiography of Maryland*, Vol. I, Part II, Maryland Weather Service, Baltimore, Md., 1899.

Laboratory Exercises. The following laboratory exercises in TARR and VON ENGELN's *Laboratory Manual for Physical and Commercial Geography*, The Macmillan Company, New York, are designed to supplement the study of plains and plateaus as presented in this chapter and to provide the problems of interpretation that will lead to a clearer understanding of the text. Exercises XIX, XXII, XXIII, XXIV, XXV, XXXVI.

Fig. 146. — The Wetterhorn, Alps, Switzerland. A view of a high peak and part of the range that it surmounts. A rugged, young mountain region. The lower levels are cultivated and in pasture; the intermediate slopes are forested; above these is bare rock and snow and ice. This view rightly gives one the impression that it is typical of mountain scenery, but mountains have many aspects.

CHAPTER VI

MOUNTAINS

75. Introductory. Mountains contrast strikingly with plains, but resemble dissected plateaus in irregularity of form (Fig. 162). The height, ruggedness, and coldness of lofty mountains make them barriers to commerce and travel. Mineral wealth may lead to a

Fig. 147. — Mt. McKinley, Alaska. This is the highest mountain in North America, 20,300 feet high. From a distant viewpoint. Notice the clouds extending across the level of the slopes of the lower mountains (see p. 415).

considerable population in mountain regions, and, in summer, people are attracted to them by the cool climate and beautiful scenery. But, not being suited to extensive agriculture, mountains as a whole are never densely settled.

76. The mountain rocks. Unlike those of plains and plateaus, the rock formations of mountains are almost never horizontal.

All kinds of folds and faults (p. 53) are found. Some mountains, like many in the Great Basin, are faulted and tilted blocks of rock, with the formations inclined in a single direction (Figs. 150, 151). Others, like the Jura in Switzerland, consist of strata folded into

Fig. 148. — Mt. Blanc, France. The highest mountain of the Alps, 15,781 feet high. This mountain looks higher than Mt. McKinley in Fig. 147 because it is seen from a nearer point and across a deep valley.

regular anticlines and synclines (Fig. 165). Still others, like the Alps, are very complexly folded and faulted (Fig. 152a). The strata of the Appalachians were originally horizontal, but are now complexly folded. If they could be straightened out to their original condition, they would occupy fully twice as much area as now. That is to say, forty miles of rock strata have, by folding, been crowded into twenty miles of mountain. The rocks of the Alps appear to have been compressed into less than one fourth the area they once occupied.

Such complex folding often so alters, or metamorphoses, the rocks that it is very difficult to tell their original condition (p. 49). Igneous rocks often cut across the mountain strata (Fig. 49); indeed they commonly make up a large part of the mountain mass. Therefore, one may in a short distance find many kinds of rock—granite, gneiss, sandstone, limestone, etc. — occupying many different positions. This complexity gives denudation an opportunity to sculpture mountains into many irregular land forms that are not possible on plains and plateaus. Mountains may be defined in general terms as elevated regions having only a small area of summit level.

Photo by Darton

Fig. 149. — Cathedral Spires, Garden of the Gods, Colorado. Originally horizontal layers made to stand vertically by mountain uplift and then weathered and eroded into relief by removal of the weaker strata on either side.

Summary. *Mountain rocks are inclined at various angles by folding and faulting, and they are also very complex in kind. In these respects mountains contrast strikingly with plains and plateaus.*

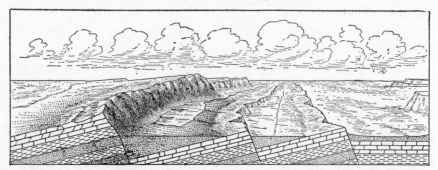

Fig. 150. — Diagram of fault block mountains as these appear in the desert region of the Great Basin country of Utah. Note the relation of the structure to the ridges; the filling of desert sand waste between the ridges; the lake impounded in a hollow where the dislocation has been greater in the middle, due also in part to the barrier of an alluvial fan.

Photo by Ransome

Fig. 151. — Mexican Canyon fault, east of Bisbee, Arizona. Fault block ridges on a small scale. If the ridges were due to denudation only, without faulting, how many strong capping layers would show in the foreground?

77. Names applied to units of mountain form. A mountain *system* is a series of mountain folds, raised by the same uplift and forming a single group. A mountain system consists of minor portions, or *ranges* (Figs. 146, 155). A group of mountain systems is called a *cordillera*. For example, the cordillera of western United States includes four systems, — the Coast Ranges, the Sierra Nevada-Cascade system, the Basin Range system, and the Rocky Mountain system. Each of these systems consists of a number of ranges; for instance, the Rocky Mountain system has many ranges, such as the Wasatch and Uinta ranges.

Denudation, wearing away the ranges, leaves some of the resistant rocks standing above the general level. If these elevated portions are long, they are called *ridges* (Figs. 154, 232, 236); if not greatly elongated, *peaks* (Fig. 158). There may be many peaks and ridges in a single range (Fig.

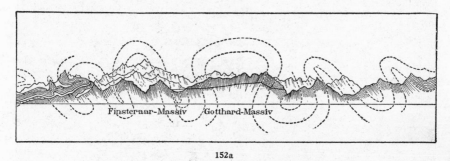

152a

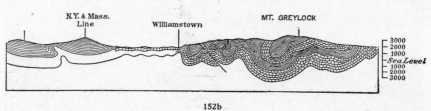

152b

Fig. 152a and b. — Complex folding of rocks in the Alps and in the New England mountains of western Massachusetts. The dotted lines in (a), the Alps, extend the layers upward, as they would extend if nothing had been removed. The New England mountains are older and worn down more; their strata if continued would extend to even greater proportionate elevations.

167). More rarely ridges and peaks are formed by folding or faulting (Figs. 165, 151).

Long, narrow ridges, commonly very steep because the rocks are nearly vertically inclined, formed on the flanks of mountains by erosion into relief of the more resistant of the upfolded strata, are popularly called *hogbacks*. If not so steeply inclined similarly durable strata give rise to escarpments (p. 126). Such escarpments may be sufficiently high and bold to cause the term mountains to be applied to the level, plateau summits they enclose. Thus the Helderberg Mountains of New York State are an escarpment-bounded plateau (Fig. 130).

There are different kinds of valleys among mountains. The largest of these are the broad plateaus between mountain systems. When they have no outlet to the sea, as in the Great Basin of the West, they are called *interior basins* (p. 33). Smaller basins without outlet are formed between mountain ranges by downfolding. Broad valleys in the Rocky Mountains, some due to folding and faulting, others to denudation, are commonly called *parks* (Fig. 155). In the Appalachians, narrow gorges cut by streams across ridges are called *water gaps* (Figs. 113, 172, 447, and Plate VI). Similar gaps, usually at higher elevations, not now occupied by

Photo by Stose

Fig. 153. — Synclinal fold near Upton, Pennsylvania. The strata are *competent,* that is they have yielded to the forces of mountain folding but have not broken under the strain to which they were subjected.

streams, are called *wind gaps* (Fig. 178). A mountain *pass* (Figs. 157, 450) is a low portion of a mountain divide. Passes are usually caused by denudation, where streams head together on opposite sides of a divide. Many have been lowered further by glacial erosion (p. 249, Fig. 235). Their position is often due to the presence of weak rock.

Summary. *The names cordillera, system, range, ridge, and peak are applied to mountains or units of mountain form. The names interior basin, park, water gap, and pass are applied to mountain valleys.*

78. Climate of mountains. The temperature of the air decreases 1° F., on the average, for every 300 to 330 feet of elevation
(p. 407). Therefore, high plateaus and mountains rise into the cool
upper layers of the air. Indeed, many mountains rise so high
that there is perpetual snow on their summits, and glaciers occupy
their valleys. The line above which there is perpetual snow is
called the *snow line* (Figs. 156, 230). Below this is a belt with a
climate too cold for tree growth. The line above which trees can-

Photo by Wheeler

Fig. 154. — Ridge after ridge, a sea of mountains, all due to the erosion of the valley
hollows between them. The mountain height and the bending and tilting of the strata
are due to the uplifting forces, but the mountain forms and the ruggedness are the
effects of differential erosion. In the Canadian Rockies. Mt. Lefroy is the highest
peak on the left.

not grow is known as the *timber line* (Figs. 146, 155, 180). These
lines are lower on the shady than on the sunny side of mountains,
and in the temperate than in the tropical zone.

Mountains in the path of vapor-bearing winds have abundant rainfall
on the slopes against which the winds blow (p. 415). The opposite slopes,
and the country beyond, are dry, because so much vapor is lost in passing
over the mountains. This is well illustrated in northwestern United

States, where winds from the Pacific cause abundant rain on the western slopes, but reach the eastern side so dry that the country is arid (Figs. 157, 473).

Summary. *On high mountains there is a line, called the timber line, above which no trees can grow; higher still is a zone of perpetual snow. Mountains are well watered on the side from which vapor-bearing winds blow, and commonly arid on the opposite slopes.*

79. Denudation of mountains. Mountain ranges owe their actual height, that is, elevation above sea level, to the uplifting forces which raised them. This height is, however, only seldom

Photo by Jackson

Fig. 155. — Timber line in winter. There is a snow cover in the woods below the timber line at this season. In summer the snow at the lower levels melts away but the sharp line of the edge of the woods on the upper slopes clearly indicates the timber line above which trees cannot grow because of snow and cold.   Ten Mile Range, Rocky Mountains, Colorado.

as great, or even nearly as great, as the uplifting forces might develop. The number and rugged relief of the individual topographic features of mountains are due to denudation. This is a fact that should be kept always in mind when studying mountain forms.

The climate and great elevation of mountains give high power to the agents of denudation. Because the rivers are well above base level, they are able to cut deep gorges (Fig. 66) and canyons. Weathering is also very active, especially on steep slopes above

the timber line (Figs. 154, 158, 159, 181), where there is little vegetation to afford protection to soil and rock. In such situations the
rock is exposed to sharp contrasts in temperature between day and
night; frost action is vigorous; and the strong winds, heavy rains,

Photo by Peabody

Fig. 156. — Mt. Washington, New Hampshire, 6,279 feet high, the highest mountain
in the northeastern United States. Snow line in early summer. Trees in leaf and
green grass at lower elevations, while a light fall of snow covers the summit ridge.
This snow will disappear later in the season. If a considerable amount of snow should
remain through one summer into the next winter, what would develop in the highest
mountain valleys? (See Chapter VIII.)

and water from melting snow all help to move rock fragments down
the steep slopes.

Among high mountains the slopes are often so steep that the rock
fragments fall to their base (Figs. 158. 180). Some of this rock waste is

carried away by streams, but very often more falls than can be thus removed (p. 63). In time this forms a mantle of rock waste, or *talus slope* (Figs. 125, 161), which covers the lower slopes, and, by its smooth, curving outline, forms a striking contrast to the rugged, irregular slopes above. Where wet-weather streams descend the mountain sides, these talus slopes grade into steep alluvial fans (Figs. 101, 167). Great accumulations of talus containing a large proportion of small size fragments may develop a flow-motion in the mass giving rise to *rock-streams*, also called *rock-glaciers* (why?) (Fig. 159), that creep slowly forward. Saturation

Fig. 157.— The arid lee slopes of the Andes Mountains in Chile, at the Pass of Uspallata. The lower slopes are nearly barren of vegetation and the summit areas are nearly free of snow because precipitation is so slight. In these high valleys the ancient civilized Inca Indians grew crops by practicing irrigation. Look carefully to find the road over the pass.

with water, and the alternate freezing and thawing of water between the particles, greatly promote such flow.

At all times small fragments of rock are falling from the steep mountain slopes; but, in addition, there is an occasional fall of large masses, forming an *avalanche* if mixed with snow (Fig. 440), or a *landslide* (p. 63). In an avalanche thousands, and sometimes millions, of tons of rock, mingled with snow and ice, come tearing down the mountain side, destroying everything in their course. Rivers are dammed, villages destroyed, and roads ruined. Mountains supply many instances of destructive landslides. They are usually started by frost, or by rain (Fig. 160) or melted snow, which saturate unstable masses of soil or rock on steep slopes, making them so heavy that they can no longer maintain their positions.

Fig. 158. — Bare rock slopes above the snow line in the Alps. Here weathering is even more rapid than on the site of Fig. 154. Frost splitting detaches great blocks of rock which then tumble down the perpendicular cliffs. Aguile du Dru, a typical "needle" peak.

As a result of rapid denudation, acting on the complex rocks, mountains are cut into a great variety of rugged forms. There are peaks almost impossible to scale, some so steep and sharp-pointed that they are called "needles" (Fig. 158) and "horns" and resulting usually from the cirque erosion of glaciers (p. 270); there are ridges that no roads cross; and, in fact, a surface often so rugged that large areas are uninhabited.

Photo by Cross

Fig. 159. — Rock stream, Silver Basin, Colorado. The accumulation of talus was here so extensive that it caused the mass, probably when saturated with water, to flow out faster than soil creep, slower than a landslide. In high latitudes ice forming between the rock fragments causes such talus accumulations to flow quite continuously, in the manner and by essentially the same process as do glaciers.

Summary. *River erosion and weathering are very active among mountains, especially above the timber line. Rock fragments, falling from steep slopes, accumulate at their base as talus slopes, alluvial fans, and rock streams. Occasionally larger masses descend as avalanches and landslides. By this rapid denudation high mountains are made very rugged.*

80. Resemblance between mountains and high plateaus. Some plateaus are more elevated than many high mountain peaks; it is only very lofty mountains that rise higher than 10,000 feet, and yet there are plateaus which reach that level. These high plateaus are often so carved by vigorous denudation as to resemble mountains closely (Figs. 161, 310 and Plate III). They are, in fact, in some instances called mountains.

The Catskill Mountains, for example, are not mountains in the structural sense, but dissected plateaus. In the Catskills, denudation has carved out peaks and deep valleys with precipitous sides; but the nearly horizontal strata prove that they were uplifted as plateaus, not as mountain folds. Such mountain-like plateaus, sometimes called *relict mountains*, are usually near mountains, and gradually merge into them (Figs. 162, 263). Of similar origin, in the sense that they remain as elevated regions because surrounding, less resistant, rock masses have been worn away,

Photo by International Newsreel

Fig. 160. — Landslide at Someo, Switzerland, 1924. Heavy rains caused a mass of rock and earth to slide down from a height of 2,500 feet on the mountain side. The mass and velocity of the slide caused it to cut a path straight through the village, utterly destroying the houses in its way. The débris of these homes is seen here mixed with the rock and earth of the slide itself. Note that the slide did not come down the stream valley that appears on the left.

are *mountains of circumdenudation* or *circumerosion*. These may be made up altogether of igneous rock; Pikes Peak is an example. Where associated with a peneplain such mountains are called monadnocks (p. 93).

Summary. *Vigorous denudation so sculptures high plateaus, like the Catskills, as to make them resemble mountains in ruggedness; but their strata are horizontal. Other mountain areas result from the widespread wearing away, hence lowering, of surrounding masses of weaker rock.*

Fig. 161. — Relict mountain, part of a dissected plateau, at Tempel Bay, Spitzbergen. Note that the strata are horizontal and that the mountain has been formed by the dissection of the flat-lying rocks. What evidence that dissection still continues do you find in the picture?

81. Distribution of mountains. Although mountains are typical of continents, there are ranges in the open ocean; for example, the New Zealand (Fig. 163) and Hawaiian islands. The latter are volcanoes rising from the crest of a submarine mountain fold,

Fig. 162. — A section showing folded mountain strata (on the right) grading into the horizontal strata of a plateau (on the left). Compare the two portions in ruggedness and elevation.

having a length of 1500 miles. There are many other ranges in the ocean, especially in the South Pacific.

Mountains are common at or near the border of continents (Figs. 28, 29). They sometimes fringe the coast, as in the case

Photo by N. Z. Tour. and Health Res. Dept.

Fig. 163. — Mountains that rise directly from the sea floor in the open ocean; George Sound, New Zealand. The valley shown was formerly occupied by an immense glacier and is a fiord (pp. 294, 364) viewed from its mouth.

of the Kurile, Japanese, and Philippine islands (Fig. 32), and the East and West Indies.   Mountain chains also extend from the land into the sea, forming peninsulas; for example, the peninsulas of Lower California, Kamchatka, Malay, Greece, and Italy.   In other places mountain systems form the very border of the continents rising directly out of the sea.   Such a condition is well illustrated by the Coast Ranges of western North America and the Andes of South America.

Mountains are also found far from the coast; for example, the Appalachians, Rocky Mountains, Sierra Nevada, and the

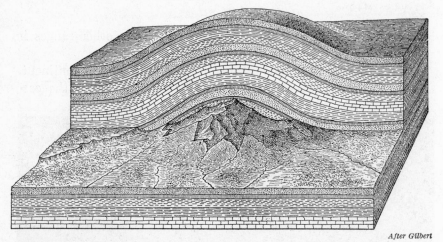

After Gilbert

Fig. 164. — The Henry Mountains, Utah, 11,000 feet high, with the dome restored as it would probably exist if denudation had removed none of the strata.

mountains of central Europe and Asia.   But most mountains of the interior, when first formed, rose from the sea.

Summary. *Mountains occur on continents, both in the interior and along the border, where they form chains of islands, peninsulas, and systems which rise at the very margin of the land.   They also form island chains in the open ocean.*

82. Cause of mountains.   The explanation of mountains most widely accepted is that of *contraction* (p. 29).   The heated interior of the earth is evidently shrinking in volume, and the more or less rigid surface shell of rocks settles down upon it.   But it cannot fit the constantly shrinking interior without wrinkling.   This causes mountains, which are either wrinkles or the result of wrinkles, in the earth's crust.   The most typical and extended of mountain ranges are those due to folding and faulting of strata by compressive force acting from one side.

Another hypothesis asserts that all the rocks of the earth to great depths contain radio-active minerals that give off heat energy, and that this fact is the basic cause of mountains. The amount of heat developed in a short time by this radio-activity is small, but two conditions make it effective in bringing about great changes. (*a*) The heat generated in the depths cannot escape to the surface by conduction through the rocks as fast as it is produced. (*b*) Millions of years are available for heat to accumulate between one mountain-making period and the next. Accordingly the heavy rock material deep below the surface of the earth may

Fig. 165. — An anticlinal fold near Münster in the Jura Mountains of Switzerland. It slants, *pitches* to the left, and is cut through by an antecedent stream.

become so hot that it melts. Then three things happen. The continents, supported isostatically (p. 41), sink deeper into the melted, hence less dense, rock below them. Melting of the deep rock stuff causes it to expand, and this expansion stretches and cracks the surface crust, permitting vast floods of the molten lava to be forced out (p. 225). In the epicontinental seas (p. 119) caused by the sinking of the continents great thicknesses of sediment accumulate.

The expansion also arches up the floors of the great oceans and the ends of such arches thrust against the sides of the continents. By this force the sediments accumulating in the basins of the epicontinental seas are crushed together. Meanwhile a tide develops in the underlying "sea" of molten rock. The effect of this tide is to cause the continents to slip around over the areas formerly covered by the oceans. Then the specially hot places, previously under the continents, cool off by losing their heat to the ocean waters. Convectional currents (p. 403) in the molten material greatly hasten the cooling process. As the molten rock solidifies and gains its earlier density the continents are caused to rise isostatically. The crushed sedimentary masses being especially light are forced up much higher than other areas. Thus mountains made up of folded strata result. This cycle is thought to have been repeated at least four times in the geological history of the earth.

Summary. *Mountains are the result of distortion, breaking, and upheaval of the earth's crust by forces originating in, or determined by, interior*

Photo by Clifford

Fig. 166. — The Columbia River, an antecedent stream, cutting across the Cascade Mountains in Oregon. The river flows in rapids because the uplift of the mountain rocks from below always furnishes more material for the stream to cut through.

conditions. The more typical folded mountains have been formed slowly and by successive uplifts.

83. Types of mountains. Perhaps the simplest type of mountain is that in which a block of rock has been uplifted, along a fault plane, and tilted (Fig. 150). Such a mountain has one moderate and one steep slope, while the crest is a ridge parallel to the fault plane. Mountains of this type are found in southern Oregon and other parts of the Great Basin. These tilted *block mountains* may reach a height of 4000 or 5000 feet, a width of 10 to 20 miles, and a length of 50 to 100 miles. They are probably parts of a great arched fold which has broken down.

Another simple mountain type is the dome, in which the upper strata have been raised by the intrusion of lava. If the intrusive rock rests below on undisturbed strata the dome is called a *lacco-lithic* mountain (p. 228). In such a mountain there is no ridge, but a central area from which the surface slopes in all directions. This

Fig. 167. — Young mountains, the Alps, Switzerland at Bergün, opposite the Piz d'Aela. The steep slopes, the sharp peaks and the evidence (what?) of rapid denudation, even though not high above the timber line, are characteristic features of young mountains.

type is illustrated by the Henry Mountains, in Utah (Fig. 164), and others in the West.

If the whole thickness of the sedimentary layers has been raised by the intrusion of the igneous rock a broader uplift, such as that of the Little Rocky Mountains in Montana, is formed. Such domes have usually a *granite core* and this is also found to be the central material of great folded ranges.

A third simple type is the evenly folded mountain, illustrated by the Swiss Jura (Fig. 165) and parts of the Appalachians. When such mountains are formed the surface is thrown into a series of regular waves, like the waves of the sea, the anticlines forming mountain ridges, the synclines, valleys. When denudation cuts deeply into these, as in the Appalachians, each durable layer is left as a ridge (Figs. 172, 173).

Mountains whose strata are greatly contorted (Fig. 180) and metamorphosed, with much igneous rock, have a far less simple form. Denudation, discovering differences in the rocks, sculptures them into very irregular and rugged outlines. The Rockies and Alps (Figs. 146, 159, 167) are types of such mountains.

Fig. 168. — Mature mountains in the Lake District of northwestern England made famous by the poet Wordsworth. The lake is Derwentwater.

Summary.—*There are simple faulted block mountains; laccolithic and domed mountains raised by the intrusion of lava; evenly folded mountains; and very complexly folded and faulted mountains. On being denuded the latter are carved into very irregular and rugged forms.*

84. Life history of mountains. Let us assume that the strata of a former sea-bottom are being folded to form a mountain system. As the strata slowly bend, the surface becomes irregular; and, when the strain becomes too great, the rocks slip along fault planes. Through the deeper fissures, lava may rise, building volcanic cones. Earthquakes and volcanic eruptions normally occur in regions of growing mountains (pp. 221, 233).

From the very first the rising land is attacked by the agents of denudation; but as the mountains are not worn down so rapidly as they are elevated, they continue to grow higher, reaching above the timber line and even into the zone of perpetual snow. Then glaciers extend down the valleys.

The durable rocks are etched out into ridges and peaks, the weak rocks are cut away, forming valleys and passes. In this stage the surface is so irregular as to preclude agricultural settlement almost entirely. Such mountains, illustrated by the Coast Ranges of western North America, the Himalayas, and the Alps, are *young mountains*. Make a list of the pictures of young mountains that are in this book.

The time comes when uplift ceases; but denudation continues

Fig. 169. — An old mountain region. Scottish Highlands around Loch Lomond, Scotland. These low knobs and ridges are the roots of an ancient mountain mass worn to the low relief and gentle slopes of old age.

to broaden the valleys and lower the peaks and ridges. As the mountains are lowered, glaciers disappear, and, in time, even the highest peaks may come below the timber line. Such mountains, which have lost the ruggedness of youth, may be called *mature;* the Appalachians and the mountains of New England, Norway, and Scotland are examples (Figs. 156, 168, 170, 184, 440). Their slopes are forested, their valleys tilled.

Further lowering may continue until the mountains are reduced to a series of low, rolling hills — *old* mountains (Figs. 169, 493); or, further still, to the condition of peneplaination (p. 93). The mountains are then, like plains, adapted to dense settlement. New York City, Philadelphia, Baltimore, and Washington are situated on such old, worn-down mountains. These ancient mountains, known as the Piedmont Plateau, extend from New England to Alabama, east of the Appalachians.

After being worn to the low relief of a peneplain (Fig. 171), a mountain region may be reëlevated, and caused to start on a new life history, as has been the case with the Appalachian Mountains to the west of the Piedmont Plateau. Then denudation etches the ridges of durable rock into relief again, and forms broad, subsequent valleys where the strata are weak (Figs. 172, 173, 447). The broad valleys are well settled (Fig. 186), but the ridges are too rough and rocky for farming, and are often timber-

Photo by U. S. Geol. Survey

Fig. 170. — Summits of the Blue Ridge Mountains in North Carolina. High mountains dissected to late mature form in the cycle of erosion. This wide prospect of smooth, flowing slopes, with no bare rock ledges or steep cliffs, gives a clear idea of the effect of long continued denudation on the form of high mountains. Even the loftiest summits are mantled in residual soil and covered with forest growth.

covered. Where streams leave the broad valleys to cross the ridges of resistant rock, they flow in narrow gorges, or *water gaps* (Plate VI), because there has not been time for weathering to broaden valleys in such durable strata.

Water gaps may originate in any one of three ways. If a stream is superimposed (p. 94) on a buried mountain structure after having had its direction of flow and valley cutting determined by the slope and structure of overlying rocks, the stream will continue in its course and a narrow

Fig. 171. — The level summit of the Labrador peneplain at the head of Saguenay fiord.

gorge will be eroded where it cuts through the stronger structures, either anticlinal, synclinal, or monoclinal, of the underlying folded rocks. Meanwhile denudation, by removing great quantities of less resistant material on either side, may bring the strong structure into marked relief as a mountain ridge and the stream course across it appears as a water gap.

In the second case a mountain fold, or other uplift, develops across the course of an existing stream. But the degrading action of the stream more than keeps pace with the rate of mountain uplift. So the stream keeps its course as the mountain folding takes place and a water gap results. This process is like pushing a log against the bottom of a buzz-saw. Such a stream course is said to be *antecedent*, that is to have existed

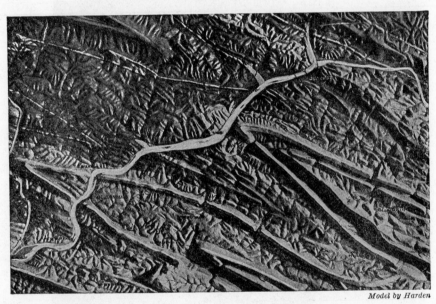

Model by Harden

Fig. 172. — Photograph of a relief model of the Appalachian Mountains in the anthracite coal district of Pennsylvania. The Susquehanna River is shown cutting across successive ridges of resistant strata which outline the anticlinal and synclinal folds.

before the mountain fold developed. The Columbia river is considered to have cut across the Cascade mountains in this way (Fig. 166).

The third way for a water gap to originate is by headwater erosion and river piracy as explained in the following section.

Summary. *As mountains rise, the effect of denudation increases, and young mountains are therefore made very rugged. Mature mountains have been lowered and the valleys broadened; and old mountains are still further lowered, and perhaps even reduced to a peneplain. Uplift allows denudation again to etch the resistant strata into relief.*

85. The drainage of mountains. In early stages, in consequence of the slopes, numerous short streams flow down the moun-

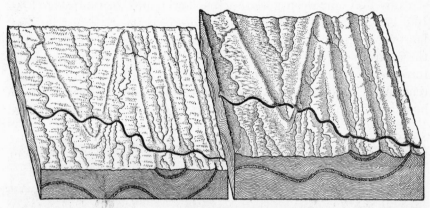

Fig. 173. — To illustrate the origin of the Appalachian ridges. The mountains were worn down to low relief, as in the left figure; then, after uplift, the ridges were etched out. The streams crossing them have cut water gaps, while broad valleys have been developed between the ridges in the weaker strata.

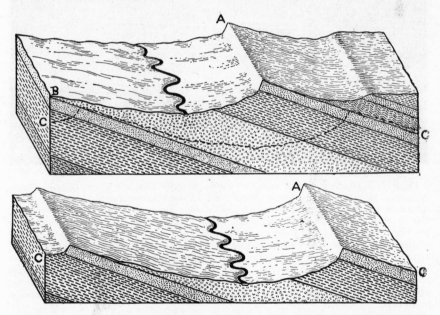

Fig. 174. — To illustrate the migration of divides. A durable layer A forms a divide ridge. When the surface has been worn down to the line CC (upper figure) the ridge A will have migrated to the right, as shown in the lower figure. A is the escarpment slope, A–C the dip slope, A–B the inner lowland; in the lower diagram a new escarpment is beginning to form above C on the left.

tain sides in gorges; and longer streams follow the broad valleys between the mountain folds. Here and there antecedent main streams may cut deep gorges across low points in the folds (Figs. 165, 173). In such *consequent mountain drainage* there are, at first, however, numerous lakes held up by the mountain dams. But these are soon filled with sediment brought by the mountain torrents or drained by downward erosion of their outlets. A slight renewal of mountain movement may warp the valleys and form new lake basins. Lake Timiskaming in Ontario is thus explained.

Photo by von E.

Fig. 175. — Headquarters of Pine Creek, opposing the Genesee River, Ulysses, Pennsylvania. Here the valley course flattens out to the shallow channel seen just below the house in the right center of the picture. Above the house, toward the foreground, this channel divides left and right, and each of these channels divides again into even less marked channels. By these minor channels the basin at the headwaters is drained at the time of rains. As run-off waters at the time of such rains concentrate at the head of the valley course they deepen and lengthen it. Meanwhile the basin at the head is being enlarged and lowered. See Fig. 176. A stream does not necessarily rise in a spring or lake, nor does it need to start in a narrow mountain gorge to permit headwater erosion to take place. Across the dividing ridge the Genesee has a similar basin head.

If the elevation of the land ceases, the valleys pass through the stages of youth, maturity, and old age. But the great elevation, and the resistant and complex nature of the mountain rocks,

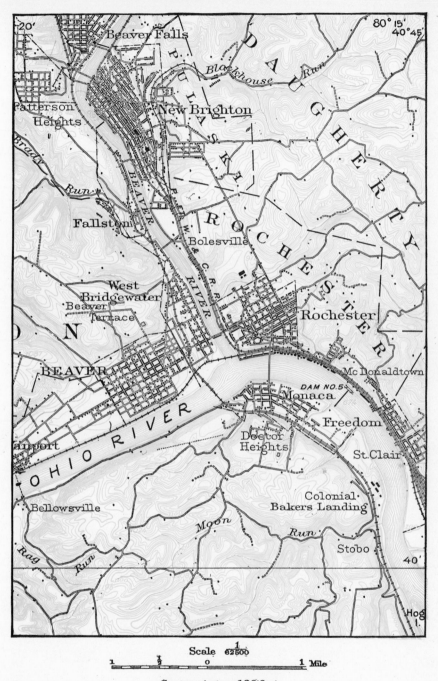

Scale $\frac{1}{62500}$

Contour interval 20 feet.

Plate V. — Part of Beaver, Pennsylvania, sheet; Topographic Atlas of the United States; U. S. Geol. Sur.

An accordant stream junction. The Ohio River and Beaver Creek have both eroded their valleys deep into the plateau, but the smaller stream has kept pace with the larger stream and comes in at grade.

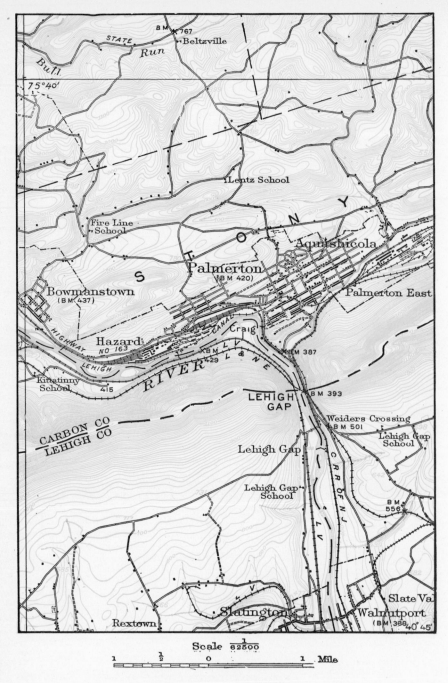

Scale $\frac{1}{62500}$

1   ½   0   1   Mile

Contour interval 20 feet.

Plate VI. — Part of Mauch Chunk, Pennsylvania, sheet; Topographic Atlas of the United States; U. S. Geol. Sur.

    A water gap. Here the Lehigh River cuts across one of the narrow ridges of the Appalachian Mountains. How did such gaps originate? See p. 182.

make the life history of a river valley in mountains longer than in plains and in most plateaus.

The wearing away of the weak rocks leaves the durable strata standing as divides (Figs. 44, 45, 46). As the surface slowly wears down, the divides still remain on the more durable strata. These mountain strata usually incline, or dip; and, as they are slowly worn away, their crests, that is the divides, not only become lower, but shift to one side (Fig. 174). This, called *the law of monoclinal shifting,* may be stated as follows: *As denudation lowers a region of inclined strata, the divide migrates in the direction of the dip.*

Photo by von E

Fig. 176. — Headwater erosion by rain-gullying; Pine Creek, opposite the headwaters of the Genesee River at Ulysses, Pennsylvania. As a particularly hard shower concentrates on some area of the headwater-basin slope a rain gully, like that in center of picture, forms. Thus the basin is lowered and the dividing ridge between it and the opposite drainage is notched. The next rain may cause more marked gullying at another point, as suggested on the left. Meanwhile weathering is reducing more of the bed rock, which is only a short distance below the surface, to fine particles ready for removal by gullying. Thus the whole basin is successively and intermittently attacked and lowered. This photograph is in the basin head of the Pine Creek drainage which opposes the Genesee drainage and is competing with it in headwater erosion.

Mountain divides may migrate for other reasons (Figs. 177, 178, 179). Thus, two streams heading on the same divide are both enlarging their drainage area by headwater erosion, and the stronger one gradually pushes the divide back into the territory of the weaker. It thus robs the weaker stream of its headwaters, and is called a *river pirate*. There are various reasons why one

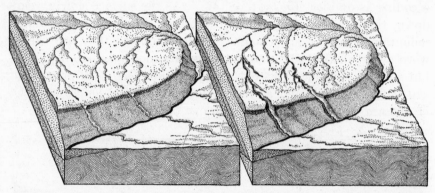

Fig. 177. — The headwaters of a tributary (left figure) rise on a highland and flow a long distance, in a roundabout course, to reach the main stream. Two short streams head in the same region, but flow in steep courses to the main stream. This gives them power to eat back at the divide and rob the long tributary of some of its headwaters (right figure). This condition is somewhat like that in the Catskills. Note that the tributaries of the captured streams join in a *barbed* pattern. In the left figure the main stream on the upper level may be regarded as a consequent stream with insequent tributaries; the lower level stream as a subsequent stream with obsequent tributaries on the left.

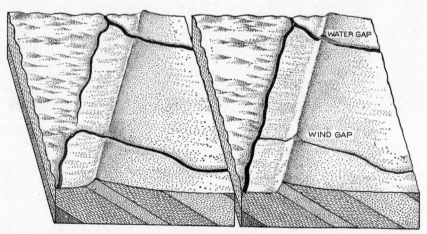

Fig. 178. — In the left figure two streams cross a mountain ridge of durable rock. A tributary of the farther one heads back nearly to the point where the nearer one turns to cross the ridge. For some reason (perhaps greater volume) the farther stream has more power to cut into the ridge, thus deepening its valley. This gives to its tributary a steeper slope which permits it to eat gradually backward until it taps the nearer stream, drawing it off through the farther water gap. This leaves a *wind gap* where the nearer stream formerly crossed the ridge (right figure).

stream may have greater ability to erode than another: one may have more rainfall; or it may have a shorter and steeper slope; or it may have only weak strata to remove while the other wears down resistant rocks.

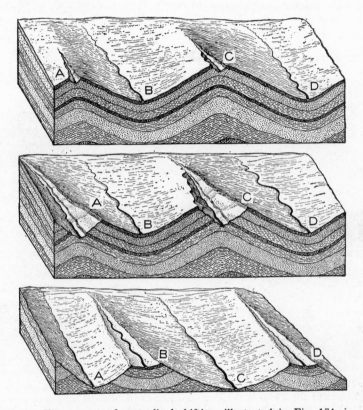

Fig. 179. — The process of monoclinal shifting, illustrated in Fig. 174, is carried further in this diagram. In the upper diagram there are four streams, A, B, C, and D; A and C in small valleys in the anticlines, B and D in broad synclinal valleys caused by down-folding. They are consequent on the mountain form. In the middle figure there is little change, except that the anticlinal valleys have been lengthened and deepened, this being possible because they are so high that the streams have much power, while the synclinal streams are held back in their work by lakes (not shown here), strong structure, and durable strata. The lower figure represents a much later stage, in which the surface has been greatly worn down. Monoclinal shifting has pushed the divides away from the anticlinal streams, broadening their valleys and narrowing the synclinal valleys. This has robbed the synclinal streams of water, and consequently weakened them, while it has increased the power of the anticlinal streams. As a result, the conditions have been reversed from the first stage, and the anticlinal streams, A and C, flow in broad, deep valleys, while the synclinal streams are in high, narrow valleys, on the tops of synclinal mountains. Instances of such change are found in the Appalachians.

There are numerous illustrations of such migration of divides. In the Catskills, for example, the streams descending the steep eastern slope to the Hudson have pushed the divide backward and captured the headwaters of streams that have a long, gentle slope (Fig. 177). The Appalachian rivers, — the Potomac, Susquehanna, Delaware, etc., — which cross ridge after ridge in water gaps (Fig. 173, 447), are thought to have slowly eaten their way across the mountains by headwater erosion and river capture. But they may have been in part antecedent or superimposed.

Fig. 180. — Summer pasture lands of the Alps, at Bergli, at and above the timber line. Trace out the bends in the rock structure of the mountains and picture in your mind the parts removed by denudation. Is more rock material gone where the rocks are arched up (anticline) or arched down (syncline)? Why? See Fig. 179.

Wind gaps of the Appalachians are also caused by river capture or *stream piracy* (Fig. 178).

Summary. *Consequent mountain streams flow down the mountain sides, along the valleys of folding; antecedent ones may persist in their courses across the ridges. The courses of both the consequent and the antecedent streams may be interrupted by lakes in the early stages of mountain development because the forces of mountain warping are ordinarily too great for the stream erosion to reduce at an equal pace. But as mountain growth ceases the lakes are eliminated by both filling and down-cutting. The divides change position by the law of monoclinal shifting, and by headwater erosion, and* *subsequent valleys develop on the less durable strata and on the weaker anti-clinal structures. The subsequent valleys develop obsequent tributaries. The more favorably situated streams capture the headwaters of opponent streams. From these processes a trellis pattern (p. 134) of drainage and broad, low valleys result on regularly folded mountains. As denudation proceeds, the mountain forms pass through the stages of youth, maturity, and old age; rapidly at first, then very slowly, until finally they are reduced to a peneplain. The cycle may, however, be interrupted at any stage by renewed mountain growth.*

Fig. 181. — The Alps at Grindelwald in winter. The mountain is the Wetterhorn. Formerly tourists and pleasure-seekers went to the Alps resorts only in summer; in recent years the winter season is almost as popular as the summer season. Visitors enjoy the dry cold air, the sparkling sunshine, and the snowshoeing, skating, tobogganing, and skiing that the picture suggests.

86. Settlement of mountains. (See also p. 601.) The soil and climate of mountains are usually unfavorable to agriculture, and, in many cases, absolutely forbid it. Large areas are even unfit for the growth of forests. For these reasons mountains are usually sparsely settled (Figs. 148, 154, 157, 159).

The relation of mountains to settlement is well illustrated by the Alps, which rise in the midst of a densely populated land, — Italy on the one hand, France and Germany on the other. If we were to cross the Alps from the Italian side, this is what we should see: first a level plain, the Po Valley, dotted with farms and villages, and densely settled. As the land becomes irregular in the foothills, there are fewer people; and, when the mountains are reached, large areas are found with a surface too steep and rocky for cultivation. Wherever there is soil enough, however, vineyards and groves of olive and mulberry trees are seen on the valley sides. Higher up, where the climate is cooler, the olive, mulberry, and grapes no longer grow (Figs. 146, 167, 503). There small grain fields and pasture lands are interspersed with rocky cliffs and forested areas, in which the chestnut is a common tree. Still higher, where the climate is that of the cold temperate zone (Fig. 232), evergreen trees prevail, and only the hardiest grains can be raised. Most of the land that has soil enough is used as pasture, and cows and goats are raised in large numbers. Between the timber line and the snow line there is an area on which no crops can be raised, but where the pastures support herds of cows and goats for a month or two in summer (Fig. 180). Above this is a wild, dreary mass of snow, rock, and ice, where no one can find sustenance (Figs. 148, 158, **181**).

Summary. *Mountains are sparsely settled. Agriculture may flourish at the base, but the area suitable to cultivation becomes smaller the higher one goes, and the climate more and more unfavorable, until, at the snow line, a barren area of snow and rock is reached on which there are no inhabitants.*

87. Mountains as barriers. Mountains are barriers to the passage of animals, plants, and men. On a plain, animals and plants spread freely; but the ruggedness and coldness of mountains check, and in many cases prohibit, the passage of animals and the spread of plants. Even the passes of high mountains, like the Alps, have deep snow until summer.

The low Appalachians served as a barrier to the westward spread of the early colonists (p. 497). The Alps (p. 602) have always been an obstacle to man, being crossed only with difficulty along the few passes, and, in modern times, by tremendously expensive railway tunnels cut completely through the highest ranges.

Fig. 182. — A carriage and automobile road crossing the valleys and climbing the slopes of the Alps to the levels of the Grimsel and Furka passes. The long zigzags ease the grade to enable the horses to draw a load up and automobiles to travel in high gear. What about the expense of building such roads? The glacier is the Rhone. It was formerly much larger (see Fig. 259).

The Himalayas (p. 601) are an even more effective barrier; and the Pyrenees although narrow are so high and unbroken that they form a perfect natural fence between France and Spain.   Name other cases where mountains serve as boundary lines.

In the past century men have found means of reducing the difficulties of crossing mountains.   Excellent automobile roads, rising with gentle slopes by great sweeping curves, now cross the principal Alpine passes (Fig. 182).   In places where snowslides and avalanches are common, the roads are covered and protected by avalanche sheds.   Railways now

Fig. 183. — The St. Gothard railway on the Italian side of the Alps.   Notice the three levels.   At this point the railway passes through two spiral tunnels in order to climb the steep slope of the mountain valley before finally plunging into the main St. Gothard tunnel.   With your finger trace the course the railway must follow inside the mountain.

cross the lofty Rocky Mountains (Fig. 450), Andes, and Alps (Fig. 183). They pass up the valleys as far as they can, curving about, first on one side, then on the other; crossing deep gorges by lofty bridges; tunneling the rock, even by curved tunnels; and finally, when it is no longer possible to climb higher, plunging through a great tunnel into the very heart of the mountain.   The St. Gothard tunnel in the Alps is nine and one fourth miles long; the Simplon tunnel, farther west, is even longer.   A tunnel six miles long has been cut through the Rocky Mountains west of Denver. However, air navigation and communication by radio are little affected by mountains.

Summary. *The ruggedness and coldness of mountains make them barriers to the spread of plants, animals, and man. Now, owing to the building of roads and railways and tunnels, mountains, although they continue to interpose difficulties to commerce and travel, are not the nearly absolute barriers to human contacts they were earlier.*

Fig. 184. — The forest-covered slopes of the White Mountains of New Hampshire; a famous summer resort at Franconia Notch, a glacially carved valley. Notice the lake and the large resort hotel.

88. Mountains as resorts. The cool summer climate and the wild and beautiful scenery attract many people to mountains. The numerous mountain lakes which offer opportunities for boating and fishing and hunting on the forest-covered mountain slopes are further attractions. The mountains of New England (Fig. 184), the Adirondacks and the Catskills of New York, and the Appalachians are visited each year by large numbers of people. In winter these American mountains are cold and snow-covered, and nearly deserted.

The Alps, the wildest and most beautiful of west European mountains, have come to be one of the greatest resort regions in the world. In the small country of Switzerland, which is only one third the size of Pennsylvania, there are thousands of summer hotels.   At every point where many tourists are likely to go, even on mountain trails far from wagon roads, a hotel is sure to be found.   In the height of the season most of these hotels are full to overflowing with tourists from all parts of Europe, in fact, from all the world.   In recent years it has even become quite the fashion to visit the Alps in winter and participate in all manner of winter sports (Fig. 181).   One of the leading industries of Switzerland is the entertainment and care of these visitors.

Photo by Waite

Fig. 185. — Guanajuato, a mining town in the mountains of Mexico. Gold and silver mines in the adjacent mountains brought about this concentration of population, 40,000 people, in this mountainous district.

Summary. *The climate, scenery, boating, fishing, and hunting attract people to the mountains for a vacation.*

89. Mountains as timber reserves. Mountain slopes are so often unsuited to agriculture that in many places the forest remains (Figs. 81, 170, 184).   About one fifth of the surface of Norway is forest-covered, and much of the remainder is either too high or too rocky for trees to grow.   The mountains of eastern and western United States still have great timber resources and are the seats of important lumber industries.

Summary. *Mountains are important timber reserves, because agriculture has not demanded the removal of the forests.*

90. Mineral wealth and water power of mountains. The Alps have little valuable mineral; but the mountains of eastern and western United States, and many other lands, are very rich in mineral. In the West, gold, silver, lead, and copper are most important; but zinc, iron, coal, and building stones are also found. In the mountains of eastern United States, coal, iron, and building stones are the leading mineral products. In modern years, as transmission of electrical power has been perfected, there has been an increasing use of the immense water power developed by moun-

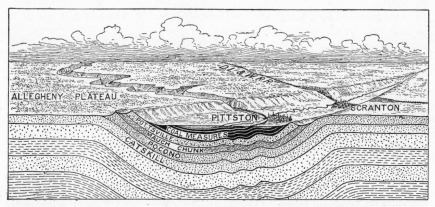

Fig. 186. — A perspective diagram to show how the anthracite coal beds were bent down in a syncline at Pittston and Scranton. Note that the coal layers once extended across the plateau area, but have all been denuded from these regions of higher elevation. Hence we have only the down-bent remnant to mine of these once very extensive coal formations.

tain streams descending steep slopes. Even small streams at quite remote points have been pressed into service by using water wheels that turn at tremendous speeds under the impulse of thin streams of water, shot from nozzles at very high pressures.

The presence of the ores of metals has attracted many people to mountain regions, where otherwise there would be only a sparse population of farmers, herders, hunters, and lumbermen. In rugged mountain valleys and on arid mountain slopes, cities with thousands of inhabitants have quickly grown up around mining centers.

The reasons why mineral resources and mining tend to be concentrated in mountain regions are various. In the first place the rocks in which the ores occur are exposed to view, partly because of the lack of a soil cover, partly because on the lee side of mountains arid climatic conditions (p. 167) make the vegetation cover scant. Second, the mountain rocks are cracked and fissured, and this has permitted mineral-bearing solutions and gases to deposit veins of ore in the openings. Third, the mountain folding brings deep-seated rocks and materials near to the surface and is accompanied by volcanic activity (p. 180) and heat, agencies which help to concentrate and even to form the valuable ore minerals.

Mineral beds and veins are revealed by folding of the strata and erosion of valleys in the mountain rocks (Figs. 145, 185). Sometimes they are preserved from erosion by being folded down in the synclines, as in the case of the anthracite coal of Pennsylvania (Fig. 186). This was formed at the same time as the bituminous coal that is found west of the Appalachians; but, during the folding of these mountains, the pressure metamorphosed it to "hard" or anthracite coal. At Scranton, Wilkes-Barre, and elsewhere, the anthracite is now being removed from the synclines in which it has been so long preserved.

Summary. *Mountains may contain valuable mineral deposits, which then attract a considerable population. Folding and erosion help to reveal these deposits; and sometimes they are preserved in the synclines. Mountain streams are now being much used for power development with electrical transmission to distant cities.*

TOPICAL OUTLINE, QUESTIONS, SUGGESTIONS, AND LABORATORY EXERCISES

TOPICAL OUTLINE. 75. **Introductory.** Influence of mountains on settlement.

76. **The mountain rocks.** Position of rocks; faulting; folding; complex folding; Appalachians; kinds of rock; effect of complexity; definition of mountains.

77. **Names applied to units of mountain form.** System; range; cordillera; ridge; peak; hogbacks; interior basin; smaller basins; park; water gap; wind gap; pass.

78. **Climate of mountains.** (*a*) Temperature: normal change; snow line; timber line; variation. (*b*) Rainfall: rainy slopes; arid slopes.

79. **Denudation of mountains.** Height and relief of mountains. Denudation. (*a*) River erosion. (*b*) Weathering: reasons for activity. (*c*) Talus: cause; form produced; change to steep fans; rock streams. (*d*) Avalanches: size; effects; cause. (*e*) Effect of denudation on land form.

80. **Resemblance between mountains and high plateaus.** Resemblance in height; in ruggedness; the Catskills, difference from mountains; relict mountains; mountains of circumerosion.

81. **Distribution of mountains.** In open ocean; fringing continents, — as islands, peninsulas, and continental borders; — in interior.

82. **Cause of mountains.** Contraction theory, radium heat and isostasy; successive uplifts.

83. **Types of mountains.** Faulted blocks; domes; laccolithic mountains; granite cores; regular folds; complex folds; cause, characteristics, and examples of each.

84. **Life history of mountains.** (*a*) Young mountains: early growth; voi-

canoes; denudation; valleys; unfitness for occupation; examples. (*b*) Mature mountains: broadening; lowering; examples; fitness for occupation. (*c*) Old mountains: further reduction; peneplain; settlement; instance; Piedmont Plateau. (*d*) Renewed elevation: Appalachians; ridges; broad valleys; settlement; water gaps, origins of.

85. **The drainage of mountains.** (*a*) Consequent drainage: antecedent stream courses; lakes. (*b*) Life history — compare with plains. (*c*) Monoclinal shifting: nature of process; law. (*d*) River pirates: competition at headwaters; favoring conditions; Catskills; Appalachians; wind gaps.

86. **Settlement of mountains.** (*a*) Unfavorable conditions. (*b*) The Alps: the base; the slopes; above the timber line; above the snow line.

87. **Mountains as barriers.** Reasons; instances; overcoming barriers, — roads, railways, tunnels.

88. **Mountains as resorts.** Attraction; mountains visited in eastern United States; the Alps; importance to Switzerland.

89. **Mountains as timber reserves.** Reasons for forests; instances.

90. **Mineral wealth and water power of mountains.** Alps; the West; the East; water power; effect on settlement; concentration of minerals; effect of folding and erosion; anthracite coal.

QUESTIONS. Section 75. Of what importance are mountains to men?

76. What is the position of the mountain rocks? What differences are there in the folds? In the rocks? What effect has this complexity? Define mountains as topographic features.

77. What are the following, and what causes each: mountain system, mountain range, cordillera, ridge, peak, hogback, interior basin, park, water gap, and pass?

78. What is the snow line? The timber line? How do they vary in elevation? What effects have mountains on rainfall?

79. To what conditions do mountains owe their variety of relief and their ruggedness of topography? Why are rivers and weathering very active in mountains? What becomes of the fragments that fall? What are rock-streams? What are the nature, effects, and causes of avalanches? What particular forms are due to denudation of mountains?

80. Compare and contrast high plateaus and mountains.

81. In what situations are mountains found? Give illustrations.

82. State the theory of contraction. Of radium heating and isostasy. What kind of mountains are most typical? How do mountains grow?

83. Give four types of mountains. What are the characteristics of each? How do they differ? Are they alike in any respect?

84. What happens when a mountain is rising? What effect has denudation? What are the characteristics of young mountains? Trace the development through maturity to old age. Give illustrations of each. What is a peneplain? What has been the history of the Piedmont Plateau? What changes have occurred in the Appalachians? Describe three ways in which water gaps may develop. Define an antecedent stream.

85. Describe the consequent drainage of mountains. What is the normal life history? What causes lakes? How does the law of monoclinal shifting operate? What are river pirates? Why do they succeed? Give illustrations. Explain wind gaps (Fig. 178). Trellis drainage. Barbed tributaries.

86. Why are mountains sparsely settled? How does the appearance of the Alps change from base to summit? How do the occupations vary?

87. Why are mountains barriers to the spread of animals and plants? Give illustrations. How are these barriers now overcome by men?

88. What attracts people to mountains? Give instances.

89. Why is there much forest among mountains? Give illustrations.

90. What mineral deposits are found among mountains? Account for the modern development of water power in mountains. What effects have mountains in the concentration, revealing, and protection of mineral deposits?

SUGGESTIONS. (1) It is not very difficult to make an apparatus for imitating the folding of rocks. Of one-inch boards make a long, narrow box, say 2 feet long, 5 inches wide, and 8 inches deep, open at one end and the top. Place four or five thin layers of wax, differently colored, on the bottom. At the open end apply slow, steady pressure, best obtained by using a screw, like that which sets a vise, fastened to a board that just fits into the end of the box. Before applying the pressure, place over the wax layers enough shot nearly to fill the box. After pushing the layers a few inches, remove the shot, unscrew one side, and the layers will show folding. Devising and perfecting apparatus for this experiment should be an interesting problem for the manual training department of a school. A simpler experiment may be made by taking a number of pieces of thick cloth and felt, cutting them to the same size, and pressing them up with the hand. (2) Is your home among mountains, or have you ever been among mountains? What are the nature and position of the rocks? Do the mountains rise above the timber line? Are they young, mature, or old? Are they well settled? Why? Are there forests? Minerals? Are they resorted to in summer? Why?

Reference Books. LUBBOCK, *Scenery of Switzerland,* The Macmillan Company, New York, 1896; and Chapters on Mountains and related topics in the following books: TARR and MARTIN, *College Physiography,* The Macmillan Company, New York, 1914; PIRSSON and SCHUCHERT, *Textbook of Geology,* John Wiley & Sons, New York, 1924; HOBBS, *Earth Features and their Meaning,* The Macmillan Company, New York, 1912; Hobbs, *Earth Evolution and its Facial Expression,* The Macmillan Company, New York, 1921; MARR, *Scientific Study of Scenery,* Methuen & Company, London, 1900; JOLY, *The Surface History of the Earth,* Oxford University Press, Oxford, England, 1925.

Laboratory Exercises. Exercises XXIX, XXX, XXXI, and XXXVIII in TARR and VON ENGELN's *Laboratory Manual for Physical and Commercial Geography,* The Macmillan Company, should be performed in connection with the study of this chapter.

CHAPTER VII

VOLCANOES, EARTHQUAKES, AND GEYSERS

VOLCANOES

91. Graham Island. South of Sicily, in 1831, a new volcano was born. During the eruption large volumes of steam and other gases rose into the air, carrying up fragments of lava. The expansion of the gases in the melted rock caused numerous cavities to form in it and broke the lava into bits of porous volcanic ash and pumice. Some of the lightest ash drifted away in the wind; much of the pumice was light enough to float on the water; but many of the heavier fragments fell back near the outlet, building a cone which rose 200 feet above the sea and had a circumference of almost three miles. With this single eruption the life of the volcano seems to have ended; and soon the waves cut the loose ash cone away, leaving a shoal to mark its site.

Other volcanoes, some in the sea, some on the land, have become extinct after a single gasp; but most volcanoes have a longer and more varied life. From some, ash is always erupted; from others, streams of molten lava; and from many, now ash, now lava. Some erupt freely and at frequent intervals; others have violent outbreaks, following long periods of quiet. These differences between volcanoes may best be illustrated by studying a few typical ones.

Summary. *Graham Island became extinct after a single eruption of ash and pumice. Its cone was washed away by the waves of the sea. Other volcanoes have a much more varied history.*

92. Eruptions of 1902 in the West Indies. On the 8th of May, 1902, the city of St. Pierre, in Martinique, was wiped out of existence by a terrible volcanic eruption from Mont Pelée (Fig. 187). Between 25,000 and 30,000 people were killed in a few minutes, and only one person in St. Pierre, a prisoner in an underground cell of the jail, escaped death (Fig. 188).

The last previous eruption of Mont Pelée was in 1851. The

people of St. Pierre had almost forgotten that danger lurked in the slumbering volcano; and, though the outbreak of 1902 was preceded by distinct warnings, few heeded them. On April 25 warm water was reported in the old crater; later, dust-laden steam rose from it; then a lake rose, overflowing the crater rim on May 5, and sending a deluge of hot water and mud down a valley.

On the 8th of May came the eruption. A huge column of steam, expelled with great force, bore heated sulphurous gases,

Photo by Hovey

Fig. 187. — The spine of Mont Pelée, March 25, 1903, from the northwest, seen from a distance. This shows also the gullied slopes of the mountain bare of vegetation. The eruptions destroyed all plant growths.

dust, ashes, and stones high in the air. The eruption was not nearly so violent as many other eruptions; but, owing to the following peculiar condition, its effect was very disastrous. On the side toward St. Pierre there was a break in the crater wall, with a valley leading toward the city. Down this valley some of the steam, with its load of hot rock fragments and gases, rushed with the violence of a tornado, destroying everything in its path (Fig.

189). It overturned trees and houses, and even carried a hollow iron statue, 11 feet high, a distance of 50 feet. Most of the deaths were probably caused by breathing the steam and hot gases, which were hot enough to melt soft metals like lead and brass.

There were several later outbursts, all, like the first, erupting ash, with no flowing lava and with no destructive earthquake shocks. The eruptions built a cone 1500 to 2000 feet high in the

Photo by Hovey

Fig. 188. — The underground dungeon (built in a cellar) in which Calbarice, the only person in St. Pierre who survived the explosion of Mont Pelée, was confined. The hot gases did not kill him because he was so far below the surface and because his cell had such slight ventilation.

old crater, and ash fell over the whole island and the sea round about. Thin films of this dust could still be found in 1921 in protected nooks on the island of Barbados about 200 miles distant. On and near the cone the ash deposit was several feet deep, and resembled freshly fallen snow. During each eruption the condensed steam caused heavy rains, which washed vast quantities of loose ash down the steep slopes in destructive *mud flows* (Fig. 190). About eight months after the first eruption, when the successive explosions had fully opened and cleared the throat of the volcano, a column of viscous lava filled the crater. This was thrust up and finally forced out as a *spine* (Fig. 187) above the crater rim, cooling and hardening as it emerged. The phenomenon was like tooth paste coming from a tube. The spine grew to be 1000 feet high, but in after years crumbled to a mass of blocks.

Photo by Hovey

Fig. 189. — The ruins of St. Pierre, from a photograph taken February 15, 1903. Mont Pelée is in the background. Notice that the walls parallel to the shore remain standing because the force of the blast came from the mountain toward the foreground of the picture.

Its unbroken continuation below the crater rim may be thought of as a plug or stopper to the volcanic bottle, holding in the gases until enough pressure develops to cause another explosive eruption. Then the "cork" of hard rock will be blown out of the vent again.

Summary. *In May,* 1902, *after a long period of quiet, Mont Pelée burst forth in explosive eruptions of gases and ash, causing much destruction. Vast quantities of volcanic ash were thrown out upon the islands and the sea* *round about. The condensed steam, forming rain, washed much ash down the volcano side, causing mud flows. Finally a stopper of lava plugged up the vent, sealing it until the time of another explosive eruption.*

93. Vesuvius. At the beginning of the Christian era, Vesuvius, like Pelée, had long been inactive, and people had no fear of it. It had been quiet, or *dormant,* for centuries. People knew it to be a mountain of volcanic kind but they had no idea of its ever erupting again. Farms and villages dotted the slopes of

Photo by Russell

Fig. 190. — Mud flow of hot volcanic ash (notice the steam jets) flowing down and filling the bed of the Wallibu River, St. Vincent, May 24, 1902. (There was an eruption from the volcano La Soufrière on the near-by island of St. Vincent on the day before the Mont Pelée eruption.) It was such a mud flow as this that buried Herculaneum, near Pompeii. As the hot, wet mud cooled and solidified it became cemented. Accordingly it has been much more difficult to excavate Herculaneum than Pompeii.

Somma, as the mountain was called, and cities were located at its base. In the year 79 it broke forth in a terrible eruption which buried the farms and villages beneath ash, and destroyed Pompeii and Herculaneum.

Before the eruption there were frequent earthquakes, one of which partly destroyed Pompeii; and, finally, a terrific explosion occurred by which half the crater wall was blown away. The ashes rose thousands of feet in the air, settling on all the country round about. The naturalist Pliny, admiral of the Roman fleet, who was at Misenum (near C. Miseno, Fig. 191), started toward the mountain and lost his life. Letters of Pliny's nephew to the historian Tacitus, telling of the death of his uncle, provide us with our only, but very vivid, description of the eruption.

The day was changed to the darkness of night by a heavy cloud of ash; hot ashes and stones fell all about; the air was filled with sulphurous gases; the ground was violently shaken; there was fierce thunder and lightning; and the cries of terror from the people, who rushed madly about, added to the din. Thousands of people were undoubtedly killed, though there is no record of the number, or even of the villages destroyed.

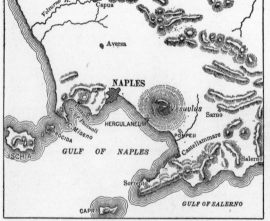

Fig. 191. — Map of the Bay of Naples. There are numerous volcanic cones from Pozzuoli to Ischia.

Pompeii and Herculaneum have been discovered and partly excavated (Fig. 192). From these excavations we learn what the life of the Romans was on the day of that fearful outbreak nearly 1900 years ago. The houses have been so well preserved beneath the ash that even the pictures painted on the walls are still quite perfect. It is a wonderful experience to walk through those deserted streets, and to see how the people lived, and what they did, as if they had left but yesterday. Yet it is a picture of life almost at the time of Christ.

Since 79 Vesuvius has had many eruptions, some violent (as in 1872 and 1906), some moderate, some of ash, some of lava (Fig. 193). The remnant of the old cone, Monte Somma, still stands on one side of the present cone, which rises 4200 feet above the level of the Bay of Naples (Fig. 191). At most times one may go to the very edge of the crater. Standing on the side from which the wind blows, the observer looks down into a deep hole, out of which quantities of steam rise with a roar, bearing sulphurous gases. Every few seconds there is a slight explosion, when masses of red-hot lava are thrown up, often higher than the crater wall. At night the lava in the crater causes a glow on the cloud that overhangs Vesuvius.

Occasionally the volcano grows more active; then hot stones rise so high that they fall on the crater edge, and it is unsafe to stand there. This may increase until the stones fall some distance

Fig. 192. — Excavating the ruins of Pompeii, 1895. The work was done under guard to prevent the theft of gems, coins, or other small valuable objects. All material removed was carefully sifted. Note that the roofs of the ancient houses are all caved in. Why? The tiled roof is a modern one erected to preserve the paintings on the walls of the house it covers; paintings that remained unspoiled through nearly 2000 years under the compact cover of dry volcanic dust.

beyond the crater. The small cinder cone that surrounds the crater is made of these loose fragments.

Now and then lava, as in the violent outburst of 1906, issues from fissures in the side of the cone, flowing in a great stream, sometimes as far as the sea. The recent flows form great black, rugged scars on the volcano side (Fig. 193); the older ones are partly decayed and covered with soil. In the violent eruptions the top portion of the cone built up during the intervening quiet period is in part blown off. But the volcanic energy has never since 79 been completely sealed off. Accordingly the explosions of Vesuvius are not so violent as that of Mont Pelée was. This may be due to the fact that the lava of Vesuvius is not so viscous as that which formed the spine of Mont Pelée.

Fig. 193. — The ordinary condition of Vesuvius. The lava in the foreground was erupted in 1858. Note that much of it has weathered to residual soil. This soil is very fertile and in places is gathered by the Italians and used in the planting of vineyards.

Summary. *In the year 79, after being long dormant, Vesuvius broke forth in violent eruption, partially destroying the cone and burying Pompeii and Herculaneum, which have been well preserved beneath the volcanic deposits. Since then Vesuvius has had many eruptions of ash and lava, some of them, 1872, 1906, very violent. Ordinarily it is so quiet that one may go to the very edge of the crater, from which steam constantly rises, and, occasionally, explodes with sufficient force to throw upward masses of hot lava.*

94. Etna. The greatest volcano in the Mediterranean is Etna, on the eastern end of Sicily. Steam rises from its crater (Fig. 194), and every few years there is an eruption. Then lava issues from fissures in the mountain side and flows in enormous masses down the slopes, even to the sea, often destroying villages on the way. There are scores of small cones, 200 to 300 feet high, built along these fissures.

Etna rises 10,870 feet above the sea, and at its base has a circumference of over 60 miles. It is so high that, although oranges and bananas

Fig. 194. — Looking down into the crater of Etna. The picture was made at a time when the activity of the volcano was very slight. One may see that the crater walls are built up of successive layers of ash and larger fragments.

grow at its base, the climate at the top is frigid. This great cone is made up almost entirely of lava. Etna has had many violent eruptions, but as the material poured out is so largely lava these are not so explosive as those of Vesuvius, much less so than that of Mont Pelée. The lava appears to burst out when the pressure of its weight is too great for the walls of the volcanic chimney to withstand. Then fissures crack open in its sides and the lava pours out. The recent lava flows, those only a few score years old, are barren masses of black rock too rough to cross. But this lava decays so readily, and forms so fertile a soil, that in a century portions of a flow are fit for cultivation. Soil is often gathered in baskets and placed between the lava blocks for the planting of grapevines.

Summary. *The huge cone of Etna is made of lava, issuing mainly as great flows from fissures in its flanks. This lava decays quickly, forming a fertile soil.*

95. Krakatoa. For a century the small volcanic island of Krakatoa, near Java, in the Straits of Sunda, was dormant. In August, 1883, it broke forth in the most terrific eruption that civilized man has known. A large part of the cone, together with ash from below, was hurled high into the air, and the site of the destroyed cone was occupied by water 1000 feet deep (Fig. 195).

Fig. 195. — The half of Krakatoa left after the eruption.

Every vestige of life on the island was destroyed, and its surface was deeply covered with ash.

For miles around, the sea was so thickly covered with pumice that the movement of vessels was interfered with. The finer ash was thrown so high into the air that it was carried all round the earth, causing brilliant sunsets in Asia, Europe, and America.

So violent was the explosion that a great air wave was started which passed three times around the earth. Windows were broken 100 miles from the volcano, and the sound of the explosion was heard more than 150 miles away. A water wave was also caused which spread all over the Pacific, being measured on the coasts of Africa, Australia, and California. This wave washed over the shores of lands and islands near the volcano to a height of 50 to 100 feet, killing 35,000 people.

Since then Krakatoa has been quiet. It may have become extinct; but more probably it is only dormant, and will again burst forth when the pent-up gases once more gather sufficient energy to force their way to the surface, exploding the rock cover that now holds them in.

Summary. *After a century of quiet, Krakatoa burst forth, in 1883, in the most violent eruption known. Half the cone was blown away; ash fell all about, and was carried far and wide by the winds; a great air wave passed three times round the earth; and a water wave spread over the Pacific. Since then the volcano has been quiet.*

96. Hawaiian volcanoes. There are numerous volcanic cones in the Hawaiian Islands, most of them extinct. The two highest are Mauna Loa and Mauna Kea, which, with the smaller Kilauea, are on the island of Hawaii (Fig. 196). This island, the greatest volcanic mountain in the world, rises nearly 14,000 feet above sea level, and 30,000 feet above the sea floor.

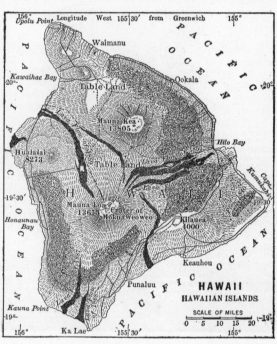

Fig. 196. — The dark areas represent lava flows which start from fissures.

On the top of Mauna Loa is a great crater, two or three miles in diameter. This is partly frozen over, but steam rises from cracks in the surface, and in one part there is a lava lake, from which jets or fountains of lava rise, sometimes several hundred feet. A similar condition exists in the crater of Kilauea; but Mauna Kea is extinct. Such extensive craters (Figs. 208, 209) are called *calderas.*

The lava slowly rises, overflowing the crater floor and solidifying on it, as water sometimes overflows and freezes on the ice of a pond. Before the lava rises high enough to pour over the rim of the crater, its weight and the steam pressure open a fissure in the mountain side through which the lava is drained (Fig. 196). There was, for instance, an eruption from Mauna Loa in April, 1926, when streams of lava from the level of 8,000 feet poured down the mountain side (Fig. 197).   Four days after its emergence the molten rock of the lava flow reached the sea into which it plunged, causing great clouds of steam to rise.   Such eruptions occur, on the average, once in about seven years, and no violent ash eruptions have ever been recorded.   The fissures are usually formed above sea level, but

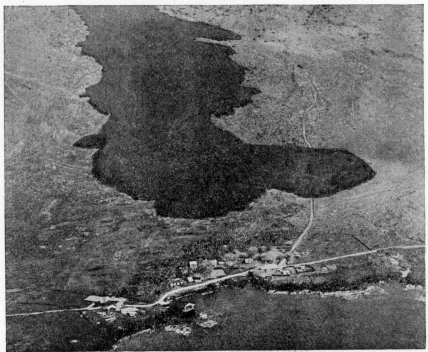

Photo by U. S. Army Air Service. © *War Department*

Fig. 197. — Lava flow, April, 1926, from Mauna Loa, Hawaii, moving down on the village of Hoopuloa, which was later buried in lava.

sometimes occur beneath the sea.   Some of the lava streams are 30 or 40 miles long and 2 or 3 miles wide.

At first the lava flows rapidly down the mountain side; but it soon cools and solidifies at the surface (Fig. 198).   Then the movement becomes much slower.   The frozen crust is broken and rolled along by the movement of the lava beneath, and liquid lava may burst through the solid front at any point.   Years may pass before it cools entirely.

Summary. *Hawaii, the greatest volcanic island in the world, has two active volcanoes with huge craters, or calderas.   In these are lava lakes* *which steadily rise, once in about seven years being drained through fissures in the mountain sides. The lava at first flows rapidly; but, as it cools on the surface, its rate of flow is checked.*

97. Types of volcanic eruptions. Krakatoa and the Hawaiian volcanoes represent the extremes of types in volcanic eruptions from cones; Krakatoa violently explosive, the Hawaiian eruptions very quiet. In between are Mont Pelée, Vesuvius, and Etna. The greater the quantity of

Fig. 198. — Lava cascades, solidified; formed by the flow over a declivity of vast quantities of hot liquid lava, from a Hawaiian volcano.

gas present and the more viscous the lava, the more violent is the eruption. The viscous lavas are made up of rock stuff like quartz; the more fluid ones have much iron in their composition.

98. Mt. Shasta and Mt. Lassen. Mt. Shasta is an extinct volcano (Fig. 199), whose elevation is over 14,000 feet. It resembles Etna in form. From its snow-covered top small glaciers descend into the higher valleys, and on its flanks is a later cone.

Until the eruption in 1914 of the supposedly extinct cone of Mt.

Lassen, 10,437 feet high, south of Mt. Shasta in California, active volcanoes were unknown in the United States. The first eruptions of Lassen were all explosive with emission of gases, volcanic ash, and rock fragments. In 1915 a cloud of gas and dust shot up nearly four miles high in the air (Fig. 200) and lava flowed over the rim of the crater, descending 1000 feet down the slope of the cone. There was another slight eruption in 1925. Mt. Lassen, hence, is intermediate in type between Mont Pelée and Vesuvius.

Although previous to these eruptions of Mt. Lassen there was no

© *Miller*

Fig. 199. — Mt. Shasta, California. Rising above the ridge of the left slope of the mountain is Shastina, a newer cone on the flanks of the main volcano. Both these cones are extinct, but Shastina still has a crater, whereas the crater of Shasta has been destroyed by denudation.

record of an active volcano in the United States in historic time, and the Indians had no traditions of such an occurrence, it was known that outbursts had taken place in the recent past (Fig. 201). Fifteen miles distant from Mt. Lassen there is an ash cone 650 feet high. The size of trees that have grown in the ash indicates that it was erupted about 200 years ago. A still later lava eruption dammed a stream, forming Snag Lake, in which are snags of trees killed by the rise of the water. It seems probable that this lava flow is not much over a century old. There are other recent lava flows in various parts of the West.

Summary. *Shasta is a lofty extinct volcano; but Mt. Lassen near by erupted in 1914, 1915, and 1925, and there have been other recent eruptions of ash and lava in the United States.*

Fig. 200. — Eruption of Mt. Lassen, 1915. The eruptions from Mt. Lassen in 1914–1915 were the first eruptions in the United States in historic times.

99. Crater Lake. Another extinct volcano in western United States is occupied by Crater Lake in Oregon. This lake, which is about 2000 feet deep, lies in a huge crater, or caldera (Fig. 202), between 3000 and 4000 feet in depth, and about 6 miles in diameter. It has been proved that a lofty volcano (Fig. 203) rose where the caldera now stands. The removal of lava from beneath the cone allowed it to collapse, forming the caldera, in which a later eruption has built a small ash cone (Fig. 202). The proof of

Fig. 201. — The steaming crater of Mt. Baker, Washington. The snow is covered with sulphur crystals brought up by the volcanic vapors. This illustrates the dormant, but not completely extinct, condition of the western volcanic cones.

Fig. 202. — Crater Lake, Oregon, the deepest lake in North America. The little island, called Wizard Island, is a cone built up from the bottom of the crater since it collapsed. The gap in the rim at the foreground is the cut-off end of one of the valleys truncated by the collapse.

the collapse of the cone after eruptions had ceased is that the entire upper sections of valleys, filled with glacial ice, and formed on the slopes of the higher peaks, disappeared when the infall took place. These valleys now end abruptly in air on the sides of Crater Lake, but the slopes of the valleys show glacial markings right up to their ends.

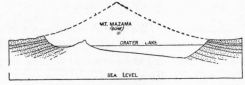

Fig. 203. — Section of Crater Lake, with the old cone, named Mt. Mazama, restored by the dotted line.

Summary. *Crater Lake occupies a huge crater, or caldera, formed by the draining off of lava from beneath, causing the cone to collapse.*

100. Materials erupted. Every volcanic eruption is accompanied by vast quantities of steam, and smaller amounts of sulphurous and other gases. These gases are commonly called "smoke," and the glow of light reflected from the melted lava is popularly termed "flame."

Fig. 204. — A deposit of volcanic ash with an imbedded volcanic bomb, Eifel Region, Germany. Explain the layering shown here with regard to size of particles, bending, effect of bomb.

If the eruption is moderate, melted rock usually flows out, and, in cooling, forms *lava flows* (Figs. 125, 193, 198). Expansion of steam in the pasty lava makes many small rounded cavities, especially near the top; and the surface is broken by the movement of the lava after a crust has been formed. In violent eruptions the expansion of the steam blows the lava to pieces, forming *scoria, pumice,* and *ash.* Pumice is so light and porous that it floats in water, and the fine ash even remains suspended in the air.

Lumps of lava thrown into the air, cooling in oval, twisted masses, are known as *volcanic bombs* (Fig. 204). They vary from a few inches to many feet in diameter. During eruptions the condensation of the steam causes heavy rains, accompanied by vivid lightning. The rain washes down much loose ash, often while it is still hot, forming volcanic *mud flows* (Fig. 190). Pompeii was buried under dry ash, Herculaneum under mud flows. Because the water in the mud flows caused the material in them to cement and consolidate, Herculaneum has been much more difficult to dig out.

Summary. *Steam and other gases accompany all volcanic eruptions. Lava comes from moderate eruptions; ash, pumice, and scoria from violent ones. Volcanic bombs are also thrown out; and rains wash down the ash, forming mud flows.*

101. The forms of volcanic cones. A volcano is a conical peak with a crater at the top. If the eruptions are of ash the cone is

Photo by Gilbert

Fig. 205. — A new volcanic cone on the plateau of northwestern Arizona. It is probably the product of a single eruption and has not since been active.

steep, because the fragments that fall back near the vent have a slope as steep as loose ash will stand (Figs. 193, 205, 206). On the other hand, cones made of flowing lava are broad and have a low slope (Fig. 207).

One reason for these differences is that lava flows away as a liquid; another, that most of it starts, not from the top, but from fissures on the slopes of the cone (Figs. 193, 196); and a third, that it all remains on the cone, while in ash eruptions a large part is drifted away by the winds. When the material is now ash, now lava, as in Vesuvius, the cone has a slope intermediate between that of lava and ash.

The crater of a volcano may be so large, perhaps from one to five miles in diameter, as to deserve the name caldera. In addition to the calderas

Fig. 206. — Fujiyama, a very perfect ash cone in Japan. The lava cones of the Hawaiian type are so broad that, although high, it is difficult to show them in a photograph.

of the Hawaiian Islands (p. 211) and Crater Lake (p. 215), there are calderas in Italy, the Eifel district of Germany (Fig. 208), and other places. The craters on the moon (Fig. 20) are perhaps enormous calderas. Calderas may be caused either by collapse of the cone, or by violent explosions

Fig. 207. — The slopes of two volcanoes, one ash (dashed), the other lava. The latter, represented by the continuous line, may be considered to be Mauna Loa. Not only is the ash cone steeper, but it contains much less material, because so much has been drifted away by winds and ocean currents.

which blow the top of the cone away. In some cases, as in Krakatoa (Fig. 195), explosions wreck the cone and make it irregular.

In Africa, just inside the northern boundary of Tanganyika Territory, formerly German East Africa, in a region known as the Highlands of the Great Craters, is found the greatest caldera on the earth's surface, that of the extinct volcano, Ngoro (Fig. 209). This caldera is 12 miles wide and 35 miles around the complete and unbroken rim that rises 2000 feet above the level floor of the caldera. As the location is in tropical Africa and as the caldera floor is sufficiently high to get more rainfall than the sur-

Fig. 208. — Caldera in the Eifel region of Germany. This is a region of extinct volcanoes; but they have become extinct so recently that lakes still occupy their craters. This is Lake Gemünden, near Daun. Each crater is probably the result of a single explosive outburst.

rounding semi-arid plains, it has a rich cover of vegetation and is a great natural zoological garden enclosed as it were by a circus ring. It is said to contain 50,000 or more wild animals, lions, leopards, rhinoceroses, hippopotami, zebras, antelopes, monkeys, buffaloes, etc.

Summary. *Ash cones have a steep slope, whereas lava cones are broader and more gentle in slope. Cones consisting of both ash and lava have a slope* *between the two.   The greatest caldera known is that of the extinct volcano, Ngoro, in Africa.*

102. Distribution of volcanoes. There are thousands of volcanic cones, only about 500 of which are known to be active.   The great majority of these cones are in or near the sea, by far the greatest number being in the mountains and islands which partly encircle the Pacific Ocean (Fig. 210).   Another great belt extends in an east-west direction around the earth north of the equator.   Starting in southern Mexico and Central America, it is continued by the

After James L. Clark

Fig. 209. — Relief model of Ngoro, the great caldera crater of Africa, that is a vast natural zoological garden.   Locate this crater on Fig. 210.

volcanoes of the West Indies, the Azores, Cape Verde, and Canary Islands in the Atlantic; the Mediterranean volcanoes; others in Asia Minor and Central Asia; then the East Indies; and finally the Hawaiian group.

Many of the lofty peaks of the Andes are volcanic cones.   From Mexico northward, through western United States, are hundreds of volcanic cones, all except Mt. Lassen being either dormant or extinct.   Among these are Mt. Rainier (Fig. 455), Mt. Shasta, Mt. St. Helens, and Mt. Hood.

The Aleutian Islands, which enclose Bering Sea, form a volcanic chain 1600 miles long, including 57 volcanoes, some of which are very vigorous.

On the Alaska Peninsula north of the island of Kodiak is the Katmai volcano that on June 6, 1912, exploded in an eruption second only in violence to that of Krakatoa in 1883. The report of the Katmai eruption was heard in Juneau, 750 miles away, and the town of Kodiak, 100 miles away, was in total darkness for 60 hours because of the density of the volcanic dust cloud that filled the air. A mass of this incandescent dust accumulated in a valley on the slope of the volcano and led to the advertisement of the place as the Valley of the Ten Thousand Smokes because of the hot steam and gases that were given off for a number of years afterward. Where such an accumulation of volcanic dust covers a wide region the area is called an *ash plain*.

Practically all the small islands of the open Pacific and Indian oceans are volcanoes (Fig. 401). Even many of the coral atolls are volcanic

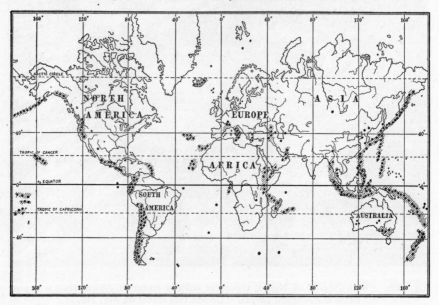

Fig. 210. — The distribution of volcanoes. The shaded sections show the main areas, and the dots locate some of the active or recently extinct volcanoes.

cones with a veneer of coral. The Bermuda Islands in the Atlantic are also volcanic peaks with a cover of coral rock. Other islands of the open Atlantic are volcanic, and some of them are active. Iceland has a number of volcanoes, several of which have had terrific eruptions. The Faroe Islands are ancient volcanoes, and there were formerly volcanoes in the British Isles (Fig. 216). St. Helena, the prison home of Napoleon, is a volcano.

Despite the great number of cones, they are really exceptional land forms. By far the greater part of the earth's surface is now free from

Fig. 211. — Volcanic peaks in the Auvergne region, a volcanic area in central France. The peaks on which the buildings are situated are remnants, or necks, of volcanoes partly destroyed by denudation. The buildings are castles and churches, and were so perched in medieval times to insure safety when enemies attacked.

volcanic action; and large areas have never been disturbed by eruptions. In other places, as in eastern United States, central France (Fig. 211), and the British Isles, volcanic action long ago died out. Both at the present time and in the past, volcanic activity has been associated with mountain growth.

Summary. *The majority of volcanoes are in or near the sea, the greatest belt being in the chain of mountains and islands which partly encircles the Pacific. There are many volcanic islands in the open Pacific, Indian, and Atlantic oceans, and in the Mediterranean. Volcanic cones are exceptional land forms. Volcanoes appear never to have been present in some places and have become extinct in others.*

103. Cause of volcanoes. The immediate cause for a volcanic eruption is undoubtedly the explosive force of pent-up steam and other gases.

It was formerly thought that surface water descending to the heated interior of the earth caused the steam explosions. It is now regarded as improbable that such water penetrates to the depths of the molten-lava reservoirs. But it is possibly true that those volcanoes that are violently explosive in their eruptions are set off by surface water reaching masses of hot rock material. If so, then, curiously, the explosive volcanoes are to be regarded as dying, the violent eruptions being only the last gasps of volcanic activity. According to this theory the surface water, as at Mt. Lassen and Katmai, reaches a mass of hot lava through the opening of a fissure made, perhaps, at the time of an earthquake. There the water changes into steam and dissolves into the lava. This helps the rock material of the lava to crystallize into solid minerals (Fig. 52). But in this crystallization much water in the form of steam at a higher heat and tremendously greater pressure than that of the steam first dissolved into the lava is given off. An explosion ensues. The first explosion opens further fissures and more water from the outside is let in. Other more violent explosions follow. Eventually quite liquid lava rises to fill in the fissures, the lava solidifies, the water from the outside is shut off, and the eruptions cease.

The volcanoes that quietly erupt great volumes of lava are the really active ones with a long life ahead of them. In these, as in the Hawaiian volcanoes, the rock material of the lava is being continuously melted and caused to rise to the surface. Although the interior of the earth is hot, the rock material at any considerable depth is apparently under so great pressure that ordinarily it cannot melt. But when mountains are being folded up (p. 180), arches are formed in the rocks. Under a strong, or *competent*, rock layer (Fig. 153) that maintains itself as an anticlinal arch weak rocks may be relieved of part of the pressure that ordinarily acts on them. These weak rocks can then melt (Fig. 223). In melting they expand and force their way to the surface as hot, liquid, rock stuff filled with gases. The lava does not come from very deep sources, for it is similar in composition and density to surface rocks. Neither does it come from one big connected reservoir, for the lava erupted by two nearby volcanoes may be quite different in composition and may stand at quite different levels in the craters.

It is by no means certain that these explanations are the correct ones. The subject is very difficult and complicated and chemical factors such as radio-activity, that are not well understood, may be important.

Summary. *Expanding steam and other gases are responsible for explosive volcanic eruptions. Lava eruptions come from local reservoirs of*

Fig. 212. — The Columbia Lava Plateau in eastern Washington. The vast expanse of level, lava-flooded country is clearly shown. Since their outpouring the lavas have in places weathered to fertile clayey soils. This is one of the great wheat regions of the United States.

molten rock material situated at no great depth below the earth's surface. The heat probably has its source in the interior of the earth; the melting of the lava is due to relief from pressure; and its rise to the surface, to the expansion on melting and to the expansion of included steam and gases.

104. Lava Floods. In western United States, in addition to volcanoes, there were great lava floods which escaped from fissures or enormous low volcanoes and deluged the surrounding country. The greatest of these floods was in the valley of the Snake and Columbia rivers (Fig. 212), mainly in Oregon, Idaho, and Washington, where an area of fully 200,000 square miles is covered with lava. By these lava floods, which extended up valleys and surrounded mountains, as lake water does, an irregular land surface was changed to a great lava plateau. Deep canyons show a depth of 3000 to 4000 feet of lava, layer on layer.

Throughout the Far West there are other instances of lava floods, for example, in the Yellowstone Park. Similar floods have been formed

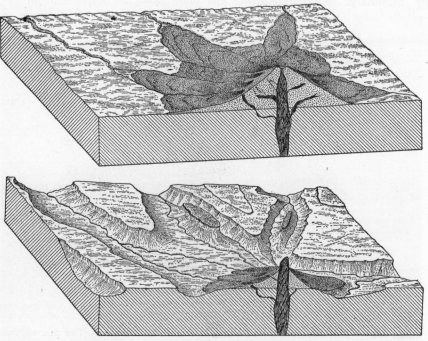

Fig. 213. — To illustrate the destruction of a volcano. Above, the cone is shown with its lava flows; below, the cone has been mostly worn away, and streams have deeply carved the land. Small areas between the streams are left capped with lava, forming mesas, and the volcanic neck rises above the general surface.

in other parts of the world, as the plateau of the Deccan in India, which in extent rivals the Columbia lava plateau.

At present such lava floods are nowhere issuing from the earth. The nearest approach is in Iceland, where lava, welling from fissures, has built a broad plateau. When such a fissure is partly closed, leaving only one or two places for the lava to escape, volcanic cones are built along it. This accounts for some of the chains of volcanic cones.

Summary. *Great lava floods, rising through fissures and great low craters, have deluged large areas of country in western United States and other regions. Iceland has the nearest approach to this condition at present. The closing of most of a fissure allows the formation of a line of volcanic cones.*

105. Lava intrusions. Not all the molten rock, *magma*, that starts reaches the surface. For example, when eruptions cease, the vent of a volcano may fill with solidified magma. This is called the *volcanic neck* or

Fig. 214. — Mato Tepee, Wyoming, a volcanic neck or plug. All the other material has been removed by denudation, leaving the resistant lava plug standing above the surrounding country. Notice also that the stratified rocks around the base of the neck are in perfectly horizontal position, showing that the lava materials here made their way upward without bending or otherwise disturbing the surrounding rock. (See Fig. 218.) What kind of jointing is shown in the lava?

plug (Figs. 40, 213, 214). The long, narrow sheets filling the fissures, through which lava escapes on the flanks of a volcano, are called *dikes* (Fig. 40). In the neighborhood of volcanoes, similar dikes are intruded into the rocks (Fig. 49) deep in the earth. These and other forms of intruded rocks are brought to light by denudation.

Sheets of lava have been intruded between strata (Figs. 40, 215). Such intruded *sheets* or *sills* frequently have a well-developed jointing, which causes them to break in columns, usually with five or six sides (Fig. 216). (Lava flows also show such jointing but less perfectly developed.)   The Palisades of the Hudson (Fig. 215); Mt. Tom and Mt. Holyoke, Massachusetts; East and West Rocks at New Haven, Connecticut (Fig. 217); the trap mountains near Orange, New Jersey; and the lava sheets in many other regions have reached their positions by intrusion into the strata.

A large mass of magma intruded between strata which raises a part of the overlying layers to form a dome is called a *laccolith*, lake of rock (Figs.

Fig. 215. — Intruded lava sheet forming the Palisades of the Hudson.   Notice the columnar appearance due to jointing.

164, 218).   Irregular, large masses of magma form *bosses* (Fig. 40) and *batholiths;* these are commonly composed of granite.   Such masses are found in the cores of old, worn-down mountains, as in the Adirondacks, New England, Scotland, and Norway.

Summary.   *Various forms of intruded igneous rocks — necks, dikes, sheets, laccoliths, and bosses — are caused by the rising of magma that does not reach the surface.   The wearing down of the surface by denudation brings these intruded masses of igneous rock to view.*

106. Life history of a volcano. While a volcano is active the cone usually grows, because each eruption adds material to it. In fact volcanic cones consist wholly of the fragmental and lava material piled up around the vent. A dormant volcano may, however, break forth in so violent an explosive eruption that the cone is wrecked and its size and form changed (Figs. 195, 200). Or, by the opening of a new outlet, the lava may be drained from beneath the cone, causing it to collapse (Fig. 203).

Throughout the life of every volcano the agents of denudation

Fig. 216. — Columns caused by the jointing of an ancient sheet of lava at Giant's Causeway, Ireland. The columnar jointing is the result of the breaking of the lava as it contracted in cooling. (See Fig. 215.) In the same way the vertical contraction made the socket and rounded forms on the surface. The breaks are so regular because the composition of the lava was very uniform. Breaking in three directions from each of a number of centers gives six-sided forms. Make a diagram to illustrate this.

are at work tearing it down; but so long as it is active, fresh supplies of lava or ash tend to repair the damage. When the volcano becomes extinct, however, denudation has full sway. At first the crater is occupied by a lake (Fig. 202), but the rim is slowly destroyed and the lake drained. Streams gully (Figs. 71, 187) the cone with deep ravines and gorges, until it bears little resemblance to a volcano. As the cone is slowly worn down, the core of solid lava

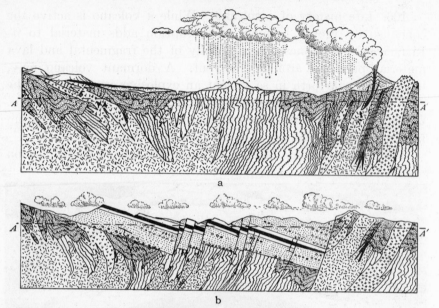

A _____ A'

a

A' _____ A'

b

Fig. 217 (a) (b) (c) (d). — Sections across the Connecticut River valley and the neighboring uplands of central Connecticut at four different periods in its topographic history. These diagrams show how this area got its present topographic features with reference to the rock origin and structure, and to the changes in elevation due to uplift and denudation.

Diagram (a) shows the conditions when the Appalachian Mountains were being uplifted. The rocks are being bent and contorted and there is much volcanic activity. Volcanic ash settles down in quantity over the area that is now the Connecticut valley. There are also lava flows (not shown) and deposits of sediments in a basin formed by later down-bending. The line A–A¹ may be thought of as having an elevation only slightly above sea level.

Diagram (b). Volcanic activity has ceased but meanwhile there have been further

that in the end fills the volcanic neck resists denudation better than the looser beds of porous lava and ash. It therefore long remains above the surface as a central divide for radiating streams (Figs. 187, 213, 214). In western United States there is every gradation from the perfect cone to the volcanic neck remnant.

Fig. 218. — Ideal section through a laccolith (see also Fig. 164).

If a volcano stands in the sea, the waves have a large share in its reduction (Fig. 401). At first, steep cliffs are cut, on which the waves beat with such force that no boat can land. As these cliffs are pushed back into the land, the crater may be reached and, if its floor is below sea level, a crater harbor be

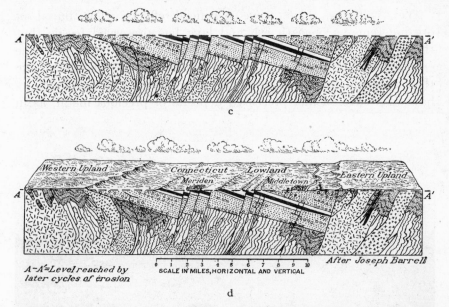

c

A-A=Level reached by
later cycles of erosion

SCALE IN MILES, HORIZONTAL AND VERTICAL

After Joseph Barrell

d

movements of the rock masses resulting in faulting and the formation of block mountains (see p. 164). Erosion and denudation tend to bring the more resistant (black)
lava layers into relief.

Diagram (c). A long period of no land movement follows, during which denudation
slowly but quite completely reduces the whole surface to a peneplain (see p. 93) at
about sea level.

Diagram (d). A slight uplift comes next. Rejuvenated streams and weathering
wear down the less resistant rocks, leaving the lava layers in relief to form the block
mountains in the valley, and uplands on either side (Fig. 439) on the ancient, strong
rocks. These are the present conditions. The differences in elevation shown by
the diagrams seem slight but this is only because the horizontal and vertical scales
are equal.

opened (Fig. 219). Further wave cutting may entirely consume the
volcano, leaving only a shoal to mark its site.

Summary. *During activity a volcano grows by addition of lava or ash
faster than denudation wears it away; but explosion or collapse may change
its size or form. When extinct, however, volcanoes are slowly worn away, the
last remnant being the solid volcanic neck. Waves aid in the destruction of
cones in the sea.*

107. Importance of volcanoes. The most noticeable effect of volcanic action is the destruction of life, — human, plant, and animal.
The ash, lava, steam, gases, hot water, mud flows, lightning, and
earthquakes that accompany eruptions all contribute to this destruction. Nothing in nature is more terrible than a volcanic eruption.

Yet volcanoes have some beneficial effects. The burial of organic remains beneath ash and lava has preserved fossils that throw much light on the history of former life on the globe. The eruption of Vesuvius in 79 has preserved a record of Roman life that we could not have obtained in any other way. Lava flows have also covered and preserved deposits of precious metal, as in

Fig. 219. — The harbor, a volcanic crater, of the island of Ischia (see map, **Fig. 191**). After the eruption that made the crater there does not seem to have been any further volcanic activity. In the distance the "smoking" cone of Vesuvius is seen.

California, where gold mining has been carried on in ancient river gravels beneath old lava flows.

Volcanic eruptions have given rise to many lake-basins, like that of Nicaragua in Central America. Volcanoes and lava floods have helped make grand scenery. There are few finer sights than a large, snow-capped volcanic cone, like Etna, Rainier (Fig. 455), Hood, or Shasta (Fig. 199).

Lava soils are usually very fertile; for example, one of the most productive wheat regions of the country is the region of eastern Washington with its rich volcanic soil (Fig. 212). Lava and ash have supplied much of the material of which the sedimentary strata are made; and igneous rocks have supplied underground water with much valuable mineral for deposit in veins. Lava also heats the water, thus giving it more power to dissolve minerals. The presence of lava in western United States has had a very important influence on the formation of the valuable mineral veins of that region.

Summary. *Volcanoes are very destructive to life; but they have some beneficial effects. They preserve records of past life; they give rise to lakes; they aid in the making of scenery; their soils are usually fertile; they have helped supply material for the sedimentary strata; and they have aided in the formation of mineral veins.*

EARTHQUAKES

108. (A) *Cause.* Any jar to the rocks, as an explosion of dynamite in a quarry, the falling in of caverns, or an avalanche, will cause earth tremors. The jar may be so slight that it can be detected only by delicate instruments; or it may be so violent as to cause widespread destruction. According to the nature of their cause, real earthquakes are classified as *volcanic* earthquakes or *tectonic* earthquakes. All earthquakes that are due to volcanic explosions, or to jars localized at a given point, are considered to be volcanic. Volcanic earthquakes are usually feeble and are not felt far from their source. Earthquakes due to the slipping of blocks of the earth's crust along fault planes (Fig. 151) are tectonic. The word comes from a Greek word meaning carpenter and the idea is that the structure of the earth is then changed. Nearly all earthquakes that cause widespread destruction and topographic changes are tectonic. Volcanic explosions, and the rush of lava into fissures, forming dikes, also cause earthquakes. During mountain growth series of jars, or vibrations, are sent through the rocks when slips along fault planes occur. These vibrations are the earthquake. Sometimes, as in Japan, in 1891, the surface of the ground on one side of a fault plane is raised at the time of the earthquake.

(B) *Characteristics.* As tectonic earthquakes are caused by the breaking of rocks, the regions of their occurrence are also commonly areas of volcanic activity. Indeed a map of the distribution of volcanoes might also serve as a map of frequent earthquakes. This association of earthquakes and volcanoes was responsible for a misunderstanding in regard to the cause of great earthquakes that persisted for a long time. But there have been violent earthquake shocks far from volcanoes; for example, those of Lisbon,

Portugal, in 1755, southern Arkansas in 1812, Charleston, S. C., in 1886 (Fig. 220), and California in 1906.

The early idea of a relationship in cause and effect existing between volcanoes and great earthquakes, an idea based on their association in occurrence, gave rise to the concept of the *focus* or *centrum*, and of the *epicentrum*. The focus was the location of the point below the earth's surface where the volcanic explosion causing the earthquake was supposed to occur. The epicentrum was the point on the surface of the earth vertically above the focus. At the epicentrum the surface shock was

Photo by Dutton

Fig. 220. — Sand craters formed near Ten Mile Hill, South Carolina, during the Charleston earthquake of 1886. In the earth movements that cause earthquakes the water-saturated mantle rock may be squeezed as though it were a sponge and the water caused to spurt out as fountains, as it did here.

supposed to be most violent. Mapping of the points of equal intensity of shock (*isoseismal lines*) led to the discovery that almost all great earthquakes had more than one focus; that the site of greatest intensity of shock was not a point but a line. From this evidence there came slowly a realization that great earthquakes are not due to volcanic explosions, but that they are almost without exception due to the slipping past each other of great blocks of the earth's crust along cracks or fault planes that extend or develop for long distances and to great depths in the rocks. This slipping causes the rocks to vibrate, and the vibration, as much or more than the actual movement of the masses, causes the earthquake phenomena. The true relationship is that both volcanoes and earthquakes are associated with growing mountains.

It appears that the rocks of the earth's crust are in certain regions subject to forces that tend slowly to move a great mass on one side of a line past the mass on the other side; either up, or down, or sideways (Fig. 221). The Andes mountains appear to be moving eastward at the rate of five feet in every hundred years; the mountains of California are moving northward by one foot every five years. Although the earth blocks as wholes do move past each other, the strength of the rock at the line of separation between movement in one direction and that in the other is for a time great enough to withstand the strain to which the rock is thus subjected. But the stress finally becomes too great and a break occurs. Then the rock on each side of the line snaps to a position of no strain, and this movement, together with the vibrations set up by the great grinding and friction of the masses as they scrape past each other, causes the earthquake.

This is the *elastic rebound theory* of earthquakes as set forth by H. F. Reid. On forcibly

Photo by Gilbert

Fig. 221. — Trace, near San Francisco, of the fault movement that caused the California earthquake of 1906. The valley at the left is probably a depression marking the effect of earlier movements along this line. See Fig. 222.

ripping apart two thin boards that have been firmly glued together, one gains an idea of how the earthquake phenomena occur. An even better parallel is found in the action of a violin bow on violin strings and the resulting vibrations. As the bow moves over the string it tends to pull the string with it. But the strain almost instantly becomes too great and the string snaps back. As it snaps back the string is caused to vibrate, and this vibration is transmitted to the body of the violin. As the violin then causes the air to vibrate and give rise to sound, so at the time of earthquakes great rumblings are heard because the rock vibrations likewise set the air in motion.

(C) *Effects.* Violent earthquakes are very destructive. They often cause landslides which dam streams and form lakes; and the shaking of the ground sometimes forms depressions in which water

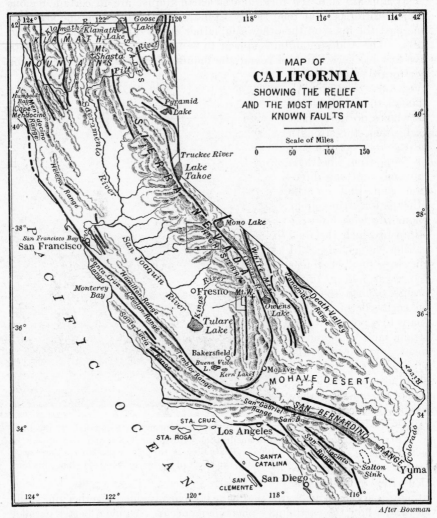

After Bowman

Fig. 222. — The black lines are those along which fault movements are known to have occurred. Notice that the mountain ranges and longer valley depressions follow the fault lines.

collects to make lakes and ponds. Trees are thrown down; cracks are opened in the ground; and great destruction of life is caused by the overturning of houses and the fires that start because of such overturning. Also the movements along the fault line cause breaks in water mains making it difficult to put out the fires. Great fires caused the destruction of San Francisco at the time of the earthquake in 1906, and of Tokio and Yokohama at the time of the Japanese earthquake of September 1, 1923. In the California earthquake the movement (Fig. 222) was horizontal with displacement of the surface by as much as twenty feet; in the Japanese earthquake the movement was up and down, a distance of four feet (Fig. 223). In consequence of the danger from falling houses, people who live in countries where earthquakes are frequent

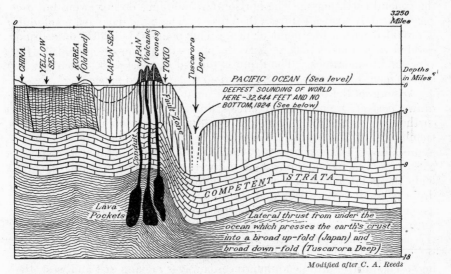

Modified after C. A. Reeds

Fig. 223. — One conception of the undersea and underground conditions of the Japanese earthquake of September, 1923, that caused such great destruction in Tokio and Yokohama. It suggests further the relations between great ocean deeps, rising mountains, earthquakes, and volcanoes.

build their homes so that they will withstand ordinary shocks. Even with this precaution, thousands of lives are sometimes lost in a single shock. If the earthquake is under the sea, a water wave may be started which causes much destruction on low coasts (p. 339).

Summary. *Earthquakes are the result of movements and vibrations of the rocks of the earth's crust and are brought about by faulting, volcanic action, and other causes. They are most common in regions of growing mountains and are associated with volcanoes. A tectonic earthquake, usually a series of shocks, is most violent at points above and along the line of dis-*

placement of the rock masses, diminishing in intensity in all directions from the source. Earthquakes form lakes, open cracks in the ground, and throw down houses, causing great destruction of life. If an earthquake occurs in the sea, a destructive water wave may be started.

109. Recording and locating earthquakes. The occurrence of distant earthquakes is now recorded at many stations by the use of *seismographs* or earthquake-recording machines. The Greek word *seismos* means earthquake. A commonly used type of seismograph consists of two horizontally mounted pendulums, one extending in a north-south line, the other in an east-west line. The pillars that support these pendulums are provided with very solid foundations. Thus these pillars become part of the general earth mass. The horizontal pendulums do not swing but are very delicately suspended from the pillars. The far end of each pendulum is provided with a fine point or pen. This point rests lightly on a drum covered with smoked paper. Like the pillars the drums are provided with very solid foundations. The drum is rotated by clockwork which has an arrangement for marking off the minutes on the smoked paper.

As long as the earth is at rest the point at the end of the pendulum draws perfect, uninterrupted circles around the drum. But when an earthquake occurs the pillars and the drums vibrate in unison with the tremblings of the earth. Theoretically the pendulums do not move appreciably. To the degree that that is made possible by fine mechanical construction each pendulum acts as if it were hanging free in space. Accordingly the point at the end of the pendulum should remain still while the drum below it swings back and forth as the earth vibrates. Practically, as one watches the recording of an earthquake, it is the pendulums that move, with great amplification of distance over that actually covered by the moving crust beneath the instrument. Thus a tracing, the record of the earthquake, is made on the smoked paper as the drum keeps on rotating. The north-south pendulum records waves moving east and west, the east-west pendulum the north and south waves.

Earthquake tremors so slight that no one can feel them are recorded by the seismograph. It is found that earthquake vibrations or waves pass straight through the earth at the rate of $6\frac{1}{4}$ miles per second. Other waves go around through the shallow crust of the earth at the rate of two miles per second. The waves that come through the earth come first and make a different sort of mark from those that come around the outside of the earth. It is possible, accordingly, to tell how far away an earthquake is by noting the difference in time between the arrival of the two sets of waves it sends out. The difference in the records of the two pendulums also gives a general idea of the direction from which the waves come. Then if three widely separated stations each get the record of the earthquake, it is possible to tell just where the disturbance took place by drawing circles on a map at the proper distance out for each station. Where the circles cross each other is the site of the earthquake. Thus it is possible to locate distant earthquakes even though they occur in an uncivilized region or under the sea, and this has frequently been done.

Summary. *Earthquakes are recorded on seismographs many miles distant from the site of the disturbance. If three widely separated seismographs each get a record of an earthquake, it is possible to locate the scene of the disturbance although no observer was at that place.*

HOT SPRINGS AND GEYSERS

110. Underground water is often heated by buried masses of lava or other causes. Where this heated water rises to the

Photo by Jackson

Fig. 224. — Hot spring deposits in the Yellowstone Park. These deposits are carbonate of lime (calcareous tufa), and they build little basins in which the hot water stands, trickling over the edge and forming icicle-like deposits.

surface, usually through a fissure, it forms a *hot spring;* and if it occasionally gushes out, it is called a *geyser.*

The rising hot water always bears mineral substances in solution, some of which may be deposited near the spring. Such deposits are found around the hot springs (Figs. 224, 301) and geysers (Figs. 393, 453) of Yellowstone Park.

There are geysers in New Zealand, Iceland, Yellowstone Park, and one near Mount Lassen — all volcanic regions. The mineral deposits made around hot springs are often very beautiful in color, and the geysers sometimes build a cone, and erupt through the crater of it (Figs. 224, 225, 393).

The geysers are exceedingly interesting. Old Faithful formerly erupted every sixty-five minutes, with such regularity that the time of each outburst could be accurately predicted. It is now erupting less regularly and at longer intervals. With each eruption a great mass of hot water and steam is thrown to a height of over 100 feet.

Fig. 225.—The Devil's Punch Bowl, a boiling hot spring surrounded by a rim of siliceous deposit.

Other geysers erupt very irregularly, and some have become extinct.

Those that erupt more or less regularly, like Old Faithful, apparently operate as follows: Surface water from rain or melting snow seeps down from elevated areas, through fine pores and fissures in the rocks, to considerable depth. At the points of the geyser occurrences this percolating water encounters wider fissures leading back up to the surface, and, in general, emerging at the level of the valley floors. The seepage water slowly fills these wider geyser tubes. But in their lower levels the geyser tubes penetrate layers of lava erupted long ago but still very hot because deeply buried under other rock material. Accordingly the water in the tubes is heated by contact with these hot lavas.

The boiling point of water rises under pressure; therefore, it may be necessary to raise the temperature to 250° or more before boiling begins down in the tube. When the boiling point is reached steam forms. The expansion of the steam lifts the whole column of water and causes some of it to flow away from the geyser crater. This overflow removes some of the water column and therefore reduces the pressure on water that is already boiling at 250°. This removal of pressure at once lowers the boiling point; and, since a large mass of water has a temperature near

Photo by Jackson

Fig. 226. — Steam from the fumaroles, hot springs, and geysers of the Norris Basin, Yellowstone National Park. Seen in the cold of the early morning.

250°, it changes suddenly to steam. This expels the water with a rush. The time between eruptions depends upon the length of time required to refill the tube and to heat the water down in the tube to the boiling point again. Fig. 228 illustrates these conditions and shows also the construction of an experimental geyser, more fully described under suggestions at the end of the chapter.

There are all gradations from the intermittently erupting geysers to freely flowing hot springs on one side, and *fumaroles* (Fig. 226), or steam vents, and *mud volcanoes* or *paint pots* on the other. If the tube is wide, the supply of water great, and the heat moderate, a hot spring results. If there is much heat and little water a steam vent develops. If there is much heat, little water, and only small fissures leading to the surface, mud

Photo by Tourist Dept., New Zealand

Fig. 227. — Paint Pots, Rotorua, New Zealand, called there the Porridge Pot. Note the plopping bubbles of mud formed by boiling stone to a paint-like substance.

volcanoes are formed. In these the rock is literally cooked to a soup (Fig. 227).

Summary. *Surface water percolating underground and coming in contact with hot lavas in volcanic regions is heated and erupted, forming a geyser. There are all gradations from hot springs through geysers to mud volcanoes, in the form of the escape of the heated water. These gradations depend on variations in the conditions of supply, heating, and escape.*

TOPICAL OUTLINE, QUESTIONS, SUGGESTIONS, AND LABORATORY EXERCISES

TOPICAL OUTLINE. **91. Graham Island.** The eruption; materials erupted; the cone; its destruction; other volcanoes.

92. Eruptions of 1902 in the West Indies. Destruction of St. Pierre; previous eruptions; warnings; eruption of May 8; cause of destructiveness; effects of later eruptions; material erupted; distribution of ash; mud flows; spine of Pelée, significance of.

93. Vesuvius. (*a*) Eruption of 79: previous condition; settlements on slopes; warnings; effect of eruption; our knowledge of the eruption; conditions accompanying eruption. (*b*) Pompeii: importance of its excavation. (*c*) Condition since 79: difference in eruptions; present condition; ordinary quiet; increase in activity; lava eruptions.

94. Etna. Position; eruptions; great height; decay of the lava.

95. Krakatoa. Former eruption; eruption of 1883; ash on the sea; air wave; water wave; conditions since eruption; future.

96. Hawaiian volcanoes. (*a*) Island of Hawaii: its volcanoes; their height. (*b*) The craters: lava lakes; calderas. (*c*) Lava flows: rising in crater; draining through fissures; length of flows; nature of flow.

97. Types of volcanic eruptions. Extremes; reasons for differences.

98. **Mt. Shasta and Mt. Lassen.** Shasta; ash cone; recent eruptions of Mt. Lassen.

99. **Crater Lake.** Size of lake; cause of caldera.

100. **Materials erupted.** Steam; other gases; meaning of "smoke" and "flame"; lava flows; effect of steam explosion on lava; bombs; mud flows; burial of Herculaneum and Pompeii.

101. **The forms of volcanic cones.** Ash cones; lava cones; ash and lava cones; calderas; wrecked cones; great African caldera.

102. **Distribution of volcanoes.** Number; general location; belt encircling Pacific; the east-west belt; Katmai eruption; ash plains; areas of extinct volcanoes; association with mountains.

103. **Cause of volcanoes.** Explosive eruptions; lava eruptions; relation to growing mountains; shallow source of lavas.

104. **Lava floods.** (*a*) Columbia valley: cause; area; lava plateau; thickness. (*b*) Other areas. (*c*) Present condition: general absence of lava floods; Iceland; relation of fissures to volcanic cones.

105. **Lava intrusions.** Volcanic necks; dikes; how revealed; sheets or sills; illustrations; laccoliths; bosses.

106. **Life history of a volcano.** Normal growth; effects of explosion, of collapse; denudation; the volcanic neck; volcanoes in the sea.

107. **Importance of volcanoes.** Destruction of life; preservation of fossils, of human records, of mineral; formation of lakes; effect on scenery, on soils, on sedimentary rocks, on mineral veins.

108. **Earthquakes.** (A) *Cause:* faults; volcanic action; other causes; volcanic and tectonic earthquakes. (B) *Characteristics:* volcanic regions; other regions; illustrations. (C) *Effects:* landslides; lakes, depressions, cracks; destruction of life; fires; movements of the surface; waves. Old ideas—focus, nature of shock, epicentrum. Modern ideas—mass movement of rocks, break, vibrations, elastic rebound theory.

109. **Recording and locating earthquakes.** Seismographs, operation of; rate of travel of earthquake waves; difference in waves; locating distant earthquakes.

110. **Hot springs and geysers.** Cause; nature of geysers; mineral deposit at surface; distribution of geysers; geyser deposits; eruption of geysers; explanation of geyser eruptions, fumaroles, and paint pots.

QUESTIONS. Section 91. State the history of Graham Island. What causes ash and pumice? How do many volcanoes differ from this one?

92. What reasons were there for expecting an eruption? Why was the eruption so destructive at St. Pierre? What were its effects? What was the nature of the material erupted? What causes mud flows? Describe the spine of Pelée.

93. What was the condition of Vesuvius in 79? Tell about the eruption of 79. How has it been of importance? What has been the subsequent history of Vesuvius? What is its present condition?

94. Describe Etna and its eruptions.

95. Describe the eruption of Krakatoa and its effects.

96. Describe the Hawaiian volcanoes and craters. Describe the eruptions. What is the nature of the lava flows?

97. What are the two extremes in type of volcanic eruptions? Account for each type.

98. What is the condition of Shasta? When and how did Mt. Lassen erupt? Why was this eruption of special interest?

99. What has been the history of Crater Lake?

100. What substances are erupted from volcanoes?

101. How do ash and lava cones differ? Why? What are calderas? Locate and describe the greatest caldera in the world.

102. Trace (Fig. 210) the principal chains of volcanoes (named in text). Describe the eruption of Katmai. Where else are volcanic chains found? Are volcanoes found everywhere?

103. What is the immediate cause for volcanic eruptions? Account for explosive eruptions, for lava eruptions. What evidence is there that lava does not come from deep within the earth?

104. Describe the lava floods of the Columbia valley. Where else were lava floods formed? How may volcanic cones succeed fissure eruptions?

105. What are volcanic necks? Dikes? Sheets or sills? Give illustrations. What are laccoliths? Bosses? How are they brought to light?

106. What may affect the form of a volcano before its extinction? What is its history after extinction? What is the case in the sea?

107. State the important effects of volcanoes.

108. (A) What are the causes of earthquakes? Distinguish between volcanic and tectonic earthquakes. (B) Where are they most frequent? What is the focus? The epicentrum? What are isoseismal lines? What is the nature of the shock? Explain the elastic rebound theory of earthquakes. How may earthquakes be imitated? (C) What are the effects of earthquakes?

109. What is a seismograph? How is the seismograph constructed? Why are two sets of waves recorded from one earthquake? How are distant earthquakes located?

110. What are hot springs and geysers? What do the waters carry? Where are geysers found? How do they vary? Give the explanation of regularly erupting geysers, of hot springs, of mud volcanoes.

SUGGESTIONS. (1) If the school is located in a region where there has been volcanic activity, ancient or recent, the class should make an excursion to places at which phenomena of extrusion and intrusion may be studied in the field. Examine the contacts between the volcanic and other rocks for heating effects. Study the effect of lava flows, etc., on land forms after erosion, the jointing and other characteristics of the volcanic rocks and materials. (2) Set up the experimental geyser as illustrated in Fig. 228 and described in the caption under that figure. Build up the background to imitate the natural relationships of the geyser, using colored pencils, red for hot lava, etc., to make a vivid drawing. Note especially the necessity for including the constricted piece of glass tubing in the supply pipe. This imitates nature in that the fineness of the pores through which the water percolating downward comes, prevents the *rapid* escape of the heated water back over the same path.

Laboratory Exercises. Exercises VIII, IX, XII, and XXXIV of TARR and VON ENGELN's *Laboratory Manual of Physical and Commercial Geography*, The Macmillan Company, New York, correlate in content with the subject matter of this chapter and may be performed most profitably in connection with this chapter.

Reference Books. RUSSELL, *Volcanoes of North America*, The Macmillan Company, New York, 1897; HEILPRIN, *Mt. Pelée and the Tragedy of Martinique*, Lippincott, Philadelphia, 1903; IDDINGS, *The Problem of Volcanism*, Yale University Press, New Haven, 1914; DALY, *Igneous Rocks and their Origin*, McGraw-Hill Company,

New York, 1914; GRIGGS, *Valley of Ten Thousand Smokes*, National Geographic Society, Washington, 1922; DUTTON, *Earthquakes*, Putnam, New York, 1904; HOBBS, *Earthquakes*, D. Appleton & Company, New York, 1907.

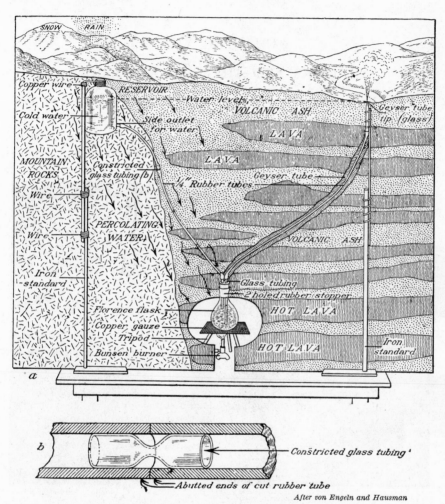

After von Engeln and Hausman

Fig. 228a and b. — Experimental geyser with background illustrating its relation to natural conditions. Note that the levels of the water in the reservoir and at the glass tip of the geyser outlet are the same. The glass tube from the supply reservoir does not penetrate the flask so far as the one leading to the geyser tube. The diameter of the nozzle of the geyser tube must be slightly greater than the diameter of the constriction in the supply tube. Have the Bunsen burner flame quite high and hot. The eruptions should succeed each other at regular intervals of about two minutes, and the jet be about two feet high. The significance of each item of the naturalistic, cardboard background should be brought out. In the drawing of this for classroom use the various labels and directions are, of course, to be omitted.

CHAPTER VIII

GLACIERS AND THE GLACIAL PERIOD

111. Valley glaciers. The snow line in the Alps is about 9000 feet above sea level. Above this line is a great *snow field* (Figs. 148, 229, 384), in which snow accumulates year after year without melting, in some places reaching a depth of hundreds of feet. Some

Fig. 229. — Snow fields in the Canadian Rockies, British Columbia. Here the snow fall, which is not so heavy or regular as on Mt. Fairweather, Fig. 230, has slid, avalanched, and been blown into the basins between the higher peaks. A glacier extends from the snow field toward the lower right-hand corner. Note and trace the névé line.

of the snow is whirled away by the wind, settling in valleys; some slides down the steeper slopes (Fig. 230), as snow slides from the roof of a house. There is so much snow falling into the valleys,

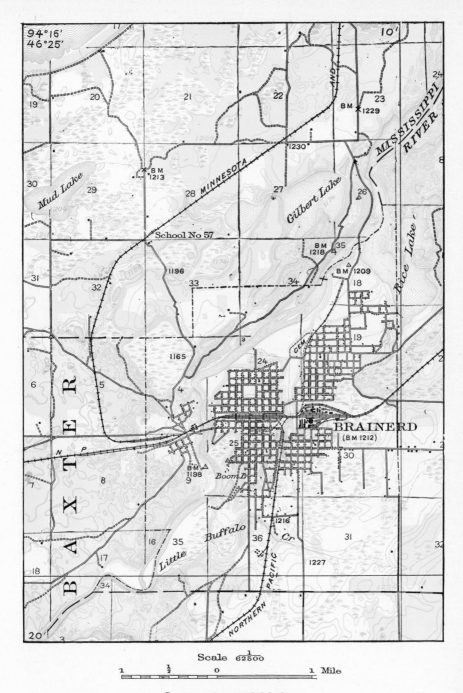

Scale 1/62500

1 — 1/2 — 0 ————————————— 1 Mile

Contour interval 10 feet.

Plate VII. — Part of Brainerd, Minnesota, sheet; Topographic Atlas of the United States; U. S. Geol. Sur.

Glacial moraine. Here the Mississippi River is shown flowing through a belt of moraine deposited by the continental glacier of the Glacial Period.

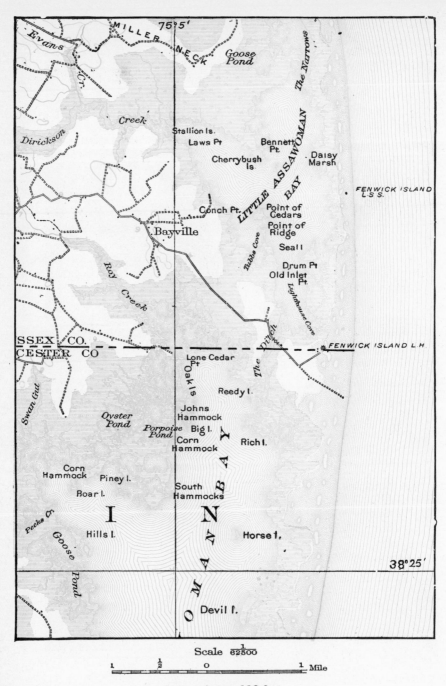

Scale 1/62500

1 ⟼ 1/2 ⟼ 0 ⟼ 1 Mile

Contour interval 10 feet

Plate VIII. — Part of Ocean City, Maryland, Delaware, sheet; Topographic Atlas of
the United States; U. S. Geol. Sur.

Offshore bars, sand dunes, salt marsh, and drowned stream valleys. Account for each of these
features. See pp. 359, 360, 375-380.

Photo by von E.

Fig. 230. — Snow fields completely mantling the summit ridges of Mt. Fairweather, Alaska, 15,330 feet high. Probably as much as 150 feet of snow falls each year on this peak.

both as small slides and great avalanches, that they would be completely filled if it could not in some way be removed.

The snow that accumulates in the valleys gradually changes to granular snow-ice, resembling the snow banks of late winter. This change is partly due to the pressure of the overlying mass, and partly to the fact that the larger snow particles absorb the smaller ones and so build up ice pellets. The granular ice, called the *névé* (Figs. 229, 231), moves slowly down the steep valleys.

Fig. 231. — *Séracs,* or ice pinnacles, in the névé region of a Swiss glacier. In the névé section the glacier surface is not solid ice. On descending over an ice fall this snow-ice becomes greatly crevassed and then melts differentially to form pinnacles such as these.

As the mass moves, pressure and further growth of the crystals gradually change it to pure, clear ice. The supply from the snow field causes the ice to move down the valley, much as a river extends beyond the place where the rain fell. Such an ice tongue, occupying a valley, is called a *valley glacier* (Figs. 1, 182, 232, 236). In the Alps the Great Aletsch glacier is over ten miles long. Glaciers there extend 4000 or 5000 feet below the snow line. They end where the warmth is sufficient to melt the ice completely, and the terminus may be below the timber line, even in the zone where grain will grow.

The glacier moves down grade, behaving much as a mass of wax does when under pressure; that is, it moves as if it were slowly flowing. The most rapid motion is near the middle, though even here it does not usually move more than two feet a day. Every glacier carries rock fragments, some of which have fallen from the valley sides, while others have been torn or *plucked* from its bed

Fig. 232. — A *valley glacier,* the Mer de Glace, descending far below the timber line in the Alps. Give all the reasons you can that show why the glacier is able to persist so far below the snow line.

by the pressure and wedging action of the moving ice. These fragments, slowly dragged along, and pressed down by the weight of the ice, groove, striate, and scour the rocks over which the glacier moves. By such plucking and scouring, known as *glacial erosion,* valleys are both deepened and broadened (Figs. 233, 234, 235, 241).

Bands of rock fragments, accumulated on the margin of the glacier, where they have fallen from the cliffs, are known as *lateral moraines* (Figs. 236, 237, 240). Where two glaciers join, two lateral moraines unite, forming a *medial moraine* (Fig. 256), near the

Fig. 233. — Valley developed by stream erosion, American Fork Canyon, Wasatch Mountains, Utah. This is in the same region as Fig. 234. Note the V shape and the overlapping alternating spurs of this valley as contrasted with the broad open U of the glaciated valley.

Fig. 234. — Valley developed by glacial erosion, Little Cottonwood Canyon, Wasatch Mountains, Utah. This has the typical trough form of such valleys; in cross section it is like a capital U with the arms pulled apart at the top.

middle of the glacier. The surface of the glacier melts in summer; but moraines protect the ice beneath from melting, and this causes them to stand up as ridges, often fifty feet or more above the surface of the glacier. See also Figs. 238, 239.

Although ice under steady pressure slowly flows, when subjected to a decided tensional or shearing stress it breaks, forming cracks, or *crevasses* (Figs. 242, 243), in the glacier. Thus *lateral crevasses* develop because the center of the ice stream moves faster than the marginal border (Fig. 244). Where the valley bottom is irregular crevasses are especially abundant; and where the slope of the bottom is steep, the ice may become so crevassed that it is almost impossible to pass over it. Such a section is called an *ice fall* (Figs. 245, 246). Morainic material is constantly sliding into these crevasses (Fig. 247), some of this finding its way to the bottom of the glacier. Water from the melting ice also falls into crevasses that have been melted broadly open, called *moulins* (mills), boring *potholes* (p. 79) in the rock floor and flowing in ice tunnels to the front of the glacier.

Photo by Ernest Beaumont Schoedsack

Fig. 235. — A mountain pass, a U-shaped glacial trough carved by ice erosion, leading down to the valley of Isfahan in western Persia. Through this snow-filled pass thousands of nomads with all their possessions and herds struggle each year in a migration from their winter grazing lands at low elevations to higher summer pastures beyond the mountains. In summer the low-level pastures are parched; in winter the high pastures are buried in snow. The picture is from the motion picture *Grass* and is reproduced by courtesy of G. P. Putnam's Sons.

The rock detritus enclosed in the bottom ice of a glacier is known as the *ground moraine* (Fig. 248), and when a glacier disappears by melting this ground moraine is left as a deposit on the

Photo by Tarr

Fig. 236. — The Mer de Glace, an *alpine* or valley glacier. A band of lateral moraine is seen on the left, and a talus, down which morainic material comes, on the right.

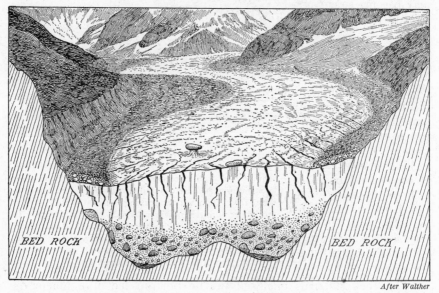

After Walther

Fig. 237. — Diagram to illustrate the relation of a valley glacier to its rock bed. Note the ground moraine, the lateral crevasses, the glacier table, and the lateral moraine. Account for each of these as it appears in the drawing.

Photo by von E.

Fig. 238. — Glacier table, Valdez glacier, Alaska. When a large block of rock comes to rest far out on the glacier surface it protects the ice beneath it from melting as rapidly as the surrounding areas, hence in time is supported on an ice pedestal and forms a *glacier table.* See Fig. 237.

Photo by von E.

Fig. 239. — Debris cones on the Valdez glacier, Alaska. When the ice surface is covered in patches by small rock fragments, *debris cones* that look like clusters of great ant-hills form by differential melting. Explain by Fig. 238 above.

Photo by von E.

Fig. 240. — Kettle pond in lateral moraine on the borders of the Columbia glacier, Alaska — seen behind the trees. Irregular deposit of the morainic debris gives rise to little hollows in which water collects.

Photo by von E.

Fig. 241. — Rock surface ground by glacial erosion. Yakutat Bay, Alaska. The rock here presented uneven resistance to the scour of the bottom ice; this made knobs and grooves. The ice has only recently melted off this area. (See Fig. 261 for plucking erosion.)

Fig. 242. — Lateral crevasses typically developed from the sides of the Illecillewaet glacier, Canadian Rockies.   (See Fig. 244.)

Fig. 243. — A great crevasse in the Valdez glacier, Alaska.   The figure is the late Professor R. S. Tarr, author of the original *New Physical Geography.*

valley bottom. To it are added the materials of the lateral and medial moraines, which slowly settle to the ground as the glacier melts.

At the end, or terminus, of a glacier, rock fragments are built into a *terminal moraine* (Figs. 250, 297). These fragments are brought by the ice and loosened as it melts, accumulating in irreg-

Fig. 244. — Diagram to show how lateral crevasses develop and why they extend in parallel lines up-glacier. The arrows indicate by their lengths the different rates of movement of the ice from the margin toward the center. The section (*a*) is supposed to have moved to the position (*a¹*) when the lateral crevasse, *c-c¹* opens. The ice has "stretched" along the line *s-s¹*. Why do these conditions cause the crevasse to open?

ular piles at the base of the glacier front (Figs. 249a, b, c). If the end of a glacier remains in one place for a long time, the hills of terminal moraine may reach a height of 100 or 200 feet.

The water that falls into crevasses and moulins emerges as a stream from the ice front (Figs. 182, 251, 252), often from an *ice cave*. It is white with suspended sediment, or *rock flour*, supplied by the grinding up of rocks beneath the glacier. In summer, the volume of these glacier streams becomes so great that large bowlders are moved along. The fine rock flour is carried far down the valley, but the sand and pebbles are usually deposited on the valley bottom, gradually filling the valley. Over this deposit the stream flows in a branching, braided course, constantly depositing sediment and changing position (Figs. 253, 254). Such *outwash deposits* may reach a depth of over 100 feet.

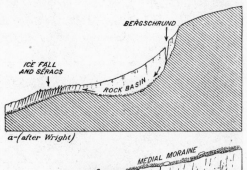

a-(after Wright)

b-(after Smith)

Summary. *Snow, derived from the snow field, accumulates in the valleys, changing to granular ice (névé), then to ice, which extends down the valley as an ice tongue or valley glacier. As the glacier moves, it plucks and scours its bed, and carries rock fragments, both on its surface (lateral and medial moraines) and at its bottom (ground moraine). Rock fragments and water descend to the bottom of glaciers through crevasses, caused by strains resulting from the ice motion. The rock fragments form a ground moraine and assist the ice in erosion; the water emerges from beneath the ice in streams, bearing rock flour, sand, and pebbles, which build extensive outwash deposits. Terminal moraines are built at the ice front.*

c-(after Davis)

Fig. 245a, b, c. — Diagrams to illustrate the occurrence and formation of cirque basins and an ice fall. See page 270.

(a) The cirque basin is excavated deeply into the rock by the plucking action of the ice at the bergschrund crevasse and its grinding as it moves downward and outward in the basin.

(b) A steep declivity in the valley floor at the cirque mouth causes an ice fall and séracs. The diagram suggests that some medial moraine here becomes ground moraine. How?

(c) A mountain mass after being denuded by cirque and glacier erosion. The dotted and dashed lines illustrate the originally higher elevations of the mountain. The glaciers were later melted away and a cirque lake now occupies the basin. Compare this picture with the photograph, Fig. 300.

Fig. 246. — Crevasses of an ice fall in the névé region of a Swiss glacier. Descent over the steep slope of the valley floor subjects the ice to shearing stresses and causes it to crack through.

Photo by Rafflus

Fig. 247. — Great crevasse near head of Coe glacier, Mt. Hood, Oregon.

112. Glaciers of Alaska. Of the many Alaskan glaciers the best known is the immense *Muir glacier*, which is fed by twenty or more glacier tributaries. These unite to form an ice tongue which advances down a broad valley and ends in the sea. Its front is a cliff, which, in 1892, rose 200 feet above the water and extended 800 feet below. From it small icebergs frequently break off and float down

Photo by von E.

Fig. 248. — Bottom ice of the Shoup glacier, Alaska, black with imbedded bowlders, rock flour, the ground moraine material.

Glacier bay. The discharge of icebergs, added to melting, caused Muir glacier to grow shorter steadily, so that its front has retreated over six miles and is not nearly so broad or magnificent as it was in 1892. Tourists now go to see the Taku glacier near by. Another splendid Alaskan valley glacier that is, like the Muir and Taku, a *tidal* glacier is the Hubbard, shown on the right in the

Photo by Libbey

Fig. 249 (a) — Terminus of the Tuktoo glacier, Greenland.

Photo by Grant

Fig. 249 (b) — Terminus of the Columbia glacier, Alaska.

Photo by Martin

Fig. 249 (c) — Terminus of the Cornell glacier, Greenland.

Fig. 249 a, b, c. — These three photographs illustrate three different processes by which terminal moraine ridges are built up. In (a) the rock fragments melt out from and slide down the steep face of the ice front; in (b) the front of the glacier is moving bodily forward and pushing up a ridge of debris before it; in (c) the end of the glacier is riding up on previously deposited material and adding to the height of the ridge through the melting out of the ground moraine in the bottom layers of the ice. What evidence do the pictures afford as to the height to which such terminal moraine ridges may be built? All three or only one of the processes may be acting at the front of a particular glacier.

Photo by Robinson

Fig. 250. — Terminal moraine of the Grinnell glacier, Glacier National Park. Here the ice has melted back from the thickness it had earlier when it deposited the moraine. Hence the moraine now stands out as ridge.

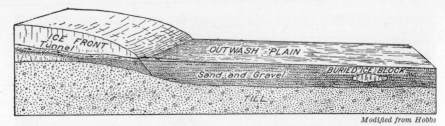

Fig. 251. — Diagram to show the structure of an outwash plain and how an ice block may be buried in the gravels of such a deposit.

Fig. 252. — Outflow stream of Hidden glacier, Alaska. The violence of the current indicates the capacity of the stream to move big bowlders.

Fig. 253. — An outwash plain and valley train in front of the Llewellyn glacier, Alaska. The gravels carried by the streams outflowing from the glacier have filled the valley deeply.

Photo by Tarr

Fig. 254. — Pitted outwash plain of the Hidden glacier, Alaska. Shows *fosse,* and pits and lakelets. These pits are due to the fact that the outwash gravels bury glacial ice which later melts out, letting the surface slump. See Figs. 251 and 283. The fosse is a ditch caused by the melting of the front of the glacier.

Photo by von E.

Fig. 255. — The end of the Hubbard glacier, Alaska. The vertical ice cliff is 280 feet high. If the end of the glacier is floating, about how great must be the full thickness of the ice? See page 277.

Fig. 256.— End of the tidal Nunatak glacier, Alaska. Notice the three bands of medial moraine. Account for the middle one.

map (Fig. 257) and in Fig. 255. Still another beautiful tidal glacier in this district is the Nunatak glacier shown in Fig. 256.

Farther west in Alaska there is still another large glacier, the *Malaspina* (Fig. 257), formed by the union of a number of valley glaciers that descend from the Mt. St. Elias range. This glacier spreads out, fan-shaped, on a plain at the base of the mountains.

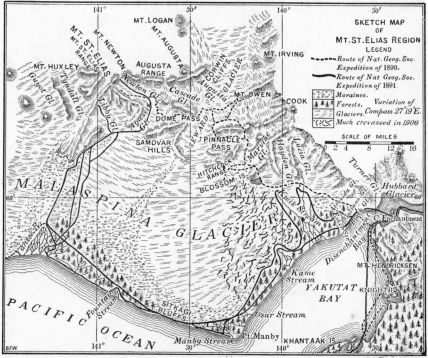

Fig. 257. — The Malaspina glacier.

For this reason it is called a *Piedmont* glacier (from *pied*, foot, and *mont*, mountain). It has a length of sixty or seventy miles and a breadth of twenty or twenty-five miles; and its movement is so slow that it is an almost stagnant, undulating ice plateau.

Melting and evaporation have caused the rock fragments originally incorporated in the upper ice of the Malaspina glacier to accumulate on its surface, especially near the terminal border. These rock fragments form a rocky soil on the glacier, called *ablation moraine*, in which a forest is growing (Fig. 258a, b).

A   *Photo by Russell*

B   *Photo by von E.*

Fig. 258a and b. — The Malaspina glacier, Alaska. The upper picture shows part of the margin of the Malaspina, so stagnant that a forest grows on the cover of ablation-moraine soil on the top of the glacier behind the 100-foot high ice cliff seen in the picture. The lower picture shows another part of the margin of the Malaspina, August, 1906, when the earthquakes of 1899 had caused the stagnant end of the glacier to advance. These earthquakes shook down abnormally large quantities of snow on the feeding valley glaciers of the St. Elias mountains. The blocks are huge ice masses, thrust up and forward through the forest that had become established on the moraine cover of the previously inert ice.

Summary. *Muir glacier, fed by over twenty tributary glaciers, ends in sea cliffs from which icebergs are discharged. Malaspina glacier, an almost stagnant ice plateau, is called a Piedmont glacier.*

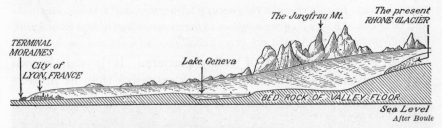

Fig. 259. — Length and thickness of the Rhone glacier in the Glacial Period. Note the size this diagram shows the present Rhone glacier and make comparison with the photograph, Fig. 182.

113. Distribution of valley glaciers. There are several hundred valley glaciers in Switzerland, and these serve as one of the attractions to tourists. With the exception of Australia, valley glaciers are found in the higher mountain ranges and peaks of all the continents. Thus in South America and Africa there are small glaciers on volcanic cones that are situated directly over the equator. Extremely long valley glaciers occur in the Himalaya Mountains. Toward the north glaciers increase in size and number, becoming especially large and abundant in western Canada and Alaska. In the United States, Glacier National Park, in Montana, has small glaciers; and many tourists now visit the Selkirk range of western Canada, which rivals Switzerland in the grandeur and beauty of its snow-capped mountains

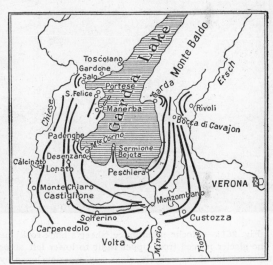

Fig. 260. — Map of the morainic loops around the lower end of Lake Garda, Italy. Here the glacier has completely melted away but the basin and deposits are exactly like those now forming that are shown in the frontispiece of this book.

and its glaciers. Outside the Arctic regions Alaska has the most magnificent valley glaciers in the world and these can be easily visited by steamer. Near one of these (see frontispiece) tourist camps are conducted like a hotel in a city. Thus it is made possible for anyone to enjoy these great natural wonders without hardship.

Summary. *Valley glaciers exist in many parts of the world, even in the tropical zone. In cold climates they occupy low valleys, and even descend to the sea; in warm climates they are confined to the upper valleys of high mountains. The valley glaciers of Alaska are exceptionally magnificent and easily visited.*

114. Former extension of valley glaciers. It is well known that valley glaciers were formerly more extensive than at present

Photo by Tarr

Fig. 261. — Roche moutonnée (sheep's back rock) near the Spencer glacier, Alaska. The glacier moved from upper right to lower left across the picture. The surface of the right side of the rock, the *stoss* side, was developed by grinding erosion of the glacier; the left or *lee* side was developed by plucking erosion. Account for this difference.

(Figs. 182, 259, 260). In fact, they once existed in places where now there is none. Nearly all Switzerland was once covered by an ice sheet, formed by the lengthening and piedmont expansion of the existing and other valley glaciers; there were many glaciers in the Rocky Mountains; and glaciers existed even in the Adirondacks and New England mountains.

The clear evidence of this former extension of glaciers is of various kinds, as follows: (1) rock fragments, called *erratics*, often weighing tons, are found in the valleys. In many cases they are different from the rock near by, but are the same as rock found higher up the valley. They have apparently been brought by some powerful agent, like moving ice.

(2) The ledges in the valleys have been polished and scratched by the dragging of rock fragments over them (Fig. 241), again as

Photo by Read

Fig. 262. — A rock basin developed by differential ice erosion. Read's Lake, Coast Ranges, British Columbia. This lake is completely surrounded by solid rock sides and is a basin that was dug out by the grinding and plucking action of glacial erosion.

if by moving ice. These scratches, or *striæ*, extend in the direction in which the erratic bowlders have been carried.

(3) Deposits like those being made by existing glaciers occur in the valleys (Fig. 297). These include lateral, medial, terminal, and ground moraines; the ground moraine making a thin sheet of mixed clay, pebbles, and bowlders, called *bowlder clay* or *till*. This till is unlike water deposits, being unassorted and unstratified; but it is like deposits from ice, which carries and drops large and small fragments with equal ease, and, therefore, side by side. In front of the terminal moraines, and sometimes mixed with them, are

outwash deposits of stratified gravels, like those now being laid down by the streams that issue from glaciers.

(4) The valleys also show signs of glacial erosion (Figs. 233, 234, 235, 265). The rocks of their sides and bottoms are polished by ice scouring, and in some places the valley floor is worn into smooth, rounded hummocks, known as *roches moutonnées* (sheep backs) (Fig. 261). This erosion has often broadened and deepened valleys (Fig. 148); and where they have been deepened a little more than elsewhere, *rock basins* have been formed, now occupied by lakes and ponds (Fig. 262). In some cases the valleys have been deepened hundreds of feet; and in the region of former névé,

Photo by National Park Service

Fig. 263. — Small remnant glacier in a cirque basin. Piegan Mountain, Glacier National Park. This hollow was carved in the mountain by cirque erosion of this and the earlier larger glacier on the same site. See also Figs. 245a, 245c, 300.

broad deep amphitheaters, called *cirques* (Figs. 245, 263, 300), have been developed by the headward erosion of the ice.

Since the ice disappeared, water streams in valleys tributary to such ice-eroded valleys have not had time to cut their bottoms down to the level of the *overdeepened* main valleys. Their bottoms therefore stand above the level of the main valley, and they are accordingly called *hanging valleys* (Figs. 264, 265, 266). From them the streams tumble into the main valley as falls or rapids. These waterfalls add to the charm of the mountain scenery in Switzerland, Norway, Alaska, and other regions in which glaciers have far receded or departed altogether.

Summary. *Erratics, moraines, till, and outwash deposits are among the evidences that valley glaciers were formerly more extensive, and even existed*

Fig. 264. — A hanging valley, tributary to Nunatak Fiord, Alaska. A tributary glacier formerly joined a main glacier extending from left to right down the larger valley in the foreground, now an arm of the sea, a fiord. Because the main glacier eroded its valley more deeply than the smaller tributary did its valley, the lip and floor of the latter are now left "hanging" far above the level of the main valley bottom.

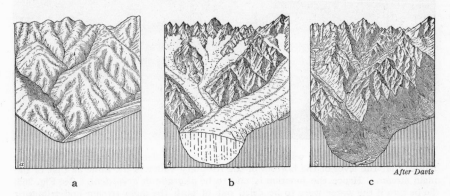

a   b   c

Fig. 265a, b, c. — Diagrams to show how the development of tributary and main valleys differs under stream and glacier erosion. In (a) valley development with accordant junctions under stream erosion is shown; in (b) the same general region is illustrated when drained by glaciers; in (c) is shown the effects of the glacial occupation on the valley forms and relations. Streams join at grade (1) because the water depth is slight, (2) because deepening of the main valley increases the slope of the tributary, hence the erosive effectiveness of the tributary stream. Hence it "keeps up" with the main stream. The tributary glacier valleys hang (1) because the ice streams are so much thicker than the water streams are deep, and (2) because glacial erosion depends for its effectiveness on the pressure of the ice on the valley bottom, and not on the slope of the bed. Hence the thicker main glacier is always "getting ahead" of the tributary glacier in down cutting.

271

*where now there is none.   Phenomena due to ice erosion are also found, in
the form of striæ, roches moutonnées, broadened and deepened valleys, rock
basins, cirques, and hanging valleys, and are further evidence pointing to the
same conclusion.*

115. The Greenland ice sheet. The island of Greenland is
mountainous, probably not greatly unlike northern New England
and Scotland.   Near the coast there is a fringe of peninsulas and
islands on which there are scattered Eskimo settlements.   The

Fig. 266. — A tributary water stream joining a main stream, Bingen on the Rhine.
Notice that the level of the bottom of the tributary valley is the same as that of the
main stream.   Hence the junction is said to be *at grade* or *accordant*.   See Fig. 265.
To be sure if the water were to be dried out of both the main stream and tributary
stream valleys the bottom of the channel of the latter would hang slightly above that
of the main stream channel.   State how these conditions are unlike and like those of
a tributary glacier joining a main glacier.

mountain valleys have valley glaciers, and small ice caps exist on
some of the larger islands and peninsulas.

Back of the fringe of coast land is a great waste of ice and snow,
with an area of over 500,000 square miles, more than ten times
the area of New York State.   This enormous ice cap is so large,
and, in a number of ways, so different from a valley glacier, that

the term *continental glacier* or *ice sheet* is a better name. A continental glacier *is a mass of ice, moving over a large area of land, hill and valley alike, and completely covering the rock topography.*

In the central interior, which Peary and other explorers have crossed, the elevation rises to 8000 to 10,000 feet, and the temperature is seldom or never above the freezing point. The surface is, therefore, always covered with loose, dry snow. Nearer the coast, where the elevation is less, the warmth of the summer sun melts the snow, leaving an ice surface quite like that of valley glaciers.

The continued fall of snow on the high interior of Greenland has caused such an accumulation that, changed to ice by pressure, it is forced to move slowly outward (Fig. 267) in all directions, — north, east, south, and west. It moves as a great pile of wax would, and in its slow, irresistible outward movement crosses hill and valley alike.

Back of the coastal fringe the only land that appears is an occasional high mountain

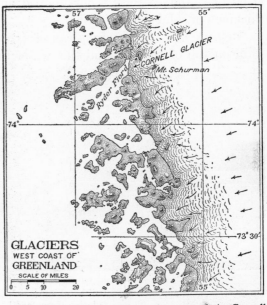

Fig. 267. — A map of the region around the Cornell glacier. The arrows show the general movement of the ice, outward from the interior, but turning down into the valleys, and ending in tongues in the bays and fiords.

peak, called a *nunatak*, which projects like an island above the sea of ice. Near the coast the ice extends down the valleys through the mountain rim, often reaching the sea as *outlet tidal glaciers* (Fig. 268). At the head of *fiords* these valley tongues end in sea cliffs 200 or 300 feet high, advancing in some cases at the rate of from 50 to 75 feet a day, and discharging huge icebergs that float south into the Atlantic Ocean. Most of these tongues are only a few miles wide; but the largest of all, the Humboldt glacier of north Greenland, is 60 miles wide. Their surface is broken by crevasses, quite unlike the smooth, unbroken ice plateau of the interior.

Unlike that of valley glaciers, the surface of the ice sheet is quite free from rock fragments, except where nunataks supply materials for a medial moraine, or, near the end of a valley tongue, where the mountain slopes rise above the ice surface. Near the bottom, however, there is much rock material, which has been worn from the land. In transporting this load of rock fragments at its base, the ice sheet scours its bed and has worn away a great thickness of solid rock.

Melting near the margin causes streams and even ponds to form on top of the ice; and this water finds its way by crevasses

Photo by Martin

Fig. 268. — Icebergs large and small breaking (*calving*) from the front of the Cornell glacier, Greenland.

to the bottom. Where this water emerges, either on the land or in the sea, deposits of gravel and clay are being made. Along the ice front, too, moraines are being built of rock fragments loosened by melting (Figs. 249 a, c). Many of these fragments are worn and scratched (Fig. 274) by the grinding they have received.

There is good evidence that the Greenland ice sheet, like the valley glaciers in other parts of the world, once extended much farther, completely covering some, if not all, of the islands and peninsulas. This evidence is supplied by moraines, erratics, glacial scratches (Fig. 465), rounded and deepened valleys, and rock basins.

Summary. *Greenland is covered by a great ice sheet, or continental glacier, with a fringe of ice-free land near the coast, and, near the margin,* *occasional nunataks projecting above the ice. From the high interior, where snow falls summer and winter, there is a movement outward in all directions, the margin of the ice consisting of valley tongues, often ending in the sea into which icebergs are discharged. The ice has little rock material on the surface, but carries much near the bottom, with which it is eroding its floor and making moraine and outwash deposits.*

116. Other ice sheets. The Antarctic continent (Fig. 269), situated over the South Pole and extending over an area comparable to that of the

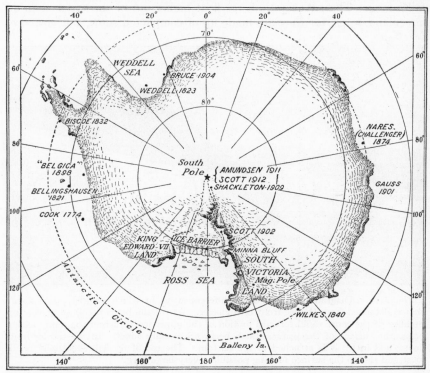

Fig. 269. — Map of the Antarctic Continent as it is known. Notice position of the Great Ice Barrier south of the Ross Sea.

United States, is completely enveloped by a vast continental glacier. So massive is this ice indeed, that explorers are not positive whether the land beneath is a group of islands bridged across by the glacial dome or a continuous land area. Mountains project above the ice in the marginal areas, but Amundsen and Scott found the South Pole to be located in a vast plateau of ice having a surface elevation of 10,000 feet above the sea. Tremendous outlet glaciers pour from this plateau through low points in the mountains, carrying the ice accumulations of the interior down to the

sea.   One such outlet glacier, the Beardmore, is ten to twenty miles wide
and over 125 miles long.   At the sea level on one side of the continent there
is a great, level ice plain 300 miles wide at its sea front and extending about
as far back from the edge.   This is known as the Great Ice Barrier because
its outer edge is an unbroken ice cliff varying from 50 to 300 feet in height.
The Great Ice Barrier seems to be a *piedmont glacier afloat*, for it is fed
on the landward side by many outlet glaciers, moves forward at the rate
of about one fourth mile a year, and rises and falls in level with the tide.
At the sea edge it breaks off in huge tabular icebergs, some of which are
miles long.   These Antarctic bergs float higher out of the water than do
Greenland bergs, for they are made up of compacted snow, not clear ice.

Fig. 270. — Diagram to show three different ways in which icebergs are *calved,*
that is detached from the ice-front of a glacier.   At (a) the bergs break off at the top
because of the more rapid forward motion of the upper ice, undercutting, and melting
below the surface of the water.   Such bergs are usually small.   In (b) the ice-front
floats; and in (c) it is attached to the bottom.   The toe of (c) will eventually break
loose and rise to the surface making possible a very large berg.

The Great Ice Barrier is built up as a level plain by the accumulation of
successive snowfalls as it moves outward under thrust from the outlet
glaciers.

On the larger islands of the Arctic, Spitzbergen, for example, there
are also ice caps, resembling that of Greenland, though smaller.   There is
evidence that ice sheets once spread completely over these islands.

Summary.   *There is a great ice sheet on the Antarctic continent, and
smaller sheets on some of the larger islands of the Arctic.*

117. Formation of icebergs.   When a glacier enters the sea the water
buoys the ice up, causing great masses to break off, forming icebergs (Figs.

1, 268, 270, 271). Other masses are broken away by undercutting along the water's edge. As the icebergs drift slowly away they melt, strewing rock fragments along the sea bottom.

It should be clearly understood that the *sea ice* and *ice floes* due to the freezing over of the Arctic Ocean do not give rise to icebergs. Such ice either remains in the Arctic seas or melts before it has drifted far south. The sea ice is comparatively thin ice, whereas the icebergs discharged by glaciers may be over a thousand feet thick. It is on this account that the Greenland bergs that drift far to the south into the steamer routes of the North Atlantic are so dangerous to shipping. A berg that is one hundred feet high above the water extends 700 to 1000 feet below the surface. A ship that collides with such a mass suffers as greatly as if it had run against an island of solid rock.

Summary. *Icebergs are discharged by moving forward of the glacier, by undercutting along the water's edge, and by buoying up of ice as it advances into the sea. Because of their great mass below as well as above the water surface, collision with icebergs causes disastrous shipwrecks.*

Photo by von E.

Fig. 271. — Small iceberg stranded at low tide, Nunatak fiord, Alaska. The notch and line mark division between parts of berg above and below the surface when the ice is afloat.

118. Former ice sheets in Europe and America. There is quite indisputable evidence that, not many thousand years ago, a great ice sheet spread over northeastern America (Fig. 272), and another over northwestern Europe. Scandinavia, Denmark, northern Germany, northwestern Russia, and all of the British Isles (Fig. 273) except southern England, were then covered by ice. Canada east of the Rocky Mountains, New England, northern New Jersey, nearly all of New York, northern Pennsylvania, much of Ohio, and the states farther west and northwest as far as Montana and as far south as the Missouri River, were also ice-covered.

These ice sheets, quite like those now covering Greenland and the Antarctic continent, have been called the *continental glaciers* of the Pleistocene or Glacial Period.

The proofs of these former ice sheets are of the same kind as those of former greater extension of valley glaciers (p. 268) and of the Greenland glacier (p. 274). These proofs include glacial

After Tarr and Martin

Fig. 272. — Centers of dispersion, lines of flow, and maximum extent of the glaciers of the Glacial Period in North America.

striations (Fig. 276), glacial *potholes*, and erratic bowlders (Figs. 275, 277, 292). The striations point toward the north, and many of the bowlders can be traced to a northern source, some of those in the United States having come from Canada. In New York State varieties of igneous rock can be traced quite definitely to the old volcanic neck, Mt. Royal, that rises above the city of Montreal. There is evidence also of ice erosion and valley deepening; and there are lakes in rock basins that the ice scoured out (p. 270).

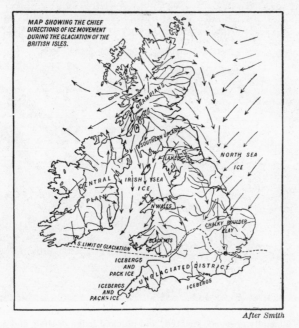

Fig. 273. — Glaciation of the British Isles. The arrows show the direction of flow of the ice. Notice that the glaciers extended across the North Sea.

Fig. 274. — A pebble with glacial scratches; taken from the Greenland ice sheet at the place shown in Fig. 268.

Fig. 275. — A pebble with glacial scratches taken from a till bed in the interior of the Labrador peninsula.

Photo by Morgan

Fig. 276. — Glacially grooved, striated, and plucked ledge of shale and sandstone bed rock along the east side of the Cayuga Lake valley, Central New York. The ice moved from left to right across the picture. See Fig. 241.

Photo by von E.

Fig. 277. — A large glacial bowlder near Slaterville, New York. This bowlder is composed of a variety of rock that occurs, as bed rock, not nearer than the Adirondack Mountains, nearly 200 miles from Slaterville.

Where the ice stood, the land is covered by a sheet of deposited ground and ablation moraine or *till*, and there are bands of terminal moraine (Fig. 278), with outwash deposits in front (Fig. 283).

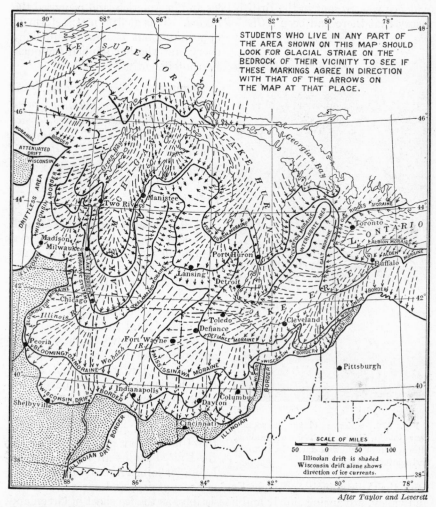

STUDENTS WHO LIVE IN ANY PART OF THE AREA SHOWN ON THIS MAP SHOULD LOOK FOR GLACIAL STRIAE ON THE BEDROCK OF THEIR VICINITY TO SEE IF THESE MARKINGS AGREE IN DIRECTION WITH THAT OF THE ARROWS ON THE MAP AT THAT PLACE.

SCALE OF MILES
50   0   50   100

Illinoian drift is shaded
Wisconsin drift alone shows
direction of ice currents.

After Taylor and Leverett

Fig. 278. — Terminal moraines in the Central States, showing the influence of the Great Lakes valleys in causing the ice tongues to extend farther south.

These glacial deposits, collectively, were years ago called *drift*, because they were thought to have been brought, or drifted, by icebergs or great floods of water; and the term *glacial drift* is still applied to them.

Louis Agassiz, in the middle of the last century, first proposed the glacial theory to account for this drift. Being a Swiss, he had studied glaciers in Switzerland, and had seen the clear evidence (p. 269) that Alpine glaciers were formerly more extensive. He saw that the same evidence was present in the British Isles and in America, and proposed the theory that there had been a *Glacial Period*. This at first met a storm of opposition, but is now accepted by every one who has studied the question intelligently.

Summary. *Striæ, erratics, evidences of erosion, moraines, etc., prove that great continental glaciers, or ice sheets, formerly covered northeastern North America and northwestern Europe. Louis Agassiz proposed the now accepted explanation, a Glacial Period.*

Photo by Sauramo

Fig. 279. — Varve clays in section near Jokela, Finland. Notice banding, alternation of light and dark, the summer and winter variation.

119. Cause of the Glacial Period. Why there should have been a glacial climate in temperate latitudes is not positively known. At present the climate of Labrador, Scandinavia, and other centers from which the ice spread, is very cold; and, if they were elevated several hundred feet, great ice caps might slowly gather on them and spread out into lower and warmer regions. Before the Glacial Period these lands actually were higher than now, and one theory is that this former elevation caused great ice sheets to form and move down into the United States and Europe. In the United States an ice sheet from Labrador joined forces with ice sheets from the Adirondack and New England mountains, and spread over hill and valley, advancing slowly and irresistibly, as the ice sheet of Greenland does. It advanced southward to a zone where melting became so great that it could go no farther. After many thousand years the climate gradually changed, perhaps because the land was lowered. Then the ice front slowly melted back, or "retreated."

This theory is not completely satisfactory however. It fails to account for the fact that not only did the continental glaciers form in the areas of North America and Europe mentioned, which may have been more elevated, but also that valley glaciers all over the world were apparently more extensive in the Glacial Period.   Even the glaciers on the mountains in the equatorial zone, descended to far lower levels than they do now. Perhaps as plausible a hypothesis as any to account for such a world-wide lowering of temperature and glacier development is that great sunspots caused tremendous storminess and cloudiness over long periods of time. The cyclonic storms (see p. 441) gave rise to heavy precipitation and also brought about the escape of much heat to the upper levels of the atmosphere.   The cloudiness in turn prevented the sun's rays from warming the earth in the degree that they would with clearer skies.

The time since the ice left is so short that the drift deposits are still quite fresh; and even delicate striæ remain (Fig. 276) wherever protected by a thin coating of soil (p. 59).   Until recently, however, there was no way of measuring with any exactness how long ago the ice melted away, although estimates of 5000 to 10,000 years were made on the basis of the rate of retreat of Niagara Falls (p. 524).   But we have now a precise method of determining the rate of melting back of the ice in certain localities.   It is found that the waters released by melting of the ice make deposits of banded clays in fresh-water ponds.

Photo by Sauramo

Fig. 280. — A small section, natural size, from the varve clays shown in Fig. 279, matched with a section for the same years from another place.   One cannot see at a glance that these match, careful measurements and comparisons must be made.

Each band or *varve* (Figs. 279, 280) (cycle) consists of a thick, light-colored and coarse layer deposited in summer, and a thin, dark, fine-grained layer deposited in winter.   Thus each varve represents a year.   The varves vary in thickness and in other characteristics. Accordingly it is possible to match the top sets in one pond with the bottom sets in the pond next north and count the years consecutively. In this way it has been found by De Geer that the ice started to melt from southernmost Sweden over 13,500 years ago.   In Finland Sauramo has determined that it took the ice 2200 years to retreat about 300 miles and that about 200 years are occupied in the building of a great morainic ridge.   Antevs has shown that about 4300 years elapsed while the ice was retreating 185 miles up the Connecticut River valley from Hartford, Conn., to St. Johnsbury, Vt.

Summary. *One theory for the Glacial Period is that when the land was higher in Labrador and Scandinavia, ice caps formed and spread out in all* *directions, and, after many thousand years, when the land was lowered, melted away. Another hypothesis is that great sunspots caused a long period of storminess with loss of heat and heavy snowfall and thus brought on a Glacial Period. Time since the Glacial Period has not been long and can now be exactly measured in years in certain locations by counting and matching layers of banded clay varves.*

120. Complexity of the Glacial Period. There were at least two advances and withdrawals of the continental glaciers over Europe and North America, of which the former seems to have been the greater both in volume and in the distance to the south to which it extended. In addition there were lesser oscillations of the ice fronts which some students dignify to the degree of terming them separate advances and retreats.

Photo by von E.

Fig. 281. — A kettle pond in morainic deposits near Dryden, New York. This is due to irregular dumping of the debris and was formed in quite the same way as the pond in Fig. 240. See also Fig. 297.

Outside of limited areas these have little significance. But between the first great advance and the second the climate of eastern North America was warmer than it is now. This is proved by the finding of remains of plants, between deposits made by the first ice sheet and those of the second, at Toronto, Ontario, of species that at present flourish in the lower Ohio River valley. Again the characteristics of the deposits made by the first ice sheet differ from those of the second. Also, outside the glaciated areas, Great Salt Lake twice expanded so as to overflow or nearly overflow (p. 310) its basin (Fig. 304). This indicates two periods of moist cold climates. We may be living in an interglacial period.

Summary. *There is good evidence that there were at least two separate advances and retreats of the continental ice sheets of Europe and North America and*

*that the interglacial period between was warmer than our climate is now.
There were also lesser oscillations of the ice fronts.*

121. Terminal moraines. While the ice sheet was melting
there were periods when it halted for a time and built terminal
moraines. These bands of moraine, which resemble those now
forming at the margin of glaciers, may be easily traced. They
consist of irregular, hummocky hills, varying from a few feet to 100
or 200 feet in height, and enclosing many basins, or *kettles* (Fig. 281),

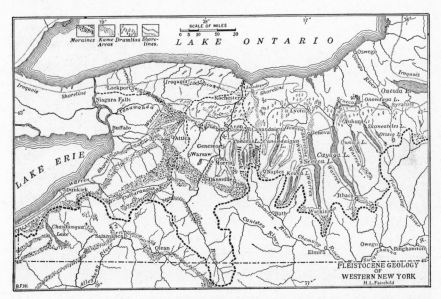

Fig. 282. — The lobate moraines of recession (dotted belts) in western New York.
The outermost moraine bends up from Pennsylvania to Salamanca and Olean. Also
location of drumlins, and of shore lines of glacial lakes. The heavy dotted line is the
divide. The lakes have all been caused by glacial action.

often occupied by ponds. The moraines are made partly of till, and
partly of stratified drift deposited by water from the melting ice.

Ice tongues, or *lobes*, during the retreat of the ice extended farther in
the valleys than on the hills, and on this account the moraines bend
southward in the valleys, forming looped or *lobate moraines* (Fig. 278).
Terminal moraines were built at each halt of the receding ice sheet, and
they are called *recessional moraines* (Fig. 282).

Summary. *At each halt of the receding ice sheet a terminal moraine
was built with lobes extending down the valleys. These moraines are low,
hummocky hills, with enclosed basins, or kettles, commonly occupied by ponds.*

122. Stratified drift. Water issuing from the melting glacier built several classes of deposits. All these are stratified, because water assorts rock fragments (p. 46). These stratified deposits are called *stratified drift*. Of these the most extensive are the *outwash plains* (Fig. 251); if narrower and hemmed in by valley walls they are called *valley trains*. These valley trains are quite identical with similar deposits now forming in the Swiss valleys (Fig. 182).

Fig. 283. — Outwash plain near Clinton, Massachusetts, with a "fossil" kettle hole. This is an extraordinary picture in the confirmation it affords of the glacial origin of this deposit. Just as in Fig. 254 buried ice melting out caused pits in an outwash plain forming in front of a living glacier, so, here too, an ice block first made a pit, then melted completely; later as deposit of the outwash gravels continued, the hollow was filled up and bridged across as we see. It was found, in digging a great reservoir, 10,000 years or more after it was formed.

Many valleys in eastern America are filled to a depth of from 100 to 300 feet with these level, gravelly plains, built by ancient glacial streams. Wherever the ice front rested on fairly level land, the glacial streams built a series of low, flat alluvial fans, the outwash plains. The plains on the south side of Long Island are of this origin. Melting of buried ice blocks gave rise to *pitted plains* (Figs. 254, 283).

At and under the ice front the water built irregular, hummocky hills of gravel, called *kames* (Fig. 285), in which deep basins, or kettles, are often found. Some of the kames were apparently made by streams, bearing much gravel, which tumbled to the bottom of, or "boiled" out of the front of the glacier through crevasses. This gravel occasionally covered blocks of ice which, on melting, allowed the gravel to settle, forming *kettle holes*.

Long narrow ridges of gravel, sometimes miles in length, and with an irregular, serpentine course, are called *eskers* (Figs. 284, 286). These are the gravel beds of streams that flowed in tunnels or gorges in the ice,

Photo by Tarr

Fig. 284. — Section through an esker at McLean, New York. Shows that these ridges are made up of rounded stream gravel.

usually at the bottom. When the ice walls that supported the sides of the bed melted away, the gravels were left in ridge form. Where these streams emerged from their ice tunnels, they built outwash plains; or, if the end was in small, ice-dammed lakes, they built deltas. These level-topped deltas are called *sand plains*. Some of the fine-grained material was carried away by the winds from these deposits and from the flood plains of the glacial rivers to form loess deposits (p. 153).

Summary. *Water from the melting ice made stratified deposits: kames where streams tumbled to the base of or emerged from the front of the ice; eskers where they flowed in ice tunnels; outwash plains where they emerged upon the land; and sand plains in small ice-dammed lakes.*

Photo by Tarr

Fig. 285. — A kame near Auburn, New York. It is made up entirely of irregularly stratified gravel.

Photo by Shaub

Fig. 286. — An esker on the west shore of Stacker Lake, Labrador peninsula, P. Q., Canada, near the center from which the eastern section of the continental glacier radiated.

123. Ice-dammed lakes. In some places the ice front stood in large lakes (Figs. 1, 287, 298), formed where north-flowing streams were dammed by the ice. Clay and gravel deposits were made in these, and along their shores deltas and beaches were built.

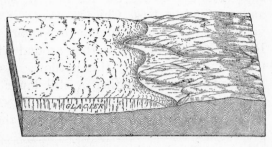

One of these large lakes was formed in the valley of the Red River of the North (p. 132, Fig. 120). The case of the Great Lakes is especially

Fig. 287. — Diagram of an ice sheet on irregular land, damming up a series of lakes along its margin. Describe what you see.

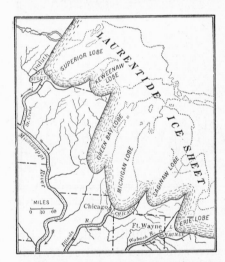

Fig. 288. — Three diagrams showing the enlargement of the glacial lakes as the ice melted from the St. Lawrence basin. Left figure, first stage of very small lakes; upper right figure, lakes larger, and eastern lakes draining into Lake Chicago; lower right figure, ice so far retreated that all the lakes drain eastward through the Mohawk, the St. Lawrence being still ice-filled. The upper lakes then flowed through the Trent river, because the land in the north was then so low that the Detroit channel could not be occupied. The dotted lines in Lake Erie and southern Lake Michigan represent the outline of the lakes at this stage, when the land was so low in the north that the water did not completely fill these basins. Elsewhere the ice dam forced the water to rise beyond the margins of the present lakes.

interesting. At first a few small lakes were formed, one outflowing past Chicago, one past Duluth, and one past Fort Wayne, Ind. (Fig. 288). As the ice melted, these grew larger, uniting and outflowing past Chicago (Fig. 288). Then an enormous volume of water, comparable to Niagara, escaped into the Illinois River. The small lake harbor around which Chicago has grown up was scoured out by this outflow. As the ice front continued to recede through melting, a still lower outlet was opened eastward through the Mohawk valley (Figs. 288, 289), the Chicago outlet was abandoned, and for a while the glacial lakes outflowed

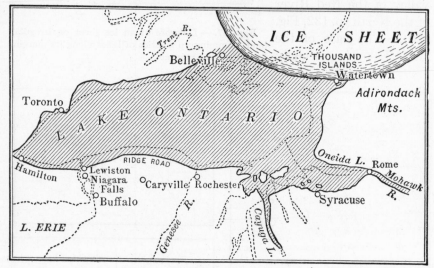

Fig. 289. — The Ontario region during the stage of outflow through the Mohawk (Figs. 282, 288).

into the Hudson past Little Falls, N. Y. Finally, when the ice had disappeared from the St. Lawrence valley and the sea retreated, the present course was established. See Fig. 290.

The beaches that were formed at the levels of the different outlets of these various lakes may still be clearly seen. For example, the beach ridge from Syracuse to Lewiston (Fig. 282), on which the "ridge road" is built, was recognized as a beach by the early explorers. The fine-grained clay that was deposited on these lake bottoms (Fig. 122) makes a level, fertile soil. Consequently, the region between the elevated beaches and the present lake shores is the seat of prosperous farms, orchards, and vineyards.

The beaches are not horizontal, but rise toward the northeast at the rate of about three to five feet a mile; and this is considered proof that the land has been tilted since they were formed. As a result of this tilting, the lakes have changed from one outlet to another (Figs. 288 and 290).

It was formerly thought that this tilting, which is still in progress, would result, in some 500 or 600 years, in causing the upper Great Lakes again to outflow past Chicago. This is not, however, the case. The uplift is like opening a trap door. The line of tilting, or hinge line, extends

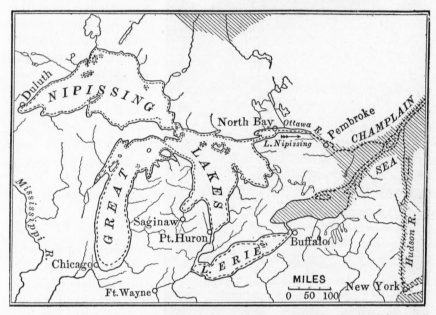

Fig. 290. — After the ice had left the St. Lawrence valley, the land in the north was so low that the sea (shaded) entered the Champlain and Ontario basins, and the upper Great Lakes outflowed through the Ottawa River. Niagara carried only the water of Lake Erie. As the land in the north rose, the sea retreated and the upper lakes were tilted until they finally overflowed past Detroit and down the St. Lawrence.

east and west across the country north of Chicago and *north* of the upper end of the Detroit River. Further uplift in the north accordingly will only result in drawing off more water through the Detroit River. Along the south shores of Lakes Superior, Erie, and Ontario, water in bays and harbors is growing deeper and the lower Niagara River is also being flooded. Why?

Summary. *As the ice was melting from the land it dammed north-flowing streams, causing temporary glacial lakes which disappeared when the ice dam* *melted away. Lakes of this sort were formed in the valleys of the Great Lakes, shifting their outlets as lower ones were uncovered by ice melting, or made available by land tilting. The tilting of the land is still in progress.*

124. The till sheet. The principal soil of a glaciated country is *till* or *bowlder clay*, which occupies the region between the moraines, wherever the surface is not covered by stratified drift. Till is a compact clay, usually unstratified, with bowlders and pebbles mixed through it (Fig. 291). It is the ground moraine and ablation moraine left when the ice melted.

The till sheet varies greatly in thickness, being usually thin where the rock was resistant to ice erosion, and thick where it was easily ground up. In Labrador, and in hilly New England, there are large areas with little or no till; but in the Mississippi Valley, where the land is more level and the rock less durable, the till sheet is sometimes 100 or 200 feet thick.

Photo by von E.

Fig. 291. — Stony till in a field in northwestern Pennsylvania, near Ulysses. The bowlders here are mostly of local origin, the last scrapings by the ice sheet, as this was near its southerly margin.

There is also much difference in composition. In places the till is made of clay with only occasional bowlders; in others it is so full of bowlders that farming is almost impossible (Fig. 292). An abundance of bowlders is likely to be found just south of mountain areas of strong rock, as in New England and south of the Adirondacks. They sometimes form trails, or *bowlder trains*, from the place of origin, growing less common and smaller as the distance from the source increases, because of the erosion to which they have been subjected. In central New

Photo by French

Fig. 292. — Glacial bowlders cleared from fields and used for fences in New England. Mt. Monadnock, New Hampshire (see p. 93) in distance.

York, where the bowlders are largely resistant rock from the north, farmers call them "hardheads."

Summary. *Till or bowlder clay, the most widespread glacial deposit, is the deposited ground and ablation moraine. It is a sheet of mixed clay and bowlders, varying in thickness and in the proportion of bowlders.*

125. Drumlins. In many sections the till sheet is smooth and regular, covering the surface to a fairly even depth; in other places it is

Photo by Gardnet

Fig. 293.—A drumlin at Ipswich, Massachusetts. Notice that its sides show modeling due to the ice pressure and movement.

ridged and irregular. One peculiar irregularity of till is the *drumlin* (Fig. 293). Drumlins vary from 100 feet to a mile or more in length, and from 20 to 100 or 200 feet in height. Some are long and ridge-like; some short and lumpy; but the most typical drumlins are oval, having the shape of a half-submerged egg, with the thick and steep end to the north; the axis of the long direction parallel to the water surface and in the line of ice movement. They are masses of till ridged up under the ice.

Drumlins usually occur in clusters. There is one group in Wisconsin, near Madison; another in central New York between Rochester and Syracuse, and northward to Lake Ontario (Fig. 282); another in the Connecticut valley; another in and near Boston (Figs. 293, 439). Boston is built on drumlins, of which Bunker Hill is one.

Summary. *Elongated ridges of till, usually in clusters, are called drumlins. They vary greatly in shape and size, the most perfect having the oval shape of a half egg.*

126. Glacial erosion. In a glaciated country wherever the rock is uncovered, its surface is likely to be polished, striated, and grooved (Fig. 276). In eastern United States the striæ point toward Labrador. Striæ and erratics found on high mountains prove that the ice was thick enough to override the tops of mountains even a mile in height.

The northern slopes of hills and mountains over which the ice moved are often rounded by ice erosion; and ledges have the smoothed and rounded form of the roches moutonnées (p. 270). Pebbles and bowlders in the till are also smoothed and scratched (Figs. 274, 275). Typical ones have rudely the shape of an old-fashioned flatiron. It is evident that great erosion was done by the ice sheet as it moved onward, pressing down with enormous weight, and dragging its rock load over the land. It acted as a great rasp tearing its way across the rock-grain of the country.

By this erosion some rock was removed from the hills, but more was worn from those valleys along which the ice moved freely. In this way many north-south valleys were so deepened that their tributaries now enter through hanging valleys (Figs. 264, 265, 294); and the same is true of bays and fiords (Figs. 163, 171, 347) on the coasts of Maine, Labrador, Alaska, and Norway. By such erosion the valleys of the larger Finger Lakes of central New York (Cayuga, Canandaigua (Figs. 282, 310), and Seneca) were deepened; and part of the depth of Lake Ontario, and of others of the Great Lakes, is also due to ice erosion. During this erosion, rock basins, in which lakes and ponds now stand, were scoured out. Thus the land surface was decidedly modified by erosion.

Fig. 294. — A glacial trough valley in the plateau of central western New York; Berby Hollow from Gannett Hill, near Naples. Notice how completely like the glacial valleys of Figs. 182, 234, 264 this is in form; that although it is a large valley, it has no stream of any consequence in its bottom, hence is not due to stream erosion.

Summary. *That the ice sheet did much erosion is proved by striated pebbles, bowlders, and ledges; by rounded north slopes; by roches moutonnées; by hanging valleys; and by rock basins. The ice sheet acted as a great rasp, digging into the surface more in some places than in others, and especially in valleys through which it moved freely.*

127. Effects of the ice sheet. In some places the surface was roughened by the deposit of drumlins, eskers, kames, and moraines. Elsewhere the drift has smoothed the surface by making thicker deposits in the valleys than on the hills (Fig. 83). This smoothing reaches its extreme in the prairie region of the Central States, where, in certain areas, drift in the valleys has a depth of 500 feet. The

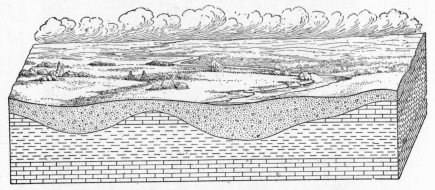

Fig. 295. — To illustrate the effect of glacial deposits (dotted) in leveling a hilly country by filling the valleys, as in the prairie region of the Central States.

level surface and fertile soil of the prairies are therefore due to the glacier (Fig. 295).

Throughout the glacial belt the drift soil shows many variations; for example, stony, clayey, sandy, gravelly, level, irregular. On a single farm there may be several kinds of soil. Sometimes this is better than the soil of rock decay that existed before the ice sheet came; in other cases a barren, sandy, gravelly, or bowldery soil (Fig. 291) has been left in place of a fertile residual soil. Usually the glacial soil is a strong one, because it consists of ground-up rock fragments, which are slowly decaying and releasing plant food.

The sheet of drift has turned many streams aside, causing them to cut new valleys for a part of their course. In these the streams have often reached the rock and cut postglacial gorges, in which there are rapids and falls (Figs. 60, 67, 441). There are thousands of instances of this, and many of the falls are of great value for water power; for instance, the falls in the Mississippi at Minneapolis, the falls of Niagara, those at Rochester, and the rapids in the Merrimac where Manchester, Lawrence, and Lowell are situated. In New England, New York, and other states in the glacial belt, this water power has given rise to much manufacturing.

Of the tens of thousands of lakes in the glacial region, the great majority are due to some interference of drift deposits with drainage (Figs. 281, 303). This is true of the small ponds and lakes, of which there are said to be 10,000 in Minnesota alone (Plate VII); and it is true of many large lakes. Even the basins of the Great Lakes, caused in part by glacial erosion and changes in level of the land, owe a portion of their depth to dams of glacial drift. What an important difference it would make in the cities and industries of northern United States if glacial action had not caused the lakes which dot the surface!

Summary. *The ice sheet caused many changes: it made some regions rougher than before, others smoother; it changed the soil, causing it to differ greatly from place to place; by turning streams aside, it led to the formation of many gorges and waterfalls; and it has made thousands of lakes, great and small.*

TOPICAL OUTLINE, QUESTIONS, SUGGESTIONS, AND LABORATORY EXERCISES

Topical Outline. 111. **Valley glaciers.** (*a*) Formation: snow field; movement of snow; névé; formation of ice; extension of ice tongue. (*b*) Movement: nature; rate; glacial erosion. (*c*) Moraines: lateral; medial; crevasses; ice falls; movement of materials to bottom; ground moraine; terminal moraine. (*d*) Outwash deposits: source of water; of sediment; rock flour; nature of deposit.

112. **Glaciers of Alaska.** (*a*) Muir: tributaries; front; withdrawal; other tidal glaciers. (*b*) Malaspina: form; size; movement; surface condition.

113. **Distribution of valley glaciers.** Europe; South America; Africa; Asia; North America — United States, Canada, Alaska.

114. **Former extension of valley glaciers.** (*a*) Instances. (*b*) Evidence: erratics; striæ; moraines; till; outwash deposits. (*c*) Ice erosion: roches moutonnées; rock basins; cirques; hanging valleys.

115. **The Greenland Ice Sheet.** (*a*) General condition: topography; coast; valley glaciers; area of ice; meaning of continental glacier or ice sheet. (*b*) The ice sheet: interior condition; outward motion; nunataks; valley tongues; size; movement; icebergs. (*c*) Rock materials: on the surface; at the base; erosion; deposits at margin. (*d*) Former extension.

116. Other ice sheets. Antarctic; Great Ice Barrier; tabular icebergs; islands of Arctic.

117. Formation of icebergs. Causes; effects; outward movement; size; danger to navigation.

118. Former ice sheets in Europe and America. (*a*) Extent: Europe; America; continental glaciers. (*b*) Proofs: striæ; erratics; ice erosion; glacial deposits; glacial drift. (*c*) Agassiz's explanation.

119. Cause of the Glacial Period. Land formerly higher; probable result; retreat of ice; theory of sunspots; time since ice withdrawal.

120. Complexity of the Glacial Period. Two advances, evidences of; warmer interglacial climate.

121. Terminal moraines. Cause; form; size; kettles; composition; lobate moraines; recessional moraines.

122. Stratified drift. Nature of stratified drift; outwash plains; pitted plains; kames; kettles; eskers; sand plains.

123. Ice-dammed lakes. Cause; Great Lakes, — early stages, changes in outflow; beaches; lake clays; changes of level — evidence; effect on outflow; present changes.

124. The till sheet. Distribution; nature of material; variation in thickness; variation in bowlders; reason for variation; bowlder trains.

125. Drumlins. Size; shape; cause; occurrence.

126. Glacial erosion. Striæ; north slopes; roches moutonnées; scratched pebbles; nature of the ice erosion; effect in valleys; illustrations; rock basins.

127. Effects of the ice sheet. (*a*) On the land surface: irregular surfaces; smooth surfaces; prairies. (*b*) On soil: differences; strength of glacial soils. (*c*) On streams: formation of gorges and falls; instances; effect on manufacturing; complete turning aside of streams; importance of this. (*d*) On lakes: cause; numbers; Great Lakes; importance.

QUESTIONS. Section 111. What is the snow field? What is the nature and origin of the névé? What is a valley glacier? Why does it extend down the valley? How does the ice move? What is happening at its bottom? What are lateral moraines? Medial moraines? Crevasses? Ice falls? What descends through the crevasses? What is the ground moraine? Terminal moraine? Account for the outwash deposits.

112. Describe the Muir glacier. The Malaspina glacier. What is ablation moraine?

113. Where are valley glaciers found?

114. Where did valley glaciers formerly exist? What are erratics? What is till? Why is it unstratified? What action of erosion did ancient glaciers perform? What are roches moutonnées? Rock basins? Hanging valleys? State the evidences of former valley glaciers.

115. What is the condition of Greenland? What is a continental glacier or ice sheet? What is the condition in the interior? How does the ice sheet move? What is the condition at its margin? Describe nunataks. How are rock materials carried? What deposits are being made? State the evidence of former extension.

116. Describe the Antarctic continental glacier. What is the nature of the Great Ice Barrier? Why and how fast does it move?

117. What are the causes for icebergs? Why do they drift away? Why are they dangerous to navigation?

118. Where were there former great ice sheets? What evidence is there of former glaciation? Why are the deposits called glacial drift? Who proposed the theory of the Glacial Period? Why?

119. Give two different explanations of the Glacial Period. How did the ice advance? Why did it retreat? How long ago? How do we know how long ago?

120. What evidence is there of two glacial advances? What was the interglacial climate like?

121. What are the characteristics of terminal moraines? What are lobate moraines? Recessional moraines? Glacier kettles?

122. What is the cause of stratified drift? What are the following: outwash plains, valley trains, pitted plains, kames, eskers, sand plains?

123. What changes occurred as the ice melted from the area of the Great Lakes? What deposits were made? What evidence is there of change in level of the land? State the past and possible future effects.

124. What is the principal soil of the glacial region? Where is it found? How does it vary? Why? What are bowlder trains?

125. What are drumlins? How do they vary? Where found?

126. What proofs of glacial erosion are there? What were its effects on the valleys? Give illustrations.

127. What effects had the ice sheet on surface features of the land? On soil? On stream courses? What effect had the ice on lakes?

SUGGESTIONS. (1) If this has not already been begun in connection with the study of preceding chapters, start with this chapter to make a special study of all the pictures and the descriptions under them. Points not covered in the text are in many instances made clear in the titles to the pictures. Discuss the pictures; how well they show what they are intended to illustrate; other phenomena they show, etc. (2) Saw thin strips out of a cake of ice, support these at one end, put weights on the other end, keep in a place where the temperature is below freezing point, and note bending. What does this show? (3) Cut out a square block of ice and float it in water. Measure it to see what proportion is above water. Place the same block in salt water and measure the proportion above water. (4) Is your home in the glacial belt? If so, the class should make several field studies of glacial phenomena that are sure to occur near by. What effects of the glacier can you find in the neighborhood, either by a study of the topographic map or, better still, on a field excursion? Is the soil till or stratified drift? To answer this question look for cuts and study them carefully. If till, look for scratched stones. Try to find a number that have the typical flat-iron shape. Consider how such a shape may have developed. Make a collection of glacial pebbles for the school museum. If stratified, why are the pebbles rounded and the scratches gone? Look for glacial scratches on recently uncovered exposures of bed rock. What is their direction? Are the bowlders and pebbles all of the same kind as the bed rock? Do you know if any of them could have come from ledges in the direction in which the striæ point? Can you find moraines, kames, eskers, or drumlins? If so, study them, — their form and the nature of the material, and consider how well the descriptions in the book fit them.

Laboratory Exercises. Exercises XXXIII, XXVII, XXII in TARR and VON ENGELN's *Laboratory Manual for Physical and Commercial Geography,* The Macmillan Company, New York, provide for map studies of the various phenomena of glaciers and glaciation.

Reference Books. HOBBS, *Characteristics of Existing Glaciers*, The Macmillan Company, New York, 1911; WRIGHT, W. B., *The Quaternary Ice Age*, Macmillan & Company, London, 1914; TARR and MARTIN, *Alaskan Glacier Studies*, National Geographic Society, Washington, D. C., 1914; GILBERT, *Glaciers*, Vol. III, Harriman Alaska Expedition, 1904; ANTEVS, *The Recession of the Last Ice Sheet in New England*, American Geographical Society, New York, 1922; HUNTINGTON and VISHER, *Climatic Changes*, Yale University Press, New Haven, 1922; WRIGHT, *Ice Age in North America*, Bibliotheca Sacra, Oberlin, Ohio, 6th ed., 1920; TYNDALL, *Glaciers of the Alps*, Longmans, Green & Company, New York, 1896; NANSEN, *First Crossing of Greenland*, Longmans, Green & Company, New York, 1892; PEARY, *Northward over the Great Ice*, P. A. Stokes, New York, 1898; SCOTT, *Scott's Last Expedition*, 2 vols., Smith, Elder & Company, London, 1914; SHACKLETON, *The Heart of the Antarctic*, 2 vols., Lippincott Company, Philadelphia, 1909; BROWN, *Spitzbergen*, Seeley Service & Company, London, 1920; COLEMAN, *Ice Ages*, The Macmillan Company, New York, 1926.

CHAPTER IX

LAKES AND SWAMPS

LAKES

128. Origin of lake basins. A lake is a body of water occupying a closed depression, or basin, in the surface of the land. Lakes form parts of river systems, but their basins usually are not made

Fig. 296. — Ox-bow lake in the Connecticut Valley near Northampton, Massachusetts. Explain how this lake was cut off from the main stream channel.

by the rivers. In their action of valley cutting, rivers tend to establish regular slopes, and are capable of developing only small basins: for example, potholes (Figs. 70, 71) and ox-bow lakes (Figs. 96, 296). Rivers are not capable of creating deep basins. In deep

301

Photo by Jackson

Fig. 297. — Lake Moraine, Pikes Peak, Colorado. A lake formed when a small mountain valley was dammed by a terminal moraine ridge, deposited by a valley glacier, now completely melted.

basins water collects and stops the flow of currents. Hence there is no erosive action.

Most of the leading causes for lake basins have already been stated. (See pages 87, 98, 104, 132, 149, 170, 186, 215, 220, 229, 236, 240, 270, 285, 289, and 297.) Make a list of these causes. From it you will see that there are various reasons why dams may be made across stream valleys changing them to lake basins, and that the majority of lakes of intermediate size, those neither very great nor very small, are of this origin. By far the most important of these barriers are the glacial dams (Figs. 260, 287, 297, 298 and Plate VII) which have so recently interfered with the drainage of large areas of Europe and

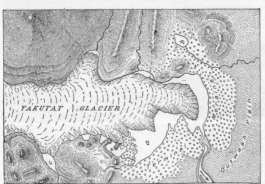

After Maddren

Fig. 298. — A glacier melting back from a terminal moraine that it deposited when it was longer and thicker. At (a) is a lake dammed by the moraine on the one side, by the ice on the other; this is exactly like the lake of the frontispiece. At (b) is a lake or pond due to the uneven dumping of the morainic deposits; this is like the lakes of Figs. 240, 281. At (c) and other points are marginal glacier lakes, like the Marjelen See of Switzerland. Explain these.

America. Many lakes, such as the Great Lakes, are due to a combination of two or more causes.

There are still other causes than those already stated for lakes and ponds. For example, beavers build dams of wood and mud across streams to make ponds for their homes and feeding grounds (Fig. 484). Man is now one of the most important agents in the making of lake basins. To supply water for power, for the use of cities, and for irrigation, men are making ponds and lakes in many parts of the earth (Fig. 299). The Ashokan reservoir in the Catskill Mountains of New York is a conspicuous exam-

Photo by U. S. Reclamation Service

Fig. 299. — A large lake made by a great man-built dam across the Salt River in Arizona, the Roosevelt Dam. The water is used for power and irrigation.

ple of a large artificial lake for a city water supply. Another such lake, also for New York City, was in 1924 formed at Gilboa in the same mountains.

For purposes of classification lake basins may be divided into three types: (*a*) those due to inequalities that the surface of the land had to begin with, or that developed by change of level; (*b*) those due to interruptions of the normal or regular excavation of valleys by streams through action of some other agency in forming a dam across a valley depression (Fig. 299) or eroding a basin in its bottom; and (*c*) those small basins due to the action of streams. Each of these types may be further subdivided,

Fig. 300. — A rock basin, cirque lake; Chasm Lake, Longs Peak, Rocky Mountain National Park. This lake has a solid bed-rock barrier across its lower side, in foreground. Notice the vertical cirque wall of the mountain at the head of the lake. The former glacier here "dug in its heel." Explain this; see Fig. 245a and c.

the second one (*b*) many times (Fig. 300); and even then close observation often reveals that a particular basin has had a complicated history and that several causes may each be in part responsible for its existence. Because of this the origin of lake basins is a fascinating study. If a lake occurs near the school, the class in physical geography should make an effort to determine the origin of its basin. Consider each of the possible causes listed to see which one or what combination best fits the observed conditions.

Summary. *Lake basins, though parts of river systems, are not generally formed by the rivers, but by some interference with drainage, usually by some kind of dam. Man is now making many lakes.*

Photo by Raffius

Fig. 301. — Pool of the Gem Geyser, Yellowstone National Park. The pool is full of heated water, so transparent that the photograph shows all details of the bottom of the basin. But the water contains dissolved mineral matter which, on precipitation, has built up a rim around the geyser mouth and made the basin.

129. Size and form of lakes. There is every gradation from mere pools (Fig. 301) to the largest of lakes. Some are very shallow; others have great depth; in many the bottom is below sea level; and the surface of some even, like Dead Sea (Fig. 302), is below sea level. The tables on page 306 give some facts regarding the size and depth of certain large lakes.[1]

[1] See "Reference Books" at end of chapter for other sources of statistical data in regard to lakes. The figures given in the tables can be only approximate in numerous instances and may be superseded as more accurate surveys are made and more complete sounding is done.

The Great Lakes

	Length, miles	Average width, miles	Maximum width, miles	Shore line, miles	Water area (including islands), square miles	Average depth, feet	Maximum depth sounded, feet	Surface above tide water, feet	Deepest point above tide water, feet	Water volume, cubic miles	Land area of watershed, square miles	Aggregate land and water area of watershed, square miles
Superior	420	70	160	1300	31,200	475	1008	602	−406	2800	51,600	82,800
Michigan	335	58	85	875	22,500	335	870	581	−289	1290	37,700	60,100
Huron	250	54	100	725	22,322	210	750	581	−169	650	31,700	55,700
Erie . .	250	40	58	590	9,960	70	210	573	363	130	22,700	32,700
Ontario	185	40	68	600	7,104	300	738	247	−491	410	21,600	28,900

Some of the Largest Lakes in the World

Name	Area (Square miles)	Elevation (Feet)	Greatest Depth (Feet)
Caspian	169,000	−85	3200
Superior	31,200	602	1008
Victoria Nyanza	26,000	3800	240
Aral	26,900	160	1200
Huron	22,322	581	750
Michigan	22,500	581	870
Nyassa	14,000	1500	2300
Tanganyika	12,650	2560	4188
Baikal	12,500	1700	4997
Great Bear	11,200	391	270+
Great Slave	10,100	520	650+
Chad	10,000+ variable	8–900	20
Erie	9,960	573	210
Winnipeg	9,400	900	80
Balkhash	8,600	780	170+
Ontario	7,104	247	738

The great majority of lakes are longer in one direction than in others. The explanation of this fact is that they occupy parts of river valleys, and, therefore, have a long axis in the direction of the valley. If the water rises into tributary valleys, the outline of the lake becomes irregular, as in the case of Lake Memphremagog, Vt. (Fig. 303). Because the basin which they occupy is round, some lakes are nearly circular. This is true, for instance, of crater lakes (Fig. 202), sink hole lakes (p. 98), and kettle hole ponds (Fig. 281).

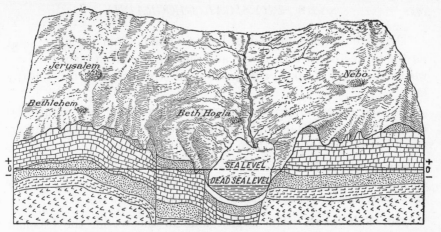

Fig. 302. — A diagram of the Dead Sea, a lake basin formed by the dropping down of a block of the rock crust of the earth between parallel faults; a trough, or rift lake. The nearly vertical lines through the strata are the fault breaks. The great lakes of East Africa are in basins made by the continuation of the same lines of break. The Lowlands of Scotland, the valley of the upper Rhine, and Death Valley in California are the result of similar down-faulting.

Fig. 303. — Lake Memphremagog, Vermont. A river valley made into a lake basin by a barrier of glacial drift in its lower course. Notice the irregularity of the shore line; each little bay marks the place where a tributary formerly entered the larger stream in the main valley. Compare with the straight outlines of Figs. 282, 310, glacially eroded basins. This illustrates also the effect of sinking of the land with penetration of sea water inland up river valleys, see Fig. 111.

Deltas built out into lakes help to make them irregular; and on the projecting deltas, towns and villages are often placed. Deltas at the head of lakes, where the inlet streams enter, shorten the lake.

On the other hand, waves tend to straighten lake shores by cutting back headlands and building beaches, which often shut in small bays, transforming them to ponds (Fig. 355).

Summary. *Lakes vary greatly in size, depth, and form; but most lakes are long, because they occupy parts of river valleys. Deltas on the sides of lakes make them irregular; but waves tend to straighten the shores.*

130. Salt lakes. The largest lake in the world, the Caspian Sea, is salt. It receives an enormous inflow of fresh water from the Volga and other rivers; but in that dry climate, evaporation is so rapid that the water does not fill the basin and overflow. Its surface is about 85 feet below sea level.

Dead Sea, whose surface is 1300 feet below sea level, is one of the saltest lakes in the world, being nearly a quarter salt, although entered by the fresh-water Jordan.

Great Salt Lake (Fig. 304) is about one fifth salt; and this amount so increases the density of the water that a man cannot sink in it. Where the water has risen over the low plain surrounding the lake and evaporated, the ground is incrusted with salt; and, by leading the water into shallow basins, and allowing it to evaporate, clean dry salt is obtained.

The explanation of salt lakes in dry climates is as follows: Streams carry salt, gypsum, carbonate of lime, and other mineral substances in solution (p. 74). Where lakes have outflows, either by surface overflow or underground seepage (*e.g.* Crater Lake), these substances are borne away by the outflowing water; but in arid climates evaporation is so great that the lakes cannot rise and overflow at the lowest points of the rims of their basins. Therefore, although the water is removed by evaporation, the mineral substances are left and the water grows gradually salter. If evaporation continues long enough, there will be so much salt that some of it must be deposited on the bottom. Great Salt Lake is not yet salt enough for this; but carbonate of lime is being deposited.

In the Great Salt Lake basin there are wonderfully perfect deltas, beaches, and wave-cut cliffs on the mountain sides, hundreds of feet

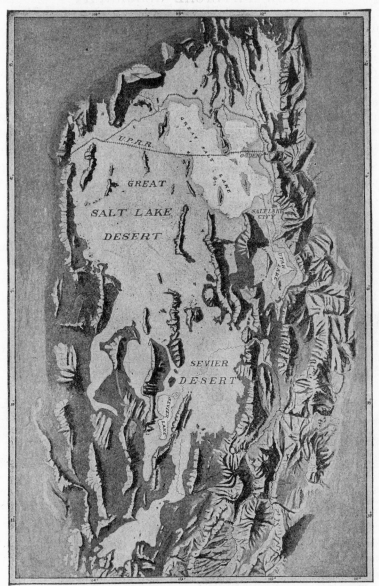

Fig. 304. — A map showing the extent of ancient Lake Bonneville, as indicated by the beaches and other shore lines on the surrounding mountain slopes. The present Great Salt Lake is shown occupying a part of the desert plain on the site of this extinct lake. That a railroad has built its line straight across Great Salt Lake by filling in an embankment, and by trestle work, indicates how shallow this lake is.

above the valley bottom. By tracing these shore lines (Fig. 305) it is found that a great fresh-water lake, now named Lake Bonneville, formerly filled this basin, overflowing into the Columbia. Its area was as great as that of Lake Huron, and on the site of Salt Lake City (Fig. 304) the water was over 1000 feet deep. Great Salt Lake is the shrunken descendant of Lake Bonneville, occupying a shallow depression on the lake-bottom plain. In other arid regions there is evidence of former periods of greater moisture. These moister periods, perhaps wholly due to diminished evaporation, probably coincide with the advances of the ice in the Glacial Period.

Summary. *Salt lakes, common in arid regions, are due to the fact that evaporation prevents the water from rising to a point of overflow, and, by remov-*

Photo by Pack

Fig. 305. — Beach terrace of ancient Lake Bonneville, Utah. The flat top of the terrace marks a former level of the lake and is the result of both erosion and deposit. See Fig. 351.

ing the water, leaves behind salt and other dissolved mineral substances. Higher level shore lines, now dry, around the basin of Great Salt Lake prove former periods of greater moisture.

131. Life history of lakes. Some lakes disappear by the rather quick and complete removal of the dam, as in the case of glacial lakes (Fig. 120, p. 132); others, like Lake Bonneville, disappear by evaporation. But most lakes have a different history, being destroyed partly by filling, partly by cutting down at the outlet (Fig. 306). Cutting at the outlet is usually slight, because the sediment has been filtered out in the quiet lake water, thus robbing the outlet stream of tools for erosion. This is illustrated by Niagara River, which, though emerging from Lake Erie with great volume, has been able to do little more than cut a shallow valley in the loose glacial drift (Fig. 461).

Every stream that enters a lake is bringing to it sediment which is helping to fill the basin; and the waves, winds, and rain wash add to this

Photo by Tour. and Health Res. Dept., N. Z.

Fig. 306. — Outlet down-cutting, Lake Ada, Dusky Sound, New Zealand. Although the overflow waters leave the lake in large volume they have accomplished little or nothing in eroding a channel in the rock rim of the basin. This is because the waters are so clear. Why do they lack rock particles to use as tools of erosion?

sediment supply. The finer rock fragments are carried out into the lake and strewn over its bottom (Fig. 121), while the coarser material is deposited near the shore, especially opposite the stream mouths, building deltas (Fig. 307).

As soon as part of a lake becomes shallow enough, vegetation commences to grow in the quiet water (Figs. 308, 475). On their death the remains of these plants — including lilies, reeds, cane, and sphagnum moss

— supply further material for lake filling.   Gradually the lake is replaced by a swampy plain (Fig. 309), the upper layers of which are made of vegetable remains.

Over this very level, swampy plain streams then meander, gradually building it higher by flood deposits until it becomes a dry-land plain. During its existence, a lake acts as a temporary base level, below which the incoming streams cannot cut.   But when a lake is filled, the outlet

Fig. 307. — The area of a lake being diminished by delta filling, the Silser See, Engadine valley, Switzerland.   Back of the delta is a hanging valley due to the lesser glacial erosion of a former small glacier that here joined a main glacier in the valley now occupied by the lake.   The modern stream has cut a gorge in the rock bottom of the hanging valley.

stream, being no longer robbed of its sediment, is able to cut more rapidly; and, as the outlet stream deepens its valley, opportunity is given for the streams on the lake plain to cut valleys.   Then the sediment with which the lake basin has been filled is slowly removed.   In the glacial belt there are many illustrations of partly or completely filled lakes and ponds; and among mountains every gradation in lake destruction is found, even to the point where all lake sediment has been removed.

Summary. *Lakes are normally removed by combined cutting at the outlet and filling with sediment; but down-cutting at the outlet is usually slight because the outflowing streams have little sediment. Plant growth, and the flood deposits of streams that flow over the swampy plain, accomplish the final stage. When filling is complete, the streams are able to cut into these lake beds and remove them.*

132. Importance of lakes. Lakes are highly important as resorts for people in search of rest and recreation. The beautiful

Photo by Yost

Fig. 308. — A pond in which vegetation is aiding in filling. Lilies are the farthest out, then low shrubs, then low trees, and finally the forest. "Bottomless Lake," near Jamesville, New York. See also Figs. 309 and 475.

scenery, cool climate, boating, bathing, and fishing attract thousands of people each summer to the Great Lakes, Lake George, Lake Champlain, and the lakes of the Adirondacks, to the lakes of New England, and to the Finger Lakes of central New York (Fig. 310) and the lakes in the Rocky and other mountains of the West.

Lakes have a decided influence on climate. In summer the water warms less rapidly than the land, and this cools the air over the lakes. In winter, on the other hand, when the land is frozen and snow-covered, deep lakes are open and the temperature is, therefore, above freezing point. This open water acts as a great stove, raising the temperature of the air, which winds carry to the neighboring land.

The lake water warms so slowly in spring that its presence chills the land near by and retards the buds of plants. It also helps to prevent late spring frosts. This is very important to delicate plants, like some of the fruits, which are greatly injured by frosts late in spring after the buds have appeared. The water, warmed in summer, also tends to prevent

Photo by Stoddard

Fig. 309. — A filled pond in the Adirondacks, showing the swamp plain and the stream crossing it. It is still too swampy for trees to grow. Valley of the Boreas, Adirondacks, New York.

early autumn frosts, and thus the growing season for delicate plants is prolonged. For these reasons lake shores are often the seat of important fruit-raising industries. One of the best vineyard regions of the United States is along the south shore of Lake Erie; and the peninsula of Ontario, between Lakes Erie, Ontario, and Huron, has so moderate a climate that peaches and tobacco are grown. A similar influence is felt quite generally along the Great Lakes.

Lakes are an important source of food fish. They are also a source of ice, which may be stored for use in summer. To freeze shallow lakes does not require great cold; but only few large, deep lakes freeze over completely. The reason for this is that, until a temperature of 39° is reached, fresh water becomes progressively denser and sinks. It is, therefore, necessary that the entire lake be cooled to 39° before the surface freezes. The settling of cold water in winter gives to the bottom of deep lakes a temperature around 39° throughout the year.

Lakes are also of great value in navigation. In early days the Great Lakes were of the highest service as pathways for the

Photo by Abrams

Fig. 310. — Canandaigua Lake, one of the Finger Lakes of central New York, noted for their scenic attractiveness. The lake basin is due to glacial erosion; note the steep beveled slopes extending in straight lines, due to ice scour. Contrast with form of Lake Memphremagog, Fig. 303.

explorers of the wilderness; to-day they are thronged with ships going in all directions. By this lake navigation and commerce the development of numerous great cities has been determined — Duluth, Milwaukee, Chicago, Detroit, Toledo, Cleveland, Buffalo, Toronto, and others (p. 499).

The building of railways into the interior of Africa is opening up the great African lakes to navigation. These lakes are already important factors in the development of tropical Africa, and were traversed by steamboats even at the time when it was necessary for all the machinery to be carried to them on the backs of men.

As storage basins and regulators of water supply, lakes serve still another important purpose. Whereas the volume of such rivers as the Mississippi varies with the rainfall, the lake-fed Niagara and St. Lawrence maintain a very uniform flow. As a deep current pours out of a narrow river valley into a lake at flood time, the flood waters spread out as a thin film over the lake surface raising the level but little because of the wide expanse to be covered. Hence the depth of the *narrow* outflow current is increased only slightly, and the flood waters that come so quickly into the lake require a long time to flow out (Fig. 306). It is because they store large quantities of water for steady supply that lakes and ponds are so useful for city water supply, for factories, and for irrigation. The fact that sediment settles in lakes makes them of further value in supplying clear drinking water, even though entered by very muddy streams. Indeed, artificial ponds or reservoirs are often made part of a city water supply for this very purpose of removing sediment.

Summary. *Lakes have decided influence on the climate of near-by land; they are important as resorts; they are a source of ice; they supply food fish; some are very useful for navigation; they act as storage reservoirs for a steady supply of water, and as settling basins for sediment.*

SWAMPS

133. Causes of swamps. A swamp is a damp place on the land, not ordinarily covered by standing water. The damp place is caused by some interference with the run-off of water, such as a gentle slope (Fig. 84), or the growth of swamp-loving vegetation. One of the most common causes of swamps is the filling of lakes, forming surfaces so level that rain water flows off very slowly. The water table (p. 96) is consequently very near the surface and in the damp soil swamp plants grow in abundance and help further to maintain the swampy conditions. During the stages of lake filling, swamps are formed on deltas, in bays, and, if the lake is small, even along the shores (Figs. 307, 308, 311).

In cool, damp, temperate climates, the most important swamp-producing plant is the sphagnum moss, which forms *peat bogs*. Sphagnum commonly grows out from the shores of small, shallow ponds, floating on the surface (Fig. 312), and, by the partial decay, detachment, and accumulation of its lower parts, causes a deposit of vegetable muck on the bottom. Eventually the sphagnum cover may extend entirely across a pond, with growing plants above and a thick, liquid mass of decaying vegetation below. It is then called a *quaking bog* (Fig. 312), because it trembles, or quakes, under the foot. For the animal or person that breaks through and sinks into the muck below, escape is difficult and often impossible. Very perfect remains of extinct animals, and even of

Photo by Rau

Fig. 311. — A swamp in the Mississippi Delta, near New Orleans, Louisiana. The shallow open water is the head of a bayou.

men, have been found in the peat bogs of Ireland, the decaying vegetation forming preserving acids.

Swampy or boggy places are common on hillsides where springs appear, encouraging the growth of sphagnum and other swamp plants. Sphagnum holds water like a sponge, and is thus able to grow some distance from the spring; in fact, it may even climb the hillside, making a *climbing bog*. In the damp climate of Ireland, climbing bogs sometimes become so heavy with water that they slide down the hillside, becoming "bursting bogs," by which both life and property have been destroyed.

The Arctic *tundra*, in winter a frozen, snow-covered desert, in summer becomes a vast swamp wherever there is soil (Fig. 116). The reason for this is that the melting frost makes the ground wet, as it does in all cold climates in spring. Every rain makes the tundra more swampy, partly because the frost prevents the water from soaking into the ground, and partly because it helps the frost to melt. In this swampy land mosquitoes develop in such numbers as to become a great pest (pp. 477, 555).

The overflow of rivers causes swamps in low places on flood plains, especially on the low ground just behind natural levees. These swamps are unfit for cultivation and are occupied by dense forests of cypress, black gum, and other swamp-loving trees (Fig. 311). Swamps are also found along the lower courses of rivers, where the river water is backed up by the tide and caused to overflow low land (Fig. 363). In the northern, coniferous forest region

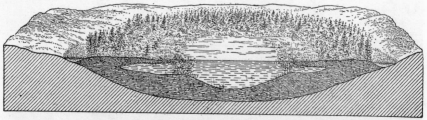

Fig. 312. — To show the growth of sphagnum moss, pond weeds, and other plants, out from the shore, forming a quaking bog. In time the moss from the sides will meet, completely covering the pond, and, by its decay, covering the entire bottom with muck.

that has been glaciated, bogs and swamps are known as *muskegs* (Fig. 313).

Coastal plains (p.122) commonly have so gentle a slope that the water cannot run off; and the drainage is further interfered with by the rank growth of vegetation which the water encourages. Such swamps are found on the coastal plain of Texas and in Florida, especially in the Everglades region. The famous Dismal Swamp on the coastal plain of Virginia and North Carolina is another illustration. By clearing off the vegetation, and cutting ditches for the water to run through, parts of Dismal Swamp have been drained.

Naturally there are few swamps in arid lands; but some are found near springs and on the river flood plains. There are also marshy places— *alkali flats* and *salines* (p. 146) — in which only a few species of plants can grow. At times of flood they may become shallow, muddy lakes, called *playas;* but, at other seasons, evaporation changes them to hardened mud, crusted over with alkali and salt. When wet, the deep, sticky mud often makes them quite impassable.

Swamps, or marshes, are also found on the seacoast (pp. 379, 380).

Summary. *Swamps are caused during the filling of lakes, one form of swamp being the peat bog, formed by the growth of sphagnum moss. Sphagnum also makes swampy places around springs, and climbing bogs on hillsides. The melting of frost in summer causes the Arctic tundra to be swampy wherever there is soil. Swamps also occur along rivers and on level coastal plains. In arid lands, where evaporation causes a deposit of salt or alkali, there are swampy tracts, called alkali flats and salines.*

Photo by Shaub

Fig. 313. — Muskeg near Trout River, Province of Quebec, Labrador peninsula, Canada.

134. Effects of swamps. Malaria and, in tropical regions, yellow fever, both transmitted by mosquitoes which breed in the water, make swampy areas unhealthful unless the mosquitoes are exterminated. In tropical regions, as along the narrow coastal plain of the central African coast, and in Central America, fever is so common that white men may contract it on a journey across the level, damp lowland. Because of malaria, parts of Italy have become quite deserted. In the Panama Canal Zone, on the other hand, mosquitoes and sources of infection have been brought so completely under control that there is now practically no danger cf becoming ill of fever in that area, which was formerly one of the most unhealthful places in the world.

Swampy conditions unfit land for most agricultural purposes, rice growing being a notable exception (Fig. 496); but, when drained, the rich, black soil is very productive. For this reason, as well as for the sake of health, swamp lands are being drained, where possible. This has been done much more extensively in Europe than in America, where land is less valuable. The most extensive drainage has been carried on in the Netherlands, where the low, swampy delta of the Rhine (Fig. 33), and even part of the shallow sea bot-

Fig. 314. — At a peat bog in Ireland. The bog is in the distance. After being dug, the square pieces of peat are piled up to dry for a time, then loaded in carts to be transported to the homes of the users.

tom, have been protected by dikes, and drained by pumping. About one half of the Netherlands is reclaimed land, a large part of it being below sea level.

The salines of arid lands have valuable stores of salt; and the peat bogs of cool temperate climates are important sources of fuel. Coal and wood are so abundant in America that this reserve of fuel is scarcely touched; but in northern Europe it is much used, being cut out with spades (Fig. 314) and dried and stored for winter. Coal beds are similar swamp deposits, made ages ago, and covered and preserved beneath thick beds of sediment.

Summary. *Swamps are unhealthful because of transmission of disease infections by mosquitoes that breed there. Swamp lands are of little value unless drained; but the salines supply salt, and the peat bogs, fuel. Coal is made of swampy deposits, slowly changed to mineral and preserved beneath beds of sediment.*

TOPICAL OUTLINE, QUESTIONS, AND SUGGESTIONS

TOPICAL OUTLINE. 128. **Origin of lake basins.** Definition; impossibility of formation of large basins by rivers; causes for lakes; most important cause; combination of causes; effect of beavers; of man; classification of lakes.

129. **Size and form of lakes.** Variation in size; in depth; long lakes; irregular lakes; circular lakes; effect of deltas; effect of waves.

130. **Salt lakes.** (*a*) Instances: Caspian Sea; Dead Sea; Great Salt Lake. (*b*) Cause: source of salt; failure to overflow; increasing saltness. (*c*) Former moist periods: shore lines; Lake Bonneville; relation to Glacial Period.

131. **Life history of lakes.** Exceptional causes for removal; cutting at outlet; slight importance; sources of sediment; places of deposit; effect of vegetation; change to dry land; removal of lake beds.

132. **Importance of lakes.** (*a*) Summer resorts: reason; instances. (*b*) Climate: summer influence; winter; spring; autumn; effect on vegetation; illustrations. (*c*) Food fish. (*d*) Freezing: ice; reason why deep lakes do not freeze. (*e*) Navigation: Great Lakes; cities; African lakes. (*f*) Water supply: effect on floods; storage of water; settling of sediment.

133. **Causes of swamps.** (*a*) Definition. (*b*) Lake swamps; filled lakes; lake shore swamps. (*c*) Peat bogs: sphagnum; quaking bogs; animal remains. (*d*) Hillside swamps: springs; climbing bogs; bursting bogs. (*e*) Tundra swamps: in winter; in summer. (*f*) River swamps: flood plains; in lower course; muskegs. (*g*) Coastal plain swamps: cause; illustrations; drainage. (*h*) Arid land swamps: scarcity; alkali flats; salines; playas. (*i*) Seashore marshes.

134. **Effects of swamps.** Effect on health; Panama Canal Zone; effect on cultivation; drained swamps; Netherlands; supply of salt; of peat; origin of coal.

QUESTIONS. Section 128. Why is it not possible for rivers to excavate large basins? State the causes for lake basins. How may lake basins be classified?

129. How do lakes vary in size and depth? In form? Why? What effects have deltas? Waves?

130. What is the condition of Caspian Sea? Dead Sea? Great Salt Lake? What causes salt lakes? Describe Lake Bonneville.

131. What happens at the outlet of most lakes? With what materials are lakes filled? What is the last stage in the life history of lakes?

132. Why are lakes favorite summer resorts? How does the lake water influence climate? What effects has this on vegetation? Why do deep lakes not freeze over quickly? Give illustrations of the value of lakes in navigation. Explain why lakes are so effective as regulators of the flow of outlet rivers. What effect have lakes on water supply?

133. What is a swamp? In what ways are swamps associated with lakes? What is the relation of lakes and swamps to the water table? What are peat bogs? Quaking bogs? Climbing bogs? Why is the tundra swampy in summer? Where, near rivers, do swamps occur? Muskegs? Why are swamps common on coastal plains? Give illustrations. What are alkali flats and salines? Play&s?

134. What effect have swamps on health?   How has the Panama Canal Zone been made healthful?   What effect have swamps on agriculture?   How may they be made valuable?   What fuel is supplied from swamps?   What is the origin of coal?

SUGGESTIONS.   (1) Make a valley in clay and pour water into it.   It is now a stream valley.   Place a dam across it and make a miniature lake.   What is its shape?   Make one or two tributary valleys into which the water rises.   What is the shape then?   Wash sediment into the lake by sprinkling the sides with a watering pot.   Notice the growth of deltas.   The lake may even be filled. (2) In a very deep jar of water, take the temperature at the top and bottom. Pound up ice and put it into the jar, and when it has all melted, again take the temperature at the top and the bottom.   Why has the bottom water this temperature?   Continue putting in ice until the temperature at the surface is 36°. What is the temperature at the bottom then?   (3) Place a large dish of warm water in a cold room.   Note the temperature of the air in the room.   As the thermometer is brought near the water does the temperature change?   Try the same experiment with a large dish of ice-cold water in a warm room.   (4) If your home is near a lake, study it.   Can you find out what caused it?   Does the outlet stream flow in a deep or shallow valley?   Are there any deltas?   Where?   Any' signs of filling by wave action?   Are there any swamps?   What kinds of plants grow on the shallow lake bottom and shore?   (5) Are there any swamps near your home?   What is their cause?   Are any of them partly or wholly drained?   How was it done?   What effect has the draining had?   (6) Make three surfaces of clay: (*a*) a steep slope, (*b*) a plain, (*c*) a plain with vegetation (made by putting pieces of grass in it).   Sprinkle with water.   Which remains wet longest?   Why?   Which dries first?   (7) Have a discussion in class as to reasons why "bottomless" lakes are impossible.

Laboratory Exercises.   Exercises XXXII, XXXIII, and XXXV in TARR and VON ENGELN's *Laboratory Manual of Physical and Commercial Geography*, The Macmillan Company, New York, will supplement the study of this chapter.

Reference Books.   TARR and MARTIN, *College Physiography*, The Macmillan Company, 1914, Chap. X, at end of which is bibliography of technical papers on lakes and swamps.   Petermann's Mitteilungen, Erganzungsheft, Nr. 185, HALB-FUSS, *Die Seen der Erde*, Justus Perthes, Gotha, 1922, contains a comprehensive tabular presentation of the known facts regarding all lakes of significant size in the world.

CHAPTER X

THE OCEAN

135. Importance of the ocean. We have already learned (p. 21) that the ocean is of importance to man in many ways. It supplies vapor for rain, and moderates the climate of the lands; it is a source of food and other products that man needs; and it is, aside from the air, the one free and connected highway of transportation to all quarters of the globe.

THE OCEAN BOTTOM

136. Oceanography. Oceanography is the study of the oceans, their waters and their bottoms. For carrying on this study there have been numerous exploring expeditions, the most important being that of the British ship *Challenger*, which spent four years in studying the Atlantic, Pacific, Indian, and Southern Oceans. One important reason for the early study of the ocean was to deter-

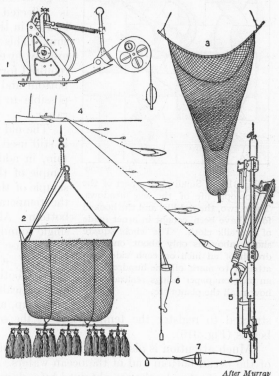

After Murray

Fig. 315. — Instruments used in exploring the oceans. (1) Lucas automatic sounding apparatus, using piano wire line. (2) Deep sea dredge used by the *Challenger*, the fringes entangle small objects. (3) Otter trawl net used as in (4). (5) Water bottle and thermometer that reverse on striking bottom. Reversing closes and locks the water bottle and causes the temperature on the thermometer to register. (6 and 7) Tow-net used vertically and horizontally.

323

mine its depth and the nature of its bottom in order to discover feasible routes for submarine cables. Such cables now cross the oceans in many directions.

Depths were formerly determined by lowering a weighted line to the bottom. Even after automatic machinery had been devised to let out and take in the line this was a slow process. It took an hour to get one sounding in water 15,000 feet deep. Now soundings are made almost instantaneously in any depth by the Hayes sonic apparatus. This is a water-telephone arrangement. Vibrations set up in the water at the stern of the ship cause a sound wave, traveling at the rate of 4840 feet per second, to go to the ocean bed from which it is reflected back to a hydrophone located in the water at the bow of the ship. This phone automatically and exactly, by electricity, records the time required for the wave to travel to the bottom and back, and thus makes it possible to compute the depth accurately.

The old method of lowering a line is still used where it is desired to obtain, in addition to the depth, (a) a sample of the bottom material, (b) a sample of the water at the bottom, (c) the temperature of the water at the bottom. All these can be got in a single sounding. A little cup smeared with grease picks up some of the bottom stuff; a strong, metal water bottle open at both ends, going down, closes automatically as the line begins to be pulled up, and thermometers are constructed to register the temperature at the second the upward motion begins (Fig. 315).

After Murray

Fig. 316. — Small plants, part of the microscopic life of the sea meadows. These two, the rod-like and the hooked form, have been caught in a net made of fine silk cloth. The whole square shown above is only about one-hundredth of an inch on each side. An attempt to mark off one-hundredth of an inch on paper brings realization of how small the plants are.

Much attention is also given to the study of the animal and plant life of the ocean bottom and of the ocean waters. Specimens of the animals from the greater depths are obtained by a deep-sea dredge, or trawl, that consists of an iron frame several feet in length with a long bag net attached. This trawl is dragged over the bottom, animals in its path being scooped up by the frame and gathered in the bag. Many weird creatures are thus obtained. Nets are towed along horizontally at intermediate depths; some of them are made of very fine-meshed silk cloth to capture organisms of microscopic size (Fig. 316). Such forms are prepared for study by means of a centrifuge, an apparatus that by very high speed of rotation concentrates all the microscopic life naturally existing in a pint of water within the volume of a single drop, which can then be put under the microscope (see p. 351).

Summary. *For a study of the ocean, or oceanography, there have been numerous government exploring expeditions, one of whose objects has been to*

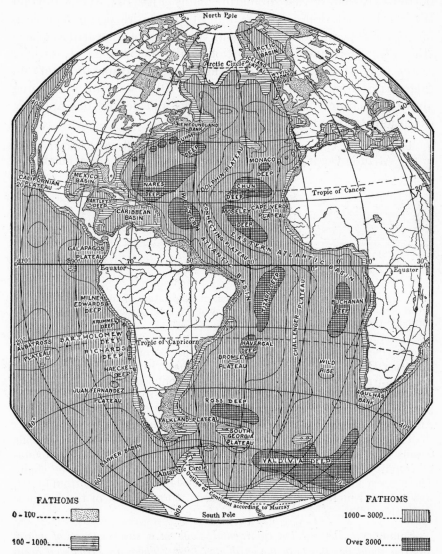

Fig. 317. — The depths of the Atlantic in fathoms (a fathom is six feet). The mid-Atlantic ridge is called Dolphin, Connecting, and Challenger plateaus. Note the continental shelves, dotted.

determine the best routes for cables. In the study of the ocean bottom the depth, nature of the water, nature of the bottom, temperature, and kind of animal life are usually determined.

137. Ocean basins. Exploration has shown that the ocean bottoms are mainly vast submarine plains (Figs. 104, 317). Beyond the continental slopes (p. 32) almost the entire ocean floor is a monotonous plain, occupying about two thirds of the earth's surface (Fig. 35). Here and there a portion is sunk below the rest, forming a *deep* (Fig. 317); and here and there volcanic peaks or mountain ridges rise from the ocean floor (Fig. 401), sometimes reaching above the surface. But these elevations and depressions are only exceptions to the general levelness.

The Nares deep, not far from Porto Rico, is the deepest known point in the Atlantic Ocean, 27,972 feet (Fig. 317). There are a number of

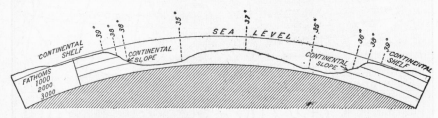

Fig. 318. — Diagram to show the conditions of temperature and depth in the Atlantic. Ocean depth and width of the continental shelf are greatly exaggerated. The raised portion in the center represents the mid-Atlantic ridge.

volcanic peaks in the Atlantic, such as the Bermudas, the Azores, the Canaries, Cape Verde Islands, and St. Helena. In the mid-Atlantic there is a low, irregular elevation, or a series of submarine plateaus (Fig. 317), sometimes called the *mid-Atlantic ridge* (Fig. 318). There are deeps on both sides of it. This upraised portion extends the whole length of the Atlantic, usually several thousand feet beneath the surface.

There are hundreds of volcanic peaks in the open Indian and Pacific oceans (Fig. 401), usually in chains along the crests of submarine mountain uplifts, — for example, the Hawaiian chain and the Ladrone chain. The deepest known point in any ocean, 32,644 feet with no bottom found, was obtained in 1924 in the Pacific Ocean, 50 miles east of the Japanese coast (Fig. 223).

Summary. *Beyond the continental slope is a vast expanse of plain, covering about two thirds of the earth's surface. There are occasional deeps sunk below its general level, and volcanic cones and mountain ridges rising above it.*

138. Deposits on the ocean bottom. (A) *Rock fragments.* The wind, rain, rivers, and waves drag fragments from the land into the sea (Fig. 41). Most of this sediment settles in the quiet water near the coast; but currents drift some of the finer particles out to sea as far as to the edge of the continental shelf.

This sediment fills depressions and tends to smooth over the irregularities of the continental shelf; and, by its accumulation, it makes beds of sedimentary rock, coarsest near the coast (p. 46). Remains of ocean animals also accumulate on the bottom and add to the deposit of sediment, being preserved in the rocks as fossils (Fig. 319).

Probably little or no sedimentary waste from the continents is deposited on the deep-sea floor beyond the edge of the continental platforms. This is because the ocean water has various salts dissolved in it (p. 332) making it an electrolytic solution. The effect of such a solution is to cause the minute clay particles, comprising the finest sediments, that would be buoyed up for long periods and carried far in fresh water, to collect in aggregates while in suspension, that is, to flocculate; and these denser lumps quickly sink to the bottom. This fact may easily be verified by experiment. Dissolve a teaspoonful of ordinary salt (NaCl) in a glass of water. Into that glass and into another glass containing fresh water place equal amounts of fine clay soil. Shake both up thoroughly and place on a shelf in the light. The salt water will become clear in a short time; the fresh water may remain turbid for a long period. This is important for it shows that the materials of the continents, despite weathering and erosion, transportation by rivers and deposition in the sea, are never lost to them. The waste accumulates on the continental shelves and is later uplifted to form a coastal plain, or folded up into mountains, in both cases becoming again a part of the dry land. On the other hand, no rocks have ever been discovered in continental masses that had a deep-sea origin. Such deep-sea deposits do, however, occur in a few places on oceanic islands, notably in Barbados.

Summary. *Near the continents the ocean bottom is covered with layers of rock fragments derived from the land.*

(B) *Ocean-bottom oozes.* As little or no sedimentary material is dragged far out to sea, the contribution of animal remains to the deposits of the ocean bottoms far exceeds that of rock waste. More than a third of the ocean bottom is covered with an ooze, composed mainly of animal and plant remains. This deposit contains a small percentage of rock fragments, especially pieces of volcanic ash and pumice that, on becoming water-logged, have settled to the

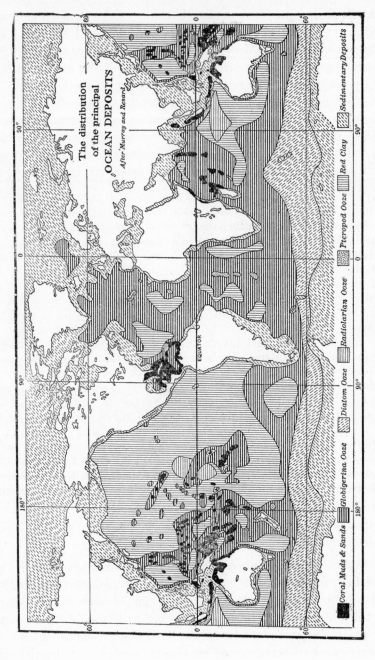

Fig. 319. — Map showing distribution of principal ocean deposits. See Fig. 320. It would be more correct to leave large areas of the polar seas, away from the continental shores, blank on the map because of lack of observations.

The distribution
of the principal
OCEAN DEPOSITS
After Murray and Renard

Coral Muds & Sands   Globigerina Ooze   Diatom Ooze   Radiolarian Ooze   Pteropod Ooze   Red Clay   Sedimentary Deposits

bottom. The ocean-bottom ooze is made partly of organisms that live on the bottom, but mainly of the shells of microscopic organisms that live in vast numbers in the surface waters and, on dying, settle to the bottom.

The ocean-bottom ooze is given different names according to the organisms that are most abundant. Thus a large part of the ocean-bottom deposit is called *globigerina ooze* (Fig. 320), because of the abundance of microscopic Globigerina (Fig. 321). Chalk is a similar ooze deposited on

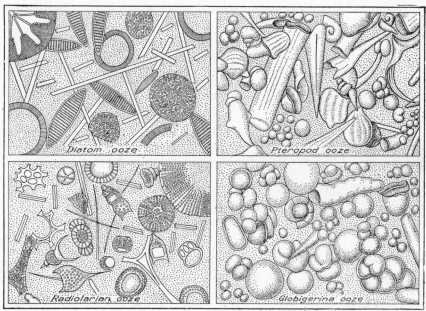

After Johnstone

Fig. 320. — Much magnified samples of the various types of deep-sea oozes.

the bottom of ancient seas. *Diatom ooze* is made of siliceous parts of microscopic diatom plants which thrive especially in the cold waters of the Southern Ocean. *Radiolaria*, similarly, are silica-secreting animals of microscopic size abundant in the Pacific and Indian Oceans. *Pteropod ooze* is from forms like the globigerina flourishing in tropical seas.

Summary. *Far from land, where there is little rock waste, the ocean bottom is covered with globigerina and other oozes, made largely of the remains of organisms, mostly microscopic surface forms.*

(C) *Red clay.* The shells that sink to make globigerina ooze are composed of carbonate of lime, but contain a very small percentage of other substances, such as iron and silica. In the very deep ocean water (12,000 to 15,000 feet or more), which contains much carbon dioxide, these limy shells are dissolved; but the iron, silica, etc., are not so readily soluble, and they pass on to the bottom forming a clay, colored red by iron oxide. It is now generally held that much, also, of the red clay is derived from the decomposition of fine particles of pumice originally carried far out to sea by the winds (p. 218) after a volcanic explosion and then slowly settling down to the bottom of the sea and undergoing chemical alteration to the clay form. More than a third of the ocean bottom is covered with this red clay, whose rate of deposit must be very slow since it is formed of minute particles of volcanic dust and of the very small insoluble portion of shells that are themselves microscopic.

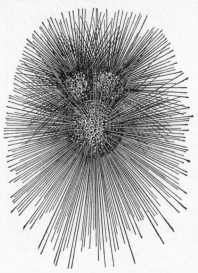

From the Challenger Reports

Fig. 321. — A living specimen of Globigerina from the ocean surface, greatly magnified.

Other facts further prove that the red clay is formed with wonderful slowness. Scattered through it are bits of meteoric iron, the teeth of sharks, and the ear bones of whales. There are not many whales or sharks in one place, nor are many meteorites falling. If the red clay were not accumulating very slowly, those objects would be so deeply covered that a small dredge would rarely find any; yet deep-sea dredging often brings them to the surface.

Summary. *Red clay covers the deeper parts of the ocean bottom, that is, over one third of the entire ocean floor. It is a very slowly forming deposit, made of decomposed volcanic dust and of the insoluble remnants of microscopic shells that have been dissolved in the deep-sea water.*

139. Land and ocean-bottom topography. There are three important reasons why the ocean bottom is far more regular than the land surface (p. 30). (1) While mountain folding and volcanic action cause irregularities both on land and ocean bottom, these forces seem to have acted much less frequently in the sea than on the land. (2) Erosion sculptures the land into hills and valleys; but the ocean water protects the bottom from erosive action.

(3) Sediment washed from the lands, and the settling of organisms to the bottom, tend to smooth the sea floor.

Because of these facts, if a sediment-smoothed, near-shore, sea-bottom plain is raised into the air, it is soon carved by erosion into a series of hills and valleys; but if an irregular, hilly land is sunk beneath the sea, it is soon smoothed over by a blanket of sediment (p. 118). There is a striking difference between the widespread smoothness of ocean-bottom plains and the pleasing irregularity of the lands. There are, however, places where fault movements have caused the plain of the ocean floor to be interrupted by cliffs.

Summary. *The ocean bottom is far smoother than the lands because of (1) less mountain folding and volcanic action; (2) absence of erosion; and (3) widespread deposit of sediment in the near-shore areas and of organic remains and volcanic dust on the deep-sea floor.*

THE OCEAN WATER

140. Surface of the sea. Elevations on the land are measured from *sea level* (commonly expressed by the abbreviation, A. T., above tide), by which is meant the approach to a spherical form which the water assumes under the pull of gravity (Figs. 4, 6; p. 15). The level of the sea is not perfectly in accord with the spherical form of the earth; for the curved water surface is distorted a little by the attraction of the continents, slightly raising its level near the coast. Tides, winds, and storms (p. 449) cause local disturbances of sea level; but, as soon as the disturbing cause has passed, gravity draws the water back to its former level.

There are two causes which are slowly operating to change the level of the sea. The less important of these is the deposit of sediment, which tends slowly to raise sea level. It would take long periods of time for this to produce a great effect, for there is a vast amount of water to be raised. Even if all of North America above sea level were put into the Atlantic, the surface of the ocean would not be raised many feet. The second cause for change in level is movement of the ocean bottoms. There is good reason for considering that, during past ages, the ocean basins have been slowly growing deeper. In certain areas of the ocean floor, samples of the bottom, up to two feet in thickness, obtained with a tube, show red clay overlying globigerina ooze. The effect of such a movement would be gradually to withdraw the waters from the lands. During the Glacial Period the withdrawal of great quantities of water from the sea to form the vast ice sheets presumably caused a temporary lowering of the sea level amounting to a number of feet.

Summary. *Sea level is slightly disturbed by the attraction of the continents; by tides; locally, and for short times, by winds and storms; and very slowly by (1) the deposit of sediment in the oceans and (2) the sinking of the ocean bottoms.*

141. Composition of sea water. Every one is familiar with the saltness of the sea. Probably salt and other mineral substances were held in solution when the oceans first gathered, but certainly some is being added every day. The vapor that rises from the ocean does not remove these mineral substances; but when it falls on the land as rain, it begins to wash more dissolved mineral matter into the sea (p. 74). It would seem, therefore, that the ocean must be growing steadily salter.

If it is assumed that all the salt in the oceans has been derived from the land and that it was brought in dissolved form by the river waters, then there is available a means for calculating, at least approximately, the age of the earth *as it exists at present.* The total volume of the ocean waters has been figured on the basis of their area and depths. The total quantity of salt in them can, therefore, be determined. The amount of salt brought to the seas each year by the rivers is also quite nearly known. Salt is a compound of sodium and chlorine. Dividing the number (14,130,000,-000,000,000 tons) representing the total sodium in the sea by the number (158,357,000 tons) brought in yearly gives, then, approximately 89,222,900 years required to furnish the oceans with the salt they now contain. Allowances made for the fact that neither the dividend nor the divisor is exactly correct show that the true quotient may be any figure between 70 million and 100 million years. The figures do make clear that geological time is very long. The age of some of the rocks of the lithosphere, as indicated by their history of radio-activity, is 1100 million years!

About three and a half per cent of ocean water is dissolved mineral matter, more than three quarters of which is common salt. Magnesium chloride and magnesium, calcium, and potassium sulphates are also present; and, in very small quantities, there are many other substances, even including compounds of gold and silver. If all the salt of the oceans could be removed, it would make a layer about 400 feet thick over the earth. In many places where the climate is dry, salt is obtained by evaporating sea water; and many salt beds, like that in central New York, were formed in past ages by the evaporation of the water in arms of the sea, cut off as the Caspian is to-day.

Carbonate of lime, though present in very small quantities,

is another important mineral substance in sea water. Many ocean animals, such as corals and shell-fish, use it in the growth of their shells and skeletons. On the death of the animals these hard parts have accumulated in beds of limestone which, raised to form land, are now used in building, smelting iron, and making lime and cement.

Some air is mixed with all ocean water, being present even on the ocean bottom, where it is brought by slowly moving currents. A few sea animals, such as the seals and whales, come to the surface to breathe; but the great majority require so little oxygen that they are able to obtain what they need from the air that is mixed with the sea water. Without it most of the ocean animals could not live.

Summary. *Salt and other mineral substances, including carbonate of lime, of which shells are made, are being constantly washed from the land into the sea. Air mixed with the water supplies the oxygen which makes most of the animal life of the ocean possible.*

142. Density and pressure of sea water. Salt water is heavier, or has a greater density, than fresh water. Calling fresh water 1, the average density of ocean water at the surface is about 1.026. The density is less than the average in the rainy tropical belt, and also near the mouths of great rivers, where a large amount of fresh water is added. It is greater than the average where there is much evaporation, as in the dry trade-wind belts, and in seas enclosed by warm, arid lands, like the Red and Mediterranean seas.

There is an enormous pressure on the bottom of deep oceans. At the depth of a mile every square inch bears a weight of over a ton of water, and the pressure on the bottom of the notable deeps (Fig. 317) approaches six tons to every square inch. One might expect that so great a weight of water would crush the animals on the ocean bottom; but it produces no more effect on them than does the weight of air (about 15 pounds to the square inch) which our bodies bear.

The reason why this great pressure is not felt is that it affects all parts of the body, both within and without. When deep-sea fish are brought to the surface, however, and the pressure from outside is reduced, that from within opens cracks in their bodies and often causes their eyes to protrude. On the other hand, substances like wood or cork having a cellular structure are "imploded" (the opposite of exploded) by the pressure of the great depths of the sea. Some pieces of soft wood sent down with a dredge on the *Challenger* expedition, came up so much compressed and so dense that they sank as if they were bricks when placed in a tub of water.

Water, unlike air, is not much compressed, even under the great load that weighs down on the bottom layers. Therefore its density at the bottom does not differ greatly from that at the surface. If it were much compressed, as air is, it might become so dense that objects could not sink through it to the bottom. They would then float around in the layer where the water had the same density they had.

Summary. *Salt water is denser than fresh water, but its density varies somewhat. There is an enormous pressure on the ocean bottom, but, as water is not much compressed under pressure, its density is not greatly increased at the bottom. Anything that will sink in a tumbler of water will also sink to the bottom of the deepest ocean.*

143. Color and light. Sunlight illuminates the upper layers of the sea and reaches to the bottom of shallow water. The beautiful blue of the open ocean is partly due to the reflection of the color of the sky, but chiefly to the same cause that makes the sky blue (p. 400). Sunlight is made of waves of many colors, and in their passage through the water they are separated, or scattered, some of them (the indigo and blue) being reflected back, giving the water its color. Near the shore, where there is more sediment, and in the higher latitudes where there is more microscopic life in the surface waters (p. 351), the green waves are reflected, giving the water its green color. The yellow water near the mouth of the Yellow River of China is colored by the mud that the river brings (Fig. 143); the color of the Red Sea is due to minute reddish organisms that float in it. The deep indigo blue seen in the tropics and in the Gulf Stream is partly due to the purity of the water; near coral islands this color is accentuated, due probably to calcium carbonate in solution.

No sunlight penetrates to the bottom of the deep sea, which, except for phosphorescence, is darker than the darkest night. Some of the deep-sea fish are blind; but many have eyes, and many are brilliantly colored. These eyes and colors are doubtless of use because of the phosphorescent glow, like that of the firefly, that many deep-sea animals emit. Indeed, some of the fish have feelers, phosphorescent on the end, which have been called deep-sea lanterns. Phosphorescence is also emitted by many surface animals, and a boat often leaves behind it a glowing trail of light, made by the multitude of animalculæ that its passage has disturbed.

Summary. *The color of the sea is due to the scattering of the waves that compose white light, and the reflection of some of them, such as green, blue, or indigo. The longer wave lengths, yellow and red, are reflected where*

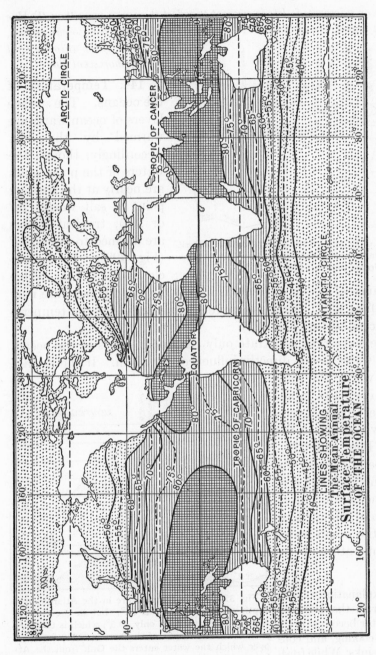

Fig. 322. — Ocean-surface temperature. The effect of the land and of ocean currents makes the temperature lines of the northern ocean far more irregular than those in the southern hemisphere. On an outline map of the world make a sketch map similar to this. Draw a line through the middle of the belt of 80° temperature. This line will be the heat equator of the oceans. Does it lie, on the average, north or south of the world equator? See p. 405 and Figs. 421, 422.

sediments or microscopic life is present to reflect them even more than the blue and green waves are reflected. No sunlight reaches the deep ocean bottom, but some of the animals emit a phosphorescent glow.

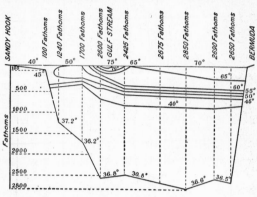

Fig. 323. — Section of the ocean from New York to Bermuda, showing the temperature at various depths. Notice the Gulf Stream.

144. Temperature of the oceans. The surface layers of ocean water are warmed by the sun. Accordingly, though the waters of the polar zones are nearly at the freezing point of salt water (28° or 29°), tropical waters are warmed to 80° or 85° (Fig. 322). In the enclosed Red Sea, where the entrance of cooler currents is impossible, the temperature may rise to 90° or 95°. Oceans currents greatly influence the temperature of ocean water (Fig. 323).

As the sun's rays penetrate only the upper layers of the ocean, deep-sea water is not directly influenced by them. If the surface water is warm, the temperature decreases rapidly in the upper layers, then slowly down to the bottom (Figs. 318, 323). Everywhere, even in the torrid zone, the temperature of the ocean bottom is low; and about four fifths of the ocean water has a temperature of less than 40°.

The explanation of the cold water in the deep sea is that water becomes more dense on cooling, and consequently sinks. While fresh water ceases sinking at 39°

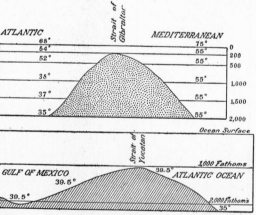

Fig. 324. — The temperature in the Atlantic at a depth of 2000 fathoms is 35°; but in the Gulf of Mexico, at that depth, only 39.5°, which is the temperature at the depth of the barrier (1000 fathoms) over which the water enters the Gulf from the Atlantic. (See Fig. 104.) The same relations prevail in the Mediterranean.

(p. 315), salt water continues to increase in density, and, therefore, to sink, almost until its freezing point is reached. For this reason ocean-bottom water is much colder than that on the bottom of lakes; it may, in fact, be as low as 29°. The settling of cold water in the frigid and cold temperate zones starts a slow circulation along the ocean bottom toward the warm belt, where there is a slow rising. It is this circulation that supplies deep-sea animals with the air they need for breathing.

One of the best proofs of this slow circulation is furnished by such seas as the Gulf of Mexico and the Mediterranean, which are partly shut off from the open ocean. In these seas the decrease in temperature continues down to the level of the barrier, but no lower, because the coldest water that can creep into them is that at the level of the barrier (Fig. 324). On the other hand, coldness of the bottom waters is not a condition that results simply because of depth. In the great age (p. 332) of the oceans (1) escape of heat from the interior of the earth and (2) warming by conduction from the surface of the ocean would have heated the tropical waters to the bottom if such circulation did not exist.

Summary. *The temperature of the surface water of the ocean in general varies with latitude; but settling of cold water, causing a slow circulation, makes the deep sea everywhere cold. Enclosed sea bottoms have the same temperature as that of the open ocean at the level of the barrier.*

MOVEMENTS OF THE OCEAN WATER

145. Wind waves. Blowing on the surface of a dish of water causes small waves. These are similar to the large waves raised on the ocean by the friction of winds that blow over its surface. The water itself does not advance with the wave, but moves up and down, with a slight forward and backward movement. It is the *form* of the wave that advances, as a wave may be made to pass through a rope by shaking it vigorously. Therefore a boat, instead of moving forward, rises and falls as each wave passes under it; but it is also carried forward and backward a little.

Some of the great ocean waves, raised during heavy gales, have a length of 500 feet, measured horizontally from the top or *crest* of one wave to the crest of the next, and a height of from 30 to 50 feet, measured vertically from the crest to the depression, or *trough*, between two waves. Each crest moves forward at the rate of 30 to 40 miles per hour—as fast as a passenger train. Then the sea presents a wild sight, as the great waves come down upon a ship, their crests broken and whitened by the fierce wind. The wind mixes much air with the ocean water in the foam and spray of these white crests, or *whitecaps*. Such waves sometimes dash over the decks of ships, carrying all loose objects along, and even tearing away massive wood and iron work.

Waves often appear when no wind is blowing, and even when the sea is smooth and glassy. They were formed in some place where the wind was high, and have traveled far beyond their place of origin. Such waves are known as *rollers,* or *ground swell.* Because waves travel so far, no part of the open ocean is ever entirely free from some form of wave or swell (Fig. 230).

As stated, water particles in the waves of the open sea move up and down in circular or slightly elliptical orbits (Fig. 325), but not horizontally forward. They are, accordingly, *oscillatory waves.* If the particles did move horizontally forward with the advance of the wave form, navigation would be a difficult business. Big waves would carry ships along with them at railway-train speed.

When, however, the sea waves advance toward a shore line where the water becomes gradually shallower they break, forming

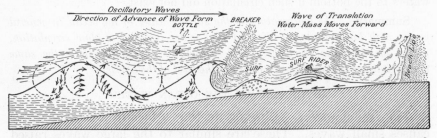

Fig. 325. — Diagram of sea waves advancing on shore and breaking to form surf. In deep water the waves are oscillatory, that is, the wave form advances but the water particles come back to their original positions. Each dotted circle traces the path of a single water particle. The dot in the circle shows the position of the particle of each circle at the instant when the wave form is as in the drawing. The arrow on the circle shows the position a particle will take an instant later. The other arrows show how near by particles are moving. In the breaker wave, owing to shallowing, there are not enough particles to fill out the wave form, but the energy of the wave motion causes the crest to develop. Left unsupported the wave breaks, forming surf. A mound of water (a wave of translation) then rushes forward. In it the water particles move horizontally forward to new positions. The returning water under the wave of translation develops the undertow current.

surf or *breakers* (Fig. 326). This happens because at a certain depth, depending on the height of the wave, there is not enough water to fill out the form of the wave crest. Consequently the wave front hollows out, the top of the wave finds itself unsupported, topples, and then is hurled forward by the energy of the wave motion.

In the reach between the line of the surf and the shore, a different type of wave motion develops. The mound of water heaped up by the surf runs forward as a ridge toward the shore; this is a *wave of translation.* Such a wave has no trough either before or behind the crest. The water particles in it each move forward as the wave advances. On the backs of such waves surf riders race in toward the shore on the long shelving beach of Waikiki near Honolulu, Hawaii (Fig. 327).

A current, called the *undertow* (Fig. 325), flows outward along the bottom beneath the surf and the shore.

Rock fragments dislodged from cliffs and ground up on the beaches, are, in part, moved offshore in the undertow. Sediment is also pushed along

Photo by Rau

Fig. 326. — A wave breaking because there is not enough water to fill out the wave form. In the middle ground of the picture a wave of translation is rushing forward on the beach. Atlantic City, New Jersey. (See Fig. 327.)

the coast (1) by the breaking of waves that reach the coast diagonally (Fig. 348), and (2) by a slow, wind-formed surface current that moves in the direction the wind is blowing.

Summary. *Sea waves, caused by friction of wind, are a rising and falling of the water, the wave form moving forward, often far beyond the place of origin. They break on the coast with great force, forming surf, dislodging rock fragments from sea cliffs. Sediment is moved offshore in the undertow, some along the coast.*

146. Other waves. Tap lightly on the bottom of a pan of water, and the water rises in a low dome. An earthquake shock in the ocean produces a similar wave, reaching from the bottom of the sea to the surface. The water may not be raised more than a fraction of an inch in the open sea, but the disturbance is so deep and affects so much water that, when the wave approaches a neighboring coast, it rises higher and higher. Such a wave is a great wave of translation (p. 339) and may then rise to a height of more than 100 feet, rushing perhaps a mile or more inland, carrying everything before it, and leaving vessels stranded. Tens of thousands of people have been drowned by a single earthquake wave (p. 210), or *tsunami,* as it is called in Japan.

© *Wide World*

Fig. 327. — Surf-boarding off the beach at Waikiki, Honolulu, Hawaii. The sea waves break at the reef and become waves of translation moving forward for nearly a mile to the shore. See Fig. 326.

Earthquake waves are often quite mistakenly referred to as tidal waves. They have no connection with the tides. Fortunately earthquake waves, or tsunamis, are not common in many parts of the world, though Japan, the East Indies, and the coast of Chile and Peru are subject to them. The waves travel great distances, some from Asia reaching the California coast; but, so far away, they are too much spread out to be destructive.

The discharge of an iceberg from a glacier (p. 276), or the breaking up of an iceberg as it runs aground, starts a similar wave. These iceberg waves dash on the shores with great force, reaching several feet above the level of the ordinary waves.

A wave of high water accompanies hurricanes and similar storms at sea (p. 449).

Summary. *Waves are also started by earthquake displacements of the ocean bottom; by the breaking off or stranding of icebergs; and by hurricanes.*

147. Tides. Twice each day (more exactly, every 12 hours, 26 minutes) the passage of tidal waves, formed by the attraction of moon and sun (Appendix E), causes the ocean surface to rise and fall (Figs. 532, 533). In the open ocean the difference in height between high and low tide, or the *tidal range,* is not over one or two feet; but, as the tidal wave approaches the coast, its height is increased (Figs. 328, 329) by the effect of the shallowing bottom.

In the ocean and on open coasts, the tide is merely a rise and fall in the water level; but in bays and estuaries this change in level starts currents, which often move with great velocity. Such currents may move so rapidly that boats cannot make headway against them; indeed, in the Bay of Fundy the tide advances over the mud flats more rapidly than a man can run. From this it is evident why, as the tide rises and falls, it is said to "come in" and "go out." During the time it is rising the tide is said to be *flowing,* or it is the *flood tide,* and when it is falling it is *ebbing,* or is the *ebb tide.*

The advancing tidal wave is greatly influenced by the form of the coast. Ordinarily the tidal range is between 3 and 10 feet; but in narrowing, V-shaped bays the range is greatly increased, as in the Bay of Fundy in Nova Scotia and Ungava Bay in northern Labrador, where the tide rises from 30 to 50 feet.

On the other hand, where bays broaden out, bag-shaped, the tidal range is greatly diminished. For instance, the Atlantic tide, passing through the Strait of Gibraltar, produces practically no effect on the broad Mediterranean; but a very small local tide is developed in the Mediterranean itself. This almost complete absence of tide in the Mediterranean was of great importance in the development of navigation in that enclosed sea (p. 589) and the growth of nations along its shores. With strong tidal currents to battle against, the movement of their small, open boats, propelled by oars, would have been a much more difficult task.

Along irregular coasts there are bays where the tidal range is greater than in neighboring parts of the coast. If there happens to be connection between two such places, rapid tidal currents, or *races,* will pass through the connecting straits. An illustration of this is found in southern Massachusetts, where rapid currents flow between Buzzards Bay and Vineyard

Fig. 328

Figs. 328 and 329. — High and low tide at Bourne, Massachusetts. Note the dead
twigs placed in a line across the middle of the pictures. What is the purpose of this?
Describe difference in conditions in the two pictures.

Sound (Fig. 330). A similar current occurs at Hell Gate, in the narrow strait between New York Bay and Long Island Sound (Figs. 331, 332).

On entering some river mouths the tidal current changes to a wave, known as the *bore* (Fig. 333), which travels rapidly up-stream. It is found in the Seine, Severn, Amazon, and several other rivers.

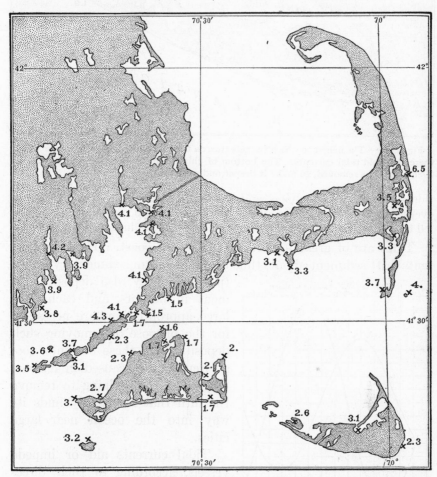

Fig. 330. — Range of tide, south of Cape Cod, indicated by figures. In Buzzards Bay it rises 4.1 feet; in Vineyard Sound, from 1.5 to 3.1; consequently rapid currents, or races, pass through gaps between the islands that separate the two bodies of water. Find these places on the map.

Not only does the tide vary from place to place, but also from time to time. At new and full moon the tidal range is greater than during the quarters. Tides with high range are known as *spring tides*, those with low range, *neap tides* (Appendix E). The correspondence of spring and neap

Fig. 331. — The height to which the tide rises on the two sides of Hell Gate, over which there are rapid tidal currents. The bottom of this channel was still being blasted in 1926 and rocks removed, to make it deeper and safer for ships.

tides to phases of the moon, and the fact that two complete tides occur every 24 hours, 52 minutes (the period between two moonrises), long ago led to the discovery that the tides are due to some influence of the moon.

Tides are of great importance along the coast. The tidal currents drift sediment about, thus helping to form sedimentary strata (p. 46). They also deposit sediment in harbors, and each year large appropriations are necessary for the purpose of removing such deposits. By these currents, too, a circulation is caused in harbors (Fig. 331), thus helping to remove the filth that necessarily finds its way into the ocean near large cities.

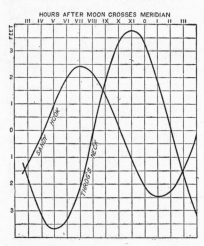

Fig. 332. — Diagram to show time of arrival and height reached by the tides on the two sides of Hell Gate. The currents at Hell Gate are therefore due to two causes (1) the time of high tide differs on the two sides; (2) the tidal range differs.

Tidal currents aid or impede vessels, according to their direction; and they sometimes drift vessels from their course, placing them in dangerous positions. Every now and then in foggy weather, when the land cannot be seen, a vessel runs aground (Fig. 340) because the tide has drifted it out of its course. The captains of all large ships carry tide tables and charts to aid them in navigation. One use of these is to tell when the tide is high, for the entrances to many harbors are too shallow to admit large ships at low tide.

Summary. *Every 12 hours, 26 minutes, the ocean surface rises and falls with the passage of a tidal wave. In the open ocean the range is a foot or two; along the coast from 3 to 10 feet; in V-shaped bays even 30 to 50 feet; but in large bays that broaden, the tide may be destroyed. Along irregular coasts the rise and fall of the tide cause currents, which may become very*

Photo by Allen

Fig. 333. — The bore wave at Moncton, New Brunswick, Petitcodiac River.

rapid races. Tidal currents move sediment about, helping to deposit sedimentary strata; they drift sediment into harbors; they keep the harbor water in circulation; they aid or impede navigation; and they sometimes place vessels in dangerous positions.

148. Ocean currents. The ocean waters are in constant circulation, not only along the bottom (p. 337), but also in well-defined surface currents (Fig. 334). The existence of ocean currents has been known for a long time; indeed, Columbus noticed them along the American coast, and Benjamin Franklin studied them and considered them the result of steadily blowing winds. It is now known that there are currents slowly sweeping through each of the oceans (Fig. 335).

Differences in temperature of the ocean water account for the settling of water in cold regions and its slow creep, in mass, toward the equator along the sea bottom (p. 337). But the surface currents are too varied to be accounted for on the basis of differences in temperature only.

The explanation that best accounts for surface currents is the effect of steadily blowing winds, as suggested by Franklin. By blowing on a pan of water with sawdust floating in it, a drift of water is seen to start; in like manner, winds blowing over lakes or the oceans start a similar drift of surface water. Such wind-drift currents continue to move for some time after the wind dies down.

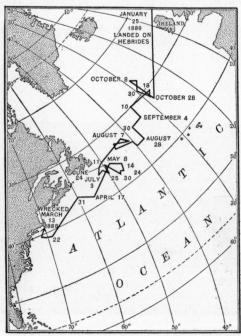

Fig. 334. — The drifting of a wreck from March 13, 1888, till it went ashore January 25, 1889. Storm winds now and then caused the wreck to leave its general course in the ocean drift.

A comparison of the ocean-current chart (Fig. 335) and the wind chart (Fig. 398) shows that there is a close resemblance between the direction of ocean currents and regular winds. We shall study the currents of the Atlantic Ocean to see how close this relationship is.

In the equatorial region there is a *drift*[1] of water, the *Equatorial Drift*, toward the South American coast. At the angle of South America it divides, the smaller portion going into the South Atlantic, the larger into the North Atlantic. This Equatorial Drift is exactly what we should expect to find, for the northeast and southeast trade winds blow steadily day after day, drifting the water westward before them.

[1] A slow current may be called a *drift*; a more rapid, and usually deeper, current, a *stream*.

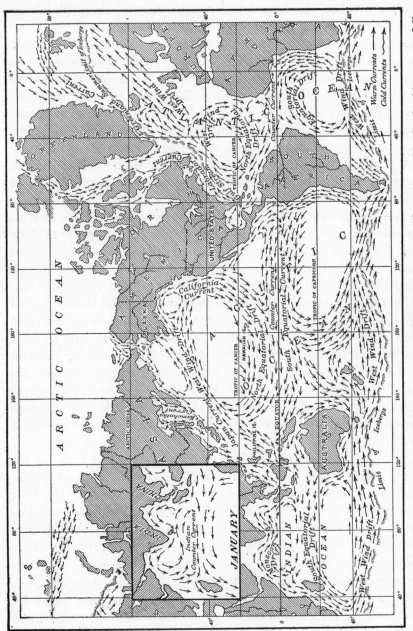

Fig. 335. — A chart showing the principal ocean currents and ocean drifts (July) of the world. Study this map carefully. Make a sketch map somewhat like it. Compare the direction of the currents with that of the winds in Fig. 398. Insert shows the reversed currents in the Indian Ocean in January.

After dividing on the coast of South America, the drift follows the coast for a while, then slowly swings to the right in the northern hemisphere, and to the left in the southern.[1] Thus a great, slowly moving eddy is formed in each ocean. Floating seaweed (*Sargassum*) accumulates in the center of the North Atlantic eddy in such abundance that it has been called the *Grassy*, or *Sargasso*, *Sea*. Columbus encountered it, and his sailors, not knowing what it was, feared that the ships would run aground in it. It is not, however, so abundant or persistent as was formerly thought.

A portion of the *North Equatorial Drift* enters the Caribbean Sea, part coming out between the West Indies, part continuing on into the Gulf of Mexico (Fig. 335). The portion that enters the Gulf is warmed still more in that enclosed sea and, because its level is about three feet higher than that of the Atlantic at New York City, flows out between Cuba and Florida as a narrow and rapidly moving stream of warm water, known as the *Gulf Stream* (Figs. 104, 323, 336). On the Florida coast it has a velocity of four or five miles an hour. The Gulf Stream rapidly broadens, a part of it joining the great *North Atlantic Eddy* that circles in the open ocean outside of the West Indies. This portion returns to form once more a part of the Equatorial Drift. There is also a current, the *Equatorial Counter Current*, that flows eastward between the two eddies and consists of water from the southern hemisphere deflected to the right on crossing the equator into the northern hemisphere. This type of counter current is better developed in the Pacific.

A smaller portion of the Gulf Stream water, and some of the North Atlantic Eddy, drifts on into the region of the west winds, which drive it on toward the coast of northern Europe, as the *West Wind Drift*, also called the *Gulf Stream Drift*. Thus water, warmed in the equatorial region, the Caribbean Sea, and the Gulf of Mexico, is carried to the European coast, and even into the Arctic. There is no similar stream in the South Atlantic, because there are no partly closed seas for the drift to enter.

Study the currents of the Pacific to see if the same great eddies are found there. Notice that in the Southern Ocean, where there are no con-

---

[1] This swinging is caused by the effect of the earth's rotation, which deflects all moving bodies, whether wind or water currents, from a straight course. In the northern hemisphere the moving body is turned to the right, in the southern hemisphere to the left of the direction of motion (p. 429).

tinents to turn the currents, the West Wind Drift extends completely around the globe.

Beside these eddies there are special currents, one of which, the *Labrador Current*, is of great importance to America. This is a cold current, flowing from among the islands of the Arctic along the Labrador, Newfoundland, and New England coasts (Figs. 335, 336). It keeps close to the American shores, being turned to the right by the influence of rotation and being kept at the surface in part because it is fresher and less dense than the surrounding waters, in part because the depths near the shore are

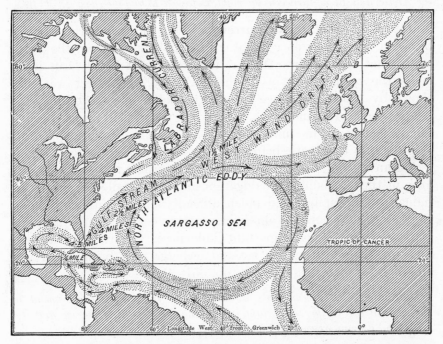

Fig. 336. — The Gulf Stream (see Fig. 104), North Atlantic Eddy, Sargasso Sea, West Wind Drift, and Labrador Current. The boundaries are not really so sharp as in this diagram, and the Gulf Stream current is not so clearly developed in the west of the Gulf of Mexico as the arrows show.

not great and hence are all occupied by the cold current. Thus, while warm water is drifted toward Europe, cold water flows along the American coast as far south as Cape Cod, where it disappears by settling and mingling with the warm water.

Summary. *The surface currents are due to the drifting of water before steadily blowing winds. In each ocean there are great eddies, started by the trade winds, which cause an Equatorial Drift toward the west. This, dividing on the continents, follows the coast northward and southward some distance;*

then it is turned, by effect of rotation, to the right in the northern hemisphere and to the left in the southern. Thus an eddy is caused in each ocean, both north and south of the equator. A part of the North Equatorial Drift enters the Gulf of Mexico and emerges as the warm Gulf Stream, a portion of which joins the eddy of the North Atlantic. A portion of the eddy and of the Gulf Stream is drifted by the west winds to the European coast and even into the Arctic. In the southern hemisphere the West Wind Drift extends around the earth. The cold Labrador Current sweeps along the American coast from the Arctic, and, being turned to the right, is forced to hug the coast till it sinks.

149. Effects of ocean currents. The most important effect of ocean currents is on climate (p. 457). For instance, the warm water that is borne into the Arctic by the West Wind Drift influences the temperature of northern Europe. Its effect was well shown by Nansen's voyage toward the pole. He started into the Arctic north of Scandinavia, where the warm drift keeps the sea fairly clear of ice in summer (Fig. 335), and was able to push his ship far into the Arctic before he met with impassable ice.

Ocean currents aid or retard vessels, according to their direction; and, in their reckonings, navigators must make allowance for this influence. Columbus had much difficulty in navigating his small ships among the currents along the northern coast of South America. Currents have other important influences, for example causing fogs (p. 415), drifting sea ice and icebergs, and bringing oxygen and food for many sea animals (pp. 351, 352).

Summary. *Ocean currents affect climate, influence the movement of vessels, and are further important in causing fogs, drifting sea ice and icebergs, and bearing oxygen and food for sea animals.*

150. Ice in the ocean. Each winter a large part of the Arctic Ocean is frozen over, often to a depth of 5 or 10 feet. The tidal currents move the ice about, opening cracks or *leads*, and closing them again with so irresistible a force that the ice is broken and piled up in ridges of *pack ice* often 50 or 100 feet high. More than one Arctic ship has been crushed like an eggshell between these moving ice fields.

In summer the ice breaks up, and the fragments drift southward till they melt. Each spring and early summer there is a steady stream of these ice fragments, or *ice floes*, passing down the Labrador coast in the Labrador current (Fig. 336).

Icebergs, discharged from the ice sheets of Greenland and other northern islands (p. 276), also drift in the Arctic waters (Fig. 268). They are huge floating islands of ice, sometimes rising more than 100 feet above the water. Far greater icebergs are discharged from the Great Ice Barrier (Fig. 269) of the Antarctic ice sheet, some of them rising 500 feet above the water. They have steep sides and flat tops, and are sometimes several miles long.

Summary. *The Arctic sea ice, formed in winter, breaks up in summer, some of it drifting southward in the Labrador current. Huge icebergs, discharged from the Greenland ice sheet, drift in the Arctic, and still larger ones in the Antarctic.*

LIFE IN THE OCEAN

151. Surface (pelagic) life. The abundance of life in the ocean is marvelous. A pail of water dipped from the surface will contain thousands of individuals, mostly microscopic (Fig. 321). These organisms are drifted about by winds and currents, and with them are many larger forms, some merely floating, some swimming. Pieces of floating wood have animals attached to them; and in the floating seaweed, many animals live in little worlds of their own.

The minute organisms are the source of food for many larger animals, even for the huge whales. The whale takes in a mouthful of water and then closes his jaws and strains the water to obtain its food, and thus the largest of animals feeds upon the smallest.

Among the many fishes some, like the mackerel, are valuable for food supply. The mackerel and other fishes swim together in vast numbers, forming "schools" or "shoals."

Summary. *Life is very abundant in the surface waters, both large and microscopic forms being present, the latter serving as a food supply for even the largest of animals, the whale.*

152. Life along coasts (littoral). Along the coast line there is also abundant animal life; but it is more varied than in the open ocean, because the coast offers so many different conditions. Some of the littoral animals swim in the surf; others cling to the rocky coast; and others burrow in the sand or mud. Many kinds, such as clams, oysters, lobsters, and a large number of fishes, are valuable as food; others, such as sponges, precious corals, and pearls, are of value for other purposes.

Plants, as well as animals, abound on the seacoast. This is true in the mangrove swamps of the tropical zone (Fig. 364) and the salt marshes of the temperate zones (Fig. 363 and Plate VIII); it is also true of rocky coasts, to which seaweeds cling, covering the rock with a mat of plant growth.

Some conditions are unfavorable to littoral life; for example, (1) frequent earthquake shocks, (2) the grinding of Arctic sea ice, and (3) the grinding of moving sand and pebbles on the beaches.

Although few parts of the earth have such an abundance and variety of animal life as the coral reefs (Fig. 366), it is a curious and interesting fact that the polar seas and particularly the North Atlantic and Arctic ocean shore zones are far more abundantly furnished with both plant and animal life than the tropical seas. The chief reason for this is that the warm tropical waters are deficient in the element nitrogen that is an essential plant food. A plentiful quantity of this element in the northern waters makes them vast meadows of microscopic plant life, *phytoplankton*, on which an equally vast assemblage of minute marine animals feed. These animals, in turn are eaten by the fish; the seals and birds eat the fish; and polar bears and foxes eat the seals and the birds.

Where, accordingly, cold, food-bringing currents are constantly renewing the supply of minute plant and animal life over shallow banks, known as *fishing banks*, large numbers of food fish congregate. This is well illustrated on the fishing banks off northeastern America, such as Georges and the Grand Banks of Newfoundland, that are bathed by the Labrador current. These are resorted to for cod, haddock, and halibut by fishing vessels from France, Newfoundland, Nova Scotia, and many New England ports, especially Gloucester, Mass. From a passing ocean liner, the schooners may be seen at anchor in the open ocean, the men busily fishing, either from the sides of the vessel or from small, open dories. It is a hazardous calling, and many a fishing vessel has been sunk during the fierce storms, or crushed by the huge transatlantic liners. Every year, also, men in dories are separated from their vessels during fogs, which are frequent on the banks. They then drift about in the open ocean, often until they starve, or freeze, or founder. In recent years, however, the fishing has been done more and more with steam trawlers.

Summary. *Animal life along the coast is abundant and varied; there is also much plant life. Cold food-bringing currents especially favor life, as is illustrated on fishing banks, from which valuable food fish are obtained.*

153. Life on the ocean bottom (abyssal).

Absence of sunlight prevents the existence of plant life in the deep sea; but, even at depths of two or three miles, there are animals (Fig. 337) on the ocean bottom (p. 324).

Photo by *U. S. Fish Commission*

Fig. 337. — A deep-sea fish.

These animals live in darkness, in water almost at the freezing point, and under a pressure of many tons.

The conditions on the ocean bottom are very uniform summer and winter alike: day and night are dark; everywhere it is cold; and the sea floor is a monotonous expanse of ooze or clay. The nature of animal life varies with the depth because of differences in temperature; and where the water is very cold, animals are scarce and have little vitality. The supply of oxygen, brought by the slowly moving bottom current (p. 337), and the supply of food, which settles down to the bottom as organisms at the surface die and slowly sink, also limit abyssal life.

After A. Agassiz

Fig. 338. — A stalked crinoid from the deep sea.

Under such uniform conditions it is not strange that many peculiar forms of animal life should be found in the deep sea. Some of them, like the stalked crinoids (Fig. 338), belong to types once abundant, but now living only on the ocean bottom. There they have been able to survive while those which were out in the world, and exposed to the struggle that goes on there, have been exterminated.

Summary. *There is wonderful uniformity of conditions in the deep sea, in which animals, but no plants, live. The abundance and distribution of animal life are influenced mainly by temperature, oxygen supply, and food supply.*

TOPICAL OUTLINE, QUESTIONS, SUGGESTIONS, AND LABORATORY EXERCISES

TOPICAL OUTLINE. **136. Oceanography.** Definition; exploring expeditions; cables; sounding; water samples; ocean-bottom mud; temperature; dredging; animal and plant life.

137. Ocean basins. General condition; deep-sea plains; deeps; elevations; Atlantic, — deepest point, volcanoes, mid-Atlantic ridge; Pacific, — volcanic chains, deepest point, other deeps.

138. Deposits on the ocean bottom. (A) *Rock fragments:* source; deposit; fossils; flocculation and its significance. (B) *Ocean-bottom oozes:* absence of rock waste; area of ooze; materials in ooze; source of organisms; globigerina ooze; pteropod ooze; radiolarian and diatom oozes. (C) *Red clay:* solution of shells; insoluble parts; red color; decomposed pumice; slowness of accumulation; proofs.

139. Land and ocean-bottom topography. Mountain folding and volcanic action; erosion; sediment; result of differences.

140. Surface of the sea. Sea level; effect of continents; of winds and storms; of deposit of sediment; of sinking ocean bottom; Glacial Period.

141. Composition of sea water. Original condition; increase in saltness; age of the ocean basins; proportion of salt; other mineral substances; amount of salt; importance; carbonate of lime; presence of air; importance.

142. Density and pressure of sea water. (a) Density: average density; effect of fresh water; of evaporation. (b) Pressure: amount; reason for no effect on animals; animals brought to the surface; "implosion"; density of ocean-bottom water.

143. Color and light. (a) Color: entrance of sunlight; blue color; green color; Yellow River; Red Sea; Gulf Stream. (b) Light: darkness of ocean bottom; blind fish; phosphorescence on ocean bottom; at the surface.

144. Temperature of the oceans. From tropical to polar zones; enclosed seas; decrease downward; ocean bottom; cooling of fresh and salt water; circulation; effect on animals; enclosed sea bottoms; cold not result of depth merely.

145. Wind waves. Cause; nature of movement; length, height; crest; trough; whitecaps; rate of movement; effects on vessels; rollers; oscillatory waves; breakers; wave of translation; undertow; movement of rock fragments.

146. Other waves. Earthquake waves, — cause, size, effects, occurrence, distance of travel; iceberg waves; hurricane waves.

147. Tides. (a) Nature of tides: time of passage; tidal range; increase on coast; movement in open ocean; currents on coast; flowing, ebbing. (b) Influence of coast; ordinary range; effect of V-shaped bays; of broadening bays; Mediterranean; races; examples; bore. (c) Influence of moon's phases: spring tides; neap tides; relation of tides to moon. (d) Effects of tides: on deposit of strata; on deposits in harbors; on circulation of water in harbors; on navigation. See also Appendix E.

148. Ocean currents. Early knowledge; effect of temperature differences; of steady winds; resemblance between winds and currents; a drift; a stream; Equatorial Drift; effect of continents; effect of rotation; Sargasso Sea; Gulf Stream; North Atlantic Eddy; counter currents; West Wind Drift; Pacific eddies; West Wind Drift of Southern Ocean; Labrador Current; comparison of European and American coasts.

149. Effects of ocean currents. Climate; Nansen's journey; effect on navigation; fog; ice; oxygen and food.

150. Ice in the ocean. (a) Sea ice: depth; leads; pack ice; travel over the ice; ice floes. (b) Icebergs: source; size; Antarctic bergs.

151. Surface (pelagic) life. Abundance; modes of life; whales; mackerel.

152. Life along coasts (littoral). Varied conditions; valuable animals; plant life; unfavorable conditions; favorable conditions; reason for abundance of life in colder seas; fishing banks — location, food fish, fishing, dangers.

153. Life on the ocean bottom (abyssal). Plants; animals; surroundings; temperature; oxygen; food; survival of types.

QUESTIONS. Section 135. In what ways is the ocean of importance?

136. What is oceanography? What was the *Challenger* expedition? How is the depth of the sea found? What facts are learned during a sounding? How is dredging carried on?

137. What is the condition of the ocean bottom? What irregularities occur? What irregularities are found in the Atlantic? In the Pacific? What is the greatest depth known?

138. (A) What is the nature of the deposit near the coast? Why are sediments not carried far from the land? (B) Why is ooze deposited far from land?

Of what is it composed? (C) What is the origin of red clay? Prove that it is forming slowly.

139. Why are land and ocean-bottom topography different?

140. What is sea level? How is this level changed? What evidence is there of such change?

141. What is the origin of the mineral substances in sea water? How may the age of the oceans be calculated? What mineral substances are there in the sea? How much salt is there? Of what importance is the carbonate of lime? The air?

142. What causes water to vary in density? What is the pressure on the ocean bottom? Why do not animals feel it? What is "implosion"? What would be the condition if the ocean-bottom water were compressed like the air?

143. What causes are there for the different colors of the ocean? What light is there on the ocean bottom?

144. What causes differences in temperature of the ocean-surface waters? What are the temperature conditions below the surface? Why is the bottom temperature lower than that in lakes? What is the cause of the slow circulation? What proof is there of it?

145. What causes sea waves? What is the real movement of the water? What causes whitecaps? How long and high may waves be? How fast may they move? What damage may they do to ships? What is the cause of rollers? Describe and diagram oscillatory waves. What causes breakers? What are waves of translation? How are rock fragments carried away?

146. What causes earthquake waves? What are some of their effects? What other causes are there for waves?

147. To what height does the tidal wave rise? Under what conditions are tidal currents formed? What is flow? Ebb? What happens where tides enter narrowing bays? Where they enter broadening bays? Give an illustration. What causes tidal races? Give illustrations. What is the bore? What reasons are there for connecting tides with the moon? Name some important effects of tides.

148. What early knowledge of ocean currents was there? What effect have differences in temperature on ocean movements? What effect has the wind? Describe the system of currents in the Atlantic Ocean and show how it is related to winds. Describe and explain the Gulf Stream. What is the Sargasso Sea? What currents are found in the Pacific? Other oceans (Fig. 335)? Describe the Labrador Current.

149. Name the important effects of ocean currents.

150. What are the characteristics of sea ice? Describe the icebergs of the Arctic. Of the Antarctic.

151. What are the conditions of pelagic life?

152. How do the conditions surrounding littoral life vary? In what situations are littoral plants found? What conditions oppose littoral life? What conditions favor it? Why is life more abundant in Arctic than in tropical waters? Why are fishing banks the home of food fish? What dangers accompany the fishing?

153. What conditions influence life on the ocean bottom?

SUGGESTIONS. (1) Prove that salt water is more dense than fresh by putting shot in a bottle until it will barely sink in fresh water, taking care to cork it; then dissolve salt in the water and again put the bottle in it. (2) Cut a cube of ice and place it in fresh water. Measure the amount above and below water.

Place it in salt water and measure again. What is the result? (3) In a large pan or tub of water place a bottle partly submerged. Start waves by blowing on one end. Note how they travel beyond their source. Note the movements of the bottle as the waves pass under it. Have the students describe its movements. At one end of the pan make a shelving beach of sand with a cliff at one end. Observe and describe the action of the waves as they approach the shore. What differences are there in the behavior of the waves on the beach and on the cliff? Are fragments removed? Where do they go? Make waves that advance diagonally on the shore and observe the movement of the fragments. To see this clearly place at one point some colored objects, like bits of colored glass, and note how they move. Note, all these observations and experiments can be made much better on the natural shore of a pond or lake or the sea; see (6) below. (4) In the pan build a coast, roughly, like that of North and South America. Sprinkle sawdust on the water and blow over its surface from both sides of a line (the equator), to imitate the trade winds approaching the equator. Watch the drift of water. Do you see any resemblance to the ocean-current systems of the Atlantic? (5) Take the temperature at the bottom of the pan near the middle line, then place ice in the water as far away from the middle as possible. Be careful not to stir the water. After the ice has melted, again take the temperature under the middle line. What is the difference? It may be possible also to imitate the conditions in the Gulf of Mexico (p. 337). (6) If the school is by the sea, or even near a lake or pond, waves and wind-formed currents should be studied. Note their force, form, and effects. (7) If by the seashore, the tides should be studied. Observe time of low and high tides for three successive days. These facts may be obtained from an almanac, or better, from the *Tide Tables* published by the U. S. Coast Survey at Washington, the tables for the year for the Atlantic and Pacific coasts. Observe the time of spring and neap tides. How do they compare with the phases of the moon? What is the range of the tide in each case? Are there any tidal currents near at hand? Are the tides of any importance in your harbor? That is, do they do any harm or good? (8) Students who live at or near the seashore should make a thorough study of Appendix E. (9) On an outline map of the world sketch the ocean currents from the chart in the book (Fig. 335).

Laboratory Exercises. Do exercises XL and XLI in TARR and VON ENGELN's *Laboratory Manual of Physical and Commercial Geography* in connection with the study of this chapter.

Reference Books. MURRAY, *The Ocean*, Henry Holt & Company, New York, 1913; JENKINS, *A Textbook of Oceanography*, Constable & Company, London, 1921; JOHNSTONE, *Life in the Sea*, Cambridge University Press, Cambridge, England, 1911; JOHNSTONE, *An Introduction to Oceanography*, Hodder & Stoughton, London, England, 1923; FOWLER (ed.), *Science of the Sea* (a guide to observations), E. P. Dutton & Company, New York, 1912; MILL, *Realm of Nature*, 2nd ed., John Murray, London, 1913; CORNISH, *Waves of the Sea and Other Waves*, University of Chicago Press, Chicago, 1911; DARWIN, *The Tides*, Houghton, Mifflin & Company, Boston, 1898; article on *Tides*, Encyclopedia Britannica; *Tide Tables for the Year*, U. S. Coast and Geodetic Survey, Washington, D. C.; MARMER, *The Tide*, D. Appleton & Company, New York, 1926; JOHNSTONE, *A Study of the Oceans*, Longmans, Green & Company, New York. 1926.

CHAPTER XI

SHORE LINES

154. Importance of shore lines. With one exception the largest city on each of the six continents is located on the seacoast: New York City (Fig. 339), the metropolis of North America, Buenos Aires, of South America, London, of Europe, Calcutta, of Asia, and Sydney, of Australia. The exception is Cairo in Africa, situated on the Nile; but its nearest rival is Alexandria, a seaport. The great and increasing trade that uses the ocean as a highway converges toward these centers; and to and from them, by railway, river, and canal, there is a steady movement of goods for shipment or for distribution.

The approach to the coast, especially in times of storm and fog (Fig. 340), is accompanied by so many dangers — from hidden sand bars and reefs, islands, and projecting headlands — that all civilized nations spend large sums in the effort to lessen these perils. To warn sailors, or to guide them into port, lighthouses are built on exposed points and light-ships anchored on dangerous shoals; and, on charts, the location and characteristics of these lights are shown. On approaching the coast at night, the first sign of land is the gleam of the lighthouse; and by the color, brilliancy, nature of flashes, or other device, the mariner knows his position. During fogs and stormy weather a fog-horn adds its warning note. In recent years the aid of radio has also been enlisted in this service.

Specially trained pilots are licensed to guide ships into port; and buoys are placed at frequent intervals to mark the channel. Some of the buoys, placed over reefs or near dangerous currents, have bells that are rung, or whistles that are blown, by the rocking of the waves, to warn the sailors of danger. Even with all these precautions vessels far too frequently run ashore. To rescue the shipwrecked, numerous life-saving stations are maintained by the state and national governments; and in these stations men with strong lifeboats, lines, and other life-saving apparatus are ever ready for the call of distress.

The coast line has become of importance to many people as a vacation resort. In summer, when the interior of the country is hot, the seacoast is cool and pleasant; there are rocky coasts to scramble over, beaches to walk upon, surf to swim in, and boating and fishing to enjoy. Conse-

357

Fig. 339.—The harbor of New York City. Arrival of the dirigible, Los Angeles, from across the Atlantic. The ocean, a river (the Hudson), railroads and roads, on both sides of the river, all serve to transport goods to the seaport metropolis. On October 15, 1924, nine years to the day after the picture, Fig. 376, of the final work on the Panama Canal was taken, the ocean of air was conquered; the dirigible, Los Angeles, flew over the Atlantic and arrived at New York City.

quently, tens of thousands of people go to the seashore for a part or all of the summer (Fig. 341).

The seacoast is ever changing. As waves are ever at work, as deposits of sediment are always being made, and as the earth's crust is constantly rising or sinking, any study of coast lines must be concerned largely with the effects of such changes.

Summary. *The seacoast is the site of most of the greatest centers of human population and commerce. It is so important that it is charted; to guard against shipwreck; lighthouses, buoys, and other warnings and guides are placed along it; and life-saving stations are established. The sea-*

Photo by Case

Fig. 340.—Wreck on Alaskan coast caused by running on a rock submerged at high tide. This may have happened (a) because the steamer got off her course in a fog, or (b) because the coast was not properly outfitted with lighthouses.

coast is also an important summer resort. The seacoast is ever changing and to understand it these changes must be studied.

155. Elevated sea-bottom coasts. The uplift of sea bottoms (Figs. 107, 108, 112, 341, 496), forming coastal plains (p. 120), produces a low, flat, straight coast line. Such coasts are found in southern United States, Yucatan, eastern Central America, and Argentina. The land back of the coast is often so level that it is swampy and unfitted for agriculture.

In tropical lands, as in Central America and Africa, such plains are the seat of deadly fevers because of infections carried by mosquitoes. Where the soil is fertile and not too damp, however, the level plains make excellent agricultural land; but the lack of good harbors is a handicap to development. Good harbors are rare, chiefly because the contact of the sea with a level plain makes a straight coast with few irregularities.

If a slight sinking occurs, as has been the case in southern United States (Figs. 111, 446; p. 121), the sea enters the valleys, forming bays and harbors; but the harbors are likely to be inferior, because the valleys of a coastal plain are shallow. Moreover, the waves and currents transporting much coarse sediment quickly build sand bars, which skirt the

Photo by Rau

Fig. 341. — An uplifted sea-bottom coast, New Jersey.   Describe its general characteristics.   Why is this a good place for bathing?

coast, enclose shallow lagoons, and even extend across the mouths of bays and harbors (Figs. 355, 373). A constant struggle is, therefore, necessary to prevent harbor entrances from being choked with sand.

Summary. *Elevated sea-bottom plains are low, level, straight, skirted by sand bars, and have few harbors, and these commonly shallow and inadequate, even where sinking of the land has admitted the sea to the valleys. Such conditions do not favor dense settlement.*

156. Straight mountainous coasts. The raising of the sea bottom is sometimes brought about by mountain uplift. This either raises narrow strips of coastal plain, between the mountains and the sea, or else causes the mountains to rise directly out of the sea. Where the mountains rise from the ocean in long chains of folds, they produce a straight and regular coast line.

Such a coast exists in western America, from Oregon to central Chile (Fig. 222). Along this coast there are few harbors, bays, capes, and peninsulas. In many places the mountains rise directly from the sea; elsewhere at the inner margin of a narrow coastal plain (Figs. 28, 29). The sea bottom slopes rapidly, and, at a short distance from the coast, the water is 15,000 or 20,000 feet deep (p. 28).

This coast has been recently elevated, and, in many places, is still rising. Both in 1822 and 1835 a part of the coast of Chile was suddenly

Fig. 342. — A drowned coast, Lofoten Islands, Norway. This is part of the "island guard" or fence that favored the early development of navigation by the Vikings.

raised 2 or 3 feet; and beaches and sea shells on the mountain slopes prove other recent uplifts. In Alaska, in 1899, part of the coast was uplifted 47 feet in one month (Fig. 105; p. 52).

For several reasons, such coasts are not suited to dense populations and high development of commerce or industries. (1) There are so few harbors that a place, even though on the shore, may be a long distance from a shipping point. (2) Between the mountains and the sea there is, at best, only a narrow strip of fairly level land, limiting the resources. (3) The mountains act as a barrier to inland communication, since few, if any, large streams break across them. The Government of the United States has only recently, and at great expense, opened railway communication across the mountain barrier between the coast and interior of Alaska. The scattered seaports, therefore, have little country tributary to them.

Summary. *Long chains of mountains, rising from the sea, form straight coasts, as in western America. The scattered harbors, the narrow area of level land, and the mountain barrier render such coasts unsuited to dense settlement or high development of industries.*

157. Irregular mountainous coasts. Mountain growth makes irregular coasts more commonly than straight ones. Irregular coasts result: (1) when mountains rise as chains of islands near continents, as in the case of the West Indies, East Indies, Philippines, and Japanese Islands (Fig. 32); (2) when the ranges are extended out from the mainland as peninsulas, as in the case of Italy, Greece, Alaska, and the Malay Peninsula; and (3) when, between mountain ranges, parts of the crust sink, thus admitting the ocean and forming gulfs or seas, like the Gulf of California and the Mediterranean.

The Mediterranean is a broad, deep depression (over 14,000 feet in depth) between the mountains of Europe and Africa. It is almost cut off from the ocean where the Atlas Mountains of Africa nearly meet the mountains of Spain at the Strait of Gibraltar; it is almost connected with the ocean at the low Isthmus of Suez (Fig. 509). Its coast line is very irregular, because there are so many short mountain chains, extending in different directions. These form the peninsulas of Tunis, Italy, Greece, and Asia Minor, besides many smaller projections; and also form chains of islands, of which Cyprus, Crete, Sicily, the Balearic Isles, and Corsica and Sardinia are the largest. The mountain chain of Italy, extending through Sicily, and along a submarine ridge to the Tunis peninsula, almost cuts the Mediterranean in two.

Many other large seas, such as the Caribbean Sea, Gulf of Mexico, Japan Sea, China Sea, and Red Sea, are partly enclosed by mountain uplifts. Still smaller seas, bays, and even harbors have been made by the uplift of mountainous islands and peninsulas. Where there has been a later sinking, as in Greece, the entrance of the sea into the mountain valleys has made many small bays and deep harbors.

Irregular, mountainous coasts are better fitted for habitation than straight, mountainous coasts. Communication by land is difficult, and the coast line is often steep and rocky (Fig. 342); but the many harbors, the great length of the irregular coast, and the quiet water of the enclosed seas and bays all encourage navigation. It is largely because of these conditions that navigation early developed in the Mediterranean (p. 589).

The same conditions occur off the western coast of Norway (Fig. 342), and this region too was the site of an early development of navigation, that of the Vikings who are reputed to have reached North America before Columbus made his voyages. It may be added that two other physiographic conditions also contributed to the early development of navigation in both places. One is the low range of the tides making the landing and launching of large boats a simple problem; the other that both coasts have many islands. Thus the navigators were always encouraged to go farther by the sight of new land ahead.

There are many places in the Mediterranean that, even to-day, can be reached only by ship; and the coasts, as in western Italy, are often so mountainous that a railway, although close by the sea, must pass through a series of tunnels near together. Wherever there is room for towns or villages, as on the delta of a small stream, the coast is well settled and, back of the coast, the settlement is especially dense along river valleys that furnish a pathway to the sea.

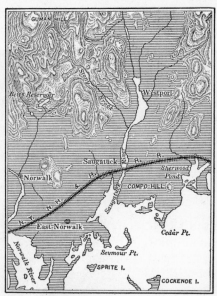

Fig. 343. — The shaded area shows the change in coast outline which would be caused in a part of southern Connecticut if the land should sink 100 feet. See Fig. 346.

Summary. *Uplift of mountainous islands and peninsulas, and sinking of the land between mountain folds, cause irregular coasts. Such coasts, like the Mediterranean, favor navigation because of the number of harbors, the length of the coast, and the quiet water; but they are in places steep, rocky, hence there sparsely settled. Communication between places along them must commonly be by ship.*

158. Coasts of drowned lands. Sinking of the land drowns a portion of it and makes the coast line irregular (Fig. 343), for the valleys are then transformed to bays, harbors, or estuaries. Sinking of the land has made San Francisco harbor (Fig. 344); it has made Massachusetts Bay, Boston harbor, and the other bays and harbors of New England (Fig. 345); and it has drowned the lower Hudson (Figs. 339, 444, 445).

When the hills of a drowned land have been completely submerged, shoals and banks (p. 352) are formed in the sea. When the hills are only partially submerged, islands are formed (Fig. 342), like the British Isles, Newfoundland, and the thousands of islands in northeastern (Fig. 346) and northwestern North America. Where there has not been submergence enough to surround the land completely, peninsulas are produced, like Scandinavia, Denmark, Nova Scotia, and innumerable capes and promontories (Fig. 33).

The outline of a sunken coast depends upon the nature of the valleys that existed on the land before it was submerged. Grand fiords, with wonderful scenery, are formed where the sea has entered the deep, steep-sided, mountain valleys of Norway and Alaska (Figs. 255, 256). These fiord valleys were first cut by streams, then broadened and deepened by glacial erosion. The lower Hudson valley is a fiord, and so is the Saguenay in Canada (Figs. 171, 347).

Fig. 344. — The harbor of San Francisco, showing the broad bay, also the gap made by the Sacramento River in cutting across the Coast Ranges. Sinking of the land has admitted the sea into the bay.

Most fiord coasts, like that of Norway, are too steep and rugged for much settlement. The villages are usually on small deltas, and very often the only communication between them is by water. Such conditions in part (see also p. 363) account for the development of that race of hardy sailors, the Norsemen.

The coast south of New York is strikingly different from the rocky coast farther north (Fig. 447). This difference is due to the fact that the coast to the south consists of weak rock and plains, crossed by broad valleys with gently sloping sides. The entrance of the sea into these valleys has formed shallow bays with gently rising margins, as in Delaware, Chesapeake, and Mobile bays. Along such coasts communication by land and water is easy and agriculture thrives.

There are several reasons why moderately low, irregular coasts, like those of the Middle States, New England, and England, are favorable to settlement and development. (1) There is an abundance of harbors, — in

Photo by Brown

Fig. 345. — Drowned stream mouth, a harbor, at Annisquam, Massachusetts. Typical of the New England coast.

fact, as in Maine (Fig. 346), often far more than are needed. (2) There is a very long coast line with protected bays and sounds for fishing and navigation. (3) Sinking of the land opens up waterways to the interior.

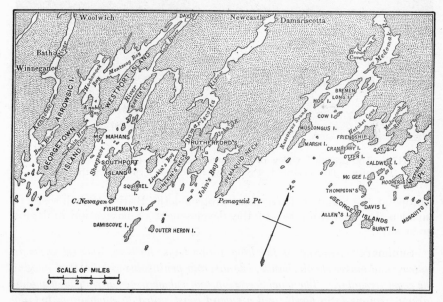

Fig. 346. — A sketch map of a part of the drowned coast of Maine. Make comparison with Fig. 343. Measure the distance straight along the coast. Measure it approximately along the greater irregularities.

The Columbia, Hudson, and Thames are navigable to ocean ships solely because recent sinking has admitted the sea. Portland, New York, and London could not otherwise be important seaports.

The formation of islands cuts off connection with the mainland and very greatly influences the ideas and affects the fortunes of the inhabitants. Thus Newfoundland is so isolated that its interests are different from those of the Canadian provinces, and it has declined to join the Canadian Confederation. The sinking of the land which separated Great Britain from

Photo by Rice

Fig. 347. — The drowned valley of the Saguenay River, Quebec, Canada, at Cape Eternity. This is a fiord; a glacially eroded valley entered by the sea.

Europe at the Strait of Dover, has protected the British from inroads of invaders by land, and led to the development of navigation and of a great navy.

Summary. *Sinking of the land forms bays, harbors, and estuaries in valleys; and makes shoals, banks, islands, and peninsulas of hills, thus making the coast irregular. The glacial erosion and submergence of valleys of mountainous regions form fiords, and a rugged coast suited to navigation, but not to dense settlement. Regions of weak rock, when drowned, have broad, shallow bays with low, level land between, adapted to agriculture. Moderately low,* *irregular coasts favor development because of the harbors, the favorable conditions for fishing and navigation, and the opening of waterways to the interior.   The formation of islands isolates people and greatly influences their history.*

159. Action of waves and currents. Waves are constantly battering at the coast, cutting cliffs, changing the outline and moving fragments about (p. 339). Some of the sediment is dragged offshore by tidal currents; some is drifted along the coast by the waves and the tidal and wind-formed currents. On rocky coasts this shore drift lodges between headlands, forming beaches (Fig. 360); on low, sandy coasts it is built into long sand bars (Fig. 361).

Photo by von E.

Fig. 348. — Diagonal approach of the waves. As, ordinarily, the whole wave does not break at once, its wash tends to move sediment in a zig-zag course along the shore. Make some observations on a sea or lake shore to verify this. Count how often waves come in during a period of five minutes.

Waves almost always approach the shore at an angle, their breaking into surf occurring first at one end and from there progressing to the other end. This is because the winds that determine the direction of wave advance happen only seldom to blow at exactly right angles to the trend of the shore line. In consequence of the average *diagonal approach* (Fig. 348) of the breaking waves, a *long-shore current* is set up, and this moves sediment with it along the coast.

An irregular coast cannot long resist the action of the waves and currents; and, were it not for the fact that there are so many changes in land level, the coast lines of the world would all be straight. Where, therefore, we find an irregular coast, we may be certain: (1) that the land has recently sunk (p. 363), and (2) that the shore has not stood long enough at the new level for the waves and currents to straighten it. This action of straightening coast lines is done in two ways — (1) by cutting back the headlands, and (2) by closing up and filling the indentations.

Summary. *Waves and currents are attacking the headlands, wearing them back, and moving the fragments either offshore or along the coast, in the latter case building beaches and bars. Ordinarily waves approach the shore diagonally and so set up longshore currents that drift sediment with them. The result of this action is to straighten the coast.*

Photo by Peabody

Fig. 349. — A sea cliff on the island of Grand Manan (Bay of Fundy) with a light-house on the top. Unconsumed portions of the cliff project above the level of the wave-cut portion of the offshore platform. The bowlders at the base of the cliff are the tools with which the waves batter the solid rock.

160. Sea cliffs. Where wave action is vigorous, as on headlands and on exposed island coasts, the waves are sawing into the land (Figs. 349, 350). The zone of most effective wave action is almost exactly at the sea level, though the spray may dash to a height of 50 or 100 feet. The advancing breakers hurl tons of water, bearing sand, pebbles, and even bowlders, against the cliffs. They act as battering-rams, undercutting the cliffs along the surf line, and thereby undermining the rock so that it falls and keeps the cliff face precipitous.

As the waves cut progressively back into the rocks of the cliff they develop a sloping plane on the rock just below the surface of the water, the *wave-cut bench* or *terrace* (Figs. 351a, b, and 350). At the outer edge of this wave-cut terrace the débris of the cutting builds up a continuation of the rock terrace, the *wave-built terrace*. It is obvious that wave attack cannot cut cliffs back or develop these offshore platforms over great horizontal distance if the land remains at the same level, for the force of the waves will be spent on the long shallow bottom. But if the land

Photo by Gardner

Fig. 350. — A cliff in glacial deposit on the Massachusetts coast at Bourne. The waves have not been able to remove the large bowlders that were in the deposit, and they, therefore, remain on the offshore platform, showing the previous extent of the land.

sinks, as the wave attack continues, wide *plains of marine denudation* may be developed by this process. Some students are inclined to the conviction that certain sloping areas with planed surfaces that others consider old peneplains (p. 93) are really old plains of marine denudation. The New England peneplain has been thus interpreted. Would there be a thick cover of residual soil on a recent plain of marine denudation? On a peneplain?

If made of strong, consolidated rock, sea cliffs are very steep (Fig. 349), though weathering, aided by the salt spray, usually prevents them from becoming vertical. If made of clay or sand, the cliffs although steeply inclined are constantly sliding down (Fig. 350). On exposed coasts, sea cliffs may rise several hundred feet; but generally they are much lower.

Cliffs in which the rocks are uniform may be straight and regular; but if the formations vary, the waves discover the differences and make

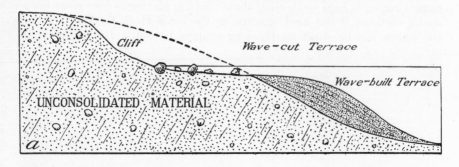

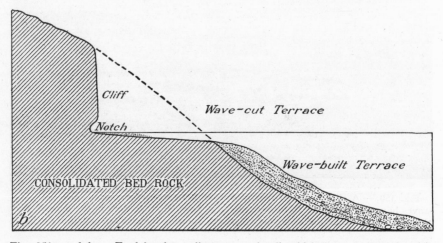

Fig. 351a and b. — Explain these diagrams and tell which one corresponds with Fig. 349, which one with Fig. 350, and why; shape of cliff, amount of cutting, etc.

the shore irregular. Then *chasms, stacks, sea arches* (Fig. 352), and *sea caves* (Fig. 353) are cut in the cliffs along the weaker strata. These irregularities cannot be cut very far back into the land, nor to a very great breadth, because the force of the waves is soon worn out on the sides and bottom. For this reason, waves cannot carve out large bays. Large bays or inlets are due to sinking of the land or to irregular uplift (pp. 362, 363).

Summary. *The sawing of the waves into the land cuts sea cliffs, leaving offshore platforms as the cliffs are pushed back. Weathering prevents most cliffs from being vertical, but all are steep, even those in sand or clay. Where there are differences in the rocks chasms, sea caves, and other small irregularities are produced.*

161. Beaches, hooks, bars, etc. Bowlder (Fig. 350) and pebble beaches at the middle of bays (Fig. 354) are built of the larger rock fragments, wrested from the cliffs at the headlands and driven

Fig. 352. — A wave-cut chalk cliff on the French coast. In cutting back the land, the waves have left a "stack" island. Another will be formed when the roof of the wave-cut sea arch falls. This picture shows low tide conditions. What is the origin of the rock shelf on which the man stands?

along the coast till they lodge in near the center. Smaller fragments make sand beaches (Fig. 341); and the still finer clay settles in the open water of protected bays, harbors, and estuaries, forming mud banks and flats.

On exposed coasts beaches are of bowlders or pebbles; in more protected places, of sand. The beaches serve as mills, sometimes called the *wave mill*, in which rock fragments are ground so fine that they can be borne off by

Fig. 353. — A sea cave that the waves have cut at Mt. Desert, Maine. At high tide and during storms the waves dash into the cave and the erosion enlarges it.

Fig. 354. — A pebble beach on the coast of Cape Ann, Massachusetts. Notice how round the pebbles are. High waves reach to the top of the beach. Here the wave mill grinds. This shows that large pebbles can be moved by the waves and longshore currents.

the currents. The rounded form of beach pebbles shows that they have been rolled about.

Rock fragments that are being moved along the coast are dropped at the entrance to bays because the current that is carrying the sediment is checked by the deeper, still waters there encountered. Thus, in time, *bars* are built across the bay mouths (Fig. 355). Drainage from the land, or wave and tidal action from the sea, may maintain an opening through the bar (Fig. 356); but a bar may

Photo by Peabody

Fig. 355. — A bar extending completely across a bay mouth; Whale Cove, Grand Manan, Bay of Fundy.

completely seal a bay (Fig. 355). A fresh-water pond then gathers behind the bar, slowly draining through it by seepage.

On many coasts, where there is an abundant supply of sand, long bars are built. For example, the waves are vigorously wearing back the high cliffs at Highland Light, Cape Cod, and building bars (Fig. 357) with the sand. By this process Sandy Hook (Fig. 358) has been built of débris worn from the cliffs of the New Jersey shore.

Such bars may be straight, or they may be curved at one end, forming *hooks* (Fig. 359), like Sandy Hook (Fig. 358) and the curved end of Cape Cod (Fig. 439). In some places, often at bends in the shore, waves and currents from opposite directions drive pebbles or sand out into the water,

Fig. 356. — A bar at North Fairhaven, New York, on the shore of Lake Ontario, partly shutting in a broad bay. The opening is maintained by the outflow of water from the land streams. The hooks are turned toward the inner bay because the waves and currents, bringing the sand and pebbles, come into the bay with greater force than the drainage water from the land flows out.

Fig. 357. — A view of the Sandy Hook bar from the Highland Light in New Jersey. See Fig. 358.

building small points, or *spits*. Bars sometimes form an angle projecting seaward, making a *cusp*, like Capes Hatteras, Fear, Lookout, and Canaveral. Other bars are often built in the lee of islands (Fig. 360).

Summary. *Rock fragments drifted along the coast build beaches along the sides and the center of bays, bars across bays, long bars where large quanti-*

ties of sand are supplied; also hooks, spits, and cusps. The material varies
from bowlders to sand, much of the fine clay going into the bays. The beaches
are wave mills in which rock fragments are ground up.

162. Offshore bars. From New Jersey to the Rio Grande
most of the coast is faced by bars at some distance from the mainland, from which they are separated by shallow lagoons (Figs. 361,
447 and Plate VIII). One of the longest of these bars extends along
the Texas coast from the mouth of the Rio Grande. River water
enters the lagoons, some of it seeping
through the bar, the remainder escaping
through gaps that the outflowing and
incoming tides are able to keep open.
The movement of sand along the shore
constantly threatens to close these channels; and for this reason, where the
channels are used as harbor entrances, as
at Galveston, it is necessary to build
jetties to keep the entrance deep enough
for large ships.

Such *offshore bars*, or *barrier beaches*, are
thrown up where large waves advance over a
shallow bottom of unconsolidated sediment
(Fig. 362). The shallowness causes the larger
storm waves to break some distance offshore.
There they tend to excavate a *submarine sea
cliff* on the sea side and to dump the excavated
material on the top of this cliff on the landward side. As the submarine cliff is pushed
back landward by the wave attack, the mass
of material deposited on its crest is also increased until eventually it is built above the

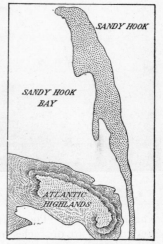

Fig. 358. — Diagram of
Sandy Hook, a spit built by
waves and longshore currents.
See Fig. 357. The "fringes"
on the inner side are due to
the action of waves driving the
sand past the point of the spit
at successive stages in its
development.

water surface, first here and there as islands, in time as a long continuous
bar. Then shallow waves and longshore currents add material and the
wind builds the bars still higher, raising sand dunes, sometimes 100 feet high.
The waves gradually consume the sand bars, eating them away on the seaward side and pushing them back toward the land (Fig. 362e, f, and g).

Beaches and bars are often useful as places for landing boats; and for
bathing they are resorted to by thousands of people. Offshore bars, are,
in addition, habitable, though usually so sterile that they are inhabited
only by fishermen, lighthouse-keepers, and pleasure seekers. Yet some
bars, like the Sea Islands off the Georgia coast, where the long-fibered
Sea Island cotton is raised, are excellent farm land. Here and there, too.

because of the absence of other kinds of harbors on such coasts, towns and cities, like Galveston, are built on the sand bars.

The sand that is drifted about in the building of sand bars often makes

Photo by Atwood

Fig. 359. — A hook, near Chignik Bay, Alaska.

dangerous shoals. The shifting sands south of Cape Cod, and those near Sandy Hook, are obstacles to safe navigation; and, on the shoals at the end of Cape Hatteras, many ships have been wrecked.

Fig. 360. — A bar joining a small island to the land on the coast of Sicily at Taormina.

Summary. *Where the waves break on shallow bottoms, the sand is thrown up into ridges, or offshore bars, which are raised still higher by the wind. Such bars, enclosing lagoons, are found along much of the coast from New Jersey to the Rio Grande.*

163. Sand dunes of the seacoast. On beaches, as in deserts (p. 147), there is dry sand, which the wind drifts about, often piling

Atlantic City Sheet. U. S. Geological Survey Topographic Atlas

Fig. 361. — Offshore bar on the New Jersey coast. On the mainland, or *old-land,* there is a wave-cut cliff, made before the bar was thrown up. Now the lagoon between this cliff and the offshore bar, or *new-land,* is being filled with sediment, a part of it being changed to salt marsh.

it up in dunes along the upper edge of the beach (Fig. 362). Sand dunes are exceedingly irregular, and their form is ever changing. Between the dune hills are basins, in which, however, there is rarely any water, because the bottom is so porous.

The movement of sand inland, doing much damage, is sometimes made possible by the removal of a forest, which gives full sweep to the wind. The removal of a forest back of Coffin's Beach on Cape Ann, Mass., over a

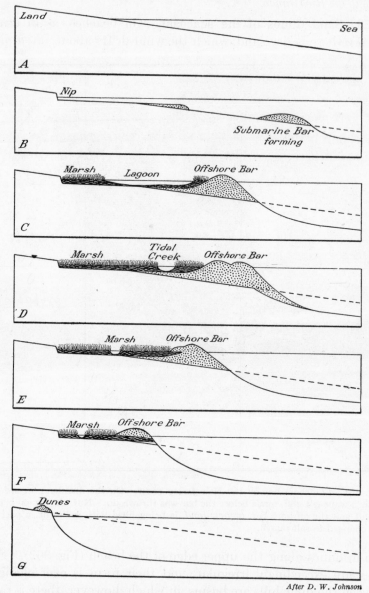

Fig. 362. — Stages in the development and migration landwards of an offshore bar. Describe the changes in each step and tell why they take place.

century ago, permitted the sand to move inland and destroy a farm. Dunes on the west coast of France moved inland two or three miles, destroying farms and villages. The French government took up the problem of how to stop their further advance. This was done by planting trees behind the dunes, and setting out such plants as will grow in the sterile, sandy soil. In the Netherlands the sand dunes protect the low plains from submergence.

Summary. *Along many coasts irregular sand hills, or dunes, are built up by the wind, and their advance inland has in some cases caused the destruction of much property. In the Netherlands the sand dunes act as a barrier, protecting the low plains from the waves.*

164. Salt marshes. Sediment deposited in estuaries, in lagoons behind sand bars (Figs. 361, 362), and in other protected arms of

Photo by Gardner

Fig. 363. — A salt marsh plain in an estuary at Cape Ann, Massachusetts. View taken at mid-tide to show the channel-ways filled with water. During high tide the entire plain is submerged beneath the salt water.

the sea, is slowly filling them. Salt-water plants that flourish in these places, such as the eel grass and salt-marsh grasses, aid in the filling. Their aid consists partly in adding their own remains, partly in checking the currents, thus causing them to drop some of the sediment they carry.

In time, the deposit of sediment and plant remains reaches to the level of high tide, forming a salt-marsh plain through which extend channels that the tide occupies (Figs. 361, 363). When, by wash from the land, the plain is built higher than the highest spring tides reach, dry-land plants take the place of the salt-marsh plants. By this process, nature is engaged in reclaiming much land from the sea.

Salt marshes as such are of little value, though a coarse grass is cut from them. Where dikes have been built to exclude the sea, and the land drained, salt marshes make excellent farm land. Much of the fertile lowland of England, a large part of the Netherlands, and the beautiful Evangeline country of Nova Scotia are diked marsh land. In the United States little has been done to reclaim salt marsh, because we have had enough land without it. But the time cannot be far distant when the

Photo by Jackson

Fig. 364. — A mangrove swamp on the Florida coast. Notice the tangle made by the roots of the mangrove, some of them descending from the limbs.

extensive salt marshes near New York and Boston will repay diking. Boston is partly built on salt marsh that has been changed to dry land by filling with earth removed from neighboring hills.

Summary. *In protected bays and lagoons, sediment and the remains of salt-water plants build up salt-marsh plains. In places these have been reclaimed by dikes or by filling.*

165. Mangrove swamps. Mangrove trees grow in protected spots on the coasts of warm countries, such as the Philippines, Bermuda Islands, and southern Florida. The mangrove tree (Fig. 364) is firmly anchored by roots that descend from the branches, forming an almost impenetrable jungle, or mangrove swamp.

Summary. *In warm countries the salt marsh is replaced by the almost impenetrable jungle of the mangrove swamp.*

166. Coral reefs. On some warm coasts animal life is so abundant that the shore is made entirely of animal remains. Of these animals, corals are the most important. Reef-building corals thrive in depths of less than 150 feet, where there is little sediment, little fresh water from the land, a temperature never below 70°, and where salt water currents are bringing abundant food.

Photo by von E.

Fig. 365. — Miniature coral barrier reef developing around a stack on the east coast of Barbados, B. W. I.

Coral is made by lowly animals, of which there are many species, varying in size from almost microscopic to individuals several inches in diameter. Some species live singly, but most unite in colonies, together forming a limy framework (as oysters form their shells), which we call coral. Some corals are massive, bowlder-like domes; others, delicately branching, tree-like forms. The individuals, or *polyps*, which form the coral, dwell in little cavities that dot its surface. The coral mass is alive on the outside, dead on the inside, and the polyps build their coral homes on foundations laid by former generations (Fig. 365).

The polyps can either withdraw into the cavities or extend their branching arms into the water in search of food. To one looking down upon a coral reef through a box with a glass bottom (Fig. 366), the sea floor seems like a garden, with flowers of all colors and many forms; and among the corals are myriads of other animals, some fixed in place, some moving freely about. The abundance and variety of life in such a place is marvelous.

Coral growth is most rapid on the outer side of a reef, where food is most abundant. This causes reefs to grow seaward, and their outward growth is increased by the action of the waves, which break off coral fragments and drag them out to sea. A reef

Courtesy of American Museum of Natural History

Fig. 366. — Staghorns and Fan Corals, Andros Island Reef, Bahamas. A submarine photograph showing how the coral stems grow on the reef. The picture was made with the aid of the Williamson Submarine Tube by Dr. R. W. Miner.

may start close to shore, as a *fringing reef* (Fig. 371a), and advance so far that it becomes a *barrier reef* (Figs. 367, 371b). Another way in which a fringing reef may be changed to a barrier reef is by a slow sinking of the land. If the coral grows upward as fast as the land sinks, it will form a reef farther and farther from the sinking land.

There are coral reefs on many coasts, the longest in the world being the Great Barrier Reef, which for over 1000 miles skirts the northeastern coast of Australia (Fig. 31) at a distance of 20 to 50 miles. Behind it is a navigable lagoon of quiet, protected water, in which, however, a good pilot is necessary because of the many coral shoals.

Uplift of the coast adds coral reefs to the land, in the form of terraces, like those in Cuba and other islands (Fig. 368). Even in the interior of

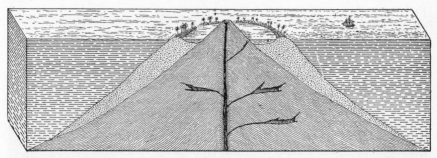

Fig. 367. — Diagram to illustrate a stage in the formation of an atoll. This corresponds to (b) of Fig. 371. Make similar drawings to illustrate stages (a) and (c) of Fig. 371.

continents, fossil reefs are found in some of the limestone strata that were deposited in ancient oceans.

Waves and winds often heap the coral fragments above sea level, forming land, as in the Bermuda Islands. The Bermudas, whose base beneath the sea is a volcanic cone, are surrounded by a fringe of coral reefs. Fragments, broken from the reefs by the waves, are ground on the beaches to

Photo by von E.

Fig. 368. — Elevated coral sea cliff, Barbados, B. W. I. Although a mile or more inland this cliff still has sea caves in it and the remains of an old beach at its base.

coral and shell sand, then drifted inland by the winds, forming coral sand dunes. It is thought that the chief period of dune accumulation was the time of continental glaciation in North America and Europe (p. 277). Windier and colder conditions probably prevailed in the region of the Bermudas during the Glacial Period.

After being built up in dunes, the coral sand of the inside of the masses is quickly cemented into a soft rock by the deposit around the grains of carbonate of lime, dissolved by rains from the surface layers.   The residual

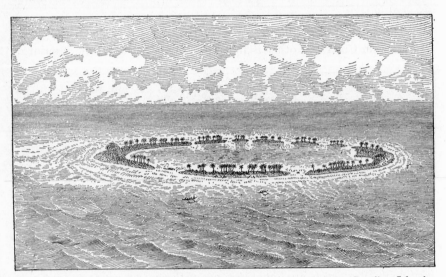

Fig. 369. — An atoll of the Pacific.   Drawing based on one of the Caroline Islands.

soil on the surface of such dunes is far better than the soil of ordinary sand dunes.

Summary.   *In warm, clear water, where there is an abundance of food for fixed animals, corals thrive, building limy skeletons, out of which reefs are made.*

Photo by U. S. Navy Bureau of Aeronautics

Fig. 370. — An airplane view of an atoll in the Pacific Ocean.   Palmyra Islands, looking east.   Note the line of the surf as the waves break on the outer edge of the reef, and the shallowness of the lagoon inside the ring of islands.

Fringing reefs are made along the coast, and these may change to barrier reefs either by outward growth or by sinking of the land. The wind forms dunes of the coral sand drifted from the beaches, thus building up and extending the area of islands in the sea.

167. Atolls. Ring-shaped islands in the open ocean, made of coral fragments, are called *atolls* (Figs. 367, 369, 370). A channel

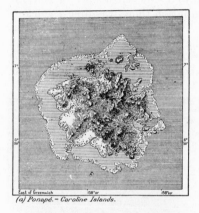

(a) *Ponapé.— Caroline Islands.*

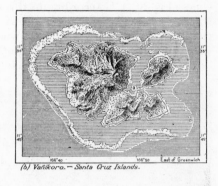

(b) *Vañikoro.— Santa Cruz Islands.*

(c) *Mayotte.-Comoro Islands in Mozambique Chan.*
After Reclus

Fig. 371a, b, c. — Development of a coral atoll. A series of maps of two islands in the Pacific Ocean and one in the Indian Ocean that show (a) a fringing reef about a sinking volcanic cone, Ponapé, Caroline Islands, Pacific Ocean; (b) a barrier reef, due to the central cone having sunk considerably, Vanikoro Island, Santa Cruz Islands, Pacific Ocean; (c) an atoll, with the cone sunken almost completely beneath the sea, Mayotte, Comoro Islands, Indian Ocean.

into the interior lagoon is kept open by the incoming and outgoing tides. Atolls are especially common in the South Pacific, and are in some cases several miles in diameter, though rarely rising more than 12 to 15 feet above sea level. They are so low that during hurricanes they are sometimes inundated by the sea. Like the Bermudas, the part above water is made of coral and shell fragments that the waves have thrown on the beach and the wind has drifted into low hills.

Few animals have reached these remote islands; but there are numerous plants, including the coconut palm. Many atolls are inhabited by man.

Atolls are built on the peaks of extinct volcanoes that rise from the sea bottom. Sometimes they seem to have been built on submerged peaks, the ring shape being due to the faster growth on the outside of the reef. In other cases the atolls appear to be due to a slow subsidence of volcanic cones (Fig. 367). According to this explanation there was first a volcanic island surrounded by a fringing reef (Fig. 371a, b, c); by slow sinking this changed to a barrier reef; finally, when the cone had entirely disappeared, there was a ring-shaped atoll where the cone formerly rose. The sinking of the cone could have been no faster than the upward growth of the reef.

Photo by Tarr

Fig. 372. — A serpula atoll off the coast of Bermuda. These are locally known as "boilers." Note how the waves bring food.

Off the coast of Bermuda small ring-shaped islands occur known as *serpula atolls* (Fig. 372). These appear to be stacks (p. 370) cut off to sea level by wave attack and then having their edges built up by deposits made by the serpula organism.

Summary. *Low, ring-shaped coral islands in the open ocean are called atolls. They are built on volcanic cones. In some cases at least, they are caused by a subsidence of the cone at about the same rate as the upward growth of a fringing reef.*

168. Lake shores. Most that has been said about seacoasts applies quite fully to lakes; and illustrations of most shore-line phenomena are found along lake shores. There are headlands, wave-cut cliffs, beaches, bars, sand dunes, islands, promontories, and harbors. There are also elevated and drowned coasts. In fact, from the form alone it is quite impossible to distinguish lake from ocean shores. Figure 356 is from a lake shore.

It is true that tides are absent in all but the largest lakes, and even there are almost unnoticeable. Because the waves are less violent, the lake cliffs are usually smaller, resembling those of bays rather than the open ocean; but along the coasts of great lakes there are some high cliffs.

The effects of life are, however, quite unlike in the two cases. Although swamps are formed in the lagoons and bays of lakes, the plants are very different from those of the salt marsh; and the absence of tide makes the difference between lake swamps and seashore marshes even more marked. In lakes there are no corals, and, consequently, no coral reefs.

Summary. *Lake shores and seacoasts are so alike that, from the form alone, they could not be distinguished. But in lakes there are smaller cliffs, tides are lacking, and the effects of life are different.*

169. Abandoned shore lines. In many places where lakes have disappeared, cliffs and beaches are now found on the land. For example, very perfect beaches, bars, spits, and cliffs are found near Great Salt Lake, marking the shore line of ancient Lake Bonneville (Fig. 305). Similar shore lines mark the level reached by the glacial lakes in the valleys of the Red River of the North (Fig. 120) and the Great Lakes (p. 289). Such beaches are seen at or near Duluth, Chicago, Cleveland, Rochester, Syracuse, and many other points. They are so much like ocean shore lines that for a time they were supposed to have been caused by a sinking of the land, admitting the sea into these valleys.

Elevated sea beaches are found from southern New England to Baffin Land. Near Boston these beaches are from forty to sixty feet above sea level; in Labrador several hundred feet. There are also elevated beaches in Norway, Scotland, and other parts of northwestern Europe. There the country back of the elevated shore lines is irregular, rocky, and not well suited to farming; but between the elevated beaches and the present shore is a narrow plain which is good farm land and well settled. It is an elevated sea bottom, from which the waves have partly removed the islands and promontories, and over which sediment has been strewn. Proof of former wave action at these higher levels is furnished by elevated beaches, marine fossils, islands partly cut away, and cliffs with sea caves and chasms.

Summary. *Shore lines, closely resembling marine shore lines, mark the sites of extinct lakes; and elevated sea beaches are found in northeastern North America and northwestern Europe.*

170. Life history, or cycle of development of a coast line. Elevations and depressions of the land are so frequent that, before the waves have carried their processes very far, some change in level may be expected to bring a new belt of land or sea bottom within the range of their activities. If a coast were allowed to pass through its normal cycle of development uninterrupted, the changes would depend on the nature of the rock, the form of the coast, and the force and direction of waves and currents.

We will start with a rocky, irregular, exposed coast, like that of New England, — a typical *young coast line* (Fig. 346) due to *submergence* or *drowning* of the land. Slowly the headlands are cut back (Figs. 349, 352, 374), some of the materials being moved offshore, some driven along the coast. Of the materials driven

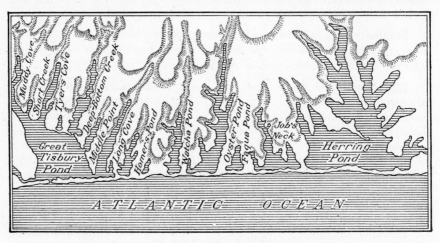

Fig. 373. — A portion of the south shore of Marthas Vineyard, showing how the growth of sand bars may straighten an irregular coast by shutting in the bays and changing them to ponds. Erosion, meanwhile, has also aided by cutting back the headlands.

along shore, bars are made, tying islands to the mainland (Fig. 360) and closing the bays (Figs. 355, 373). Sediment slowly fills the bays, transforming them to salt marshes (Fig. 363), then to dry-land plains. This straightened coast is a *mature coast line*. As the waves continue to cut back the headlands, the beaches and bars are also pushed back, and thus the entire coast line retreats.

If the rock is weak, less time is required for this life history; and if at the beginning the coast is not very irregular, less time is required to straighten it. On coasts of loose sand and clay, with gently sloping bottom, cliffs are first cut, then offshore bars are thrown up (Figs. 375, 106,

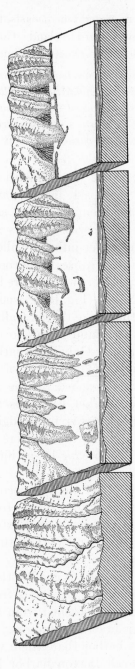

Fig. 374. — To illustrate the changes in a coast line of strong rock, like that of New England. First figure (left) shows a hilly land; second, the same land partly drowned; third, same after cliffs have been cut, bars built, and deltas formed; fourth (right), same after headlands have been cut back farther and bars built completely across bays. Describe the changes illustrated in these four pictures.

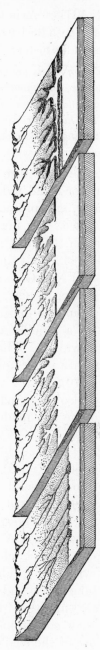

Fig. 375. — To illustrate the life history of a low coast of weak rock, like that south of New York. First figure (left), a sandy coastal plain with streams in shallow valleys; second, the same lowered; third, the first stage of wave action, forming cliffs and short bars (see Fig. 361); fourth, offshore bars have been formed with salt marshes behind, partly filling the lagoons. This is the stage shown in Fig. 361. In a further stage the offshore bar would be pushed back and the waves once more allowed to attack the mainland.

361, 362, and Plate VIII). As in the case of other straightened coasts, the waves then gradually push the barrier beaches back toward the land. Coral coasts have a different life history, for they depend on the growth of animals.

Summary. *Young coasts are irregular: as they advance toward maturity headlands are cut back, bay mouths are closed, and irregularities are filled; then both headlands and beaches are slowly moved backward as the land is consumed. This life history requires a longer time in strong than in weak rock. On gently sloping coasts of weak rock, one of the earliest stages is the building of offshore bars.*

171. Harbors. No feature of the seacoast is more important than the harbors, or small indentations of the coast, deep enough for vessels to enter, and protected enough for them to remain safe from wind and wave. By far the greater number of harbors are caused by sinking of the land, admitting the water into the valleys (Figs. 339, 344, 345, 442); but there are many other causes for harbors.

Some, like that of New Orleans, are on large rivers where there has been little or no sinking; others, like that of Naples (Fig. 191), occupy bays formed by mountain uplift; and still others, like that of Callao, are merely part of a straight coast where an island serves to cut off the winds and waves. What is the cause for Galveston harbor (p. 375)? There are others of similar origin. The lagoon of an atoll (Figs. 369, 370), and a volcanic crater breached by the sea (Fig. 219), may also form harbors. Among other causes is the work of man: for he has made many harbors, either by dredging shallow tidal rivers, as at Glasgow, or by building breakwaters on harborless coasts. He has also connected the oceans by artificial straits (Figs. 376, 509).

For a harbor to be useful at the present day and to become the site of a great city, it must be easily entered, afford shelter from wind and wave, be deep enough to admit large vessels, and extensive enough to accommodate many large ships and permit them to be moved about. It should also be free of obstruction by ice and of difficulty with strong tidal currents. If there is good bottom for anchors to take hold, and if the water in the harbor is fresh enough from river supply so that barnacles are loosened from the ship's bottom, such conditions are further favorable factors. It was partly because of the shallowness of its harbor that Salem was outstripped by its neighbor Boston; but even Boston harbor has needed deepening and improvement to admit large modern ships.

Photo by Isthmian Canal Commission

Fig. 376.— Digging the Panama Canal, Gaillard Cut, October, 1915. Where the oceans were unconnected, man cut a passageway for ships through the land.

To become the site of a great city, a harbor should also have a large area of productive country tributary to it. Baltimore, Philadelphia, New York, and Boston harbors are open to shipment not only from the country round about, but also from the great interior; and New York owes its superiority over the others largely to the fact that it has connection with the interior by water as well as by rail. On the other hand, Castine, Maine, has a better harbor than New York; but it is not connected with an extensive productive country, and consequently has not developed.

Summary. *A harbor is an indentation of the coast, deep enough for vessels to enter and so situated as to be protected from winds and waves. There are numerous causes for harbors, of which sinking of the land is most important; man also makes harbors by dredging or by building breakwaters. To be the site of a great city, a harbor must be deep enough for large vessels and have an extensive area of productive country tributary to it.*

TOPICAL OUTLINE, QUESTIONS, SUGGESTIONS, AND LABORATORY EXERCISES

TOPICAL OUTLINE. 154. **Importance of shore lines.** Sites of the world's largest cities; shipping; dangers of approach; lighthouses; lightships; foghorns; pilots; radio; buoys; life-saving stations; summer resorts. Seacoast ever changing.

155. **Elevated sea-bottom coasts.** Nature of coast; illustrations; unhealthfulness; agriculture; harbors; sinking of coast; sand bars.

156. **Straight mountainous coasts.** Effect of uplift; western America, — straight coast, mountains, narrow plain, sea-bottom slopes; recent uplift; settlement, — few harbors, limited resources, mountain barrier.

157. **Irregular mountainous coasts.** Cause of islands; of peninsulas; sinking of crust between ranges; Mediterranean, — cause, entrance, irregular coast; other large seas; small irregularities; sinking of coast; settlement; communication by land; development of navigation; western Italy.

158. **Coasts of drowned lands.** (*a*) Resulting irregularity: bays and harbors; instances; drowned rivers; shoals and banks; islands; peninsulas. (*b*) Fiord coasts: origin of fiords; instances; settlement. (*c*) Regions of weak rock: effect on coast form; settlement. (*d*) Importance of irregular coasts: harbors; length of coast line; fishing and navigation; interior waterways; instances. (*e*) Islands: isolation; Newfoundland; Great Britain.

159. **Action of waves and currents.** Movement of fragments (*a*) offshore, (*b*) alongshore; diagonal approach of waves; longshore currents; result; reasons for irregular coasts; straightening coast.

160. **Sea cliffs.** Zone of wave action; action of breakers; wave-cut and wave-built terrace; plain of marine denudation; steepness of cliffs, — strong rock, weak rock, height; chasms; stacks; sea arches; sea caves; limit to wave action.

161. **Beaches, hooks, bars, etc.** Disposition of fragments; grinding of pebbles; wave mill; bars across bays; bars supplied from sea cliffs; hooks; spits; cusps.

162. **Offshore bars.** Instances; lagoons; gaps in bars; closing of gaps; cause of offshore bars; effect of wind; occupants of bars; cities on bars; shoals.

163. **Sand dunes of the seacoast.** Location; form; effect of removal of forest; instances; encroachment; Netherlands.

164. **Salt marshes.** Location; aid of plants; channels on marsh; change to dry land; value; diked land; illustrations; United States.

165. **Mangrove swamps.** Location; jungle.

166. **Coral reefs.** Favoring conditions; differences among corals; polyps; abundant life in a coral reef; growth of reef; fringing reef; barrier reef; two causes for barrier reefs; Great Barrier Reef; elevated reefs; making of land; Bermudas.

167. **Atolls.** Form; lagoon; size; elevation; cause of elevation; plants, animals, and man; two explanations; serpula atolls.

168. **Lake shores.** Resemblance to ocean shores; phenomena in common; absence of tides; smaller cliffs; effects of life.

169. **Abandoned shore lines.** Lake shores; instances; resemblance to ocean shore lines; elevated seashores; instances; characteristics.

170. **Life history, or cycle of development of a coast line.** Controlling conditions; young coast; changes in young coast; mature coast; consuming of land; effect of weak rock; offshore bars.

171. **Harbors.** (*a*) Definition. (*b*) Causes: sinking of land; rivers; mountain uplift; islands; lagoons behind barrier beaches; atoll lagoons; crater harbors; work of man. (*c*) Sites of great cities: summary of favorable harbor conditions; tributary country; illustrations.

QUESTIONS. Section 154. For what is the coast most important? What facts in regard to the location of large cities prove this? What does the government do to fit it better for commerce? To warn sailors of danger? To protect them? Why is the coast a summer resort? Explain the changing conditions of the seacoast.

155. What conditions are unfavorable to the utilization of elevated sea-bottom coasts? Why are the harbors so poor?

156. What are the results of the rising of long chains of mountains? What is the condition on the coast of western South America? Why are such conditions unfavorable to dense population?

157. How does mountain growth cause irregular coasts? What are the conditions in the Mediterranean? Give other instances of irregular coasts. What is the condition in Greece? Why were such coasts favorable to the early development of navigation? Why unfavorable to dense settlement?

158. What results are produced by entrance of the sea into valleys? Give illustrations. What are the results of complete or partial submergence of hills? How do the nature of the rock and the valley form influence the coast outline? What effect has this on settlement? Why are moderately low, irregular coasts favorable to settlement? What effect has sinking of the land on island people? Give illustrations.

159. What changes are the waves and currents producing? What effect does this have on irregular coasts? Account for the diagonal approach of waves, longshore currents. Why are not all coasts regular?

160. How are sea cliffs formed? Account for wave-cut and wave-built terraces. For plains of marine denudation. How do cliffs in strong and weak rocks differ? What effect has variation in rock formation?

161. What becomes of the rock fragments drifted along the shore? Explain the wave mill. How do the materials vary? What forms are assumed by the bars thus built?

162. Describe the bars along the Texas coast. How are they formed? Of what importance are barrier beaches?

163. What are the characteristics of sand dunes? What damage do sand dunes cause? What is the condition in the Netherlands?

164. Where are salt marshes formed? How? What is the result? Of what importance are salt marshes?

165. What are mangrove swamps? Where are they found?

166. Under what conditions do corals thrive? How is coral made? How do the polyps live? How do the reefs grow? In what two ways are barrier reefs formed? Describe the Great Barrier Reef. What is the origin of the Bermudas?

167. What are the characteristics of atolls? Where are they found? How are they caused?

168. Compare and contrast lake and sea shores.

169. Give instances of abandoned lake-shore lines. Of elevated seashore lines. What is their nature?

170. What causes are there for variation in the life history or cycle of development of a coast line? State the life history of a strong rock, irregular coast. What differences are there where the rock is weak?

171. What is the cause for most harbors? State other causes for harbors. What factors are of importance in determining the growth of cities about harbors? Give two instances.

SUGGESTIONS. (1) Take some angular fragments of a weak rock, or brick, and shake them for a few moments in a fruit jar containing water. What causes the water to become muddy? Find out how marbles are rounded. (2) In a shallow pan, mold an irregular land of clay. Carefully pour in water until the land is partly drowned. Study the land forms produced. (3) If the school is near the seashore or the shore of a lake, at least one excursion should be made to study shore phenomena. Are there beaches? Where does the material come from? Are there cliffs? What is happening there? Have any portions been recently removed by the waves? Do the bowlders or pebbles show signs of rounding? What is the cause? Where does the finer ground-up material go? Are there any mud flats? What is the source of the material? Ask some fisherman what material covers the bottom offshore. Are there salt marshes? What are their characteristics? Are tidal currents effecting any changes? (4) If the school is on a sea or lake port, the harbor should be studied; its form; depth (making use of a Coast Survey map); cause; nature of bottom; improvements made; others needed; lighthouses; other guides and aids to entrance; source of principal materials received for shipment; of principal imports; places to which these are distributed; reasons for importance of port.

Laboratory Exercises. Exercises XXXVIII and XXXIX in TARR and VON ENGELN's *Laboratory Manual for Physical and Commercial Geography*, The Macmillan Company, should be done in connection with the study of this chapter.

Reference Books. One recent volume, JOHNSON, *Shore Processes and Shoreline Development*, John Wiley & Sons, New York, 1919, contains so comprehensive an account and so complete a bibliography of other works on its subject that it will serve as a handbook and guide. Other books of special interest are: SHALER, *Sea and Land*, Charles Scribner's Sons, New York, 1894; DARWIN, *Structure and Distribution of Coral Reefs*, D. Appleton & Company, New York, 1889; DANA, *Corals and Coral Islands*, Dodd, Mead & Company, New York, 1895.

CHAPTER XII

THE ATMOSPHERE

172. Composition and functions of the air. (A) *Oxygen, Nitrogen, Argon, and Carbon Dioxide.* We live at the bottom of a vast ocean of air, the atmosphere, that surrounds and is part of the earth, and is held to it by surface gravity. Unlike the hydrosphere which consists almost completely of the one substance, water, the ocean of air is a mixture of a number of gases and other materials. At the bottom levels, where we live, four gases comprise almost the whole bulk of dry atmosphere. There is very nearly 21% of *oxygen*, a little over 78% of *nitrogen*, almost 1% of *argon* and 0.03% of *carbon dioxide*. Together these gases make up 99.99% of the *dry* atmosphere near the surface of the earth, thus leaving only 0.01% not accounted for. This small remainder consists of the rare gases *helium, neon, krypton,* and *xenon.* Hydrogen and helium are the main constituents of the upper atmosphere (Fig. 377). Oxygen is of vital importance to man and all animals, because through breathing it energy is released. Nitrogen and argon are inert; they add to the bulk of the air and dilute the oxygen.

Carbon dioxide (often called carbonic acid gas), in spite of its small quantity, is very important. It is composed of one part of carbon and two of oxygen, and plants have the power of separating the carbon dioxide into its parts, building the carbon into their tissues.

In the bodies of animals, on the other hand, oxygen unites with carbon by a process of slow combustion, and with each breath carbon dioxide is returned to the air. Fire is a more rapid form of combustion, oxygen combining with the carbon of the wood, coal, oil, etc., and forming carbon dioxide. All forms of combustion, whether rapid or slow, produce heat. In such rapid combustion as fire, sufficient heat is produced to do much work, — for example, the heat used in the production of steam, the energy of which is used to run locomotives or machinery. In the gas engines of auto-

395

mobiles the heat of such combustion is used to make the engine turn; hence these are called internal combustion engines. Man and animals are slow internal combustion engines. Food, in the same way as gasoline, furnishes the carbon, and the oxygen we breathe combines with it. By such slow combustion the necessary heat is produced to form the energy needed for life and movement.

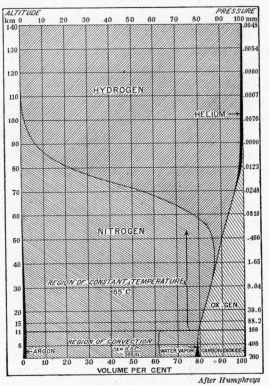

The inertness (that is, its resistance to entering into combination with other elements) of nitrogen is indicated by the fact that it is so successfully used to fill electric light bulbs. In nitrogen-filled bulbs the fine tungsten filament heats up without burning. If, instead of tungsten and nitrogen, steel and pure oxygen were used, the steel would burn up like paper, forming iron oxide.

After Humphreys

Fig. 377. — Diagram to show the composition of the atmosphere at different altitudes above the earth's surface. In the lower levels the figures are based on actual determinations; the composition at the upper levels is calculated. Note how small the per cents of carbon dioxide, water vapor, and argon are, and how great the per cent of nitrogen is in the lower levels. The altitudes on the left are given in kilometers; change these to miles. The pressures on the right are in millimeters of mercury; change these to inches.

Summary. *The atmosphere is a mixture of gases. Argon and nitrogen are quite inert; carbon dioxide, which exists in very small quantities, is of vital importance to plants; oxygen is breathed by all animals, in them it produces slow combustion, which gives the necessary heat for life. It also causes rapid combustion in fire.*

(B) *Water vapor.* Water vapor rises from all damp surfaces and water bodies; that is, liquid water is *evaporating* or changing to an invisible gas, and mingling with the other gases of the atmosphere. The quantities of the other gases do not change, but up to 5 per cent of water vapor particles is added to them. The water vapor particles may be thought of as being distributed through the air much in the same way as fine dust particles floating in air are. The evaporation, or mingling into the air of the water vapor particles, causes wet clothes to become dry when hung on a line, and the water on sidewalks to dry up after a rain. The amount of water vapor varies from place to place, some regions having very dry air, others damp or humid air. Even in the same place the amount of vapor differs from time to time, some days being humid, others dry. When the air is dry, evaporation is rapid and the sky clear; but when there is much vapor, there may be clouds and rain. The condensation of this water vapor gives rise to dew, frost, fog, clouds, rain, snow, sleet, and hail. The higher the temperature of the air is, the greater is the amount of water vapor it may include in its volume without condensation.

Summary. *Invisible water vapor, which rises from water bodies and damp surfaces, is also mixed with the air, in varying amounts.*

(C) *Dust particles.* Solid particles that float in the air are called dust. Some of these are whirled up from the ground by winds; some are bits of carbon from smoke, or pollen of plants, or microbes. Dust particles accumulate around cities, causing a dull, hazy atmosphere; but during long periods of drought, or when forest fires are burning, the air even in the country becomes hazy with dust. Rain washes dust from the air, so that it is usually clearer after a rain storm. Over the ocean, and on high mountains, the air is notably free from dust particles.

Dust is important in furnishing solid particles around which vapor condenses to form fog and rain. Injurious microbes drifted about by the winds contribute to the spread of disease.

Summary. *Particles of dust, smoke, microbes, and other solids often cause the air to be hazy, especially near cities.*

(D) *The upper atmosphere.* At elevations of over six miles in the arctic regions and nine miles in the tropics above the sea-level surface of the earth, the temperature of the atmosphere remains nearly constant at 67° below 0° F. (—55° C.) and its composition changes. Water vapor is not present above the 6 to 9 mile level.

Carbon dioxide and argon diminish rapidly in per cent of total volume with increasing elevation, as does oxygen. The nitrogen percentage increases up to 37 miles and then diminishes very rapidly. Above 60 miles the atmosphere is considered to consist almost exclusively of hydrogen and helium gases. These conditions are shown graphically in Fig. 377. There is evidence that at the very topmost surface of the ocean of air another gas, *coronium*, exists. This is unknown, as yet, on the earth, but is considered to be also a constituent of the gases of the sun. The other different upper atmosphere gas, helium, is obtainable from certain natural gas wells and because of its lightness and incombustibility is mixed with hydrogen for filling the gas chambers of dirigible airships. (See Fig. 339.)

Summary. *At elevations of over seven miles on the average the temperature of the atmosphere remains nearly constant and its composition differs from that of the air at lower levels.*

173. Effect of gravity. Although light and invisible, the atmosphere has perceptible weight. One particle, drawn down by gravity, presses on those below it, as a stone in a pile presses on those beneath. Since the atmosphere may extend in appreciable quantity to a height of two hundred miles or more, this great column has a weight that can be measured. At sea level, its normal or average weight is nearly 15 (14.7) pounds to every square inch of surface. This is equal to a column of about 30 feet of water, or 30 inches of mercury.

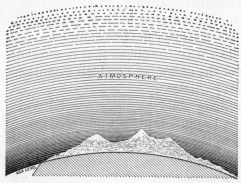

Fig. 378. — To illustrate the decrease in density of the atmosphere from sea level to higher regions.

Since there are many square inches on the surface of a human body, it is evident that each of us bears a great weight of air; but as the pressure is equal, both inside and out, we do not notice it (p. 333). If this pressure were suddenly removed from the outside, the expansion of the air within our bodies would burst many of the tissues.

Pressure pushes the molecules of gases closer together; and, therefore, the air is denser near the earth than higher up (Fig. 378). As a result of this, fully two thirds of the atmosphere is within six miles of sea level; and the air is less than one half as dense at the top of a high mountain, like Mt. St. Elias, as at its base. The air on mountain tops is so thin, or *rarefied*, that it is difficult to breathe oxygen enough for the needs of the body. Some men and animals have become accustomed to this rarefied air and are able to live in high altitudes; but a traveler from lower levels finds his breathing greatly quickened by the effort to get enough oxygen, and not uncommonly he becomes quite exhausted.

Air is so extremely elastic that even slight differences in temperature change its density or weight. For example, the air filling a room $10 \times 20 \times 20$ feet weighs 301 pounds at 60°; but when the temperature is raised to 80°, the air is so expanded that there are only 291 pounds in the room. Air that includes much water vapor is lighter than dry air.

The pull of gravity is greater on heavy than on light air, and these differences in weight start movements of the air, causing winds (p. 426).

Summary. *Air has weight—at sea level about fifteen pounds to the square inch. It is compressed, or more dense, at the bottom; and lighter, or more rarefied, higher up. It is very elastic, varying in density with temperature, and is easily set in motion.*

174. Light.[1] Part of the energy emitted by bodies having a high temperature, for example, burning coal, red-hot iron, and the white-hot sun, we perceive and experience as light and heat. This energy, coming from the sun, travels at great speed, crossing the distance of 93,000,000 miles which separates earth and sun in about eight minutes.

The sunlight which comes to us is made of a series of waves, differing in length and color, the union of which forms white light. If a beam of sunlight is allowed to pass through a three-sided glass prism these waves are turned, each at a slightly different angle. The beam enters as white light, but comes out with the color waves separated, among which violet, indigo, blue, green, yellow, orange, and red may be recognized. This bending of light rays is called *refraction;* the colors are called the *colors of the spectrum*, or of the rainbow.

Some of the rays that reach a body are sent back or away from it, or are *reflected*. This is especially true of smooth surfaces, like water or the glass of a mirror; but it is true even of irregular surfaces, like the ground. It is reflected sunlight that makes the moon

[1] A thorough study of the nature and behavior of light belongs to physics, but the student of physical geography should understand the main reasons for the color phenomena of the atmosphere.

and planets appear light; and the earth would have the same appearance if seen from them.

Refraction and reflection cause many changes in light as it passes through the atmosphere. *Mirage* is caused by reflection when layers of air have different temperatures and, consequently, different densities. It is especially perfect in deserts and on the sea, commonly showing objects inverted — a vessel with the masts downward, for instance — and above their real position. Because of such elevation the mirage image may be seen many miles distant from the object reflected. In deserts mirage causes an appearance of water which is often very deceptive.

Photo by Lee Russell

Fig. 379. — Mock sun and halo due to refraction of light by the ice crystals of cirrus clouds high up in the atmosphere.

Rainbows are caused by refraction of light in its passage through raindrops and reflection of the spectrum colors thus produced. The *halos* around sun and moon are due to similar changes in the light rays, in their passage through the ice crystals of thin, fleecy clouds high in the air. (Fig. 379.)

The colors of leaves, flowers, and other objects are due to reflection. When light reaches some objects, for example white paper, all the waves are reflected and the paper appears white. Other objects, like black cloth, reflect very little light, the rays being absorbed. Still other objects absorb some of the waves and reflect others, thus giving color. A red flower, for instance, reflects an excess of red waves; and green leaves, green waves.

Diffraction, or *selective scattering*, is an important cause for color effect in the sky. The gas molecules and dust in the air interfere with the passage of light waves, as small pebbles in shallow water interfere with water waves. By this interference, some of the waves that make the white light are turned aside, or *scattered*. The waves having the shortest length, or those on the violet end of the spectrum, are most easily turned aside; that is, they are selected for scattering.

The blue color of the sky is due to the selective scattering of the short blue waves by the gas molecules of the air itself. Dust, in addition to its action as a scattering medium, reflects all colors of light equally, so that at times the sky is milky white, or mixed blue and white in directions away from the sun. The gas molecules and fine dust reflect the scattered blue rays; the coarser, or more abundant, dust reflects all rays. When there is much dust in the air, the longer red and yellow rays may also be scattered by it, giving red and yellow colors to the sky. These colors are especially common at sunrise and sunset, when the rays pass for a long distance through the dust-filled lower layers of the air (Fig. 380). The varied cloud colors of sunrise and sunset are the result of reflection of colors caused by refraction and diffraction.

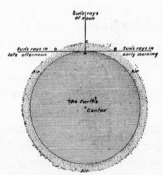

Fig. 380. — To show that the sun's rays pass through more air when the sun is low in the heavens than when it is high.

Summary. *White light is made by the union of a number of waves of different length, which, when separated by refraction, give the colors of the spectrum. These colors may be reflected, as in colored objects, rainbows, halos, and clouds at sunset. The scattering, or diffraction, of waves by the interference of gas molecules and dust gives the blue color to the sky and the reds and yellows of sunrise and sunset.*

175. Heat. (A) *Radiant energy.* On approaching a radiator or hot stove one feels its warmth, even at a distance of several feet. Waves of heat from the stove have passed that distance through the air. If the stove is very hot, the cover may be red; then the waves from it produce not only heat, but the sensation of light on the eye. This form of energy, which we call heat and light, is known as *radiant energy,* and the process of emitting it is called *radiation.* The greatest well-known center of radiant energy is the sun; but doubtless some of the stars are still larger and hotter, though so far away that they do not influence us.

Radiation causes a loss of heat, and by it bodies grow cooler; thus, in a few hours, a stove with the fire out will by radiation (and other processes) lose all its heat and become cold. The sun is also losing heat, radiating it outward in all directions; but millions of years will be required for the sun to grow cold because it is apparently developing heat almost as fast as it radiates it. A very small proportion of the heat radiated from the sun is intercepted by the earth (Fig. 21), where it causes many important effects.

Summary. *Radiant energy, i.e., heat and light, which is emitted from hot bodies is being radiated in all directions from the sun, at an almost constant rate.*

(B) *Passage of radiant energy.* Certain substances, such as glass and the gases of the air, allow light to pass so freely that they are said to be *transparent.* Air also allows heat to pass freely, or is *diathermanous.* For this reason, notwithstanding the thickness of the atmosphere, the sun's rays at midday, near the equator, reach the earth's surface with little change.

Dust particles interfere with the passage of light rays, as we have seen; and, in much the same way, they interfere with the passage of heat. This is clearly proved by the difference in brightness and warmth of the sun at midday and late in the afternoon; for often it is possible to look directly at the setting sun. Then many of the rays are intercepted in their passage through the great thickness of dust-laden air near the surface (Fig. 380).

Summary. *Air and other substances are transparent to light. Air also allows heat waves to pass through it, or is diathermanous. The interference of dust greatly lessens the sun's power when it is low in the heavens.*

(C) *Radiation from the earth.* Bodies that are warmer than their surroundings emit waves of radiant energy. The earth itself is radiating into space the heat that comes to it from the sun; if this were not so, it would grow warmer and warmer. During the day more heat comes than can be radiated; but at night, when the sun's rays are cut off, radiation cools the ground. In summer, when the days are longer than the nights and the sun is high in the heavens, the ground grows steadily warmer; but in winter, when the days are short and the sun low in the heavens, radiation is so far in excess of the supply of heat that the ground becomes cold.

Some bodies are much better radiators than others. Rocks and earth radiate heat better than water, and hence cool more quickly. This is one reason why, in winter, the land becomes colder than the water. On cold nights those objects that radiate their heat most quickly have most frost. Perhaps you can observe this difference early some frosty morning.

Summary. *The earth is always radiating heat, and this is why it becomes cool or cold at night and in winter. Some objects, such as water, are poorer radiators than others, such as the ground.*

(D) *Reflection and absorption.* Bodies that reflect light also reflect heat. Water, for example, reflects a large percentage of the rays that reach its surface, and one becomes sunburned so easily on water because the reflected rays are added to the rays received directly, and also because the reflected rays fall on parts of the skin ordinarily shaded from the direct rays. Quarries and city streets are warmer than the open country, partly because the sun's rays are reflected from their walls.

Some bodies reflect little, the sun's rays being used mainly in warming them. Such bodies are said to *absorb* heat. This is especially true of black objects, whereas white objects reflect; therefore white clothing is cooler than black. This can be readily proved in winter by placing two pieces of cloth, one black, the other white, on a bank of snow in the sunlight. The black cloth soon sinks into the snow because the sun warms it, whereas the white cloth remains at the surface.

Summary. *Some bodies, such as water and white objects, reflect much heat; others, such as black objects, absorb heat and, therefore, warm more rapidly.*

(E) *Conduction.* With a fire inside of it a stove becomes warm; and an iron placed on the stove is also heated. In this case heat from the fire is transmitted, or *conducted*, through the stove. In the same way, some of the sun's heat is conducted below the surface of the water or ground, and some of it into the air which rests on these; but water, air, and ground are not such good conductors as iron. The ground is so poor a conductor that, at a depth of from ten to twenty feet, there is practically no difference in temperature from summer to winter.

Summary. *Heat is transmitted, or conducted, into the water and ground and from these into the air; but air, water, and ground are all poor conductors.*

(F) *Convection.* The lower layers of water in a kettle on a stove are warmed by conduction. Warm water is lighter than cooler water, and, since gravity tends to draw the heavy water to the bottom, these warm lower layers cannot stay there. They are, therefore, crowded up at the center by the settling of the cooler layers of the same height at the sides of the kettle. This transfer of heat by movement of the medium is convection, and, if the heating is continued, all of the water is finally made boiling hot.

Similar convection occurs in air warmed by a lamp. As fast as it is warmed near the lamp it grows lighter and is pushed up by heavier surrounding air. The movement of heavier air to crowd up warm air is what causes the draft in a fire; and the crowding upward of the warm air is what causes it to go up the chimney. When a great forest fire is burning strong air currents moving in along the ground toward the fire are experienced.

Heat from the sun is the cause for very extensive convection of the air in all parts of the earth. Warmed in one place, usually by conduction of heat from the ground or water, the warm light air is pushed away by heavier air drawn down by gravity. This is a chief originating cause of winds (p. 426).

Summary. *Heat makes both water and air lighter; and gravity, by drawing down heavier air, causes a transfer, or convection, of the heat through the rising of the warmed lower layers. Winds are started by convection.*

176. Warming of land, water, and air. (A) *The lands.* The lands are warmed by absorption during the day, and some of the heat is conducted into the ground, warming the upper few feet into which the roots of plants reach. The ground nowhere becomes excessively warm, because much of the heat is lost by reflection, by radiation, and by conduction into the air. Everywhere the ground warms during a hot, sunny day, and cools by radiation at night.

In the tropical zone the ground does not become very cool at night, because radiation is unable to remove all the heat absorbed during the hot days. A similar condition exists during the summer with its hot and *long* days in the temperate zones; but, in winter, radiation during the long nights so chills the ground that it freezes. In the frigid, or polar, zones, radiation during the long winter causes the ground to freeze to depths of hundreds of feet, and the short, cool summer supplies only heat enough to melt the upper two or three feet (pp. 128, 535).

There are other differences in the warming of the lands. For example, dark-colored surfaces warm more quickly than light, and bare soils more quickly than those covered by vegetation. There are also differences according to exposure; for instance, in the northern hemisphere, between shady north slopes and sunny south slopes, and between hilltops and valleys, whose sides reflect heat into the valley and also interfere with winds and with radiation. A clayey soil which holds water warms slowly and is said to be a cold soil; a porous sandy soil, on the other hand, warms up quickly under the spring sun and is called an early soil. (See also Appendix C.)

Summary. *The lands are warmed by absorption and cooled by reflection, conduction, and radiation. The effect of the sun's heat varies in different zones; also according to the color of the surface, the cover of vegetation, the exposure, and the nature of the soil.*

(B) *The waters.* It is a well-known fact that water warms less quickly than land. There are a number of reasons for this. (1) Water reflects heat more readily than land, and, consequently, there is less heat to warm it. (2) When one part is warmed more than another, it is set in motion, convection, so that there is a tendency for the heat to be distributed. (3) Water is so transparent that, unlike ground, some of the rays pass into it, warming layers below the surface. Sunlight penetrates, though dimly, to depths of several hundred feet. (4) Twice as much heat is required to raise the temperature of a pound of water one degree as of an equal quantity of rock. (5) Some of the heat is expended in evaporating the water, and this is called "latent heat," or *heat of vaporization.*

It is for these reasons that even a small body of water warms more slowly during the day, and during summer, than the neighboring land (p. 313). At nighttime and in winter, on the other hand, because it is a very poor radiator, and because a considerable depth of it has been warmed, water cools much more slowly than land. Therefore, from day to night, and from summer to winter, there is slight range of temperature in large water bodies, and the climate over them is far less extreme than over land (Fig. 322). A climate with such slight changes of temperature is called *equable.* Be careful not to confuse this word with equitable.

Summary. *Water warms more slowly than land because it reflects more heat, is movable, is transparent, and some of the heat it receives is expended in evaporation. It cools more slowly because it is a poorer radiator and because so much of it has a high temperature. Therefore near large water bodies the climate is equable.*

(C) *The air.* The air is not perfectly diathermanous. Therefore some of the sun's rays, and some of the heat rays radiated from the earth, are intercepted in their passage through the atmosphere. Dust is especially effective in intercepting heat waves (p. 402). A still more important cause for the warming of air is conduction from the ground to the lower layers, which, being lighter, are then forced to rise by convection. In the same way a stove warms the air in a room, by radiation, conduction, and convection. At night and in winter the air cools by radiation; and contact with the ground is another important cause for cooling.

Water vapor and dust interfere with radiation, and for this reason more heat is retained in the lower atmosphere on hazy and muggy days than in clear, dry weather. At such times radiation fails to cool the ground, and a hot, muggy day may be followed by an oppressive, almost stifling night. It is under such conditions that our most oppressive summer weather comes.

Summary. *The air is warmed somewhat by the passage of heat rays through it, but far more by conduction from the ground, and by convection. It is cooled by radiation, and by conduction to the ground. Vapor and dust interfere with radiation.*

177. Causes for differences in temperature on the earth. (A) *Position of sun.* The sun is higher in the heavens at noon than in

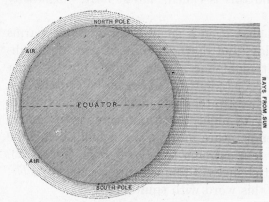

early morning and late afternoon; in summer than in winter; and in tropical than in temperate zones. When low in the heavens, the sun's power is less than when high, because (1) the rays pass through a great thickness of dust-laden air when the sun is low (Figs. 380, 381), and (2) fewer rays then reach a given area of surface (Fig. 382).

Fig. 381. — To show that near the poles the sun's rays reach the earth in a more slanting way and after passing through more air than at the equator.

There are three important results of these different positions of the sun. (1) Every day, as the angle at which the sun's rays pass through the air varies (Fig. 380), the amount of heat received from them on a given area varies. (2) As the sun changes position, from high in the heavens to lower, the seasons of summer and winter occur in both hemispheres (Fig. 525). (3) Where the sun is highest all the year round, that is in the tropical zone, the year-round climate is uniformly warm or hot near sea level; and the

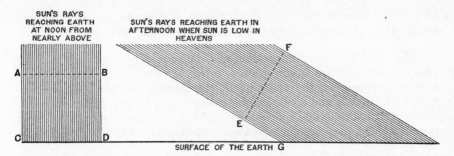

SUN'S RAYS
REACHING EARTH
AT NOON FROM
NEARLY ABOVE

SUN'S RAYS REACHING EARTH IN
AFTERNOON WHEN SUN IS LOW IN
HEAVENS

SURFACE OF THE EARTH G

Fig. 382. — Two bundles of rays having the same width (**AB** and **EF**); but, owing
to the difference in angle at which they reach the surface CH, those that are inclined
cover about twice as much ground as those that come straight down from above.   Therefore, on the same area there are about half as many inclined rays as vertical.

climate grows cooler away from the equator as the sun appears
lower in the heavens (Figs. 381, 383, 519).

Summary. *When the sun is low in the heavens it warms less than when
high, because (1) the rays pass through so much air, and (2) fewer rays reach a
given area.   Changes in the
sun's position in the heavens
from morning to night, from
season to season, and from place
to place, therefore cause differences in temperature.*

(B) *Altitude.* Observa-
tions on mountains and in
balloons show that, as the
elevation increases, there is
in general a gradual decrease
in temperature at the rate
of about 1° F. for every
300 feet, up to altitudes of
from six to nine miles (Fig.
377).   There is no warm
ground to impart heat to
these upper layers of the
atmosphere; and warm air,
rising from the surface, expands and cools as it rises.

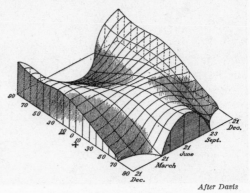

After Davis

Fig. 383. — A diagram in three dimensions to
show the amount of heat received by an equal
area of land or sea at (a) different latitudes and
(b) at different seasons.   The solid part of the
figure shows the amount of heat received at any
latitude, shown on the left side, and at any date,
shown at the front.   Note that (although the
amount of *daylight* in a year is the same at the
equator and at either pole) less than one half
as much heat is received at the poles as at the
equator.   (See Figs. 381, 382.)

Because the upper air is so cool, a
frigid climate is found at the equator at a height of a few miles;

and the average day temperatures on highlands are everywhere cooler than those of neighboring lowlands (Figs. 384, 420).

That air warms on compression may be proved by a tire pump. Air pumped into the tire is compressed, or made more dense, and therefore warmed. When, on the other hand, this compressed air is allowed to escape, it expands and cools, and its coolness may be felt as it comes out.

Although surrounded by cold air, parts of highlands exposed to direct rays of the sun may become quite warm at midday. On a high mountain

Fig. 384. — Snowfall above, rainfall below on a winter's day on a mountain in England. This shows the effect of altitude on temperature. This mountain does not have a snow cover in summer. Saddleback and Druid's Circle, England.

one may, therefore, be very warm in a protected, sunny place, while a few feet away, in a shady spot, or one exposed to the wind, it is very cold. Radiation is so rapid in the clear, thin, upper layers of air that even the warm places quickly cool off when the sun disappears; in fact, the temperature may rise to 90° at midday and descend to 10° at night. High plateaus are especially subject to these rapid and great changes of temperature.

Summary. *Highlands are cooler than lowlands, the temperature changing about 1° for every 300 feet. There is no warm land to warm the upper air.*

and air cools as it rises and expands. Rapid radiation in the clear, thin air causes cold nights. High plateaus are especially subject to great temperature changes between day and night.

(C) *Other reasons for differences.* We have already learned several reasons for differences in temperature according to situation; for example, nature of soil, exposure (p. 404), and influence of water bodies (p. 405). The nature and direction of the wind also influence temperature (p. 442). These causes for differences in temperature are more fully treated in Chapter XIV.

178. Daily and seasonal temperature changes. (A) *Daily range.* The warmest period, normally, is not midday, when the sun is highest, but two or three hours after noon (Fig. 385). The reason

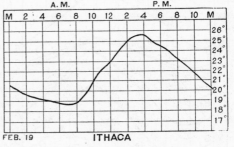

Fig. 385. — Normal daily temperature range in winter at Ithaca, New York.

for this is that in the morning it is first necessary to warm the ground that was cooled by radiation the night before. After the ground is warmed, the temperature continues to rise until the sun has sunk so low that heat is radiated away faster than it is received. Then the ground and air commence to cool, continuing to do so until sunrise. Therefore the coldest period is not mid-

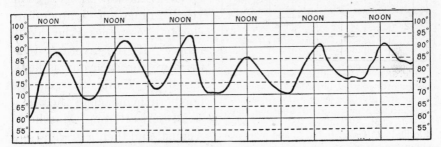

Fig. 386. — Change in temperature for six successive summer days at Ithaca, New York.

night, but just before sunrise (Fig. 385). Because of these conditions there is a normal daily change, or range, of temperature similar to that shown in the diagram (Fig. 385).

There are a number of conditions which may occasionally interfere with the normal daily range (Fig. 386). A cloudy sky, interfering with the passage of the sun's rays, may prevent the temperature from rising **after** noon. On the other hand it also interferes with the loss of heat by reradiation from the earth. Accordingly the range of temperature on cloudy days is not normally so great as on clear days. Winds may bring air so cold that the temperature falls, even during the daytime; or warm winds may cause the temperature to rise throughout the night.

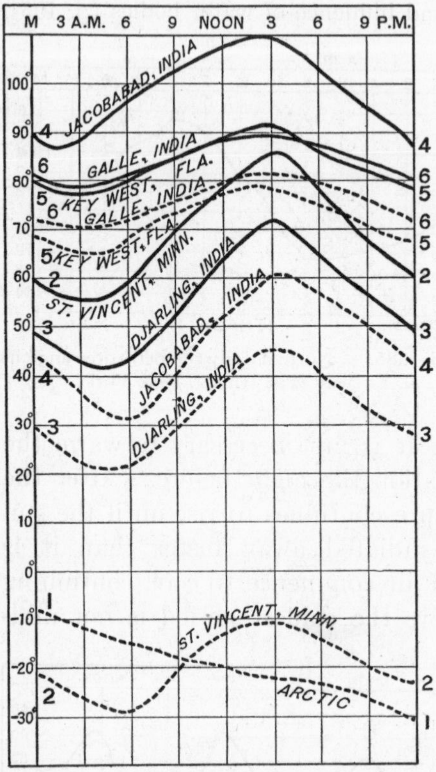

Fig. 387. — Normal summer (heavy line) and winter (dotted line) daily temperature range for several places. (1) Arctic; (2) St. Vincent, Minnesota; (3) Djarling, India; (4) Jacobabad, India; (5) Key West, Florida; (6) Galle, India; 5 and 6 are near the warm ocean.

The amount of change from day to night varies from time to time and from place to place. Thus the range is great when warm days are followed by cool nights, and less when cool days are followed by cool nights. The daily range in winter is quite different from that in summer; it is different at the equator from what it is in temperate latitudes; and on the land from what it is at sea (Figs. 322, 387).

Summary. *In the normal daily range the temperature is highest after midday, and lowest just before sunrise. The amount of daily range varies from time to time and from place to place.*

(B) *Seasonal range.* The yearly range of temperature closely resembles the daily range. If the average temperature for each day is kept, it will be found that in the northern hemisphere there is a steady rise from March to August, and then a gradual fall until February (Fig. 388). The reason why the coldest weather comes after midwinter (December 21) is that radiation continues to cool the ground and air until the days become long enough, and the sun high enough, to overbalance the effect of radiation. The hottest period of the year comes after midsummer (June 21), for the same reason that the hottest time of day is after noon. Thus the seasons are said to *lag*.

While there is a normal seasonal curve as described, it differs greatly in various parts of the world (Fig. 388). For example, the December 21 temperature at the equator is very high, in the polar zones very low; the range over the equable ocean is far less than that over the land; in the southern hemisphere the lowest temperature comes at the time of our summer.

There are also differences caused by altitude, deserts, and other influences.

Summary. *The average temperature rises until after midsummer and descends until after midwinter. The normal curve of seasonal temperature range varies from place to place.*

FORMS OF WATER

179. Humidity. Water vapor, which rises from the ocean and all damp surfaces (p. 396), is diffused through the air and drifts about with it. It finds its way to all parts of the earth; not even the Sahara has absolutely dry air. The *actual amount*

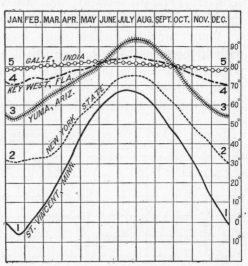

Fig. 388. — Seasonal temperature range in several places. (1) St. Vincent, Minnesota; (2) New York State; (3) Yuma, Arizona; (4) Key West, Florida; (5) Galle, India; 4 and 5 are near the equable ocean.

of vapor in the air, that is, the amount in pounds or quarts in a given volume of air, is known as the *absolute humidity*. If there is as much as possible, the air is said to be *saturated*. For example, in a room $10 \times 20 \times 20$ feet, the air at a temperature of 80°, if saturated, has $6\frac{1}{4}$ pounds of water in the form of vapor. This is its absolute humidity.

To represent the amount of vapor present in air, compared with the amount that might be there, the term *relative humidity* is employed. Relative humidity is measured in percentages. Thus the relative humidity of saturated air is 100 per cent, for it has all it can contain; of absolutely dry air, 0 per cent; and of air having only half as much as it might include at any given temperature, 50 per cent.

If the relative humidity is low, as in deserts, there is a chance for so much more vapor in the dry air that evaporation is rapid;

if the humidity is high, as in the tropical forest, there can be little evaporation, and surfaces remain damp. We notice this difference in summer, for some days are clear and dry, others are humid or muggy. When the humidity is great, the weather is most oppressive; we perspire sensibly, and are very uncomfortable, because there can be little evaporation from the surface of the body.

Warm air can include more water vapor in a given volume without condensation than can cool air, for the amount of vapor possible depends on temperature. For this reason, when the temperature in the room mentioned above is 60°, there can be only $3\frac{1}{4}$ pounds of water vapor in the air at the saturation point, or

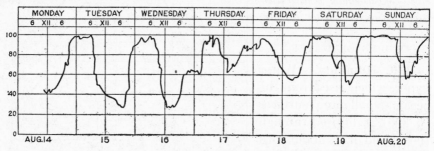

Fig. 389. — Daily changes in relative humidity at Ithaca, New York, for one week. Notice that at night the humidity rises nearly or quite to the dew point (100 per cent), but in the warmest part of the day is very low.   This does not mean any change in the absolute humidity, but is the result of changes in temperature from day to night.

100 per cent relative humidity.   There is, therefore, far less vapor in the air of the polar zones than in that of the tropical zone.

From this it is evident that if saturated air is warmed, it ceases to be saturated; that is, its relative humidity falls (Fig. 389) and evaporation is possible.   This is illustrated by the Sahara.   There the winds are blowing toward a warmer region, and the relative humidity is being constantly lowered, making the air so dry that the ground is dried and a desert produced.   If, on the other hand, damp air is cooled, its relative humidity increases, and the temperature point is soon reached when it becomes saturated.   Further cooling then forces some of the vapor to condense to liquid water, or, if the air temperature at the saturation point is below freezing, to snow or frost. This condensation to water or snow is *precipitation*.

These facts explain many phenomena.   Thus, when one breathes against a cool window pane the breath is cooled to the point of saturation, and some of the vapor caused to condense. A glass of water "sweats" on warm, muggy days, because the cool glass reduces the temperature of the air near it, and raises the relative humidity to the point of saturation. Then some of the vapor must condense. This point of saturation is often called the *dew point*, because, when it is reached, dew forms on the ground. Precipitation is caused whenever the air is chilled to the dew point.

Summary. *Absolute humidity is the actual amount of water vapor in the air at a given time; relative humidity is the percentage present compared to what might be present at that temperature. The relative humidity decreases with rising temperature, and increases with falling temperature. When it decreases, evaporation becomes more rapid; when it increases, if it reaches the point of saturation, or the "dew point," there is precipitation.*

180. Dew and frost. (A) *Dew.* At night the lower air is chilled by contact with the ground, which is cooled by radiation. If the air is damp, some of the vapor is then condensed as dew; and if it is *very* humid, or the temperature drops fast enough, dew may begin to form even before sunset. The formation of dew is checked (1) when the air is quite dry, (2) when winds stir the air and prevent any of it from being in contact with the ground long enough to cool to the dew point, or (3) when radiation is interfered with by clouds.

One reason why dew forms so readily on grass is that vegetation is a good radiator and hence cools quickly. Another reason is that there is water rising from the plants, as there is also, to less extent, from the ground. During the day this water disappears by evaporation and is, therefore, unnoticed; but at night, when the air is saturated, evaporation is so checked that the water gathers on the surface of the leaves and grass.

Summary. *Dew is caused (1) by the chilling of air to the dew point by the cool ground, and (2) by the rising of water from plants. Dry air, winds, and clouds are unfavorable to the formation of dew.*

(B) *Frost.* Frost is not frozen dew, but the solid, ice form assumed when vapor condenses from air that has a temperature below freezing. That is, if air at 31° F. reaches the saturation point when it cools to a temperature only a fraction of a degree lower, frost forms. Even when the general temperature is above freezing, frost may visit some localities. Low, swampy ground is first affected because (1) the air is damper, and (2) air cooled on the hillsides slides down to these low places and becomes saturated at a temperature below freezing.

Sometimes frost comes so early in the fall that fruit not yet quite ripe is destroyed; and late spring frosts often do great damage to buds. Such frosts occur during nights when the air is so clear that radiation proceeds readily.

The kinds of crops that may be successfully and profitably grown in different regions depend to a considerable degree in many instances on the number of frost-free days that can be counted on between the last killing frost of spring and the first killing frost of autumn.

A light, or white, frost may not kill vegetation if the air temperature does not fall below 28° F. Frost, as it affects plants, is a drying

Photo by von E.

Fig. 390. — Fog (low cloud) over Keuka Lake, New York, September 4, 1924. On the first frosty morning of fall the warm humid air over the lake condensed to fog in the cold air at the higher levels. As seen from Italy Hill.

process; it changes the water of the plant juices to ice. If too much of this water is thus dried (iced) out, the plant is unable to reform its juices with a return of warmer temperatures; and the cells may be broken by the expansion of the ice inside them, for water expands on freezing.

Summary. *Frost is the solid form assumed by vapor condensing at temperatures below freezing. Frosts first occur in low, damp places; and early fall and late spring frosts do damage to plants.*

181. Fog and clouds. (A) *Fog.* When we breathe into cold air, the vapor of the breath is condensed into particles of water so small that they float, forming a tiny fog. Fog is formed when damp air is chilled in other ways. For example, it often forms at night when the air over low, damp land or a lake is chilled to the dew point (Figs. 309, 390); or it may form when two currents of air are mixed, one cool, the other damp and warm. Fogs at sea are often caused in this way.

One of the foggiest places in the world is on the path of transatlantic steamers south of Newfoundland. There the warm Gulf Stream drift and the cold Labrador current are near together; and winds from one to the other cause vapor to condense into fog particles. Vessels rarely pass the Banks of Newfoundland without encountering some fog; and in it many a boat has been lost by collision with another or with an iceberg, or by running aground on the shoals.

Dust particles, by supplying solids on which the water may collect, may bring about the formation of fog. It is considered that the fogginess of London is partly due to the large amount of dust in the neighborhood of that great city. This dust is of such nature that it favors the condensation of fine particles of moisture on it, but, on the other hand, acts to prevent the collection of the small particles into larger raindrops. Hence town fogs are quite persistent. The fog of London is sometimes so dense that it is necessary to stop all traffic on the streets, and even to close the stores.

Summary. *Fog is caused by the chilling of air to the dew point, forcing some of the vapor to condense to tiny drops. Dust particles supply solids for the water to condense on.*

(B) *Clouds.* Clouds are also made by the condensation of vapor. Most clouds are fog or mist, that is, not water vapor, which is invisible, but water particles, though the higher ones, where the temperature is below freezing, are composed of snow or ice particles. Many clouds, especially on summer days, are caused by the rising of warm, damp air. As the air rises, it expands and cools; and when the dew point is reached, fog particles appear, forming clouds. The water particles are buoyed up, kept floating, by the ascending and other air currents. Clouds are also caused when damp air blows against a cold surface, for example, a mountain slope (Fig. 391). Still another cause for clouds is the contact of two currents of air, one above the other, one cold, the other warmer and humid.

Clouds assume many weird and beautiful forms (Fig. 392). Those that overspread the sky, having the appearance of layers, or strata, are called *stratus* ("layer") clouds (Fig. 376). They are common during stormy weather, and are usually low in the sky, often so low that they hide the tops of the hills. Frequently, especially in winter, they cover hundreds of square miles and last two or three days, while from them large quantities of rain or snow fall.

The clouds formed by the rising of air on warm summer days are called *cumulus* ("lump") clouds (Figs. 392, 393). A flat base, usually several thousand feet above the surface, marks the height at which the rising vapor begins to condense. Extending above this base, sometimes to a height of a mile, are a series of cloud domes which are often very beautiful,

Fig. 391. — Clouds forming on a mountain side. Damp winds blowing upon the cold mountain slopes are there chilled until the dew point is reached.

especially when lighted and colored by the rays of the setting sun. Cumulus clouds often develop into thunderheads.

A third common type is the *cirrus* ("curl") cloud (Fig. 392), which is often five or six miles above the surface. Unlike the other two types, these clouds are made of transparent ice particles; and they are so thin that the sun shines through them. It is in cirrus clouds that rings around the sun and moon are often seen (p. 400 and Fig. 379). The cirrus clouds vary greatly, some having a most delicate and beautiful feathery and plumed form.

There is every gradation between the three types of clouds. To these intermediate forms compound names are given as follows: cirro-stratus, cirro-cumulus, alto-cumulus, alto-stratus, and strato-cumulus. A fourth pure type, the rain cloud, is called *nimbus*. The thundershower cloud is cumulo-nimbus (Fig. 394).

Summary. *Clouds are made of fog, mist, snow, and ice particles. They are caused by the condensing of vapor from various causes, — rising and expanding, blowing against cold surfaces, and contact of cold and warmer, damp currents. Stratus clouds are low, and spread over large areas; cumulus clouds rise in domes above a flat base; cirrus are thin, fleecy clouds high in the*

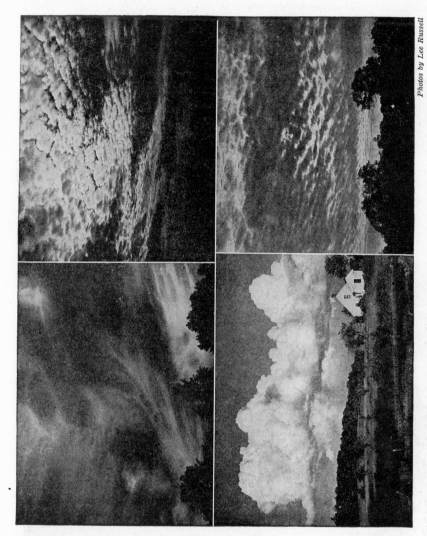

Photos by Lee Russell

Fig. 392. — The upper left picture shows typical plumed cirrus clouds; upper right, alto-cumulus; lower left, typical cumulus of the thunder-head form; lower right, stratus, breaking up — hence more exactly fracto-stratus. (See also Figs. 82, 187.)

air and are made of ice particles. The rain cloud is called nimbus. There are many variations between these types.

182. Rain, snow, and hail. (A) *Rain.* Fog particles in clouds may grow to such size that they can no longer float or be buoyed up

Fig. 393. — Fracto-cumulus clouds, torn and driven by the wind. Also Lone Star geyser in eruption, Yellowstone National Park.

Fig. 394. — Cumulo-nimbus cloud over west slope of Conesus Lake valley, New York. Upper part of cloud shows typical cumulus form. Rising air currents have their moisture condensed at the level of the flat base of the cloud. The particles of moisture collect into larger drops and are falling as rain in the dark area below the cloud on the right of the picture.

by ascending air currents. They then fall as raindrops. The growth of raindrops is due to several causes: (1) continued condensation of vapor; (2) union of fog particles, driven together by currents of air; and (3) union of particles as they fall through the cloud. Thus rain is merely the result of a continuation of the process of cloud formation. If the vapor condenses rapidly as in summer thunderclouds, the drops may grow to great size.

Photos by W. A. Bentley

Fig. 395. — Snowflakes, photographed under the microscope. Thousands have been studied; no two exactly alike have ever been found. Those shown above range from the most solid triangular forms to the most feathery six-pointed kind. Consider the wonderful suggestions these give for design.

Rain may evaporate on its way from the clouds and fail to reach the ground. Such streamers of rain, descending part way to the earth, may sometimes be seen in summer. In other cases, rain on its way down may freeze in passing through a cold layer of air, forming *sleet*. Some sleet is snow that has partly melted, and then frozen before reaching the ground.

Summary. *Continued condensation of vapor in cloud formation, and the union of the fog particles, form raindrops so heavy that they must fall to the earth.*

(B) *Snow.* Snowflakes are not frozen raindrops, but are formed when vapor is condensing in a cloud at temperatures below freezing point. If the snowflake grows without interference, it is a regular and beautiful crystal (Fig. 395). It grows as regularly as salt or alum crystals in a solution that is slowly evaporating. The feathery frost on window panes is also caused by crystal growth, when vapor condenses at temperatures below the freezing point.

There are several reasons why snowflakes are usually irregular: (1) the crystals are often broken; (2) several are commonly united, forming a matted mass; (3) as the snow falls it is sometimes partly melted in passing through a warmer layer of air. Frequently the snow melts entirely, reaching the ground as rain. This occurs often in hilly countries; then the hilltops are covered with snow, while 100 or 200 feet lower, in the valleys, rain is falling (Fig. 384).

Summary. *Snowflakes are crystals, built up by the condensing of vapor at temperatures below freezing. They are commonly broken, matted, or partly melted on the way down, becoming irregular.*

(C) *Hail.* Hail is formed in violent storms, such as tornadoes and thunderstorms, in which there are strong, whirling currents of air. Hailstones are balls of snow and ice, built up by condensing vapor as they are whirled up and down in the violent currents, freezing, melting, and freezing again as they pass from warm to cold currents. For this reason they are often made of several layers, or shells, of snow and ice. They may grow to great size, and may be kept suspended by the rising currents long after they are heavy enough to fall through quiet air. When they fall, usually at the margin of a storm, they often break window glass and do great damage to crops. Conditions favoring the formation of large hailstones are fortunately not common, and their effects are confined to very limited areas. Winter hail is frozen raindrops (p. 420) and is called sleet.

Summary. *Hailstones are made of ice and snow, formed by vapor condensing in whirling air currents. They may grow to large size before they fall; such large hailstones often do considerable damage.*

TOPICAL OUTLINE, QUESTIONS, SUGGESTIONS, AND LABORATORY
EXERCISES

TOPICAL OUTLINE. **172. Composition and functions of the air.** (A) *Oxygen, nitrogen, argon, and carbon dioxide:* percentage of each; rare gases; importance of oxygen; of nitrogen; of carbon dioxide; slow combustion in animals; rapid combustion; production of heat; inertness of nitrogen. (B) *Water vapor:* source;

evaporation; variation in amount; condensation. (C) *Dust particles:* nature of materials; distribution; effect on condensation: microbes. (D) *The upper atmosphere:* height of; constant temperature; composition; use of helium.

173. Effect of gravity. Cause of weight; amount at sea level; reason for not noticing pressure; density of lower air; rarefied air; effect; effect of temperature on density of air; movements started by gravity.

174. Light. Nature of light; speed of passage; combination of waves; effect of prism; refraction; colors of spectrum; reflection; instances; mirage; rainbow; halos; color of objects; diffraction; blue color of sky; sunset colors.

175. Heat. (A) *Radiant energy:* heat from a stove; light from a stove; radiant energy; radiation; radiant energy from bodies in space; effect of radiation on stove; on sun; part reaching earth. (B) *Passage of radiant energy:* diathermancy; effect of air on heat; effect of dust. (C) *Radiation from the earth:* earth as a radiator; cause of cool nights; of cold winter; difference between land and water; difference in radiation and frost effects. (D) *Reflection and absorption:* water; quarries; black objects; white objects. (E) *Conduction:* in a stove; air, water, and ground as conductors; depth of conduction in the ground. (F) *Convection:* in water; in air, — near a lamp, near a fire, by heat from sun.

176. Warming of land, water, and air. (A) *The lands:* warming; loss of heat; day and night; tropical zone; temperate zone; polar zones; color of surface; vegetation; exposure; soils. (B) *The waters:* comparison with land; heat of vaporization; equable climate. (C) *The air:* causes for warming; causes for cooling; interference with radiation.

177. Causes of differences in temperature on the earth. (A) *Position of sun:* differences in height; reasons why sun low in heavens is less powerful; results. (B) *Altitude:* decrease in temperature; explanation; illustration of effect of expansion; sunny spots; effect of radiation. (C) *Other reasons for differences:* soil; exposure; water; wind.

178. Daily and seasonal temperature changes. (A) *Daily range:* lag of warmest period; lag of coolest period; reasons; interference with normal range; difference in amount of range. (B) *Seasonal range:* resemblance to daily range; coldest period; warmest period; lag of seasons in temperate zones; reasons; causes for differences in curve.

179. Humidity. Source; distribution; absolute humidity; saturated air; relative humidity; measuring relative humidity; effect of low humidity; of high humidity; influence of temperature on humidity; cause of deserts; precipitation; illustrations of effect of cooling; dew point.

180. Dew and frost. (A) *Dew:* cause; unfavorable conditions; reason for dew on grass. (B) *Frost:* cause; most favorable places; early and late frosts; effect of frost on plants.

181. Fog and clouds. (A) *Fog:* the breath; chilling of air; fog off Newfoundland; dangers to navigation; aid of dust particles; London fog. (B) *Clouds:* materials; causes; stratus; cumulus; cirrus; intermediate forms; nimbus; thundershower clouds.

182. Rain, snow, and hail. (A) *Rain:* reason for falling; causes for drops; large drops; failure to reach earth; sleet. (B) *Snow:* cause; snowflakes; frost on windows; irregularity of snowflakes; melting of falling snow. (C) *Hail:* formation; reason for shells of ice; size; effects; winter hail.

QUESTIONS. Section 172. (A) What elements make up the bulk of the air? What is the importance of each? A question frequently asked in examinations is:

What are the functions, or purposes, or uses of the different materials of the atmosphere? It will be a good exercise for the student to set down in tabular form the answer to this question, going through the whole chapter to get together a full statement. Considerable ingenuity may be displayed in arranging and presenting the facts in the most concise and convincing way. This problem may be made the basis of a class contest. (See also Chapter II.) (B) What is evaporation? What difference is there in the amount of vapor in air? What results when it is condensed? (C) What are dust particles? Where are they most common? What are their effects? (D) How high does the lower atmosphere extend at different latitudes? What are the temperature conditions above those altitudes? What is considered to be the composition of the upper atmosphere? For what is helium used?

173. Has air weight? Why? How much? Why do not we feel the weight of the air? In what three ways does the density vary?

174. What is light? What is refraction? What is reflection? What phenomena are produced by refraction and reflection of light in its passage through the atmosphere? What is the cause of color in flowers? What is the cause of the blue color of the sky? Of sunset colors?

175. (A) What is radiant energy? What is radiation? What effect is radiation having on the sun? (B) What are diathermanous bodies? Give examples. Why does the sun lose power in late afternoon? (C) Why does the ground become cool at night and cold in winter? What difference is there in the radiation from bodies? (D) Give illustrations of reflection. Give illustrations of absorption. (E) What is conduction? What effect has it on earth, air, and water? (F) What causes convection in water? Give illustrations of convection of air.

176. (A) Why is not the ground excessively warmed? What differences in temperature are there in the three zones? What are other causes for differences? (B) State the reasons why water warms more slowly than land. What is heat of vaporization? Compare land and water in winter and at night. What is an equable climate? Distinguish between the words equable and equitable. (C) How is air warmed? How is it cooled? Why is muggy air oppressive?

177. (A) Why is the sun less powerful when low than when high? Why is the soil of a steep hill slope facing south (in the northern hemisphere) warmer in fall and spring than level land near by? Show this by diagram. State three important effects of differences in sun's position. (B) Why are highlands cool? Are any parts warm? What is the effect of radiation? (C) What other reasons are there for differences in temperature?

178. (A) When are the warmest and coolest times of day? Why? What causes are there for interference with the normal daily range? For differences in the amount of daily range? (B) When are the warmest and coolest times of the year? Why do the seasons thus lag? What reasons are there for differences in the normal seasonal curve?

179. What is absolute humidity? What is saturated air? What is relative humidity? What is the result of raising the temperature? What is the cause of some deserts? What is the result of lowering the temperature? What causes precipitation? Illustrate. What is dew point?

180. (A) What is the cause of dew? Under what conditions is there no dew? Why is there so much dew on grass? (B) What is frost? Why does frost first visit low, damp places? What are its effects?

181. (A) What are the causes for fog? What are the conditions on the

Banks of Newfoundland? Why? What is the effect on navigation? What relation have dust particles to fog? (B) Of what are clouds made? How are the water particles kept in the air? How are they caused? Name and describe each of the cloud types.

182. (A) What is the cause of rain? Why do the drops vary in size? What is sleet? (B) What are snowflakes? How formed? Why are they often irregular? (C) What is the cause of hailstones? Why do they sometimes grow so large?

SUGGESTIONS. (1) Recall Experiments 1, 2, 3, 4, and 6 of Chapter II, p. 43. (2) Let a beam of sunlight enter a darkened room and notice the dust that it lights. Watch the sky to see if it is sometimes hazy. Is it clearer after a rain? Why? (3) By means of an air pump show that air has pressure. The teacher of physics can tell how this is to be done. (4) Obtain a prism of glass from the physical laboratory and allow a ray of sunlight to pass through it in order to study the prismatic colors. (5) Place a stick in water and notice that it appears to bend below the water. This is due to refraction. (6) Heat a brick or a stone and suspend it by a wire. Why does it become cool? Does the thermometer show rise of temperature when placed near it? Why? (7) Try the experiment with black and white cloth, mentioned on p. 403, using ice instead of snow. (8) Place a thermometer in the shade in such a position that sunlight can be reflected on it by means of a mirror. Does the temperature rise? (9) Place one end of a bar of iron in the fire. Does the other end become warm? Why? Place an equal bulk of several substances — for example, iron, soil, and rock — on the stove for a short period to test which first becomes warm by conduction. Use a thermometer to determine this. It can also be told by putting a thin layer of paraffin on each, noticing on which the paraffin first begins to melt. (10) Study convection in water, using a glass dish with muddy water so as to see its movement. Study the convection of air near a lamp, clouding the air with smoke (this can be obtained by lighting a piece of cloth) so that its movement may be seen. Explain the principle of a lamp; of a fireplace. How is your schoolhouse ventilated? Does the fresh air come in above or below? Why? (11) Place a brick and a pan of water (as deep as the thickness of the brick) on a hot stove or over a Bunsen burner. Carefully weigh each before placing them there. When the brick has become warm, take the temperature of each at the top. At the bottom. Why is one the same temperature throughout, the other hot at the bottom and only warm at the top? Which shows the higher temperature? Why? When cool, weigh them again. Has either lost weight? Why? (12) Do the same with water and soil, leaving a thermometer in each and recording the changes. In which does the temperature rise faster? Which cools faster? (13) Take the temperature at 6, 8, 10, 12, 2, 4, 6, 8, and 10 o'clock for one day. Construct a curve similar to Fig. 385. Keep records for a week, and construct curves to find if they are all alike. (14) A seasonal curve can also be made by getting the data from the Annual Report of the United States Weather Bureau in which daily averages are given for many places. (15) With a tire pump illustrate the warming of air by compression and cooling by expansion (p. 408). A little fog can be produced by placing a dish of hot water where escaping cool air from an inflated tire passes over it. (16) Make observations on condensation, — blowing on a cold window, for example. In warm, damp air, watch drops collect on a glass of ice water. That the water does not come from within the glass may be proved by placing a glass, without water, on ice until it is cold, then putting it in the room. The same thing may also be shown by putting salt and ice in a bright tin dipper. The temperature of dew point can be determined by putting a thermometer in the salt and ice, reading the temperature at the moment water begins to cloud the surface of the dipper. (17) Study frost: the time of its coming; the places where it comes first; and any other facts you can find out by observation. (18) For a number of days observe the clouds carefully, classifying those you see.

Laboratory Exercises. Exercises XLIII, XLIV, XLV, XLVI, and XLVII in TARR and VON ENGELN's *Laboratory Manual for Physical and Commercial Geography*, The Macmillan Company, New York, provide for systematic study, observation, and experiments bearing on the facts and principles set forth in this chapter. Additional material in the form of temperature records, tables, etc., is also made available in the exercises. Exercise XLIV provides for weather observations to be made during all the period that the atmosphere is being studied and longer if desired.

Reference Books. MILHAM, *Meteorology*, The Macmillan Company, New York, 1912; DAVIS, *Elementary Meteorology*, Ginn & Company, Boston, 1894; HUMPHREYS, *Physics of the Air*, J. B. Lippincott Company, Philadelphia, 1920; McADIE, *The Principles of Aerography*, Rand, McNally & Company, Chicago, 1917; McADIE, *A Cloud Atlas*, Rand, McNally & Company, Chicago, 1923; MOORE, *Descriptive Meteorology*, D. Appleton & Company, New York, 1910; TYNDALL, *The Forms of Water*, D. Appleton & Company, New York, 1872; *Illustrative Cloud Forms*, U. S. Hydrographic Office, Washington, 1897; *Annual Reports* and *Monthly Weather Review*, U. S. Weather Bureau, Washington.

CHAPTER XIII

WINDS AND STORMS

WINDS

183. Relation between winds and air pressure. Winds are the result of differences in the air pressure, or weight. It is easier to understand their cause if we consider the atmosphere to be composed of a great number of air columns which gravity holds to the earth. If the sun's heat warms the land or the sea, and these surfaces, by conduction, warm the bottom of the air in one place, the columns at that place expand, overflow at the top and thus, by convectional movement, become lighter than in places not so warmed (p. 399). Light air is said to have a *low pressure*, heavy air a *high pressure*, because the heavier the air, the higher it pushes the mercury up in the tube of the barometer (Appendix G). The air moves, or flows, at the bottom of the atmospheric ocean from places of high toward places of low pressure, thus causing winds. On a larger scale, the phenomenon is much the same as the movement of the cooler and heavier air which crowds in and up the warm, lighter air in a lamp (p. 403).

The difference in air pressure which causes winds is often known as the *barometric gradient*. It is so named because the air flows from a region of high pressure, or high barometer, to one of low, as if it were going down a grade, or gradient, as flowing water does. It is not to be understood, of course, that there is a real slope or grade, but merely lighter air in one place than in another. It is necessary that at the start of the process there be an overflow from the top of the heated column of air to the cool ones on either side; for it is this addition of an extra quantity of air to the tops of the cool columns that makes them heavier than the heated, expanded column of air. Once the flow is started, the columns of both heated and cool air being of equal height, it is clear that the columns of cool air being denser will be heavier and exert more pressure than the columns of expanded, lighter, heated air. If the difference in pressure is great, the barometric gradient is so high that the air moves swiftly.

Summary. *Winds are due to a flowing of air from regions of heavy air, or high pressure, to regions of low pressure; and the difference in pressure is known as the barometric gradient.*

184. Sea and land breezes. A simple illustration of winds is often found along ocean and lake shores on hot days. On such days the land, and the air over it, become much warmer than the water and the air above it. Then the top of the column of expanded air over the land overflows onto the top of the cool air over the sea. Thus the balance of pressure is disturbed. Then, soon, the weighted, or heavier air (p. 405) from the water flows in as a cool, refreshing *sea breeze*, pushing inward and upward the warm, lighter air that rests on the land. Once started the process continues as long as the heating of the air over the land is effective.

When the sea breeze begins to blow, the temperature, which may have risen to 80° or 90°, commences to fall, and the rest of the day is pleasantly cool. It is partly because of the cool sea breezes that so many people go to the seashore to spend their summer vacations. Along tropical coasts, sea breezes are very pronounced and of almost daily occurrence.

At night a *land breeze* often blows out over the water. The reason for this is that at night the land cools by radiation faster than the water, reversing the hot, day, pressure conditions (p. 405). Then the cooled, land air slides out over the sea, pushing up the warmer air that rests there. Sailboats, becalmed offshore when the sea breeze dies down, are able to reach port late in the evening when the land breeze begins to blow.

Summary. *Sea breezes are caused by cool air from the sea flowing in on hot days and pushing in and up the warm, light air over the land. At night, land breezes blow out over the sea because the air over the land is then cooler and heavier than that over the sea.*

185. Mountain valley breezes. Winds similar to the land breezes are noticed at night in hilly and mountainous regions. As the land cools by radiation, heavy air, cooled by contact with the cold ground, slides down the slopes, causing winds that often gain great force late at night. During the day, as the valley sides are warmed, the air moves up the valleys; but this movement does not cause winds so strong as those at night, when the air is flowing down grade and gathering from many tributary valleys into one main valley.

Summary. *At night, cool air slides down valleys, forming winds; and air passing up the valleys during the day causes lighter breezes.*

186. Monsoon winds. On some of the continents, there are changes in wind direction from summer to winter. These seasonal winds, known as *monsoons*, are best developed in India (p. 432).

In summer the land becomes warmer than the water, and air moves from the Indian ocean toward the warm interior, forming the summer monsoon (Fig. 396). In winter, when radiation cools the northern plains and mountain slopes of India, the heavy air moves outward toward the warmer oceans, forming the winter monsoons. Thus twice each year the winds change. In the Indian Ocean the changes are so regular, and the winds so steady, that in early times sailing vessels went to India in summer and left in winter, in order to have fair winds both ways. China has similar winds.

All continents show some tendency toward the development of monsoon winds; but in most cases other winds are too well established for the mon-

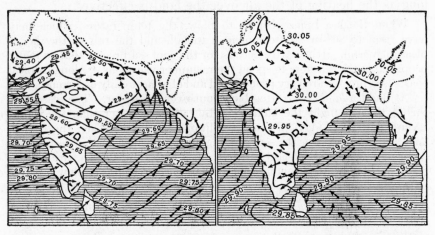

Fig. 396. — The summer (left figure) and winter (right figure) monsoons of India. Note that the cold air of the winter monsoon does not come over the mountains from the interior of Asia, as is commonly stated. Instead this cold air moves out from a high pressure area centering over the northwest plains of India and the south slopes of the mountains. The isobars (p. 436) show air pressure in inches of mercury.

soons to develop perfectly. For example, the regular winds of northeastern United States are from the west; but they are much steadier in winter than in summer (Figs. 399, 400). The reason for this is that in winter the outflow of cold air from the land strengthens the west winds, while in summer the inflow of cool air from the ocean weakens them; but the summer inflow is not strong enough completely to destroy the west wind movement and form regular monsoons.

Summary. *Monsoon winds, best developed in Asia, are due to the inflow of air from the ocean to the warmer land in summer, and the outflow of air from the cold land in winter.*

187. Wind systems of the earth. Even greater air movements than those just described are caused by differences in temperature between the warm tropical belt and the cooler zones north and south of it. The winds thus started affect all zones, all continents, and all oceans. As they act together they make up what are known as the *planetary winds* or *primary circulation*.

(A) *Comparison with a stove.* In certain respects this great circulation may be compared to the movements of air in a room heated by a stove. The air around the stove is warmed, and the cooler, heavier air in other parts of the room crowds in and pushes the warm air upward. There is, therefore, (1) a movement toward the stove; (2) a rising above it; (3) an upper current away from it; and (4) a settling at a distance from it.

Because of the heated belt of the tropical zone there are similar movements on the earth (Fig. 397). These are (1) a movement of air along the surface toward the equator; (2) a rising in

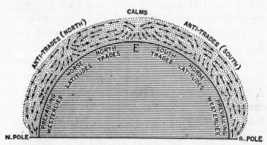

Fig. 397. — A diagram to illustrate the air circulation of the earth. **E** is the equator. The actual circulation is much more complicated and is partly governed by regions of persistent low pressure, e.g., the low pressure region near Iceland (Fig. 402).

the torrid zone; (3) an upper level movement to the north and south away from this zone; and (4) a settling north and south of it.

Summary. *Both in a room heated by a stove, and on the earth warmed in the torrid zone, there is a movement of air toward the warm place, a rising, an outflow above, and a settling. This starts the system of air movements known as the planetary winds.*

(B) *Effect of rotation.* While air currents in a room move straight toward the stove, the winds of the earth are gradually turned from a straight course by the influence of the earth's rotation. Currents of air, like water (p. 348), are turned, or deflected, in the northern hemisphere toward the right, in the southern toward the left. This effect of rotation is therefore called *right-hand deflection* in the northern hemisphere, and *left-hand deflection* in the southern.

Students are always curious to know the reason for this deflection, but the explanation is not usually attempted in an elementary text. Although not exact and complete, the following account is sufficiently accurate to give a true comprehension of the phenomenon and yet simple enough to be understood by the beginner.

It is to be appreciated, first, that the deflection is always to the right (in the northern hemisphere) of the direction of motion. Thus with a wind or current moving toward the north the deflection is to the east; with a wind moving east the deflection is toward the south, and so on.

Second, the deflection of north and south winds is due to one set of conditions, that of east and west winds to another. But in each case the deflection is to the right. Consequently a wind or current moving in some intermediate direction, like northeast, is affected by both sets of deflecting forces, and though by only one half the full strength of each, the sum of their action gives the full deflecting effect.

Consider, now, north and south winds or currents. At the equator all matter, including the atmosphere, is being carried west to east at the rate of over 1000 miles per hour due to the earth's rotation. Near the pole the movement from this cause is reduced to only a few miles per hour. A current started north at the equator will tend to continue moving in the same straight line on which it started. But it starts north as part of a mass having an eastward motion of 1000 miles per hour. It tends to keep that motion too. Hence as the current flows north and arrives successively at latitudes where the rotational motion is slower and slower, its original easterly motion becomes more and more apparent; it seems to run ahead of the earth's rotation, is thus deflected to the right, that is, becomes a west-to-east flow of air or water. Contrariwise, a wind blowing from north to south, from a region of low rotational speed to one of high, seems to lag, hence tends to become a wind blowing from east to west. If one will imagine a ball rolled from the rim (the equator) of a rotating disk toward its center (the north pole) and how the ball would be carried along in the direction of rotation; and how the ball would lag behind the rotation when rolling from the slow-moving center toward the fast-moving edge — the idea will be grasped.

A current moving east or west disturbs the equilibrium that exists on the surface of the earth between the gravity pull toward the center of the earth and the centrifugal force of rotation. Because of the centrifugal force the earth is flattened at the poles and bulges at the equator. A perfect adjustment has been established and is maintained as long as material on the surface does not move east or west. That is, the bulge at the equator does not grow larger or less. But if a wind or water current at a point north of the equator starts moving eastward it, in effect, rotates faster than the earth rotates at that latitude. Hence the equilibrium between gravity and centrifugal force is disturbed by an increase in centrifugal force. This, then, tends to deflect the east-moving current toward the equator; that is, to the right in the northern hemisphere, to the left in the southern. Contrariwise, a current moving toward the west has the effect of increasing the pull of gravity, that is, resists the centrifugal force by so much, hence tends to move away from the equator toward the poles.

At the equator there is no deflection of east- or west-moving currents. Why not? But at the equator an airplane should rise more easily taking off toward the east, and less easily taking off toward the west. Why? The student may test his understanding of this topic by applying the principles in explanation only of the "left-hand" deflection of the southern hemisphere.

Summary. *The effect of the earth's rotation turns winds toward the right (right-hand deflection) in the northern hemisphere, and toward the left (left-hand deflection) in the southern.*

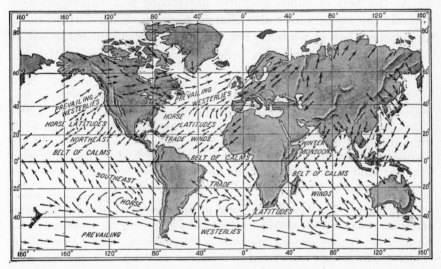

Fig. 398. — A sketch map showing the prevailing winds and wind belts of the earth in winter.

(C) *Belt of calms.* In the torrid zone, where the air is rising, there is normally little wind, because the air movement is vertical (Fig. 397) instead of horizontal. This is normally a region of calms, sometimes called the *doldrums*, sometimes the *tropical belt of calms* (Figs. 398, 400). This belt does not remain stationary, but, as the belt of greatest heat changes position with the season (Figs. 399, 400), migrates northward or southward.

Summary. *Where the air is rising, in the torrid zone, there is a region of calms which changes position as the seasons change.*

(D) *Trade winds*. The air currents that move toward the belt of calms, known as the *trade winds* (Figs. 397–400), blow with great steadiness, especially over the ocean. Indeed, islands in the trade-wind belts commonly have steep, wave-cut cliffs on the windward side (Fig. 401), against which the surf is ever beating. Instead of blowing directly from the north in the northern hemisphere, and from the south in the southern, the trades are deflected by the influence of rotation, becoming northeast winds in the northern hemisphere and southeast in the southern. These are, therefore, called the *northeast trades* and *southeast trades* respectively. A wind is named by the direction *from* which it blows.

As the belt of calms migrates northward and southward each season, the trade winds also change position, being farther north in summer than in winter. For this reason, places near the border of the trade-wind and calm belts have alternate seasons of calms and trade winds (Figs. 399, 400).

The monsoons are best developed in Asia (p. 427) because (a) the continent is so vast, (b) so much of its interior is arid, and (c) the belt of calms is near. The winter outflow of cold air strengthens the northeast trades; but in summer the belt of calms migrates, northward and the southeast trades extend across the equator to the land. That is, in summer the land is so warm that, in this region the southeast, trades are strengthened and the northeast trades destroyed.

Summary. *The steady movement of air toward the torrid zone forms the trade winds, which, deflected by rotation, blow from the northeast in the northern hemisphere and the southeast in the southern. These belts migrate northward in summer, southward in winter.*

(E) *Antitrades*. The air that rises in the belt of calms flows northward and southward, high above the earth (Fig. 397). Turned by the influence of rotation, these upper currents, or *antitrades*, move from the southwest in the northern hemisphere and from the northwest in the southern hemisphere; that is, opposite in direction to the lower trade winds. The movement of higher clouds, and of ash erupted from volcanoes, proves this. On high peaks which rise above the trade winds, as in the Hawaiian Islands, the antitrades may be felt.

Summary. *The outflow of air that rises in the belt of calms is known as the antitrades, which blow above the trades and in the opposite direction.*

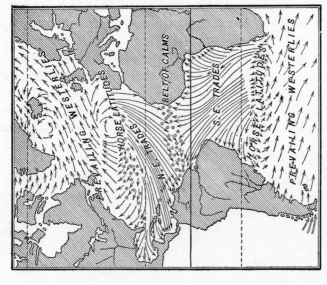

Fig. 400. — Wind belts of the Atlantic in summer. Notice how much less strongly the prevailing westerlies are developed than in winter, when cold air from the interior flows outward from North America. Locate the heat equator, on Figs. 400 and 399, and note how it shifts. See Figs. 421 and 422.

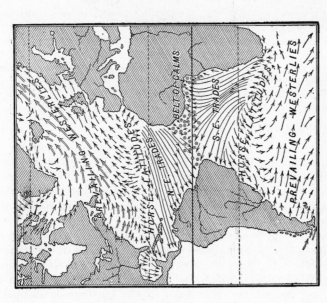

Fig. 399. — Wind belts of the Atlantic in winter. Compare with Fig. 400 to note migration of the wind belts. Length of arrows indicates steadiness; double line, strong winds; circles, calms.

(F) *Prevailing westerlies.* On its way toward the poles some of the upper air settles to the surface, but much continues on to high latitudes.

The direction that this air takes is determined by the influence of rotation; that is, the air currents are turned toward the right in the northern hemisphere and toward the left in the southern. This causes winds from a westerly direction in each hemisphere. Therefore these wind belts are called the *prevailing westerlies* (Figs.

Photo by U. S. Navy Air Service

Fig. 401. — Wave-cut cliffs on the windward side (left of picture) of a small volcanic island (Manana Island) in the trade-wind belt of the Pacific Ocean.

397–400). They cover the greater part of the two temperate and the two polar zones.

These winds, as well as the others of the planetary system, are interfered with by various conditions. For example, they are often strongest during the day because of differences caused by the warmth of the sun. When the sun sets, the wind often dies down at the surface. Storms, sea breezes, and the effects of topography, such as the influence of valleys, also interfere with the force and direction of the winds.

Winds are commonly less steady and strong on land than on water. The reason for this is that the roughness of the land, and its differences in temperature, interfere with their movement. Since in the southern hemisphere there is so little land to interfere, the prevailing westerlies are better developed there throughout the year than in the northern hemisphere (Figs. 398–400). In the Southern Ocean, a vessel could sail eastward around the earth with the prevailing westerly winds fair all the way.

There is so much land in the northern hemisphere that the westerlies

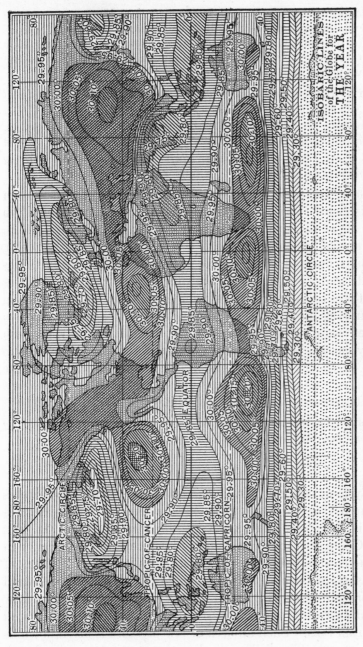

Fig. 402. — Isobars (lines of equal pressure) for the world. The dark shading represents high pressure. The figures (29.85 for example) are inches to which the mercury in a barometer rises, being highest where the air pressure is greatest. In the dark zones of high pressure, the horse-latitude belt, air is settling; it moves thence toward the low pressure belt of the warm torrid zone, forming the trade winds, and toward the low pressure areas near the poles, forming the prevailing westerlies.

are greatly interfered with; but high in the air, above the influence of the surface, they blow with great strength and steadiness. Any one can confirm this for himself by watching the upper clouds and noticing how uniformly they move eastward, sometimes even when the wind at the surface blows in the opposite direction.

Summary. *Some of the air of the antitrades continues on northward and southward. Turned by the influence of rotation, these winds blow from westerly directions in both hemispheres, forming the prevailing westerlies. They are better developed over the Southern Ocean and high in the air, than at the surface of the northern hemisphere, where they are interfered with by irregular land and by local winds.*

(G) *Horse latitudes.* Between the trades and westerlies, in each hemisphere, there is a belt known as the *horse latitudes*, in which the air of the antitrades is steadily settling (Figs. 397, 402). Since the air movement is vertical, this is a belt of relative calm, with irregular, unsteady winds, quite in contrast to the steady trades on one side and west winds on the other (Figs. 398, 400). It is said that these belts received their name from the fact that sailing vessels, carrying horses to the West Indies from North America in early times, were often becalmed there until the supply of fresh water they carried became nearly exhausted and the horses had to be thrown overboard or died of thirst. As the belt of calms and the trade-wind belts migrate northward and southward with the seasons (p. 432), the horse-latitude belts also shift.

Summary. *The horse latitudes are belts (one in each hemisphere) of relative calm, where the air of the antitrades is settling.*

STORMS [1]

188. Cyclonic storms. (A) *Characteristics.* The United States weather map (Fig. 405) shows an area where the air pressure is light. It is, therefore, called a *low pressure area*, or a *Low* (Fig. 403; p. 426). Going out from this center of low pressure the mercury in the barometer stands higher, and this fact is indicated by lines of equal pressure, or *isobars*. Air is moving from all directions toward the low pressure area (Fig. 404). Next day (Fig. 406) the Low has moved eastward; but winds still blow toward it, and around its center rain falls. Such an area of low pressure is also known as a *cyclonic storm.* The following day the storm has moved still

[1] See also Appendix H, and pp. 471–477.

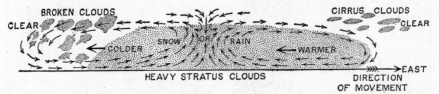

Fig. 403. — Diagram showing theoretical movement of air (by arrows), and other conditions, in a low pressure or cyclonic storm area. Describe this diagram.

farther east (Fig. 407), and, if we should continue to follow it, we could trace it out into the Atlantic, and possibly even across northern Europe into Asia.

Summary. *A cyclonic storm is an area of low air pressure toward which winds blow from all directions, and in which rain falls. Such storms move eastward.*

(B) *Anticyclones.* West of the cyclonic storm (Fig. 406) is an area of high pressure (marked *High*), from which winds blow outward in all directions, while the sky is clear and no rain falls. A high pressure area is often called an *anticyclone,* because in it conditions are the reverse of those in cyclones (Fig. 408). Anticyclones move eastward as cyclonic storms do, even crossing the Atlantic.

Summary. *Anticyclones are areas of high pressure with outward blowing winds and clear sky. They also move eastward.*

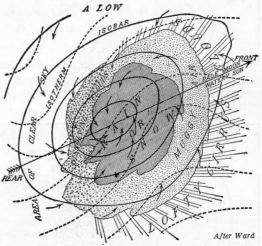

After Ward

Fig. 404. — Diagram of a cyclonic storm, or Low, in horizontal plane, in the northern hemisphere. The whole storm may be 500 to 1,000 miles in diameter. The long arrow shows the direction in which the storm as a whole is moving. The short arrows show the movement of the winds in the storm. They would blow directly into the center of the storm but the deflection to the right due to the earth's rotation gives them a curved path. Thus a *counter-clockwise spiral rotation* is developed. The air also moves upward at the center, see Fig. 403. The solid black lines are isobars, or lines of equal air pressure; the one at the center shows the lowest pressure. The dotted lines are isotherms or lines of equal temperature; the temperature decreases from the lower right hand to the upper left hand portion of the figure. Account for the labeled cloud conditions in the storm.

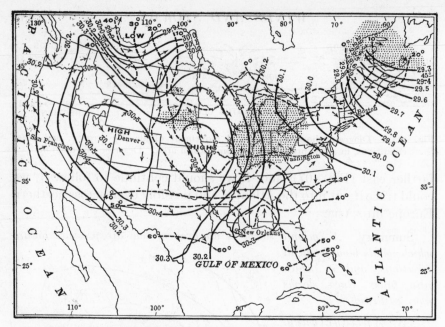

Fig. 405. — Chart to show weather conditions on January 7, of a certain year. Isobars, heavy lines; isotherms, dashes; wind directions indicated by arrows; areas of rain, dotted. Compare with Figs. 406 and 407.

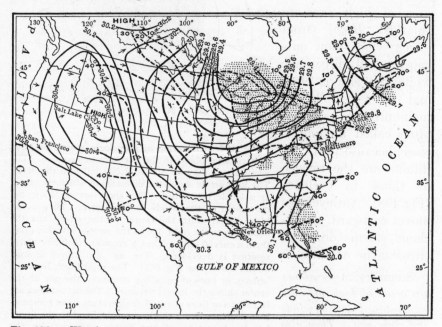

Fig. 406. — Weather map for next day, January 8 of same year as preceding Fig. 405. Path pursued by storm center indicated by chain of arrows.

(C) *Succession of cyclones and anticyclones.* Almost every weather map shows similar areas of high and low pressure (see Figs. 433–435). At intervals of from three to seven days, places in northern United States are likely to be visited, in fairly regular

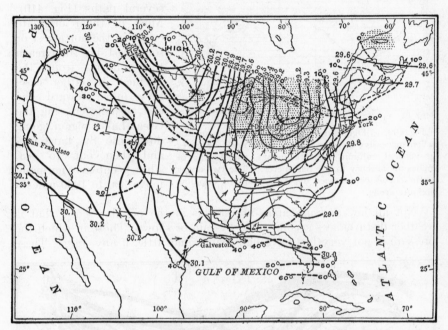

Fig. 407. — Same storm as Figs. 405 and 406, showing its position on January 9. Trace the changes for these three days. These conditions repeat themselves from year to year, never exactly the same, nor on the same days, but in general aspects quite similar.

succession (see also p. 472) by two low pressure areas with a high between (Fig. 409). The passage of these areas is readily observed by watching the rising and falling of the barometer, or by observing the weather. Cloudy weather, rain, and high tempera-

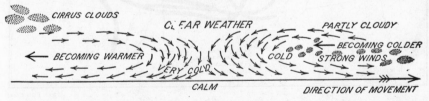

Fig. 408. — Diagram showing theoretical circulation (by arrows), and other conditions in a high pressure, or anticyclonic, area. Describe this diagram. On the basis of this and using Fig. 404 as a model, construct a diagram for a High.

tures usually accompany the Lows, and clear, cool or cold weather, the Highs; while the wind direction varies as these areas pass.

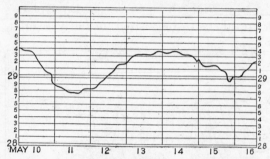

Fig. 409. — Diagram showing change of pressure for seven successive days at Ithaca, New York. Figures in vertical column indicate inches and tenths of inches of mercury in the barometer. The two drops in the curve were caused by the passage of two low pressure areas.

These high and low pressure areas follow several paths (Fig. 410). Most of them originate either in the northwest or southwest, but some reach the country from the Pacific. In either case, they move toward the east, usually crossing the Great Lakes region, going down the St. Lawrence, and then out to sea. The centers normally move 300 to 1000 miles a day.

Not all low pressure areas are storms in the popular sense, that is weather disturbances accompanied by rain or snow. Those in which the pressure is not very low have light winds and little, if any, rain. These

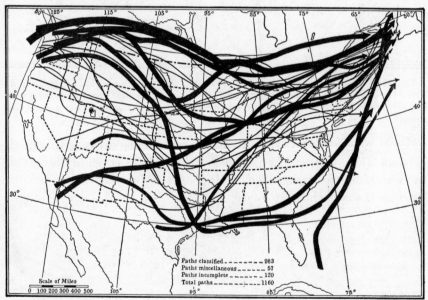

After Van Cleef

Fig. 410. — Paths followed by a number of low pressure areas, cyclonic storms, Lows, across the United States. The width of the lines indicates the comparative frequency of storms following each track.

poorly developed low pressure areas sometimes die out entirely; in other cases they rapidly develop into vigorous storms. It is such irregularities as these that make storm prediction uncertain; but, because they usually follow regular courses, most storms can be accurately predicted.

Summary. *Cyclonic storms and anticyclones usually develop in the northwest or southwest, but often come from the Pacific, passing eastward across the country in fairly regular succession.*

(D) *Causes of cyclonic storms.* Cyclonic storms are great eddies in the prevailing westerlies, and they occur both in the northern and southern hemispheres. They may be compared to the eddies in a river (Fig. 411), that move downstream with the current at the same time that water is whirling from all directions toward their centers. In the same way, while the storm whirls are moving eastward with the prevailing westerlies, the air in them is eddying from all sides toward their centers.

Fig. 411. — An eddy moving downstream, but with water whirling toward its center. Each water particle starts in a straight line toward the center of the eddy but is continually pulled, or deflected, to the right as it moves in. Thus a counter-clockwise whirl is set up.

Why these eddies develop is not a completely solved problem. Modern study and observation point to the conclusion that they have their origin in differences in the amount of heat given off by the sun. Although the variation in the amount of sun heat from day to day or year to year is not great, it is sufficient to disturb the equilibrium and regular flow of the atmospheric currents. In consequence a pulsation or wave-like ebb and flow is set up in the atmosphere. But such oscillation would not of itself develop cyclones and anticyclones. To explain the occurrence of these another notable characteristic of the air in the prevailing westerlies must be taken into account. That is, that close to the surface of the earth, wide horizontal expanses of air of greatly different temperatures may lie closely alongside each other. Thus in winter the air over the continents is much colder than that over the oceans. When a wave of cold air, due to extra solar heating at the equator, advances from the polar regions and overflows these adjacent warm and cold air masses, it upsets the pressure equilibrium at the line of contact of the adjacent cold and warm air masses. Thus a flow is started at the surface across the line of separation. Under the influence of the earth's rotation the flow movement is deflected from the original direction and localized. Thus cyclones, with winds blowing spirally inward, and anticyclones, with winds blowing spirally outwards, are developed. The solar radiation, or heating, varies as sunspots increase in number and intensity on the sun; though the sunspots are not themselves the cause for the increase in the solar heat. (See also p. 283.)

Summary. *Cyclonic storms are eddies in the prevailing westerlies, with air whirling toward their centers from all sides. These eddies are low pressure areas, caused, probably, by air waves and surface currents started in the westerlies by variations in sun heat and deflected to spiral motion by the effect of the earth's rotation.*

(E) *Influence of cyclones and anticyclones on weather.* WINDS. (See also p. 471.) During the passage of high and low pressure areas the wind changes. On the east side of a storm the wind is from an easterly quarter, on the south side from the south, and between the cyclone and the anticyclone, from the west. The winds do not move along straight lines toward the center, but are turned by the effect of rotation, so that they blow spirally (see and study carefully Figs. 404 and 411 and the accompanying explanations), and if the differences in pressure are considerable, they blow with great force. Near the center the air rises (Fig. 403); but in an anticyclone it is steadily settling (Fig. 408).

TEMPERATURE. With these variations in wind direction the temperature also changes. Air from the south is warm, from the north, cool or cold. The settling air of the anticyclones brings to the earth some of the cool upper air. For these reasons, when low pressure areas pass over a region there is usually hot, humid air in summer, and damp air and rising temperature in winter. But when the high pressure areas approach, the air becomes clear and cool in summer, and cold in winter. Radiation through the clear air of an anticyclone cools the ground far more than through the humid, cloudy air which mantles the earth during the passage of a low pressure area.

RAIN. When air is settling it is being heated by pressure; therefore its relative humidity decreases and its water vapor does not condense. Consequently anticyclones cause periods of dryness. In cyclonic storms, on the other hand, the rising air is expanding and becoming cooler, and its vapor is condensing, forming clouds and rain. The cloudy and rainy portions of a well-developed cyclonic storm may cover an area with a diameter of over 1000 miles.

There are three other important reasons for rain in these storms: (1) those winds which are blowing from the south are steadily advancing toward a cooler region; (2) in some places the air is forced to rise over highlands, like the Appalachians and New England; (3) the centrifugal force of the whirling storm also tends to lower the pressure of the air at its center and thus to cause further expansion and cooling. If, in either case, the air cools until it reaches the dew point, some of its vapor condenses.

In central and eastern United States the rain-bearing winds of cyclonic storms are mainly from the south and east. Winds from these quarters bear vapor from the ocean, and those from the south are, in addition, blowing toward cooler regions. In New England, well-developed cyclonic storms in winter are commonly called *northeast storms*, because the damp ocean winds blowing from that quarter toward the center of low pressure bring heavy snows. Ordinarily precipitation takes place in the southeast quarter of a Low. Why?

When vapor condenses to form clouds and rain, the so-called "latent heat" (p. 405) is liberated, and this helps warm the air. It is partly for this reason that storms commonly increase in violence in passing over the Great Lakes and the ocean; for in these places more vapor is provided, and the heat from its condensation causes lower pressure and, therefore, a more rapid inflow and rising of air. A cyclonic storm has been called a great engine, furnishing some of its own energy as the vapor condenses.

Summary. *As high and low pressure areas pass, the winds vary in direction, the Lows bringing warm air, clouds, and rain, the Highs cool, clear air settling from aloft. The rain of cyclonic storms is caused (1) by the rising of air, (2) by its passage from warmer to cooler regions, (3) by its rising over highlands, and (4) by expansion and cooling through centrifugal force. The heat liberated by condensing vapor causes the air to rise with increasing energy, and, therefore, storms when passing over water increase in vigor.*

189. Thunderstorms and tornadoes. (A) *Thunderstorms.* These are local storms that develop in low pressure areas, usually in the southern portion where warm, humid air moving in from the south meets colder air coming from the west and north, or where on muggy, oppressive days the air is warmed during the day over level and moist areas. This humid air rises, and patches of cumulus clouds appear (p. 416). As the day passes, these grow larger and darker, rising as masses of rolling, surging clouds, perhaps a full mile above the level base.

Eventually there is so much expansion, cooling, and condensation in the upper cloud levels that raindrops too large to be buoyed up by the ascending currents are formed. These fall. The condensation liberates latent heat in the cloud, warming and further expanding the rising air and so increasing the uprush from below. Then the storm is on in earnest and the rain falls in torrents. The upper central storm area begins to whirl and lightning and thunder are produced. As a thunderstorm approaches, the observer experiences the phenomena illustrated in Fig. 412.

Thunderstorms may be small, perhaps only a few hundred yards in area; but sometimes they are 50 to 100 miles long, 15 to 25 miles broad, and

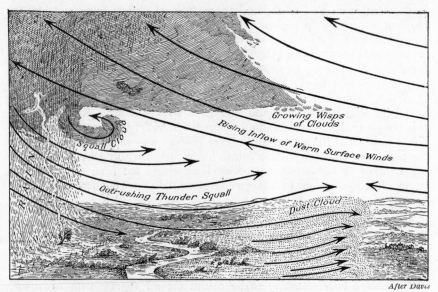

After Davis

Fig. 412. — Diagram of a thunderstorm. Note the different phenomena shown and when you see a thunderstorm again try to observe each of these and how they occur in succession.

3 to 5 miles high. They travel eastward in the west winds at the rate of 20 to 50 miles an hour, and may last from 2 to 10 hours before dying out. *Lightning* results from the fact that the raindrops of two cloud masses may be differently charged with electricity. When, owing to the turmoil in the thunderstorm cloud, a large mass with a heavy charge is brought in contact with a similar mass having a lesser or the opposite charge, a tremendous electric spark is produced—lightning. This great spark causes violent and sudden expansion of the gases of the air. An air wave, like that caused by an explosion results and is heard as *thunder*. It takes nearly five seconds for the sound to travel one mile.

Sometimes the earth has a charge of one kind of electricity, the thunderstorm cloud the opposite, then the lightning spark jumps from the cloud to the earth (Fig. 413). Trees or houses standing alone help the spark to make the jump, hence are likely to be struck. Therefore it is not safe to seek shelter under a single big tree during a thunderstorm, and isolated houses and barns should have good lightning rods.

Thunderstorms occur in other places where warm, humid air is rising to a level at which its vapor rapidly condenses. For example, they are of almost daily occurrence in the belt of calms. Around mountains, too, as the air rises on a hot day, clouds often gather and develop into thunderstorms. In arid lands these storms are sometimes accompanied by such rapid condensation of vapor and such heavy rain that they are called *cloudbursts*.

Summary. *Thunderstorms are caused by the rising of warm, humid air in low pressure areas, usually in the southern portion; they are overdeveloped cumulus clouds. They also occur in the belt of calms, and where air is rising around mountains.*

(B) *Tornadoes.* Tornadoes (Fig. 414) develop in the southern portion of low pressure areas under conditions

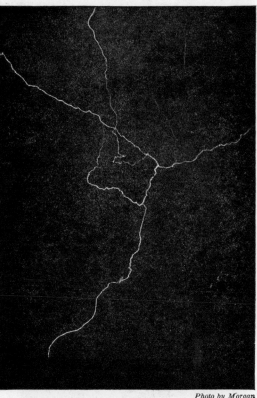

Photo by Morgan

Fig. 413. — Photograph of a great lightning flash seen from Rehoboth Beach, Delaware. Note that the lightning is like an electric spark, not jagged as sometimes pictured.

similar to those causing thunderstorms. The warm, humid, lower layers of air, brought by south winds, have above them cooler layers moving from the west. As the lower air warms and rises, a whirl starts around the center of rising, and the winds blow with great force. Like thunderstorms, tornadoes often occur in groups,

Photos by Loveland

Fig. 414. — Photographs of a tornado at Ashland, Nebraska. The picture on the left shows the narrow whirling storm at a distance and the thunderstorm condition of the upper clouds; the one on the right is a near view of the same "twister," as such storms are called in the tornado belt.

several developing at one time, and not very far apart, as in the case of the very destructive tornadoes of March 18, 1925, in Missouri, Illinois, and Indiana.

Photo by Ikenberry

Fig. 415. — Thin wooden laths driven through the heavy boards of a barn by the force (due to high velocity) of a tornado wind at Mt. Morris, New York.

The winds of the tornado whirl are so strong (Fig. 415) that houses are overturned, heavy bodies picked up and carried long distances, trees uprooted, and paths cut through the forest. In the center of the whirl there is a partial vacuum, and, as it passes, the air inside of houses expands with such force as to blow out the windows and even the walls. The air inside the quills of the feathers on chickens expands and pops the feathers right out of the skin, so that, if they survive the storm, the fowls go about plucked quite naked. The blackness (Fig. 414) of the funnel-shaped cloud is due in part to the dust there collected, in part to the sudden and complete condensation of all the water vapor of the air as it expands in the vacuum of the center, caused by the centrifugal whirl.

The path of great destruction is only a few score yards wide, though it may reach a length of several miles before the tornado dies out. Although the passage of a tornado lasts but a minute or two, its work of destruction is so complete that tornadoes are much dreaded; and, in regions visited by them, holes, called "cyclone cellars," are made in the ground for shelter.

Fortunately destructive tornadoes do not occur everywhere. They develop most frequently in the level, open country of the Mississippi Valley. There it is easily possible for warm, humid air from the Gulf of Mexico to slide in under the cooler, upper air and thus bring about the unstable conditions which are so favorable to tornado formation. They seldom develop in arid countries, because the air is rarely humid enough; nor are they common in mountainous or hilly lands, because the irregular surface causes the intermingling of warm and cool air to take place in small quantities and progressively. They rarely occur east of the northern Appalachians.

Photo by Ward

Fig. 416. — A waterspout off Marthas Vineyard, Massachusetts. Note how similar it is in form to a tornado.

Summary. *Warm, humid air, creeping under cooler layers in the southern part of low pressure areas, especially on the level plains, causes an unstable condition; and at times, as the air rises, the in-moving winds start a violent whirl, forming a tornado.*

(C) *Waterspouts.* At sea conditions favoring tornadoes produce waterspouts (Fig. 416). In their centers the sea water is raised in a low cone, and some salt water is actually carried up into the spout, the rest is supplied by the rapid condensation of the great quantities of water vapor in the humid air.

Summary. *Waterspouts are tornadoes at sea.*

190. Hurricanes and typhoons. The cyclonic disturbances of the temperate latitudes are known to meteorologists as *extratropical cyclones*. Very violent storms, *tropical cyclones*, known in the Pacific as *typhoons*, and in the Atlantic as *hurricanes*, develop in the tropical zone and move into the temperate zones. On passing into the cooler temperate zones they become larger and less violent, and then closely resemble extratropical cyclonic storms. The path followed by the Atlantic hurricanes is usually across the West Indies, off the coast of the southern Atlantic states, then out to sea, curving eastward under the influence of the earth's rotation. Sometimes they depart from this course (Fig. 417), visiting the Gulf coast and even the Great Lakes. The typhoons of the Pacific and Indian oceans have various courses, some

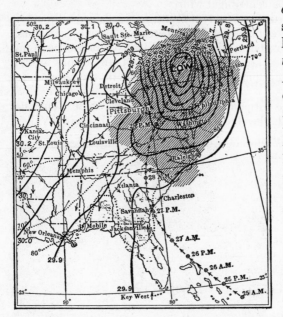

Fig. 417. — A diagram tracing the path of a hurricane from the West Indies. It has gone a little out of the usual course and passed over the land. Rain area shaded.

of those in the northern hemisphere passing over the Philippines.

These storms start by the rising of warm, humid air in the torrid belt, forming a whirl similar to that in a tornado, though much larger (Fig. 418).

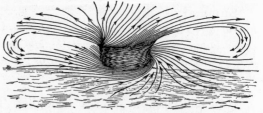

Fig. 418. — Graphic sketch to illustrate wind movement in a hurricane.

They originate on the ocean rather than on the land. The humid air over the sea supplies much vapor, which, on condensing, liberates heat that warms the air and causes it to rise still more rapidly.

The pressure is very low in the center, though not approaching a vacuum. Toward this center violent winds blow (Figs. 418, 419), often with such force as to overturn trees and houses. At Samoa in 1889, several warships were destroyed during a typhoon. Along the south Atlantic coast of the United States the most violent storms are hurricanes, which often leave the coast strewn

with wreckage. A hurricane did great damage along the east coast of Florida, September 18–19, 1926.

Heavy rains, vivid lightning, and loud thunder accompany these storms. With them also travels a wave of high water, which, advancing on low coasts, causes great damage, destroying houses, towns, and life. It was one of these waves, rising over Galveston, that, together with the winds, caused such terrible destruction in 1900, killing thousands of people and almost destroying the city. Such a wave is due to two causes: (1) drifting of water toward the storm center by the spirally inblowing winds (Figs. 418, 419); (2) rising of water in the center because the weight of the air there is less than in the ring surrounding it.

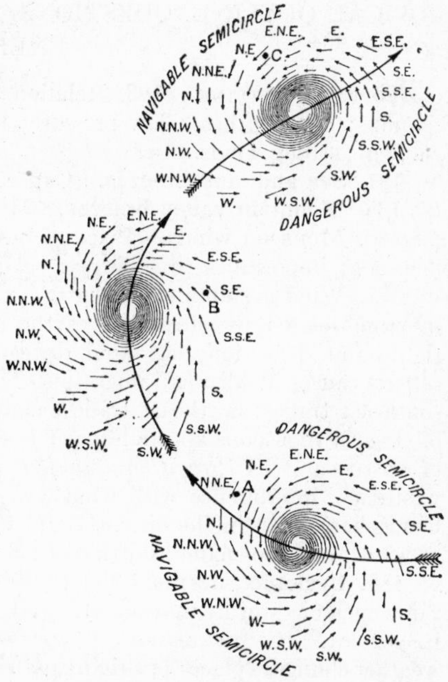

Fig. 419. — Diagram of a hurricane. In the "dangerous semicircle" a ship will be in the path of the approaching storm and the spirally inflowing storm winds are more violent because they blow with the prevailing winds: trades, south; westerlies, north.

Most hurricanes, the tropical cyclones of the West Indies, occur in late summer and early fall, because then the belt of greatest heat is farthest north. At the equator, winds are not turned by the influence of rotation; but, as the distance from the equator increases, they are turned more and more. Whirls can develop only when the winds are turned to one side so as to start a spiral movement around the center of rising. For this reason tropical cyclones cannot start at the equator; but they can start in the hot belt when it has migrated some distance from the equator. In the North Atlantic the period when the belt of calms is farthest from the equator is in late summer, and then hurricane whirls start in the rising air.

Summary. *Hurricanes and typhoons are violent whirls, starting in the tropical zone, and resembling tornadoes, though larger and less violent. They* *start over the ocean because of the great amount of vapor, whose condensation supplies heat which causes more rapid rising of the air. Their fierce winds and the water wave which accompanies them cause great destruction. West Indian hurricanes occur chiefly in late summer or early autumn, when the belt of calms is farthest from the equator, because then the effect of rotation can deflect the winds and start the spiral movement which causes the whirl.*

TOPICAL OUTLINE, QUESTIONS, SUGGESTIONS, AND LABORATORY EXERCISES

TOPICAL OUTLINE. **183. Relation between winds and air pressure.** Air columns; effect of heat; low pressure; high pressure; cause of winds; barometric gradient; strong winds.

184. **Sea and land breezes.** Cause of sea breezes; effects; land breezes.

185. **Mountain valley breezes.** Movement down valleys; up valleys.

186. **Monsoon winds.** Place of best development; summer monsoon; winter monsoon; importance to sailing vessels; condition in northeastern United States.

187. **Wind systems of the earth.** (A) *Comparison with a stove:* air movements in room heated by stove; on earth; planetary winds. (B) *Effect of rotation:* right-hand deflection; left-hand deflection; reasons for deflection. (C) *Belt of calms:* cause; doldrums; migration. (D) *Trade winds:* steadiness; deflection; southeast trades; northeast trades; naming of winds; change in position; relation of Asiatic monsoons to trades. (E) *Antitrades:* upper outflow; direction; proof of existence. (F) *Prevailing westerlies:* source of air; effect of rotation; prevailing westerlies; interference with winds; westerlies over Southern Ocean; in northern hemisphere; high in the air. (G) *Horse latitudes:* location; settling air; condition of winds; origin of name; shifting of belts.

188. **Cyclonic storms.** (A) *Cyclones:* low-pressure area; isobars; winds; rain; cyclonic storm; movement. (B) *Anticyclones:* pressure; winds; sky; name; movement. (C) *Succession of cyclones and anticyclones:* regular succession; weather changes; places of origin; paths; weak Lows; irregularities. (D) *Cause of cyclonic storms:* comparison with river eddies; theory of wave origin; relation of cyclonic storms to solar radiation and sunspots. (E) *Influence of cyclones and anticyclones on weather:* (a) Winds, — variation in direction; deflection; variation in force; rising air in Lows; settling in Highs. (b) Temperature, — south winds; north winds; settling air; passage of Lows; of Highs; radiation. (c) Rain, — reason for dryness in Highs; effect of rising in Lows; other causes for rain; source of vapor; northeast storms; effect of liberation of heat; storms over water.

189. **Thunderstorms and tornadoes.** (A) *Thunderstorms:* place of occurrence in low-pressure areas; cause; growth; conditions in; lightning; thunder; size; path; rate of movement; occurrence elsewhere; cloudbursts. (B) *Tornadoes:* favoring conditions; the whirl; comparison with thunderstorms; effect of winds; condition in center; reason for blackness; path; time of passage; cyclone cellars; occurrence in Mississippi Valley; absence in other sections. (C) *Waterspouts:* nature of.

190. **Hurricanes and typhoons.** Typhoons; hurricanes; places of development; movement into temperate zones; paths followed; cause; reason for development over the sea; accompanying phenomena; effects of water wave; cause of wave; time of occurrence; explanation of this.

QUESTIONS. Section 183. What is the cause of wind? What is barometric gradient? When are winds strong?

184. Explain sea breezes; land breezes.

185. Explain the day and night breezes of mountain valleys.

186. Where are monsoons best developed? Explain them. What is the condition in northeastern United States?

187. (A) Compare the circulation in a room heated by a stove with that of the earth. What are planetary winds? (B) In what direction, and why, are winds turned from a straight course? Why is a north wind deflected? An east wind? (C) What is the condition in the belt of calms? Why does it change position? (D) What are the directions of the trade winds? Why? How are winds named? What effect has the migration of the belt of calms? Why are the monsoons so well developed in Asia? (E) What is the direction of the anti-trades? How is this known? (F) What is the direction of the winds in high latitudes? Why? What are the prevailing westerlies? What interferes with the regular winds? How do the westerlies of the northern and southern hemispheres differ? (G) What are the conditions in the horse latitudes? Why?

188. (A) What is a low pressure area? What are isobars? A cyclonic storm? State its characteristics. (B) What are anticyclones? Contrast with cyclonic storms. (C) What changes accompany the Highs and Lows? What paths are pursued? What irregularities are noticed? (D) Compare cyclonic storms with eddies in a river. State the solar radiation and sunspot theory for these storms. (E) What is the nature of the winds in high and low pressure areas? What changes in temperature occur as these areas pass over a region? What are four causes of rain in the cyclonic storms? Why do storms commonly increase in violence when passing over large water bodies?

189. (A) Under what conditions do thunderstorms appear in low pressure areas? Why? What is the lightning? The thunder? How are these caused? What are the characteristics of these storms? Where else do thunderstorms occur? (B) Under what conditions do tornadoes develop? What are some effects of tornadoes? Where are they most common? Why? Why are they so black? In what situation are tornadoes rare? (C) What are waterspouts?

190. What are hurricanes? Typhoons? What paths do they follow? Why do they start over the sea? What destruction do they accomplish? Give instances. What destruction is done by the water wave? What is the cause of this wave? When are these storms most common? Why at that season?

SUGGESTIONS. (1) Recall the previous experiments on convection (Chapter XII, p. 424). (2) Open a window on a cold day when no wind is blowing. Why does the cold air enter the room? (3) Keep a record of the wind direction for twenty days. How many days did the wind blow from each of the four quarters (north, east, south, and west)? For the same period keep a record of the direction that the higher clouds are moving. How many days do they move from each quarter? (4) On an outline map make a sketch of the winds of the globe similar to Fig. 398. (5) If the instruments are available, keep a record of the wind direction and force, humidity, temperature, clouds and rain, and barometric pressure (Appendix G). Tell when cyclonic storms and anticyclones are passing, and carefully record the relation between air pressure and the other phenomena. From your observations predict the weather for the following day. Make an enlarged copy of the diagram of a Low (Fig. 404) on tracing paper. Place this in varying positions on a wall map of the United States and discuss the weather different localities will probably have for each position. (6) Study weather maps (Appendix H). (7) With apparatus obtained from the physics laboratory make an electric spark. This is a lightning flash on a small scale and the noise is thunder. A similar flash and noise may sometimes be noticed as a trolley car passes. (8) If thunderstorms occur, keep a record of all the phenomena and report upon them. (9) Watch in the fall for newspaper reports of hurricanes or typhoons; also, in spring and summer, for reports of tornadoes.

Laboratory Exercises. Exercises XLII, XLVIII, XLIX, L, LI, and LIII in TARR and VON ENGELN's *Laboratory Manual for Physical and Commercial Geography*, The Macmillan Company, New York, should be performed in connection with the study of this chapter. In city schools especial emphasis may to advantage be put on the chapters and exercises on the atmosphere. Not that these topics are of less importance in rural districts but because in cities weather and climate are the only natural phenomena that come directly into the pupil's experience.

Reference Books. FERREL, *Popular Treatise on the Wind*, John Wiley & Sons, New York, 1889; CLAYTON, *World Weather*, The Macmillan Company, New York, 1923; VISHER, *Climatic Laws*, John Wiley & Sons, New York, 1924; in addition to the references at end of Chapter XII.

CHAPTER XIV

WEATHER AND CLIMATE

191. Difference between weather and climate. *Weather* refers to daily changes in temperature, wind, clouds, and rain. *Climate* is the average result of these weather changes. For example, certain parts of the tropical zone are said to have a rainy climate. This does not mean that it rains every day, but that, though the weather on some days is clear, on still more it is rainy. Thus the average condition, or the climate, is rainy.

The following are some of the more important kinds of climate: dry, hot desert climates; hot, rainy climates, as in the belt of calms; damp, equable ocean climates; extreme and variable climates, common in the interior of continents; and polar climates. The greater part of the United States has a variable climate. These different climates, and the reasons for them, can best be understood by studying the conditions in various parts of the world.

Summary. *Climate is the average of weather, which is the daily condition of temperature, wind, clouds, and rain. There are a number of very different climates on the earth.*

192. Zones of heat. (A) *The five zones.* The most fundamental cause for variations in climate is the distribution of sun's heat

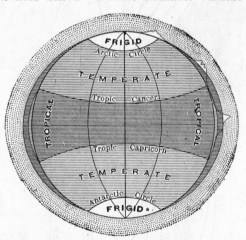

Fig. 420. — The five zones, showing, also, how on highlands a frigid climate may extend even into the tropical zone.

from equator to poles. This results from the differences in angle at which the sun's rays reach the earth in different latitudes (p. 406). From this has arisen the common division of the earth

Fig. 421. — Isothermal chart of the world for January. Determine the position of the *heat equator*, line of highest temperature around the world, at this time. What is its position in relation to the latitudinal equator, (a) over the Pacific, (b) over the Atlantic, (c) over Africa and Asia? Account for this in each case. Do the same for July, Fig. 422.

into five climatic zones, — two frigid or polar, two temperate, and one torrid or tropical (Fig. 420).

It is customary in the conventional diagrams used in grade school geographies to draw the boundaries between these zones of heat along the parallels of latitude; but the actual boundaries are by no means so regular. Indeed, there are some portions of the tropical zone that have as low temperature as parts of the polar zones; and some parts of the temperate zones have summer climates that are quite tropical. Several reasons for these irregularities are the following influences.

Summary. *Owing to the angle at which the sun's rays reach different latitudes, the earth may be divided into five zones; but, for a number of reasons, the boundaries of the actual climatic zones are irregular.*

(B) *Influence of altitude.* One important cause for irregularities in the boundaries of the heat zones is altitude. The climate of highlands is cooler than that of neighboring lowlands (p. 407). The isothermal charts[1] (Figs. 421, 422) show numerous places, as in the Rocky Mountains, where the isotherms are bent toward the equator in crossing highlands. The influence of altitude is also well shown along the Pacific slope (Fig. 423), where winds from the equable ocean blow upon a rising coast with mountains extending north and south. Along this coast the climate is warm and equable; but on the mountain slopes the temperature becomes lower. Therefore the isotherms extend north and south instead of east and west, as is commonly the case.

Summary. *Highlands are cooler than neighboring lowlands. Therefore highlands cause the isotherms, or lines connecting places having the same average temperature, to follow irregular courses.*

(C) *Influence of water.* Distance from water (p. 405) is another cause for variation in temperature. Oceanic islands have cooler summers and warmer winters than the mainland in the same latitude; and seacoasts have more equable climates than interiors. This is clearly illustrated by comparing the isotherms in the interior and on coasts of continents.

[1] An *isotherm* is a line connecting places having the *same average temperature*. An *isothermal chart* is one showing these isotherms for a given area (as the world, the United States, or a state) for a certain period of time. A chart for the year has isotherms passing through places whose average temperature for the year is the same; a chart for January averages all the temperatures for that period, etc.

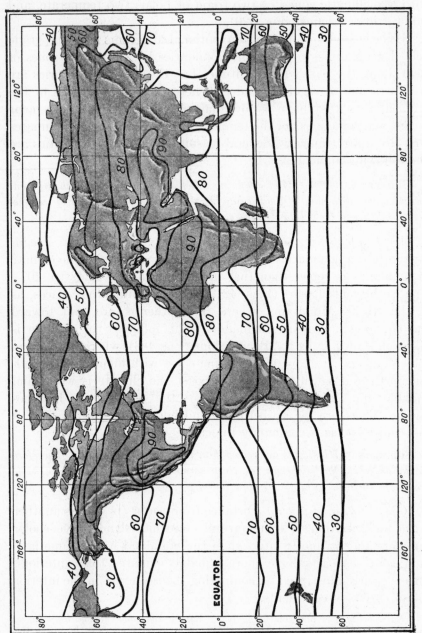

Fig. 422. — Isothermal chart of the world for July.   See Fig. 421.

Examine Figs. 423 and 424, for example, to see how much difference there is in January and July between Minnesota, the state of Washington, and of Maine. Find other illustrations on the world charts (Figs. 421, 422). Contrast the range over the Atlantic with that over Asia and America; and the range over the Southern Ocean with that over the lands of the northern hemisphere.

Summary. *Oceans and coasts have a far more equable climate than the interiors of continents.*

(D) *Influence of winds.* The influence of winds in causing irregularity in the isotherms is best illustrated, on a large scale, where winds blow from water upon land, as in northwestern United States and Europe (Figs. 421–424). In these places the prevailing west winds, influenced by the water over which they pass, moderate the cold of winter and the heat of summer. It is for this reason that in western Europe agriculture thrives, and large cities are found in latitudes that, in eastern North America, are frigid and almost uninhabited. London is in the same latitude as southern Labrador, and Leningrad as northern Labrador. For the same reason, the January temperature at San Francisco is the same as that at Charleston, S. C. (5° farther south), while the July isotherm is that of Halifax (6° farther north).

Summary. *Prevailing winds influence the temperature, the most pronounced influence being where winds from the ocean prevail, thus carrying the equable temperatures of the water upon the land.*

(E) *Influence of ocean currents.* Ocean currents and drifts bear water from one zone to another (p. 349). Winds blowing over these currents have their temperature influenced, and, blowing upon the lands, bear to them some of the warmth or cold brought by the currents from other zones.

This effect of ocean currents is well illustrated in the North Atlantic (Figs. 322, 421, 422). The great northward bend of the isotherms off the European coast shows the influence of the warm west wind drift (Fig. 336). Off northeastern North America, the cold Labrador current bends the isotherms toward the equator. Therefore, the isotherms are crowded together on the American coast and spread apart, fan-shaped, on the European coast. In other words, there are much greater differences in temperature in a short distance in eastern America than in western Europe. Notice also the influence of ocean currents on the isotherms along the west coasts of the United States, South America, and Africa.

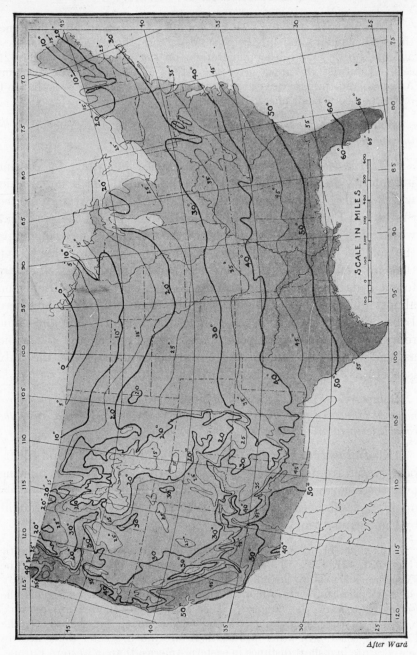

Fig. 423. — Isothermal chart of the United States for January,

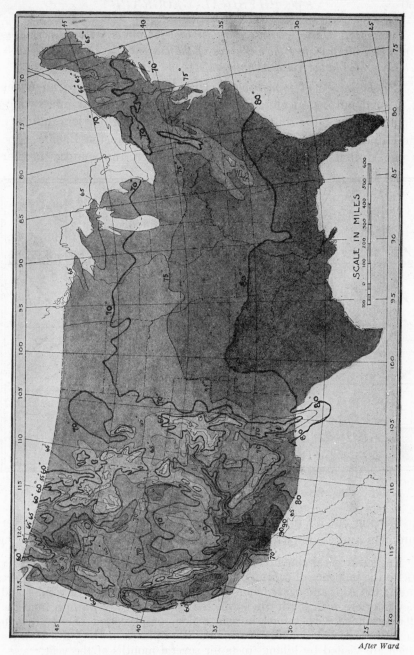

Fig. 424. — Isothermal chart of the United States for July.

Summary. *Ocean currents warm or cool the air over them; moving as winds this air transfers the influence of the currents to the land. This is well illustrated in the North Atlantic.*

(F) *Influence of topography.* Hills and valleys have an effect of a local nature on climate. Mountains produce far more wide-spread effects. By shutting off winds, mountain barriers influence the climate of places behind them. Thus, while the Pacific slope of the United States has an equable climate, the country farther

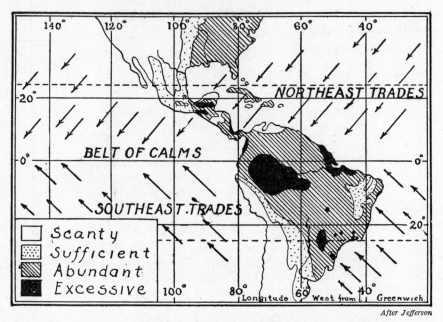

After Jefferson

Fig. 425. — Rainfall of calm and trade-wind belts of America.

east, being cut off from ocean winds by the mountains, has hotter summers and colder winters than the coast lands.

The subtropical climate of Italy, southern Spain, and France is partly due to the influence of topography. The waters of the Mediterranean are warm; the Alps and other mountains shut out the cold north winds; and they interfere with south winds which might bear away warmth from the Mediterranean. Therefore, in this region, oranges and palms grow in the latitude of Boston, New York, and other places in the United States which are visited by killing frosts for several months of the year.

Summary. *Hills and valleys have a local influence on climate, and mountains far greater effects, especially in shutting out winds.*

CLIMATIC BELTS OF THE TROPICAL ZONE

193. Belt of calms (Fig. 398). The vertical position of the sun in the equatorial belt of calms (p. 431) causes the climate to be hot (p. 406). This belt is also a very rainy one (Figs. 425–427, 429), because the rising air heated by contact with the warm sea and land surface soon reaches an elevation where its vapor condenses (p. 445).

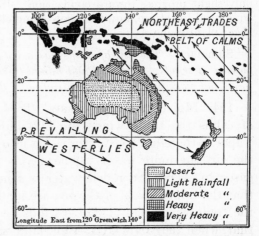

Fig. 426. — Rainfall of calm, trade-wind, and westerly belts of Australia.

The weather of the belt of calms is monotonously uniform. On the ocean, or on oceanic islands, the air grows warmer each day after the sun rises; and from the clouds which form, and which often develop into violent thunderstorms, heavy rain falls. During the night the humid air is still warm, for there is not enough radiation to cool it. Both day and night there is an absence of steady winds, and the many sailing vessels of earlier

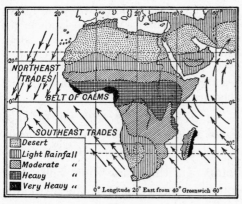

Fig. 427. — Rainfall of calm and trade-wind belts of Africa.

times were often becalmed there for days. These conditions are repeated with marked regularity. One day is like the next throughout the year. It is said that night is the winter of the equatorial lands, and at seacoast stations the night temperatures are seldom more than 4° to 6° F. lower than those of the day. At inland points the daytime temperatures are higher than on the sea, and winds are often caused by such differences in temperature; thus, along the coast sea breezes may blow (p. 427).

The rainfall although extremely variable in total quantity is nevertheless always so heavy in the wet tropical regions that dense forests thrive, and the air within these is reeking with moisture. So warm and damp is the climate that it is difficult to work; the clearing away of vegetation for planting is a laborious task.   For these reasons the equatorial forest is inhabited by tribes depending directly upon nature for food.   Having little ambition for improving their condition, these peoples have made only slight progress toward civilization.   Increasingly larger areas of the equatorial forest are, however, now being cleared for rubber, banana, and sugar plantations.

Summary.   *The belt of calms has a hot, humid climate with a general absence of winds.   The heat and humidity cause a rank growth of tropical forest, but make progress in the utilization of these lands slow.*

194. Moist trade-wind coasts.

To the north and south of the belt of calms the trade winds (p. 432) blow toward warmer regions. Vapor is therefore constantly rising into them, because, the warmer the air, the more water vapor may be included in its mixture of gases (p. 411).   So much water is removed by such evaporation that the upper levels of the sea are made more salt (p. 333) where the trade winds blow.   These winds bear such quantities of vapor that, when they blow over rising land where the air rises and cools, vapor is condensed.   Therefore east-facing coasts, against which the trade winds blow, are very wet (Figs. 425, 427, 429).

The east coast of South America, both north and south of the equator (Fig. 425), the East and West Indies, northeastern Australia (Fig. 426), and southeastern Africa (Fig. 427) have heavy rains, because the trade winds blow upon them from the sea.   These places have a tropical forest, resembling that of the belt of calms.   Mountainous oceanic islands in the trade-wind belt, like the Hawaiian Islands, have heavy rains on the eastern or windward side while the opposite side has a dry climate.   Because of this it has become a usual practice to bore a tunnel through mountains in such areas to collect the water of a river flowing down the rainy side and to carry this water to the arid side for irrigation purposes.

Summary.   *East-facing coasts in the trade-wind belts have a rainy climate, because, as the damp air cools in rising over the land, some of the water, evaporated from the ocean, is condensed and precipitated.*

195. Desert trade-wind belts.

In the trade-wind belts arid conditions are far more common than rainy; in fact, the evaporating effects of the trade winds furnish the most important cause for deserts.   They take up vapor in passing over the land for the same reason as on the ocean; but as there is so little moisture to be obtained on land they become very dry winds, into which nearly all available moisture is evaporated.   This leaves so little water for plants that the land is made desert; but there is some vapor even in the driest desert air and rain occasionally falls. In the Mohave desert the rainfall is less than two inches a year.

Because of these conditions both north and south of the equator, there is a broad belt of arid and desert country extending almost completely across the continents, though on east-facing coasts interrupted by rainy belts. These desert belts include parts of Australia (Fig. 426), South Africa (Fig. 427), western South America (Fig. 425), and southwestern United States; but the largest desert tract is in the great land area of northern Africa and the extension of this into Asia. Commencing in western Africa, there is a series of deserts extending far toward the east coast of Asia (Fig. 429). The great Sahara is a part of this belt.

In many places the deserts of the trade-wind belts merge into the arid regions of the horse latitudes (p. 436). Here the air is warming by compression as it sinks toward the surface of the earth, and evaporation, therefore, proceeds rapidly.

Life in the deserts presents a far different picture from that in the tropical forest. Only a few species of plants are adapted to life amid the unfavorable conditions, and even these are scattered (p. 541). Therefore, the desert is a barren, open country; and neither animals (p. 561) nor men (p. 600) find it a favorable place for a home. Deserts are among the most sparsely settled parts of the world.

The weather is nearly always dry, the sky usually cloudless, and the winds often strong, blowing sand about (p. 146). Even in the deserts of the temperate zone the days are warm, and in summer hot. For example, in the desert of southern Arizona, though far north of the tropic of Cancer, the thermometer sometimes rises to 120° F. in the shade. The very high air temperature of 127° F. was recorded in the Algerian desert. But radiation is rapid in the dry desert air, and at night the ground and air cool so quickly that a blanket may be necessary before morning.

Summary. *Where air is growing warmer as it passes over or settles down on the land as in the trade-wind and horse-latitude belts, the climate is dry and the land arid or desert. Most of the deserts are in these belts. Deserts are unfavorable to life,— plant, animal, and human. The desert climate is dry, often windy, and hot days are followed by cool nights.*

196. Savanna belts. Between the rainy belt of calms and the trade-wind deserts there is, in each hemisphere, a region, called the *savanna* belt, that has alternate dry and wet seasons. This peculiar climate is caused by the migration of the belt of calms (p. 432). In the hot season the belt of calms migrates to the savannas and there is heavy rain; but in the opposite season the savannas are under the influence of the drying trade winds.

As a result of these changes, the hot season of the savanna regions (the time of our summer for those in the northern hemisphere, and of our winter for those in the southern) has copious rainfall, and vegetation freshens and grows vigorously; but in the opposite season the ground is parched, and vegetation withers. The season of drought is too severe for many forms of vegetation, such as trees. Therefore, the savannas are covered with those plants, such as grass, which are able to survive a period of drought (p. 541).

The *downes* of Australia, the *park lands* of Africa, the *llanos* of Venezuela and Colombia, and the *campos* of Brazil are examples of savannas. Their grass supports large numbers of plant-eating animals, upon which flesh-eating mammals prey. It is on these areas and not in the equatorial forests of Africa that lions abound.

Savannas are probably destined to become the most productive and best-settled lands in the tropical zone. The open country favors agriculture, and the drought makes necessary some provision for that season. Being thus forced to industry and thrift the negroes of the savannas have become farmers and cattle raisers, and are the most advanced blacks of Africa.

Summary. *The migration of the belt of calms brings abundant rain to the margin of the desert trade-wind belt during the hot season, giving rise to alternate seasons of drought and rain. This makes such regions, called savannas, great pasture lands, well adapted to support life.*

197. The Indian climate. As a result of the influence of the monsoons (p. 427), parts of India have a peculiar climate with three well-defined seasons, — the hot season, the rains, and the cool winter. During the hot season, which lasts from March to June, hot, dry winds from the land cause the temperature to rise above 100° in the shade. In June the air becomes calm and the heat almost suffocating, and every one longs for the summer monsoon. When this begins (it comes so suddenly that it is said to "burst") clouds appear, rain falls, and for two to three months rains are of almost daily occurrence, causing vegetation to grow profusely.

A short period of calm follows the summer monsoon, and again the heat is intense; but cool air from the interior soon begins to flow down toward the sea, and by October the winter monsoon is established. The air is then clear and cool, and by January, in many parts of India, fires are necessary. In February a sort of spring visits the land. Vegetation then bursts forth, only to be withered by the scorching drought of the hot season, which postpones the real growing season until the summer rains. If these summer rains fail to develop in their normal intensity, as sometimes happens, the crops fail and famines result in the densely populated lands of India.

So heavy is the rainfall on the mountain slopes that in places the soil is completely washed away. A tract of the heaviest rain-fall in the world is at the base of the Himalayas (Fig. 428). In a year about 400 inches of rain fall. If it should all stand where it fell, it would form a layer of 33 feet. Of this amount about two thirds falls in the five summer months. On a single day there have been 40 inches of rain, or more than falls in most parts of the United States in a year.

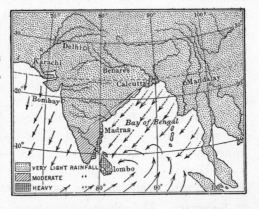

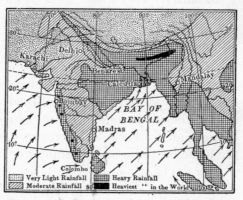

In southeast Asia, including China, the monsoonal reversal of the winds extends from the high interior plateaus of the continent. Here the winter monsoon (the opposite of the India conditions) is much stronger than the summer monsoon, and brings down icy blasts and clouds of dust to the China Sea.

Fig. 428a and b. — Winter (top) and summer (below) rainfall of India, the difference resulting from the monsoons. The winter rains of Ceylon and Madras are due to the recurving of the retreating, southwest, or summer, monsoon.

Summary. *The Indian climate consists of a hot season (March to June); a rainy season, during the summer monsoon (June to October); and a cool season, during the winter monsoon. In parts of India the rainfall during the summer monsoon is very heavy, the rainiest part of the world being in northern India. In China the winter monsoon brings icy blasts from the high interior plateaus of Asia.*

CLIMATES OF THE TEMPERATE ZONES

198. Variation (in temperate zones) from north to south. (A)
Temperature.   The temperature varies greatly, though not regularly
everywhere, from near the tropics toward the poles; but, except
near the tropics, there is everywhere a decided difference between
summer and winter.   Near the Arctic circle the summers are so
cool, and the winters so cold, that the climate is often called subarctic.   Except in a few favored localities large trees do not grow
there (p. 535); agriculture is confined to the production of a few
hardy grains and vegetables; and there are few human inhabitants,
except along the seacoast, or in cities and towns based on mining
camps like that of Fairbanks, Alaska.

These regions merge into the treeless tundras on the north; on
the south into a forest belt.   On the south vegetation becomes
more and more luxuriant until, near the tropics, the climate is so
warm that it is called subtropical.   In this warm belt cotton, sugar,
oranges, and even bananas, pineapples, and coconuts are grown.

Summary.   *The climate of the temperate zones changes from cold, or
subarctic, near the Arctic circle to hot, or subtropical, near the tropics; and
with these changes there are variations in vegetation from treeless tundra to
subtropical forest.*

(B) *Rainfall.*   The rainfall also varies from north to south.
Most temperate regions have a moderate rainfall, decreasing toward
the arctic zone and also toward the tropics.   The rainfall decreases
toward the arctic zone, because there can be less vapor in cold than
in warm air (p. 412).   It decreases toward the tropical zone because
the horse latitudes are naturally arid regions (p. 463).

The arid horse-latitude belts, in which are included southern California,
southern Texas, Spain, Italy, Greece, and the steppes of Russia, grade in
one direction into the deserts of the trade-wind belts, and, in the other, into
the damp climate of the mid-temperate zone. They may be called the belts
of *steppes.*   Some parts of the horse-latitude belts have abundant rainfall,
because exceptional conditions cause winds to blow from the ocean.   Some
parts, on the other hand, are true desert.

Steppes are dry in summer; but some sections are reached by the west
winds when they migrate southward in winter, bringing snow and rain.
Therefore irrigation is necessary for agriculture, as in Italy, which has dry
summers and rainy winters.   Where best developed, steppes are too dry for
trees; but grass grows in spring, curing to a natural hay during the warm, dry
summer, thus continues to serve as a food for cattle during the dry months.

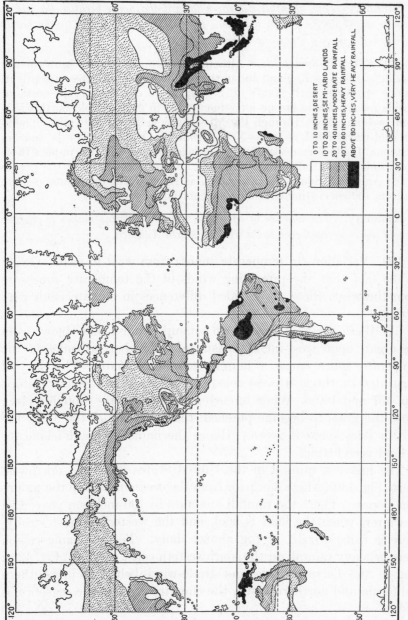

Fig. 429. — Rainfall map of the world.

Summary. *The rainfall decreases toward the north because the air is cool; in most places it also decreases toward the south; and, in the horse-latitude belts, there are regions of arid steppes.*

(C) *Effect of mountains.* Although subtropical plants grow in the latitude of the New England and of the Middle Atlantic states in southern Europe (p. 460), such plants do not thrive in our country in northern Florida even. There are no lofty mountains to prevent cold north winds from sweeping down through the Mississippi valley to the Gulf. Therefore cold waves reach as far as New Orleans and northern Florida, causing occasional frosts very destructive to orange culture. In one respect these cold winds are an advantage, for they are invigorating, and the people of the American South do not suffer, as some warm temperate peoples do, from the enervating effects of too continuous warmth.

Summary. *The absence of east-west mountain chains makes it possible for cold waves to reach even to the Gulf in North America.*

199. Variation (in temperate zones) from west to east. Owing to the fact that the prevailing winds of the temperate zones are from the west, there are decided differences in climate from west to east.

(A) *West coasts.* The warm, damp winds that blow from the ocean upon west-facing coasts in the higher latitudes of the temperate zones cause a humid, equable climate. This is well illustrated on the northwest coast of the United States and Europe (pp. 457 and 460). While in eastern United States droughts often cause the grass to become parched, the dampness of the air in the British Isles keeps it green. Hence the name Emerald Island for Ireland is so fitting.

The heaviest rainfall in the United States is on the northwest coast (Fig. 430), where damp air from the ocean moves up the mountain slopes. There the rainfall amounts to 100 inches a year; and in winter, when the land is cool, and the westerlies most steady, there is rain, drizzle, or fog almost daily. For the same reason there is heavy rainfall on the southwestern coast of Chile (Fig. 429). But in the horse-latitude and trade-wind belts, as in southern California and northern Chile, the climate, even on the seashore, is arid.

Summary. *On west coasts of the temperate zone, where reached by the prevailing west winds, the climate is damp and equable. The heaviest rainfall in the United States is on the northwest coast.*

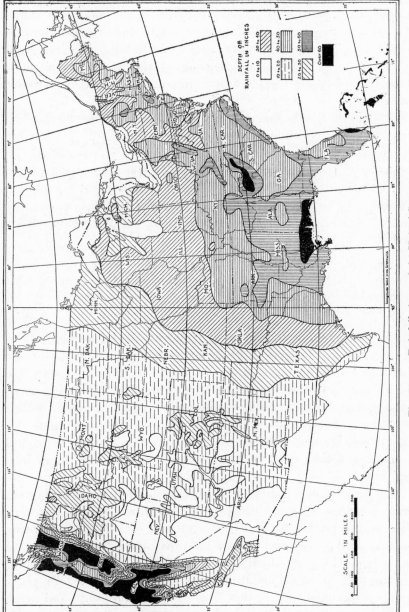

Fig. 430. — Rainfall chart of the United States.

(B) *Effect of north-south mountains.* Along the west coast of Europe there is especially heavy rainfall on the mountain slopes, as in Wales, Scotland, and Norway. But, since these mountains are not very high or continuous, the winds are able to carry vapor far inland, even into Asia. Because of this fact Europe, north of the horse-latitude belt, is well watered and the seat of extensive agriculture.

In western North America, on the other hand, as the air rises over the high, continuous mountains, so much of its vapor is condensed that it descends on their eastward slopes as dry air. Accordingly, from the Sierra Nevada-Cascade ranges eastward to the 100th meridian — the part of North America that corresponds in position to Germany, Austria, and eastern Russia — most of the country is arid; and even farther east, in the Mississippi valley, there are frequent and destructive droughts.

Summary. *Western United States differs from Europe in the greater influence of its higher, more continuous mountains, which cause the winds that cross them to reach the other side dry, forming arid regions as far east as the 100th meridian.*

(C) *Interior of continents.* The interior of a continent, being far from the sea, receives much less rainfall than a windward coast. Thus there are frequent periods of drought in central western Asia and in central United States. These droughts are less destructive in the northern part, because in a cool climate lighter rainfall suffices for crops. There are two reasons for this: (1) in cool climates the slight evaporation allows the dampness to remain long in the ground; (2) melting of the "frost" in the ground keeps the soil damp for a long time.

One striking peculiarity of the interior of continents in the temperate zones is the great range of temperature between the warm or hot summers and the very cold winters (Figs. 421–424). During the summer day the temperature may rise above 100° F. — greater than equatorial heat which averages only 80° to 85° F. at places near the sea; and in winter it may descend to 40° below zero, giving a range of perhaps 140° F. in a single year. Minnesota and neighboring states illustrate this extreme, or *continental climate.* The other characteristic of continental climate, as already pointed out, is its liability to experience droughts. Continental climate is also illustrated in central northern Siberia, near the Arctic circle, where moderately warm summers are followed by bitterly cold winters. In fact, this area is the coldest known place (Fig. 421), and has been called the *cold pole* of the earth. However, equally severe cold probably occurs at the South Pole and in interior northern Greenland.

Distance from the sea and freedom from its influence account for the extreme climate of the interior of continents in the temperate zones. The land warms in summer, when the sun, though low in the heavens, stays long above the horizon. In winter, on the other hand, the nights are very long, and during the short days the sun is very low in the heavens. Under these conditions radiation is far in excess of the heat supplied, and the land becomes exceedingly cold.

Summary. *Interiors of continents, being far from the sea, are subject to drought; and there is great range in temperature, from warm or hot summers to very cold winters. This combination gives rise to what is known as a continental climate.*

(D) *East coasts.* As the prevailing westerlies must cross the continent before reaching east coasts, one might expect to find arid climates there. Aridity is prevented, however, by the winds of the cyclonic storm eddies (p. 436), which frequently replace the west winds. Some of these winds blow from the Atlantic or Gulf of Mexico, bringing the vapor which gives eastern United States its abundant rainfall. Study Figs. 433-435 and 436-438.

Because of the influence of the cyclones and anticyclones of the prevailing westerlies, the climate of east coasts is variable. The west winds are dry and cool in summer, and dry and cold in winter; but whenever cyclonic winds blow from the sea, both the temperature and humidity are influenced by the ocean. Thus in northeastern United States the east winds are damp and chilly, being cooled in passing over the Labrador current; and in summer they often bring fogs. The south winds, warmed in passing over the Gulf Stream or the Gulf of Mexico, are warm and damp. From day to day the weather varies (p. 442), one day being like the interior of continents, another like the equable ocean.

Summary. *The cyclonic storm eddies of the west-wind belts give east coasts a very variable climate, with rain when winds bring abundant vapor from the sea.*

200. Variable winds of the prevailing westerlies. Among the winds caused by the passage of cyclonic storms and anticyclones (p. 442) are some so distinctive that they deserve special names.   The gentle south wind, which causes oppressively warm weather in summer, and unseasonable warmth in winter, may be called the *sirocco*, although this Italian term is not much used in the United States.   It is when the sirocco blows that thunderstorms and tornadoes develop in summer, and thaws occur in winter.

Of the very opposite type are the west and northwest winds that sometimes blow on the rear of vigorous winter cyclones and at the front of equally vigorous, following, anticyclones (Fig. 431).   These cold winds, often filled with snow, are called *blizzards* in Dakota and *northers* in Texas.

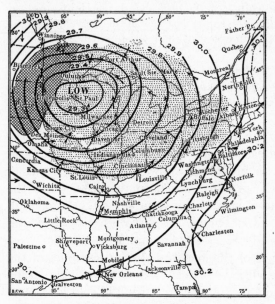

Fig. 431. — A winter storm, showing winds blowing toward a Low, and the large area over which rain (dotted) and snow (cross-lined) are falling.

Because of the marked difference in the barometric gradient (p. 426) between the cyclone and the anticyclone the air moves with great velocity, perhaps 40 to 60 miles an hour.   The cold, and the fierce snow squalls, often cause destruction of life among sheep and cattle; even men are sometimes lost in the blinding snow, and frozen by the fierce cold.   Milder forms of blizzard occur occasionally in northeastern United States

A *cold wave* (Fig. 432) is a rapid drop in temperature during the passage of a well-developed anticyclone (p. 437).   At such times a wave of cold air spreads over a large part of the country, even down to the Gulf (p. 468).   This blanket of air descends from the cold northern interior and from aloft (Fig. 408); and since it is, therefore, warming as it spreads out, it is clear and dry.   Through it radiation proceeds readily, causing very low temperatures in winter, refreshingly cool weather in summer, and early and late frosts in fall and spring (p. 414).   The term cold wave, however, is commonly applied only to the winter condition (Figs. 433-435).

The passage of cyclonic storms sometimes causes an exceedingly warm, dry wind, known as the *föehn* in the Alps and the *chinook* in the Rocky Mountains.   These winds are caused by the rapid passage of air across mountains toward a storm center.   As the air rises on one side it loses much of its vapor, descending as dry air on the opposite side.   It descends so rapidly that it is warmed by compression, as the air in a tire pump is warmed (p. 408). This warming lowers the relative humidity (p. 411) until the air becomes very dry; in fact, the Swiss formerly believed that the foehn came from the Sahara. In the warm, dry air, snow disappears rapidly, and houses become so dry that fires are greatly feared. Whole villages in Switzerland have been wiped out by fire during the foehn winds.

Summary. *A sirocco is a warm, gentle south wind blowing toward a cyclonic storm; a blizzard, or norther, is a fierce, cold wind, with squalls of snow, in the area between well-defined cyclones and anticyclones; a cold wave*

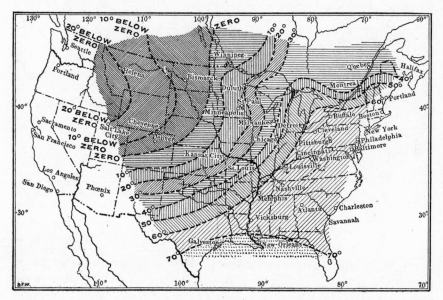

Fig. 432. — A cold wave spreading outward from an area of high pressure in the north-west, on November 27 of a certain year.

is the outspreading blanket of cold air in an anticyclone; the foehn, or chinook, is a warm, dry mountain wind made warm and dry by rapidly descending the mountain slopes in its passage toward a low pressure area.

201. Climate of the south temperate zone. Owing to the fact that there is so much water in the southern hemisphere, the changes in tempera-ture are less extreme there than in the northern hemisphere (Figs. 421, 422); and the winds blow with more strength and steadiness than over the irreg-ular lands (p. 434). Otherwise the climates of the two temperate zones are much alike. Over the Southern Ocean the summer weather is damp and chilly, the winter raw and cold, though without extreme changes from warm to exceedingly cold weather.

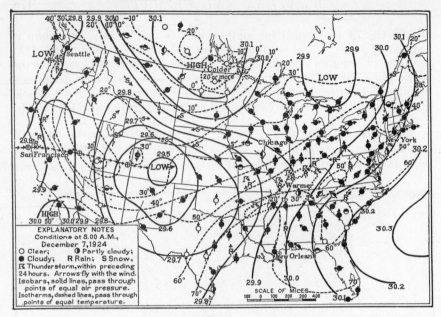

Fig. 433.

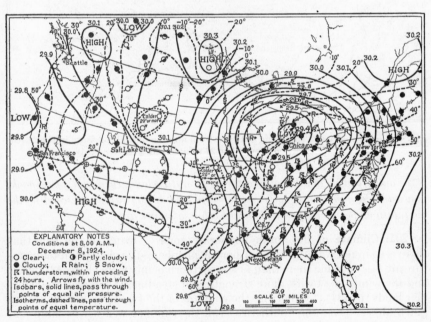

Fig. 434.

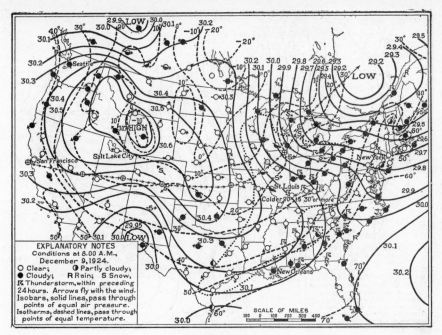

Fig. 435.

Fig 433. — Weather map, December 7, 1924, showing a low pressure area (Low) in the southwest. The solid lines (isobars) show the barometric pressure (29.5 being the number of inches the air pushes the mercury up in the tube of the barometer). The dashed lines (isotherms) pass through places with equal temperature. See "Explanatory Notes" on map for other symbols. Note that cold wave areas are marked: "Colder — 20° or more." The line of arrows shows the path pursued by the storm. Copy this and the following maps on an outline map of the United States and color in the areas of rain and snow for each day.

Fig. 434. — Weather map, December 8, 1924, showing the storm, Low, (Fig. 433) moved northeastward and its intensity greatly increased. Two anticyclones, Highs, appear in the northwest.

Fig. 435. — Weather map, December 9, 1924, showing the storm (Fig. 433) passing out to sea north of the St. Lawrence. Note that the anticyclones in the northwest of the preceding day (Fig. 434) have merged into a single, well-developed High. Select some place (one near your home if possible) and describe the changes in pressure, temperature, and wind direction accompanying the passage of this storm. (Figs. 433, 434, 435.)

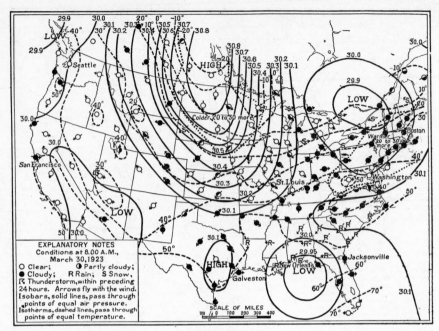

Fig. 436.

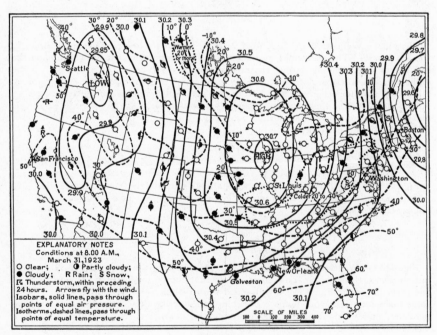

Fig. 437.

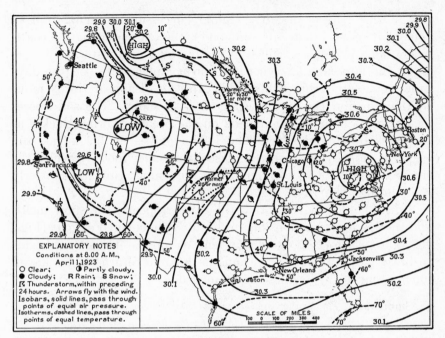

Fig. 438.

Fig. 436. — Weather conditions, March 30, 1923, showing a marked high pressure over the central northern part of the United States and southern central Canada. What effect has this on the isotherms?

Fig. 437. — Weather conditions, March 31, 1923. The High has moved southward and eastward.

Fig. 438. — Weather conditions, April 1, 1923. The High has moved eastward to the Coast. Where were cold waves experienced? How great was the drop in temperature in twenty-four hours? Compare wind and cloud conditions for a selected place during the passage of a Low, (Figs. 433, 434, 435) and a High, (Figs. 436, 437, 438.)

Summary. *Except for stronger, steadier winds, more uniform coolness, and less decided changes in temperature, the climate of the south temperate zone is similar to that of the north temperate.*

202. Polar climates. (A) *Near the circle.* In summer, when the sun is above the horizon both day and night, the air, though cool and sometimes raw, is never very cold. The warmth melts the frozen ground two or three feet down, making the soil damp and swampy. Then the grass becomes green, flowers blossom, and birds and insects appear. As in other places visited by the westerlies, storms appear in fairly regular succession, bringing rain or squalls of snow. Fogs are common on the sea and along the coast, where damp winds are chilled in passing over cold water.

In the late summer, when the sun commences to set, the days grow cooler and the nights cold. Insects disappear, birds move southward, and the land is covered with snow. The soil freezes again, and a skim of ice appears on the ocean, growing thicker as the days become shorter. The Eskimo gives up his kayak and takes to the sledge in search of seal, his chief food. Finally the sun is absent even at noon, and then the temperature stays bitterly cold through the arctic night.

With the coming of spring the sun reappears, the snow melts, and the Eskimo abandons his turf- and stone-covered dugout (Figs. 465, 500) or snow-igloo for a skin tent, or topek. The sea ice begins to break up and float away, and the Eskimo returns to his kayak for hunting. Then comes the summer day.

Summary. *The arctic summer, near the circle, is cool, damp, and stormy. In winter, when the sun is below the horizon even at midday, the ground is frozen and snow-covered, the sea covered with ice, and the weather bitterly cold.*

(B) *Nearer the pole.* Near the North Pole the climate has been found similar to that just described; but the arctic winter night is longer and colder, the summer cooler. Even there the warmth of the summer sun is sufficient to remove the snow from much of the low ground near the coast. In upper Greenland, the northernmost land known, and far north of the highest Eskimo settlements, Peary found flowers blossoming, insects humming, and musk oxen roaming about in summer.

(C) *At the poles.* The sea which surrounds the North Pole is everywhere covered with ice floes (p. 350), over which Peary went on his successful trip to the pole. Peary, and those who had tried before him, made their dashes in early spring, because in summer the ice is too broken to cross on sledges, yet not open enough to allow ships to pass through. Consequently explorers who tried to reach the pole went as far north as ships could carry them, and remained through the cold, dreary arctic night in order to be ready for an early start. At last Peary overcame the difficulties of ice and climate that had so long baffled him and other explorers, and in April, 1909, reached the North Pole. Even so, one member of Peary's party, Ross Marvin, who had been a student of physical geography at Cornell University, where this book was written, lost his life on the return trip by breaking through the thin, new ice that covered a *lead* or place where the winter ice had split through and drifted apart thus early in the season. But on May 9, 1926, Commander Byrd, U. S. N., using an airplane succeeded in flying to the pole from Kings Bay, Spitzbergen, and back to his starting point in fifteen and one half hours. Three days later the pole was crossed again, this time by the airship Norge, under command of Amundsen, who discovered the South Pole.

Amundsen, December, 1911, and Scott, January, 1912, were the first to attain the South Pole, which, unlike the North Pole, is situated near the center of a vast dome of glacial ice, and at an elevation of ten thousand feet (see p. 275). Accordingly (p. 471) the temperatures even during the Antarctic summer are always far below freezing and during the winter night it is probable that the lowest temperatures of the world occur there.

Summary. *At the North Pole, the climate is similar to that near the Arctic Circle, though cooler in summer and colder in winter, because the sun is lower and longer below the horizon. Plants and animals live on the northmost known land. In summer the sea ice breaks up so that travel over it by sledge is impossible. In the high interior of the Antarctic ice-capped continent the temperature does not rise above the freezing point the year round.*

TOPICAL OUTLINE, QUESTIONS, SUGGESTIONS, AND LABORATORY EXERCISES

TOPICAL OUTLINE. 191. **Difference between weather and climate.** Weather; climate; illustration of difference; kinds of climate.

192. **Zones of heat.** (A) *The Five Zones:* reason for division; the zones; boundaries. (B) *Influence of altitude:* effect of highlands; isotherms; isothermal charts; Pacific slope. (C) *Influence of water:* contrast ocean and land; illustrations; temperature ranges. (D) *Influence of winds:* contrast western Europe and eastern United States; eastern and western United States. (E) *Influence of ocean currents:* effect on winds; transference to land; contrast western Europe and eastern America. (F) *Influence of topography:* local influences; mountain barriers; western United States; Mediterranean.

193. **Belt of calms.** Warmth; rain; weather on the ocean; on the land; uniformity; forests; mankind.

194. **Moist trade-wind coasts.** Effect of warming air; evaporation of sea water; east-facing coasts; instances; forests; Hawaiian Islands; irrigation.

195. **Desert trade-wind belts.** Explanation; rainfall; desert belts; horse-latitude arid climate; desert life; weather conditions.

196. **Savanna belts.** Location; cause of peculiar climate; effect on vegetation; instances of savannas; animals; man.

197. **The Indian climate.** Hot, windy season; hot, calm season; the rains; short, hot period; winter monsoon; effect of these changes on vegetation; heavy rains at base of Himalayas. Monsoon of China.

198. **Variation (in temperate zones) from north to south.** (A) *Temperature:* near polar circles; near tropics; vegetation. (B) *Rainfall:* in the north; in the south; steppes. (C) *Effect of mountains:* contrast southern Europe and United States; effect on people.

199. **Variation (in temperate zones) from west to east.** (A) *West coasts:* climate of west coasts; contrast British Isles and eastern United States; rainfall

of western United States; Chile. (B) *Effect of north-south mountains:* western Europe; interior of Europe; western United States; country east of mountains. (C) *Interior of continents:* rainfall; droughts; the cool north; great temperature range; continental climate; instances; explanation. (D) *East coasts:* effect of storms on rainfall; in causing variable climate; changes from day to day.

200. Variable winds of the prevailing westerlies. (a) Sirocco: nature; cause; effects. (b) Blizzards or northers: location; reason for strong winds; effects. (c) Cold waves: nature; location; cause of cold; effects. (d) Foehn or chinook: location; cause of warmth; cause of dryness; effects.

201. Climate of the south temperate zone. Effect of water on temperature; on winds; summer weather; winter weather; storms.

202. Polar climates. (A) *Near the circle:* summer climate; plants and animals; storms; fog; change in autumn; effect on life; winter climate, its effect on the Eskimo; spring climate, its effect on the Eskimo. (B) *Nearer the Pole:* resemblance to conditions farther south; differences; life; sea ice. (C) *At the Poles:* discovery of the North Pole; of the South Pole; conditions at each pole.

QUESTIONS. SECTION 191. What is weather? Climate? Illustrate the difference. Name some different kinds of climate.

192. (A) How is the earth most simply divided into zones? What about the actual boundaries of climatic zones? (B) What is the influence of highlands? What is an isotherm? What is the condition on the Pacific slope? (C) What differences are there over land and water? Give illustrations. (D) Give illustrations of the influence of winds on climate. (E) How do ocean currents affect climate? Give instances. (F) What effect has topography on climate? Give instances.

193. What is the climate of the belt of calms? What is the weather on the ocean? On the land? What effects has the climate on man?

194. What effect have the trade winds on the sea? On rising coasts?

195. Why are there deserts in the trade-wind belts? Where are the great desert belts? Why are the horse latitudes arid? What are the life conditions in the desert? What are the weather conditions?

196. What is the cause of the savannas? What are the conditions there? What effect have these conditions on life?

197. Describe the Indian climate; the seasons; their cause; their effect on vegetation; the heavy rains; the winter monsoon of China.

198. (A) What are the conditions near the polar circle? How do the temperature and vegetation change toward the tropics? (B) How does the rainfall vary from north to south? What are steppes? Where found? What are the conditions there? (C) What is the result of the absence of lofty mountains in southern United States?

199. Why are there differences in climate from west to east? (A) What is the climate of west-facing coasts? Why? Give illustrations. (B) Contrast central Europe with the arid West. (C) What is the condition of rainfall in the interior? Why are droughts less destructive in the north? What are the temperature conditions? Why? (D) What is the cause for rainfall on east-facing coasts? How does the climate vary? Why?

200. What is the sirocco? The norther? The blizzard? What is the cause of each? Their effect? What is the cause of cold waves? Explain the foehn or the chinook wind. What are their effects?

201. How does the climate of the south temperate zone differ from that of the north temperate zone?

202. (A) Describe the Polar climate in the different seasons. How do these changes influence life? (B) What are the conditions in the northernmost lands? Describe the discovery of the North Pole. What are the conditions at the North Pole? At the South Pole?

SUGGESTIONS. (1) Trace one or two of the isothermal lines across the charts for the United States (Figs. 423, 424) and endeavor to explain the irregularities. Do the same for one or two isotherms in the northern hemisphere of the world charts (Figs. 421, 422). Follow one or two in the southern hemisphere and account for the difference between their regularity and the irregularity of those in the northern hemisphere. Locate the Heat Equator in January and July and its average position for the year on an outline map of the world, and discuss its position at the different periods and with reference to the different continents and oceans. (2) Make isothermal charts of the United States and the world, copying upon outline maps the isotherms in the book. (3) Study the Appendix on weather maps (Appendix H) and work out the suggestions. (4) Select and study weather maps illustrating cold waves. (5) From a series of three weather maps for successive days, describe the weather changes at a given place — say Boston or Chicago. Write down the temperature, wind direction, etc., for each of the days. (6) Make a record of local weather changes for a week. Write a short description of these changes. (7) Write a description of the climate of your home.

Laboratory Exercises. Exercises LII, LIV, LV, and LVI in TARR and VON ENGELN's *Laboratory Manual for Physical and Commercial Geography*, The Macmillan Company, New York, are designed to correlate with and supplement the study of the topics considered in this chapter.

Reference Books. KENDREW, *The Climates of the Continents*, Oxford University Press, Oxford, England, 1922; WARD, *The Climates of the United States*, Ginn & Company, Boston, 1924; HUNTINGTON, *Civilization and Climate*, Yale University Press, New Haven, 1915; HUNTINGTON, *Earth and Sun*, Yale University Press, New Haven, 1923; SMITH, *Agricultural Meteorology*, The Macmillan Company, New York, 1920; KOPPEN, *Die Klimate der Erde*, W. de Gruyter & Company, Berlin, 1923 (in German); *Atlas of American Agriculture, Part II, Climate, Sections A and B*, United States Department of Agriculture, Washington, D. C.; 1922. (See also references at ends of Chapters XII and XIII.)

CHAPTER XV

PHYSIOGRAPHY OF THE UNITED STATES

The United States illustrates in many ways the influence of physiography on the development of the various sections. In this chapter the larger physiographic provinces, regions having uniform physical geography, are described and these relations discussed.[1]

203. New England. New England is a region of very ancient masses of resistant rock, including crystalline gneisses, schists, and granites. These rocks are complexly folded, and, in the south and east, worn by denudation to the condition of hills and low mountains (Figs. 156, 439). It is held by many that this region was worn down to a peneplain (Fig. 217c), with here and there a peak, or group of peaks, rising above the general level. Such peaks have been called *monadnocks*, after Mt. Monadnock, New Hampshire (Fig. 292), which rises well above the fairly uniform sky line of the surrounding hilltops. Another theory is that the uniformity of level is due to marine erosion.

After the mountains were reduced to a low hilly condition, there was an uplift of the land, which permitted the streams to sink their valleys into the ancient mountains. This rejuvenation occurred so long ago that, even in the resistant rocks, the valleys have been broadened to the condition of early maturity. The Connecticut valley, in weaker sandstones and shales, has been broadened to a wide lowland, a *local* peneplain (Figs. 82, 217d), with here and there hills of more resistant trap rock, like Mt. Tom and Mt. Holyoke, rising above the valley floor.

There is little mineral wealth in New England. The exception is abundant building stone, including granite, slate, and marble, which finds a market in many parts of the country. There is hardly any coal, and very little iron or other metals.

[1] The various sections of this chapter may very profitably be studied in connection with the performance of the correlating Exercises in TARR and VON ENGELN's *Laboratory Manual for Physical and Commercial Geography*, The Macmillan Company. Accordingly these exercises are indicated by number at the appropriate paragraphs.

Fig. 439. — Relief map of southern New England. Note the nearly uniform level of the peneplain upland east of the Connecticut Valley; the valleys cut into the peneplain by streams rejuvenated by uplift; the broad lowland that the Connecticut River has excavated in the weak rocks of its middle valley; and the irregular coast due to recent slight sinking of the land. What other physiographic features do you find? Explain each.

Over all this region the ice sheet spread, rounding the hills and deepening some of the valleys (Figs. 184, 440). The residual soil was swept away, and in places, especially on steep slopes, the rock was left bare; but usually it was covered by a glacial soil. Over a large part of New England the glacial soil is too thin, or too sandy, or too rocky, for cultivation (Fig. 292).

Because of the hilly nature of the land, the many steep slopes, and the poor soil, New England, in general, is not a good farming country. Under such conditions the farms are necessarily small (Figs. 83, 441), and the area suited to farming is not nearly large enough to supply the needs of the busy manufacturing towns and cities. The great food staples, such as wheat, are brought from the West, while New England farms are devoted mainly to the production of vegetable, dairy, and similar products for neighboring towns.

The glacial deposits have formed many lakes and turned aside many streams, which now tumble in rapids and falls over ledges which they have encountered. Hundreds of cities and towns use this water power for manufacturing, which stands at the foundation of New England's prosperity. The lakes aid in regulating the water supply (Fig. 303).

During the glacial period the land sank and the sea entered the valleys, forming a very irregular coast line (Figs. 345, 346, 442), with many bays and good harbors. This irregular coast line is favorable to fishing, one of the most important industries of New England; and it early encouraged ship building, for which the forests supplied the lumber. The beautiful scenery of this irregular coast, and the cool climate, attract many people in summer. (Exercise XXXIX, see footnote p. 482).

The many harbors have encouraged navigation. This navigation aids manufacturing by furnishing a means of bringing bulky raw materials and fuel to New England. Railway lines radiate from the leading ports to cities both inland and along the coast. In this respect New England differs greatly from mountainous Norway, where communication between points along the irregular coast must be by boat.

Many of the busy manufacturing cities of New England (Fig. 439), such as Providence, Fall River, New Bedford, New Haven, Bridgeport, and Portland, are on the sea. Others, like Worcester,

Fig. 440. — The old mountains of New England. One of the higher peaks, Mt. Lafayette, New Hampshire. Note the avalanche tracks. If these mountains had local glaciers during the Glacial Period what is the probable origin of the amphitheater-shaped basins below the summit ridge?

Fig. 441. — A typical valley-and-hill view in New England, showing the large percentage of wooded surface on the upland areas. Note the cultivation of the lower slopes, the river terraces, the dam and power-site with the gorge above it on the stream, and the village utilizing this power.

Lowell, Lawrence, Hartford, and Springfield, are in the interior, generally near water power. By far the largest city is Boston, on the sea. Its size depends upon a number of favorable circumstances. It is in a central position on that part of the coast which extends farthest into the interior of New England, and it has an excellent harbor. Communication along the coast is possible by rail and boat; the interior is easily accessible by rail; and all parts of the world are open to its commerce. All eastern Massachusetts is tributary to this port, which lies in the center of a semicircle of

Fig. 442. — Harbor and city of Gloucester, Massachusetts. The protected, deep-water harbor is a result of the sinking of the land along the New England coast. Note the granite rock in the left foreground.

manufacturing towns (Fig. 439), one of the busiest manufacturing regions of the world.

In its physical geography, New England resembles parts of Great Britain and Scandinavia. In each case the coast is irregular, the land hilly, and much of the soil poor. Scandinavia, like the more hilly part of New England, has a large proportion of its area uncleared of forest. It is more mountainous than most of New England, and has little manufacturing, but its irregular coast has encouraged the development of fishing and shipping. Great Britain pays far more attention to manufacturing than to agriculture, and, like New England, depends upon other regions for a large part of its supply of food and raw materials.

Summary. *New England is a region of worn-down, ancient mountains, with hilltops rising to a fairly even sky line, but with peaks and groups of peaks rising above this level, especially in the west and north. Many of these summits are still forest-covered. The ice sheet has left a bowldery glacial soil which, together with the hilly condition, makes this a poor farming region. There is little mineral wealth, except building stone. In spite of the general absence of raw products, the water power, due to glacial interference with streams, has encouraged the development of manufacturing. Industrial progress has been further aided by the irregular coast, caused by sinking of the land. This irregular coast is favorable to fishing and to navigation. Of the many manufacturing cities Boston is most favorably situated and is, therefore, the largest.*

204. New York. The physiography of the Empire State is more varied than that of New England. New York may be divided into four quite different regions: (1) the Adirondacks, resembling the more mountainous parts of New England; (2) the low, hilly region of southeastern New York, which resembles southwestern New England; (3) the high, hilly plateau, including the Catskills and southern and western New York; and (4) the plains which border Lakes Erie and Ontario. The ice sheet covered the entire state, except a small area in the southwest (Figs. 272, 278). Therefore, in various parts of the state, there are moraines, outwash plains, drumlins, and other glacial deposits, and gorges, waterfalls, rapids, and lakes (Figs. 60, 62, 67, 294, 310, 394, 443, 467).

A chief basis for the prosperity of New York is agriculture, in which it ranks high among the states of the Union. In mineral wealth the state is not especially rich, though building stone, clay, and salt are found in excess of local needs. There is also some iron, oil, and gas, but no coal. However, the oil and coal of Pennsylvania are readily accessible; and the iron of the Lake Superior region is easily brought by water to Buffalo. Hence, manufacturing cities have developed wherever these facilities for transportation have favored a location. Water power, due to glacial action, has also aided in the growth of many towns and cities.

The Adirondacks, like the higher parts of New England, are rugged, mountainous, rocky, and forest-covered. Water power is used in a series of towns around their base, partly in manufacturing the products of the forest, i. e., as in making paper from wood pulp. As in New England, these beautiful mountains are much resorted to by sportsmen and summer visitors.

The uplands of the Catskills, and the hilly plateau of the south and west (Figs. 294, 310), have a thin and in many places a stony soil. This plateau is, therefore, sparsely settled, and there are large areas that are still forest-covered. The valley floors, however, are level, and having thicker and better soil, are dotted with farms and country villages. The abundance of creameries, for the manufacture of butter and cheese, shows that much of this region is adapted to pasturage.

The hills are so difficult to cross, and so sparsely settled, that railways are found mainly in the larger valleys; and it is often a long, roundabout railway journey from one valley to the next. The towns and cities, such as Binghamton and Elmira, are in the larger valleys, usually at points where railways from tributary valleys enter, making these places railway junctions.

The level plains along the shores of the Great Lakes have a deep soil, deposited by the glacier and in the glacial lakes (p. 289). These lake-shore plains are among the best farming

Photo by von E.

Fig. 443. — Taughannock Gorge in the Finger Lakes region of central New York. The scenery of this section of central plateau rivals that of western mountain states in impressiveness in certain places.

lands of the East, and the influence of the lake water gives them a climate especially suited to fruit culture (p. 314). From near Buffalo to Rome, the New York State Barge Canal crosses these plains. Its route is followed by trunk line railways; and the excellent facilities for transportation have encouraged the growth of numerous towns and cities, including

Rochester, — at the falls of the Genesee, — Syracuse, Utica, Troy, and Albany.

Numerous broad, mature valleys lead back into the plateau. In some of them are large lakes, such as Canandaigua (Fig. 310) and Seneca, which have been caused by ice erosion and dams of glacial drift. These lakes, and many other smaller ones, give especial charm to the scenically beautiful Finger Lakes district. The valleys and lakes afford opportunities for

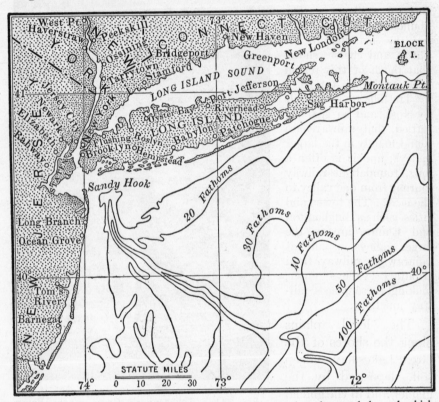

Fig. 444. — New York City and surroundings, showing the submerged channel, which extends offshore from the Hudson to the edge of the continental shelf. Before the land was lowered the Hudson occupied this channel.

communication by water, road, and railway with the heart of the plateau country. In early days the Erie Canal, which later became the New York State Barge Canal, was the only great artery connecting this interior with the sea; but railways now accommodate the steady stream of trade, between the West, the interior of the state, and the sea.

The movement of goods along the lake plains, Mohawk valley, Hudson route, which has aided in the growth of many towns and cities, has especially favored the cities at the two ends — New York, on the sea, and Buffalo, on Lake Erie. The unloading of goods at Buffalo and New York, for reshipment, accounts in part for their growth. They are, moreover, supplied with abundant raw material for manufacture and have, therefore, become great centers of manufacturing and of commerce.

By reason of its very favorable physiographic situation New York has become the largest city of the country, and one of the largest and busiest in the world. Sinking of the land (Fig. 444)

After Newberry

Fig. 445. — Ideal restoration of the neighborhood of New York, if the land were reëlevated to its former level.

has caused a fine harbor with extensive water frontage. This sinking has admitted the sea into the Hudson (Fig. 445) and into several small tributaries, even flooding low divides, thus forming islands which add greatly to the water front. As a result, an enclosed waterway has been formed behind Long Island, opening connection with New England, and another along the Hudson (Fig. 339) into the interior. The latter route, extended to the Great Lakes by canals and railways, has concentrated in New York the shipping of a large part of the interior of northern United States.

Thus the growth of New York City has kept pace with the growth of the interior.

The peculiar conditions surrounding this rapidly growing city have made the problem of living there difficult to solve. The harbor is in two states, but the main city is on a long, narrow island. There is no space for the population to spread easily outward in various directions from the harbor, as in many cities. Accordingly development has had to extend up the narrow island and across the channels of the harbor. This has crowded Manhattan Island, and has forced many New York business men to live at a distance, large numbers going across North River to New Jersey or across East River to Long Island. Therefore a number of cities have grown up around the splendid harbor, such as Hoboken and Jersey City, in New Jersey, and Brooklyn, now a part of New York City, on Long Island. In consequence of these conditions the problem of transporting people is more serious than in any other city; and surface, elevated, and underground lines, added to bridges, ferry boats, tunnels ("tubes"), and railway trains, are not yet sufficient. As the city grows, and automobiles are more and more generally used, the problems of transportation increase.

Summary. *The Adirondacks resemble mountainous New England in physiography and industries; and the low, hilly region of southeastern New York resembles southwestern New England. The plateau section is hilly, sparsely settled on the uplands, but has better soil, and more inhabitants in the broad valleys. The lake-shore plains are excellent farming land, and the old Erie Canal, now the Barge Canal, and the railways which cross these plains have caused the growth of many towns and cities, and made much manufacturing possible. The two cities at the ends of this route, Buffalo and New York, have become of special importance. New York, having the best physiographic situation of all the cities of the country, has become the metropolis.*

205. The coastal plains. From New Jersey to Mexico there is a belt of low, level land (Figs. 108, 446, 447), so recently raised above the sea that its streams are young and large tracts are undrained (Figs. 107, 112, 364). This coastal plains region is broadest in Florida, and extends up the Mississippi valley, which at its lower end is a filled bay. As it is south of the glacial belt, rapids and falls are practically absent from the streams; but there are lakes in the irregularities of the raised sea bottom, especially in Florida. (Exercises XXI and XXIII. See footnote p. 482.)

Much of the surface is too sandy for general farming and is covered with pine forests (p. 120). The coast is low and often swampy, especially near the rivers, into whose mouths the sea has been allowed to enter by a

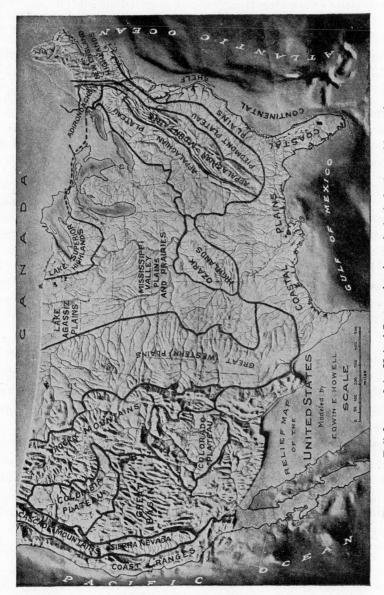

Fig. 446. — Relief map of the United States, showing principal physiographic provinces.

slight sinking of the land (Figs. 111, 361, and Plate VIII). The larger bays, especially Delaware and Chesapeake bays, admit ships far into the land; and, because of their gentle slope, and the absence of falls and rapids, many of the rivers are navigable to small boats.

The larger cities are located either on the Fall Line (Figs. 110, 113, 457), along the inner margin of the coastal plain, or at the head or mouth of the bays.

Summary. *The level coastal plains extend from New Jersey to Mexico. The low, sandy coast has many navigable bays, due to sinking of the land. The chief cities are on the Fall Line or on the coast, either at the head or mouth of a bay.*

206. The Piedmont belt. The low, hilly country, from New York to Alabama, between the coastal plains and the Appalachians, is known as the Piedmont belt (Figs. 109, 113, 446). It is an uplifted peneplain with hilltops rising to a nearly uniform level, and with isolated monadnocks standing above this upland surface. That this was once a high, rugged, mountain region is proved by the fact that the rocks are intensely folded. (Exercise XXXI. See footnote p. 482.)

Except in New Jersey the Piedmont region is south of the glacial belt, consequently the residual soil has not been removed from its undulating surface. This soil is usually deep and fertile, and, since the climate is favorable and the surface fairly level, this is a splendid agricultural region. It is one of the greatest cotton and tobacco belts, and, in addition, produces fruits and farm crops of various kinds.

The Piedmont belt is dotted with towns and cities, and crossed by many railway lines. The Fall Line cities (Fig. 113) are along its eastern margin, the two largest being Philadelphia and Baltimore, which are also near the head of navigation on large bays. Philadelphia and Baltimore, like Boston and New York, have become great seaports because of good harbors and connection with a productive interior.

The largest city away from the Fall Line is Atlanta, which, like many other towns and cities of the South, has become of importance as a center for the manufacture of cotton, lumber, and other local products. Atlanta owes its development largely to the fact that it lies at the point of inter- section of a number of railway lines, including those that pass around the southern end of the Appalachians.

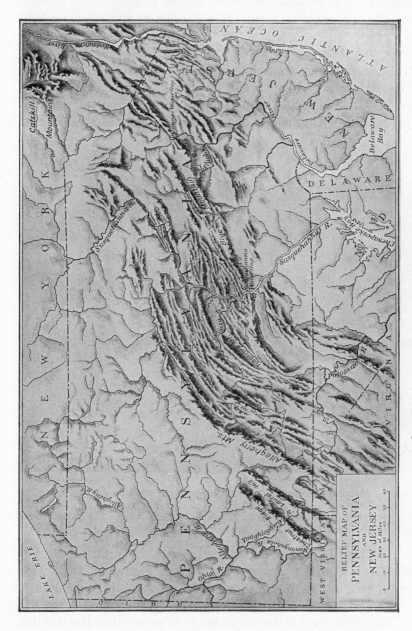

Fig. 447. — Relief map of Pennsylvania and New Jersey. Coastal plain in extreme east; next the rolling Piedmont belt; then the long mountain ridges of the Appalachians, with broad valleys between; and, still farther north and west, the rugged plateau, extending into New York.

Summary. *The Piedmont belt is an uplifted peneplain, with a fertile residual soil and a favorable climate. It is, therefore, an excellent agricultural region, producing especially tobacco and cotton. It is dotted with towns and cities, the largest of these being on the Fall Line.*

207. The Appalachian belt. This belt, extending from New York to Alabama, parallel to the Piedmont, may be divided into two parts, — the eastern, or Appalachians proper, and the western, or Appalachian (Allegheny) plateau (Figs. 130, 446, 447, and

Photo by Lehigh Valley R. R.

Fig. 448. — Mauch Chunk and the Lehigh River in the Appalachian Plateau. The river valleys afford routes, although winding, through the hilly plateau country. Farther east they pass through the Appalachian Mountains in water gaps. The Lehigh River and the Lehigh Water Gap are used by the Lehigh Valley Railroad.

Plates III and VI). The eastern section is a true mountain region of folded rocks, while the western portion is true plateau with horizontal strata. Both are so rugged that much of their area is unsuited to settlement and, therefore, still forest-covered (Figs. 81, 294). The ruggedness is due to an uplift so recent that the streams have cut only steep-sided, narrow valleys. (Exercises XXV, XXIX and XXX. See footnote, p. 482.)

For a long time these rugged, forest-covered belts served as a barrier to westward migration; and even now, along all but a few lines, they are passed with difficulty. The ridges are crossed by water gaps (Figs. 172, 178, 447, 448), which the trails of the Indians and trappers, the wagon roads of the early settlers, and the railways and highways of present-day commerce all have followed. The principal lines of passage are along the Cumberland, Potomac, Susquehanna, Lehigh (Plate VI), Delaware, and Mohawk gaps.

Photo by U. S. Geol. Sur.

Fig. 449. — A broad valley developed over limestone in the Appalachian Mountains of Virginia, near Natural Bridge, Virginia. The soil of the fields is residual clay from the weathering of the limestone. Note the alternating spurs of the small valley in the foreground. To what stage in the erosion cycle has it been developed?

This belt includes some of the most sparsely settled regions (Fig. 170) of eastern United States (p. 142), and is an important timber reserve. It would be still less populous if it were not for two important facts. In the first place, where the rock is weak the valleys have been so broadened by weathering and denudation as to invite an agricultural population (Fig. 449). This is illustrated by the broad, fertile limestone valleys of New Jersey and Pennsylvania, the Shenandoah valley of Virginia, and the Tennessee valley. In the second place, the rocks contain stores of valuable mineral (p. 197), the most important being coal, iron, oil, and gas. The coal and iron have been exposed in many of the deep valleys. In recent years there has been great development of electrical power by utilization of the steep descents of the streams.

These conditions have led to the establishment, not only of mining industries, but of important manufactures. Of the many busy centers of mining and manufacturing the greatest is at Pittsburgh, where the Monongahela and Allegheny rivers unite to form the Ohio (Plate V). This point has water connection with a wide area; and the meeting of railways where the valleys come together has added facilities for extensive railway transportation. Therefore iron and other raw products for manufacture are easily obtained, and the finished products are readily distributed.

Scranton and Wilkes-Barre, farther east in the anthracite coal fields, have also developed into important mining and manufacturing cities. Indeed, all Pennsylvania has had its growth stimulated by its great mineral resources, especially its coal. See Fig. 186.

Throughout the Appalachian belt similar mineral wealth is causing development. In no place is this better illustrated than at Birmingham, Alabama, where, within a radius of a few miles, are found abundant stores of coal, iron, and limestone, the three materials necessary for iron smelting. Under such favorable conditions a large manufacturing city has rapidly grown up.

Summary. *The Appalachian belt, extending from New York to Alabama, consists of (1) true mountains, and (2) a plateau portion. Both are for the most part rugged, sparsely settled, and, over large areas, forested; forming a barrier which was first and most easily crossed through the water gaps. Some of the broad valleys are good farm land, and there is much mineral wealth, especially coal. This has given rise to a number of important mining and manufacturing centers, of which the Pittsburgh and Birmingham regions are the most important.*

208. The Central Plains. The region that slopes toward the Mississippi River, from the Rocky Mountains on one side and the Allegheny plateau on the other, is for the most part an expanse of level plains (p. 129). This levelness is due to two facts: (1) the rock strata are nearly horizontal; (2) the valleys are mature. In a few places the strata have been disturbed by mountain uplift, as in the Black Hills and the low mountains of central Texas,

Oklahoma, Arkansas, and southern Missouri (Fig. 446). (Around Lake Superior is another low mountain area, a southward extension of the ancient mountain land of northeastern Canada.)

In so level a country railways may be built almost anywhere, though they naturally follow the valleys. These are so broad and open that they are well settled, quite unlike the steep-sided valleys of the Allegheny plateau. The large rivers have so nearly approached grade that they are navigable for long distances. The Mississippi, for example, is navigable for 1900 miles from the sea, as far as St. Paul.

The ice sheet covered the northern part of these plains (Plate VII), filling the valleys with drift and thus making the surface more level (Fig. 295). (Exercise XXII. See footnote p. 482.) These glacial deposits have turned many streams out of their valleys, causing falls and rapids, as in the case of the Falls of St. Anthony at Minneapolis. Many ponds and lakes were also formed, of which there are said to be 10,000 in the low, hilly country of Minnesota.

One of the most important effects of the glacier was to make the Great Lakes water route (p. 297), which, supplemented by canals, offers facilities for interior water transportation that are not equaled on any other continent. Continuous water transportation is possible from the sea to Duluth, a distance, via Montreal, of over 2000 miles.

The generally level surface, the fertile soil, and the climate have combined to make these plains one of the greatest of agricultural regions (Fig. 119). The further fact that large sections of prairie were treeless helped in the rapid development of the region. The agricultural products vary with the climate from hardy grains in the North to tobacco and cotton in the South. In the hilly lands and along the rivers, especially in Michigan, Wisconsin, and Minnesota, there is forest, from which much valuable timber is obtained. (Exercises XXVI and XXVII. See footnote, p. 482.)

The western part of this plains region (west of the 100th meridian) has a semi-arid climate (Figs. 117, 118) unsatisfactory for agriculture without irrigation (p. 470) or the practice of dry farming. This part is called the Great Plains and is the seat of an important grazing industry. (Exercise XXIV. See footnote, p. 482.)

There are great stores of mineral wealth, including building stone, clay, salt, lead, zinc, oil, gas, and coal. The copper and iron of the Lake Superior region contribute to the natural resources. The almost unlimited supplies of coal, widely distributed, make manufacturing possible throughout almost the entire area. The farms, mines, and forests supply the raw materials, and the excellent facilities for transportation permit the ready distribution of raw and manufactured products.

It is natural that there should be busy manufacturing cities along the large, navigable rivers. The greatest of these river cities are St. Louis on the Mississippi, near the mouth of the Missouri, and Cincinnati and Louisville on the Ohio. The position of St. Louis makes it a manufacturing and distributing point for products from north, south, east, and west, and it has the advantage of receiving the electrical energy from a great power development on the Mississippi. (Exercise XXVIII. See footnote, p. 482.)

Another great industrial community is found at the head of navigation on the Mississippi — the twin cities of St. Paul and Minneapolis. The latter has the further advantage of a fall in the Mississippi, supplying water power. New Orleans, near the mouth of the Mississippi, and Pittsburgh at the head of the Ohio River, are closely related in prosperity to the fertile interior plains, for they are in close communication with them by water and rail.

Along the lake route many important cities have developed: in Canada, Montreal and Toronto; in the United States, Buffalo, Cleveland, Toledo, Detroit, Chicago, Milwaukee, and the two neighboring cities of Duluth and Superior, besides many smaller places. Each of these cities profits by the commerce that the water route opens to it; and each is able to receive the raw products of the entire lake region (Fig. 446). Iron ore, one of the most important of these products, is for the most part carried to the coal fields for smelting, and all lake ports near the coal fields share in the resulting commercial and industrial activity. With the recent wonderful development of the iron region there has been a corresponding growth of the lake ports.

Each of these cities has some special reason for its growth at that particular point. Duluth-Superior and Buffalo are at the two American ends of the lake route. Toronto is on a good harbor on the Canadian side of Lake Ontario, opposite the Welland Canal. Montreal is at the head of navigation for large ocean vessels, and at the foot of rapids in the St. Lawrence, around which a canal has been built. Cleveland and Toledo are on good harbors on Lake Erie, and near extensive coal fields. Detroit is on a narrow strait, through which lake traffic must pass, and at a point where railways cross from United States to Canada. It is, moreover, practically at one end of Lake Erie. Milwaukee is on a good lake harbor backed by a fertile country. (Exercise XXXII. See footnote, p. 482.)

Of all the cities in this section, Chicago has the best natural site and has, therefore, grown the fastest. It is no accident that it has become the second city of the country in size; nor is there reason to expect that its growth will not continue. The small harbor, around which Chicago started, was scoured out by the overflow stream of the glacial lakes that existed while the ice sheet was melting away (Fig. 288). The city soon outgrew its small natural harbor, but continued to prosper because of its favorable situation. Like Buffalo, Toledo, Detroit, and Duluth, it occupies a position near the end of a great lake. With other lake ports it shares all the advantages of lake shipping; and, like several of them, it is near coal fields, and in the midst of a fertile agricultural region which supplies raw products and a market for manufactured goods. More than this, it is a natural railway center; railroads from the East swing around the southern end of Lake Michigan to reach Chicago, where they unite with railroads from other sections. For these reasons Chicago has become a great manufacturing and commercial center, being a distributing point for a wide area of country. It is a center of distribution for some products, such as meat products, for cities from coast to coast and for export.

Summary. *The Central Plains region, though mostly level, has a few low mountainous sections. The northern portion was covered by the ice sheet. The greater part of the plains region is adapted to agriculture; but some of the more hilly portions are forested. The western portion is arid, and hence devoted mainly to grazing. The Plains have great mineral resources, notably coal and iron, and consequently have become an important manufacturing section. The navigable rivers and broad valleys have encouraged the growth of a number of large river cities of which St. Louis is the greatest. The Great Lakes water route is far more important than the rivers for navigation, and hence has a series of large and busy manufacturing cities. Of these Chicago is the largest. This, the second city in the country, has a fine natural situa-*

Photo by Jackson

Fig. 450. — A railway line crossing the Rocky Mountains near Georgetown, Colorado. This is the old type of construction. Such places are in modern days replaced by tunnels. Trace the course of the railroad, also the course of the stream. State why these many long curves were built.

Photo by U. S. Geol. Sur.

Fig. 451. — A view in the Rocky Mountains of Colorado, near the timber line. On account of the steep slopes and the high altitudes there is not much farming. The view shows a typical small Rocky Mountain Park valley, bottom of which is filled with glacial gravels that the stream is now excavating. Teocalli Mt., 13,220 feet high. The top of the mountain is probably the bottom of a synclinal fold. Explain this (Fig. 179).

tion at the end of one of the lakes, in the midst of a fertile agricultural country, and near extensive coal fields.

209. The West. This broad area is mainly a great plateau region with mountain ranges rising above it. Both the mountains (Figs. 28, 155, 233, 234, 263, 450) and plateaus (Figs. 28, 446, 452, 458, 459) are so young that they are very rugged. Yet there are

Photo by National Park Service

Fig. 452. — Bryce Canyon, Utah, a National Monument established 1923. Illustrative of the new scenic wonders still being discovered in the West. This is a gash in the edge of the Pink Cliff. The minarets are the result of weathering processes acting on a rock structure with conspicuous joints, bedding planes, and earth column formation. Explain.

many broad mountain valleys (Fig. 451) and extensive areas of level plateau. If the climate were favorable these areas might be much more utilized as an agricultural region. Over much of this territory the climate is, however, so arid that the land is suited only to grazing; and vast numbers of cattle, sheep, horses, and goats are raised on the plains, plateaus, and mountain slopes. Parts of Nevada, southern California, and Arizona are true deserts, with too little grass and water even for grazing (Fig. 473). (Exercise XXXV. See footnote, p. 482.)

On the other hand, some of the high plateaus and mountain valleys have rainfall enough for agriculture, although the cold of the higher altitudes is an unfavorable condition. Many of the mountain slopes and higher plateaus are forested. One very large area, including the northern half of California, western Oregon, and much of Washington, is sufficiently low and has enough rainfall to make it a very important agricultural region. (Exercise XXXVII. See footnote, p. 482.)

The mountain rocks contain great stores of mineral. There is a large production of precious metals; and, in addition, much copper, lead, zinc, coal, and oil are obtained. Various other mineral products, though found in many places, are not produced in large quantities.

Photo by von E.

Fig. 453. — Eruption of Riverside geyser in the Yellowstone Park. The water falls directly into the Fire Hole river which flows steaming warm the year round because it is fed almost wholly by geysers and hot springs.

Scattered through the Far West are many thriving towns and cities, some engaged in mining (Fig. 145), some in manufacturing, and all serving as distributing centers for surrounding sections. Of these the largest are Denver, at the eastern base of the Rocky Mountains, Salt Lake City in Utah, and Los Angeles, San Francisco, Portland, and Seattle on the Pacific slope. Denver is a railway focus and an important distributing and manufacturing center

Photo by Hillers-Walcott

Fig. 454. — Granite walls and dome in the Yosemite valley, California. The surface curves of the upper dome are the result of exfoliation weathering; the arched jointing is the result of relief of pressure as the former overlying masses have been weathered and eroded away.

for a great mineral section. The Moffat tunnel, six miles long, straight through the solid mountain, to be completed in 1927, opens up a previously undeveloped, wide and fertile, interior agricultural and grazing country to Denver, and provides a route shorter by seventy miles to San Francisco. (Exercise XXXIII. See footnote, p. 482.)

On the Pacific slope Seattle, Tacoma, and Portland are manufacturing and shipping points for a productive agricultural country.
Their harbors, like that of San Francisco (Fig. 344), have been
caused by sinking of the land. The great agricultural and mineral
resources, gold formerly, oil more recently, of California have made
Los Angeles and San Francisco busy manufacturing and shipping
centers.

The West is justly noted for its magnificent scenery (Fig. 452). No
part of the world rivals in grandeur the canyon of the Colorado (Figs.

Fig. 455. — Mt. Rainier (Mt. Tacoma) from the campus of the University of
Washington, Seattle

128, 458); in no part of the world is there the equal of the Yellowstone
Park, with its hot springs (Figs. 224, 225), geysers (Figs. 393, 453), and
canyons; nowhere is there another Yosemite (Fig. 454). But these are
only some of the best known of the points of scenic interest in the West.
Symmetrical volcanic cones (Figs. 199, 455), rugged peaks and glaciers,
and grand mountain valleys (Figs. 66, 166) and lakes, whose surroundings
are nowhere excelled in picturesqueness, are found in various parts of the
West. Each year the stream of travel toward these centers of scenic
attraction increases.

The dry climate, unfavorable to agriculture, is favorable to health; and,
consequently, many parts of the West — Colorado, New Mexico, Arizona,

and southern California, especially—are much frequented. The building of reservoirs, to store the winter and spring floods for use in summer, has greatly increased the area of agricultural land. The city of Los Angeles owes a large part of its early growth to the number of people who went there in search of a healthful climate. The climate of southern California is so sunny and balmy, that, wherever irrigation is possible, the orange grows to perfection. More recently this dependable sunniness attracted a large part of the productive activities of the motion picture industry. It is one of the most attractive parts of the country.

Summary. *Except in the northwestern part, and on some high plateaus and mountain slopes, the plateau and mountain area of the West has a climate too dry for agriculture without irrigation. Much of it is, therefore, essentially a grazing region. The West is an important mineral belt. Of the cities, the largest in the eastern Rockies is Denver. On the Pacific slope are several cities, of which Los Angeles is the largest. San Francisco has a fine location, on a splendid harbor, the outlet of a productive country. The West is noted for its wonderful scenery, especially the Colorado Canyon, Yellowstone Park, and Yosemite Valley; the arid climate also makes the Southwest a favorite health resort.*

TOPICAL OUTLINE AND REVIEW QUESTIONS

TOPICAL OUTLINE. 203. **New England.** (*a*) Surface features: rocks; effect of denudation; monadnocks; uplift; nature of valleys; mineral products. (*b*) Farming: glacial soil; small farms; food supply. (*c*) Manufacturing: water power; lakes. (*d*) Coast line: cause for irregularity; fishing; shipbuilding; summer resorts; navigation; effect on manufacturing; comparison with Norway. (*e*) Cities: location; Boston, reasons for size. (*f*) Comparison: with Scandinavia; with Great Britain.

204. **New York.** (*a*) General features: four divisions; glacial action; agriculture; mineral resources; manufacturing. (*b*) Adirondacks: forests; manufacturing; summer resorts. (*c*) Plateau region: uplands; valleys; agriculture; railways; cities. (*d*) Lake plains: cause of levelness; farming; New York State Barge Canal route; cities; valleys leading into the plateau. (*e*) Two largest cities: influence of route; causes of growth. (*f*) New York: cause of harbor; water communication with New England; with the interior; peculiar situation; effect on homes; on transportation.

205. **The Coastal Plains.** Extent; surface features; coast line; interior navigation; location of cities.

206. **The Piedmont belt.** Surface features; peneplain; soil; agriculture; Fall Line cities; Philadelphia and Baltimore; Atlanta.

207. **The Appalachian belt.** (*a*) Surface features: extent; two divisions; ruggedness; effect as barriers; river gaps. (*b*) Industries: lumber; agriculture; mineral resources; water power. (*c*) Cities: Pittsburgh; Scranton and Wilkes-Barre; Birmingham.

208. **The Central Plains.** (*a*) Surface features: extent; cause of levelness; mountain areas; broad valleys; navigable rivers; effect of glacier; Great Lakes water route. (*b*) Industries: agriculture; lumbering; grazing; mineral resources;

manufacturing. (*c*) River cities: St. Louis; Cincinnati; Louisville; advantages of location of St. Louis; St. Paul and Minneapolis; New Orleans; Pittsburgh. (*d*) Lake cities: cities on the lakes; importance of situation on the lakes; location of Duluth-Superior; Buffalo; Toronto; Montreal; Cleveland; Toledo; Detroit; Milwaukee; Chicago, — origin of harbor, position, commerce, surrounding country, railway center, manufacturing and distributing center.

209. **The West.** (*a*) Surface features: plateaus; mountain ranges. (*b*) Climate and agriculture: arid climate, — grazing, desert; humid sections, — location, forests, agriculture. (*c*) Minerals: precious metal; other minerals. (*d*) Cities: Denver; Los Angeles; Seattle; Tacoma; Portland; San Francisco, — its harbor, region tributary, growth of city. (*e*) Scenery: Colorado; Yellowstone; Yosemite; other attractions. (*f*) Health: favorable climate; Los Angeles.

QUESTIONS. Section 203. What are the surface features of the uplands? What is a monadnock? What is the **condition** of the valleys? Why? What mineral products are there? What effects had the ice sheet on the soil? Explain the condition of farming. What effect has this on food supply? What conditions have favored manufacturing? Explain the irregular coast. What important effects has this coast? Where are the cities located? What conditions have favored the growth of Boston? Compare New England with Scandinavia and Great Britain.

204. What are the four divisions of the state? What effect has the glacier had? What are the natural resources? What is the condition and what are the industries of the Adirondacks? What is the condition of the plateau upland? In the valleys? Where are the cities of the plateau section? What causes the levelness of the lake plains? What are the industries there? What results did the Erie Canal route produce? What is the condition of the valleys leading into the plateau? Why have cities grown at the two ends of the water route? What conditions of physiography have favored the growth of New York City? What effect has the peculiar location of the city on homes? On transportation?

205. What is the condition of the coastal plains? What is the condition of the coast line? What favors internal navigation? Where are the cities?

206. Explain the surface features of the Piedmont belt. What is the condition of agriculture? What accounts for the greatness of Philadelphia and Baltimore? What accounts for the growth of Atlanta?

207. What are the two divisions? What are the surface features? How is this rugged barrier crossed? What are the resources of the belt? What conditions have favored the growth of Pittsburgh? Scranton and Wilkes-Barre? Birmingham?

208. Why are these plains level? Where are the mountainous sections? Why are the rivers favorable to navigation, and the valleys to settlement? What effects had the ice sheet? Of what importance is the lake route? What conditions favor agriculture? Where are forests found? What is the condition in the western part? What important mineral resources are there? What conditions favor manufacturing? Locate the three largest river cities. How is the situation of St. Louis especially favorable? What advantages of location have St. Paul and Minneapolis? How are New Orleans and Pittsburgh related to this region? Name and locate the leading lake cities. What general advantages do they share? What especial reason is there for the growth of each? What is the reason for the exact location of Chicago? What special advantages has it?

209. What are the surface features? What is the general condition of the

climate? What is the effect of this on industry? Where are the humid sections? What valuable minerals are found? For what is Denver important? Los Angeles? Seattle, Tacoma, and Portland? What causes the harbors? What has favored the growth of San Francisco? What scenic attractions are there in the West? In what way is the dry climate favorable? What effect has this had on Los Angeles?

Reference Books. JONES and BRYAN, *North America*, Dial Press, New York, 1924; SMITH, *North America*, Harcourt, Brace & Company, New York, 1925; POWELL, *Physiographic Regions of the United States*, National Geographic Monographs, American Book Company, New York, 1895; MILL, *International Geography*, D. Appleton & Company, New York, 1920; BOWMAN, *Forest Physiography*, John Wiley & Sons, New York, 1911; GREGORY, KELLER and BISHOP, *Physical and Commercial Geography*, Ginn & Company, Boston, 1910; GOLDTHWAIT, *The Geology of New Hampshire*, New Hampshire Academy of Science, Handbook, No. 1, Concord, New Hampshire, 1925.

CHAPTER XVI

RIVERS OF THE UNITED STATES

Almost the entire United States is tributary to seven large river systems (Fig. 456) and a series of smaller streams, most of which flow eastward or southward into the Atlantic (Fig. 457) and Gulf of Mexico. The greatest amount of drainage is into the Atlantic, including the Mississippi, which drains two fifths of the whole country; next in area is the Pacific drainage; while a small section drains into the Arctic through the Red River of the North. As has been shown in previous chapters, the river systems have been highly important factors in the development of the country. They have been a source of food; they have supplied water power; and they have served as pathways of exploration and commerce. The present chapter considers this subject more specifically.

210. The Columbia. The Columbia rises on the western slopes of the Rocky Mountains, flows across an arid region, and enters the sea in a region of abundant rainfall. Its length is 1400 miles, and it drains over 200,000 square miles. The lower Columbia is formed by the union of two rivers, the Columbia and Snake. From the Rocky Mountains to the Cascades, both the Snake from the south and the Columbia from the north flow across a vast lava plateau (p. 225). These rivers and their tributaries have cut young canyon valleys in this plateau, in some places 2000 to 3000 feet deep, out of which it is impossible to lead the water for irrigation. There are many rapids and falls, including the Shoshone Falls, so that, throughout the greater part of their course, the rivers would be, under natural conditions, unnavigable. Canals have now been built around these difficult reaches. (Exercise XXXIV. See footnote, p. 482.)

In its lower course the Columbia is an important aid to travel, for it crosses both the Cascade and Coast Ranges, thus opening gaps, which are followed by railways. Sinking of the land has

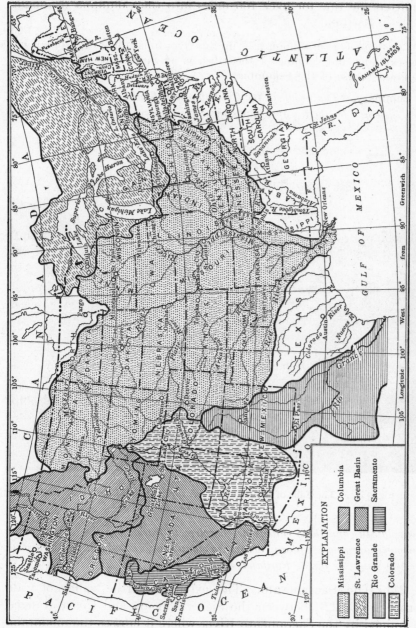

Fig. 456. — Main drainage basins of the United States.

admitted the tide for over 100 miles into the Columbia drainage, as far as Portland.

Large numbers of salmon pass up this river to lay their eggs, or spawn. The catching and canning of these fish is an important industry along the lower course of the Columbia.

Summary.   *The union of the Columbia and Snake rivers makes a great river system.   In their upper parts these rivers occupy canyons in a broad*

Photo by U. S. Geol. Sur.

Fig. 457. — The Falls of the Potomac.   A typical "Fall Line" waterfalls. Account for it.

lava plateau, and these valleys are barriers to travel; but the lower river is navigable, opening a pathway across the mountains, and admitting ocean ships for 100 miles, as far as Portland.

211. The Sacramento.   The extensive fertile valley of California (Fig. 222), between the Sierra Nevada and Coast Ranges, is drained by the Sacramento River where it crosses the mountains at the Golden Gate.   Sinking of the land has admitted the sea, forming San Francisco Bay and connecting the valley of California with the sea (Fig. 344). The Sacramento drainage is 400 miles long and has an area of about 58,000 square miles. It is made by the union of two rivers which extend along the great valley, — the Sacramento from the humid north, the San Joaquin from the arid south.

These rivers are fed by short streams from the enclosing mountains, where they occupy canyons. At the base of the mountains these tributaries are building low alluvial fans (Plate IV), and are engaged in slowly filling the great valley (p. 113). Over the alluvial fans the streams flow in shallow valleys, from which water is easily led for purposes of irrigation.

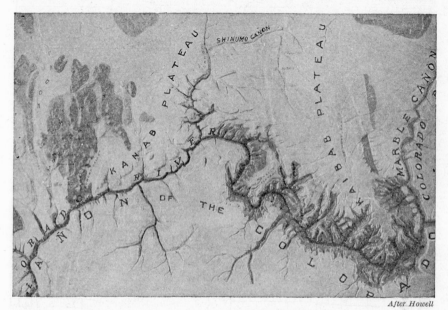

After Howell

Fig. 458. — Photograph of a relief model of the Grand Canyon of the Colorado River. This shows the level plateau surface and its cliffs; the wide upper and the narrow inner gorge of the canyon.

At the outer margins of the fans underground water is obtained plentifully from shallow wells, and this water also is used for irrigation.

Summary. *The Sacramento, formed by union of the San Joaquin and Sacramento, is fed by small mountain streams whose water is useful for irrigation. Breaking through the Coast Ranges at the Golden Gate, this river connects the great California valley with the ocean.*

212. The Colorado. The Colorado River, like the Nile, has its source among mountains which supply it with so much water that it is able to flow completely across a vast stretch of arid and desert country. Its length is about 2000 miles, and it drains about 225,000 square miles. It is formed by the union of two large streams, — the Grand and Green. For fully half its length the Colorado flows in canyons cut in a high plateau, which in places is over 8000 feet above sea level. The depth of the canyons varies from a few hundred feet to over 6000 feet in the Grand Canyon,

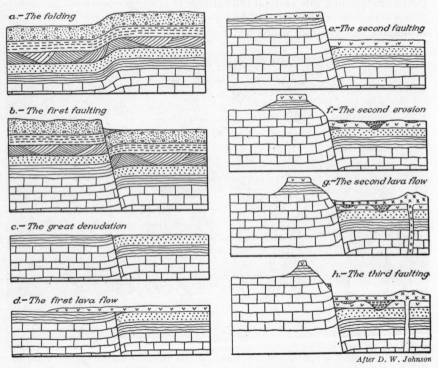

After D. W. Johnson

Fig. 459. — Physiographic history of the Colorado Plateau country shown in eight labeled diagrams. Tell the story of each of these. The last of the diagrams shows the present conditions.

which is over 200 miles long (p. 138). At the lower end of the Grand Canyon the country becomes open and the river crosses fully 300 miles of desert to the Gulf of California. In its lower course the river flows over a flood plain and delta. (Exercise XXXVI. See footnote, p. 482.)

Without exception the Colorado is the most remarkable river in the world (Figs. 128, 458, 459). No other canyon equals the Grand Canyon in size or grandeur. For long distances it is impossible to descend to its bottom over the precipitous sides, and the canyon forms an absolute barrier to travel. It would make an excellent boundary between unfriendly countries. Only by undergoing hardships and dangers is it possible to pass through the canyon; and few explorations in America have been more daring than that of Major Powell's party, which made the first descent.

On both sides rise steep, impassable precipices, commonly from the water's edge; and the river tumbles over a succession of rapids, in which it is difficult for a boat to exist. Here and there short tributaries enter, with slopes so steep that the occasional heavy rains wash large bowlders down them into the main stream. These are the chief cause of the rapids.

A mile of successive rock strata is revealed in this enormous gash in the crust. At their base is a buried mountain area. The inner, deeper canyon cut in the metamorphic rocks of the ancient mountain region is narrow and has nearly vertical walls. The river is flowing with so steep a slope that it is rapidly cutting its canyon deeper, and in the upper, sedimentary rock series weathering is wasting back the cliffs, which form a multitude of irregular and rugged mesas, buttes, ridges, and spurs. Where resistant rocks outcrop, there are steep cliffs; where weaker layers occur, the slopes are gentler; where the cliffs have wasted back, flat terraces often extend from their base; and everywhere there is a wonderful and varied coloring of the rock walls.

In this arid country few large tributaries enter the river, and these bring little water, for throughout most of the area the annual rainfall is less than 10 inches. The tributaries themselves are in canyons, and between them are broad areas of table-land with many mesas and buttes, — a typical young, arid land plateau (p. 140).

Summary. *The Colorado, fed by rains and snows from the Rocky Mountains, flows for nearly 2000 miles across an arid and, in places, a desert country, for a large part of the distance in deep canyons sunk in the plateau. The Grand Canyon has a depth of 6000 feet. Its steep sides are commonly impassable, and they are carved and sculptured into a great variety of forms. There are few large tributaries, and these bring little water.*

213. The Great Basin. The Great Basin (Fig. 456), a region of interior drainage with an area of over 200,000 square miles, lies between the Rocky and Sierra Nevada Mountains. It is bounded on the north by the Columbia plateau, and on the south by the Colorado plateau (Fig. 446). A number of disconnected parts unite to form this general basin, one of them, Death Valley, being below sea level. The surface of the Great Basin is crossed by a number of short mountain ranges, known as the Basin Ranges. (Exercise XXXV. See footnote, p. 482.)

The entire region is arid, and in places a true desert. The short mountain streams quickly disappear, either by evaporation or by percolation into the loose gravels of their alluvial fans. Some of the streams terminate in salt lakes, such as Great Salt Lake; others in alkali flats or playa lakes (p. 318).

There is too little water for extensive irrigation, consequently most of the Great Basin is sparsely settled. The most thickly settled part is the fertile, irrigated region of which Salt Lake City (Fig. 304) is the center. If the rainfall were greater, water would gather in the basins, forming several hundred lakes. During the glacial period, when the climate of the Great Basin was moist, large fresh-water lakes filled the greater basins to overflowing at least once (pp. 284, 310).

Summary. *The Great Basin is an arid region of interior drainage consisting of a number of smaller basins. It is in places true desert, and, for the most part, sparsely settled.*

214. The Rio Grande. This river resembles the Colorado in some respects. It is almost as long (1800 miles), and has a greater drainage area (240,000 square miles) (Fig. 456). Like the Colorado, the Rio Grande receives so large and permanent a water supply from its mountain sources that it is able to flow across an arid country to the sea. Like the Colorado, too, it has cut deep canyons in the plateau; but they are neither so deep, so long, nor so continuous as the canyons of the Colorado. In a number of sections the valley broadens, and is bordered by flood plains and low, terraced land, over which the river water is easily led for irrigation. Therefore, from Colorado to Mexico, there are many irrigated sections and numerous thriving towns and cities. The only large tributary is the Rio Pecos, which resembles the main river.

Owing to the openness of parts of its valley, and the sandy nature of its bed, the Rio Grande loses much of its volume in crossing the arid country and is sometimes dry in summer. But in winter and spring it is a large river, rising especially high during the melting of the mountain snows. It is always heavily charged with sediment, and in places is aggrading its valley.

Summary. *The Rio Grande, supplied with water from the Rocky Mountains, flows across an arid region to the sea, receiving only one large tributary, the Rio Pecos. Its course is marked by alternate canyons and open valleys, which are irrigated and well settled.*

215. The Mississippi system. This vast river system, the longest and one of the largest in the world, has a length, including the Missouri, of 4194 miles and a drainage area of 1,250,000 square miles. (The Nile, 3670 miles, is the longest single river.) It receives a large number of tributaries, some very long, including the Red (1200 miles long), Arkansas (2170 miles), Missouri (3000 miles), and Ohio (975 miles). Each of these tributaries has large feeders, some of them great rivers; for example, the Platte (Fig. 103) (900 miles) and the Yellowstone (1100 miles) are tributaries of the Missouri. There are over 10,000 miles of water in the Mississippi system that have been navigated (Fig. 456).

The Mississippi valley is a broad depression, a lowland left by the greater uplift of the land on either side. This depression has existed for many ages, at first as an interior sea, into which sediment was brought by streams from the neighboring highlands; later it was transformed by uplift to dry land plains.

The Ohio drains part of the Allegheny plateau on one side and of the Central Plains on the other. Since the climate of its valley is humid, with a rainfall of over 40 inches a year, the Ohio carries more water than the Missouri. The water supply varies greatly, being least during summer droughts, when the river may be only two or three feet deep, and most in spring when the snows are melting. It may then reach a depth of from 50 to 60 feet.

The Ohio and most of its tributaries occupy mature valleys (Plate V); but those in the plateau are deep and steep-sided, dissecting the plateau into the rugged condition of early maturity (p. 142). Throughout most of its course the Ohio is bordered by a flood plain, behind which the valley slopes rise to a height of 200 or 300 feet. The valley is easily followed by railways and the river is navigable even above Pittsburgh, though in some places rapids have made dams and locks necessary.

The upper Mississippi resembles the Ohio in most important respects. In both cases the valleys have been considerably modified by glaciation, which has caused rapids and falls. In its headwaters, the Mississippi passes through a series of lakes and swamps of glacial origin.

Below the junction of the Mississippi and Ohio at Cairo, the Mississippi flows in a flood plain which it is building up because it has more sediment than it can carry down the gentle grade. This flood plain is about 600 miles long and from 20 to 75 miles wide. Memphis and Vicksburg are situated on high ground, at points where the river swings against the slopes above the eastern side of the flood plain. Over this immense fertile flood plain the river sweeps in a series of meanders, many of which are five miles in diameter. These nearly double the length of the lower river. (Exercise XXI. See footnote, p. 482.)

The river is slowly changing its position in the flood plain and, now and then, the neck of a meander is cut off and a ring-shaped ox-bow lake is left. There are many such lakes which are slowly being filled with sediment. Floods, seepage from the river (water table, p. 96) and lack of drainage on the level flood plain cause the abandoned channels, or *bayous*, and other low places, to remain either as lakes or swamps (Fig. 311). The higher parts are drier and make excellent farm land. At times of great flood, when the river may rise from 30 to 50 feet, the water sometimes opens gaps, or *crevasses*, in the levees which men have built to confine the river. Then the water tears away the levees, spreading over the flood plain and doing great damage. It is the deposits made during such inundations that are building up the flood plain.

Sediment, washed from the slopes of the entire Mississippi system, has built a large delta at its mouth (Fig. 99). This is still growing outward, for each year enough sediment is poured into the Gulf to build a pyramid a mile square at the base and 268 feet high. Much of the delta is too low, level, and marshy for habitation, and over it the river flows sluggishly through a series of distributaries. On the higher and drier parts sugar cane, oranges, and truck are grown. Sediment is constantly being deposited on the river bed, interfering with navigation, especially at the river mouth. To check this, *jetties*, or piers, have been built at the mouths, or *passes*, in order to confine the current and cause it to flow rapidly enough to keep the channel open for large vessels.

Summary. *The Mississippi, with its many large tributaries, occupies a valley left as a lowland by the greater uplift of the sides. Some tributaries cross the arid western plains. They are supplied from the mountains with water, which is of value for irrigation. These tributaries bring much sediment. The Ohio and upper Mississippi valleys are mature, have abundant rainfall, and are excellent agricultural regions. They have been affected by glaciation. Below Cairo is a broad flood plain, between higher slopes, and farther down a delta, both made of sediment brought by the river. Where dry enough, both are excellent farm land.*

216. Does the Mississippi River flow uphill? The question is often asked: Does the Mississippi River flow uphill? The question has two origins. The first is that on inspection of a globe it seems unreasonable that a river should flow over the convex curve of a ball. But if it is remembered that the surface of the ocean is the level of water at rest, and that the surface of the sea is, like the rest of the earth ball, convex in form, this difficulty disappears, for the source of the Mississippi is 1500 feet above the level of the sea surface.

The other origin of the question is, however, a little more discriminating but fails to make its point because it does not take all factors into account. Its basis is this. Down means toward the center of the earth. At the equator it is thirteen miles farther to the center of the earth than at the poles, going straight down. At intermediate latitudes the distance varies between these limits. As the source of the Mississippi is 19° of latitude farther north than its mouth, it is found that its source is four miles *nearer* the center of the earth than is the mouth. Four miles many times offsets the 1500 feet of elevation above sea level that the source is above the mouth. Hence it would appear that the Mississippi is flowing up, that is away from the center of the earth, to the extent of over 19,000 feet in proceeding from its source to its mouth. And so it does, but it is to be remembered that the surface of the sea in the latitude of the source of the Mississippi is also four miles nearer the center of the earth than the surface of the sea at the mouth of the river. Consequently the source of the Mississippi is 1500 feet above the surface of the sea *in its own latitude*. This relationship is maintained at all latitudes along the course of the river. Hence the Mississippi is everywhere flowing downhill toward the sea surface.

Summary. *The Mississippi River flows away from the center of the earth in its long journey from source to mouth, but it does not flow uphill; for uphill and downhill are governed by the level of the surface of the sea at any latitude.*

217. The St. Lawrence system. This remarkable river system includes five of the eight largest fresh-water lakes in the world (p. 289). These five lakes are connected by short rivers and straits, in several cases containing rapids or falls, including the wonderful Niagara. The lake basins are very deep (p. 306), the bottoms of all but Erie being below sea level.

The St. Lawrence flows out of Lake Ontario, not in a well-defined valley, but straggling over a low, hilly land, the higher parts of which rise above the water as the so-called Thousand Islands. From this point down to Montreal the river consists of a series of broad, lake-like expanses, with intervening rapids around which canals have been built. The lowest, or the Lachine Rapids, are just above Montreal. Thence, onward to the sea, there is uninterrupted navigation through a broad valley, into which the tide has been admitted by sinking of the land. Below Quebec the valley is a broad bay, and ocean steamers ascend to Montreal. By means of canals around the rapids and falls, large ships may go on to the western end of Lake Superior (p. 499).

The exact preglacial condition of the St. Lawrence system is not yet fully known. It is certainly drowned at one end, and the continuation of its valley, between Nova Scotia and Newfoundland, may be traced on the sea bottom. When this submerged valley was formed, northeastern North America was more than 1000 feet higher than now, and the mouth of the St. Lawrence was off Newfoundland at the edge of the continental shelf.

The inland continuation of this valley seems not to have been the present St. Lawrence, but the Ottawa River, the only large tributary of the St. Lawrence system. Above Montreal the system appears to be made of parts of several systems, united by the effects of glacial erosion, dams of glacial drift, and land tilting. These processes have also transformed parts of the valleys into the deep, boat-shaped basins of the Great Lakes (Fig. 290). Neither the St. Lawrence above Montreal, nor the rivers and straits that connect the lakes, are in preglacial valleys of large streams.

Notwithstanding the great volume of water, little erosion is being done along most of the St. Lawrence. The explanation of this is that the lakes, and other quiet stretches, rob the current of its sediment. The quiet reaches, by depriving the river of its tools, reduce its erosive effectiveness. Consequently most of the St. Lawrence streams flow, not in gorges, but in young shallow valleys.

The gorge and lower part of Niagara River furnish the one striking exception to this. But the Niagara River has peculiar conditions. Leaving Lake Erie clear and free from sediment, the broad Niagara loiters along past Buffalo, in its very young valley almost on the surface of the plain (Fig. 460). At only one point in its upper course is there rapid water: where it crosses a ledge of rock near Buffalo. The river divides into two channels around the low Grand Island. The valley is so young and undeveloped that the larger channel on one side of the island has not been deepened enough to rob the other of its water. Just above Niagara

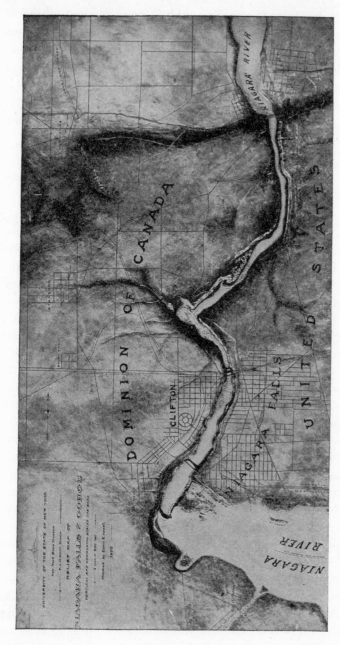

Fig. 460. — Relief map of Niagara River. Notice the broad, shallow, upper valley; the falls; the gorge; the whirlpool; the lower shallow valley; the escarpment separating the two plains; and the depression leading from the whirlpool to St. Davids, marking the site of the buried gorge which causes the whirlpool. The teacher should secure from the U. S. Geological Survey, Washington, D. C., a copy of the Niagara Folio (50c) which gives detailed information about all features of Niagara Gorge and Falls.

Falls, fifteen miles from Lake Erie, the stream is again divided, this time around Goat Island. Here the flow in each branch quickens, and soon the water is tumbling along tumultuously as a series of violent rapids.

These upper rapids are thought to have resulted from the fact that at this point the retreat of the falls has uncovered a shallow valley. This was filled with glacial débris, but was cut into the upper limestone and extended at right angles to the course of the Niagara River. The rapids, then, are due to the fact that the current of Niagara, just above the falls, is now flowing down the side of this old channel, which it has swept clean of its loose fill. The brink of the falls is on a line with the bottom axis of the old channel. Figure 461 shows the situation clearly.

At the foot of the upper rapids the river drops as a great cataract, 160 feet high. This is divided by Goat Island into two parts, — the larger, or Horseshoe Fall, on the Canadian side; the smaller, or American Fall, on the American side. For seven miles below the cataract the river rushes rapidly through a gorge 200 or more feet deep, and 200 or 300 yards wide (Fig. 461). In two parts of the gorge there are decided rapids, and at one point a whirlpool.

The top of the gorge is at the level of the plain over which the river flows from Buffalo to the Falls; and the gorge cut in this plain reveals its rock structure. It is made of nearly horizontal strata, some strong, some weak, dipping gently southward at the rate of about 35 feet a mile. The upper stratum in the gorge wall is massive limestone (Fig. 462), beneath which is a series of weak shales. It is these strata, also present under the cataract, that make the waterfall possible.

The plain ends toward the north in a steep slope, or escarpment (Fig. 460), faced by a plain about 200 feet lower. Emerging from its gorge at this escarpment, the river flows quietly over the lower plain to Lake Ontario.

An enormous quantity of water, estimated at 167,000,000 gallons a minute, falls over the Niagara limestone (Fig. 462), which forms the crest of the Falls. The underlying shales are being removed by the swirl of waters, and by the grinding against them of great blocks of fallen limestone by *plunge-pool* action (p. 82). This undermines the limestone, causing huge blocks to break off occasionally, slowly changing the outline of the cataract.

There is too little water in the American Fall for such results;

© Kohne and Wasmuth

Fig. 461. — Airplane view of Niagara. Note the broad shallow upper river, the rapids above the falls (explain, see p. 522), the two falls, and the gorge below. Notice also the level Erie plain in the background and on it the city of Niagara Falls, U. S., a rapidly growing center of industrial importance. Why? Find other features of interest in the picture and explain them.

instead, the fallen blocks of limestone protect this fall from recession. Records kept since 1842 show that, while the Horseshoe Fall has receded at the rate of about five feet a year, the outline of the American Fall has scarcely changed. Long before the cataract has receded to Lake Erie, the southward dip of the shales will have carried them so far into the ground that there will no longer be an opportunity for the river to undermine the limestone. Then the waterfall will disappear.

There is clear evidence that when the ice sheet permitted Lake Erie to outflow over the plain toward Ontario, the Niagara cataract was born, falling over the edge of the escarpment. Since then the cataract has

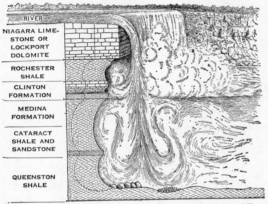

Modified from Gilbert

Fig. 462. — To illustrate the undercutting in progress at Niagara.

received for seven miles, making the gorge. When the cutting of the gorge first began, the river occupied a broad valley on the upper plain, similar to the present valley above Goat Island. The river gravels and banks made at that time may be clearly seen on the plain, 200 feet or more above the present river. The gorge could not have existed then. Another proof that the gorge has been cut by river action is the existence of an abandoned fall, similar to the American Fall, at Foster Flats, or Niagara Glen, more than halfway down the gorge on the Canadian side.

As the cataract receded, it discovered a buried valley beneath the glacial drift; and where this buried valley leaves the gorge, at the whirl-pool, there is a break in the otherwise continuous rock wall of the gorge. The removal of the glacial drift that filled this buried valley has formed the elbow in which the whirlpool is situated (Fig. 460). The rapids above the whirlpool are considered to be in the narrow upper section of this buried valley.

It was formerly thought that Niagara gave a basis for telling the time in years since the close of the Glacial Period. Three important facts are known: (1) the length of the gorge; (2) the present rate of retreat of the cataract (five feet a year); (3) that the cataract began as the ice was leaving. It therefore seemed simple to divide the distance by the present rate; but later studies show that there are many causes for variation in the rate of retreat, of which the following are most important: (1) the limestone is thinner at the northern end; (2) the time required to remove the loose drift in the buried gorge is unknown; (3) the volume of water has varied; indeed, at one time Niagara received the waters of Lake Erie only (Figs. 288, 290). Since it is impossible to tell just how much these variations have influenced the rate of retreat, the time that Niagara has taken to cut its gorge could not be known positively; but it was estimated to have been between 5000 and 25,000 years. These estimates were made before more accurate (p. 283) methods of measuring time since the glacial ice retreated had been discovered. Now it is held that the larger figure is nearly right, but that after Niagara began to flow and cut its gorge, a remnant of the great glacier lingered over northeastern Canada for some 10,000 years.

Summary. *The St. Lawrence drainage is an immature river system made by combining parts of various pre-existing valleys, primarily through glacial action. It consists of (1) a drowned lower portion; (2) a middle section with a series of quiet, lakelike stretches and intervening rapids; and (3) an upper portion of great lakes, with connecting straits and rivers, interrupted by rapids and falls. Little erosion is being accomplished because the lakes rob the water of sediment for cutting-tools. Niagara Gorge is an exception to this because of the existence of weak shales beneath a massive limestone. At the Horseshoe Fall the removal of these shales is causing the cataract to retreat upstream. There is good evidence that the falls has receded through the seven miles of the gorge. The cutting of the gorge, which began 10,000 years before the close of the Glacial Period, required 25,000 years.*

TOPICAL OUTLINE AND REVIEW QUESTIONS

TOPICAL OUTLINE. 210. **The Columbia.** Climate; length; area; two large branches; valleys in lava plateau; effect of these canyons; lower valley, — crossing mountains, navigation, fishing.

211. **The Sacramento.** Position; outlet; size; large tributaries; small mountain tributaries; uses of water.

212. **The Colorado.** Source of water; size; enclosing plateau; canyon valleys; lower course; Grand Canyon, — barrier, difficulties of passage, rapids, canyon walls; tributaries; young plateau.

213. **The Great Basin.** Area; situation; minor basins; Basin Ranges; rainfall; streams; irrigation; former lakes.

214. **The Rio Grande.** Comparison with Colorado; irrigation; tributaries; variation in volume; sediment load; delta; navigation.

215. **The Mississippi system.** (*a*) *The system:* length; area; principal tributaries; navigation. (*b*) *The valley:* origin of lowland; ancient sea. (*c*) *Ohio:* rainfall; floods; mature valley; flood plains; navigation. (*d*) *Glacial influence:* rapids and falls; upper Mississippi. (*e*) *Flood plain of lower Mississippi:* cause; area; meanders; changes in river position; lakes, bayous, and swamps; floods; levees; deposits. (*f*) *Delta:* outward growth; swampy surface; distributaries; jetties; passes.

216. **Does the Mississippi River flow uphill?** Why the question is asked. Elevation of source in relation to sea level and significance of this. Distance of source and mouth from center of earth. Why not effective. Meaning of uphill and downhill flow.

217. **The St. Lawrence system.** (*a*) *Description:* lakes; connection of lakes; Thousand Islands; rapids below the lakes; drowned lower course; navigation. (*b*) *Preglacial condition:* submerged valley; former elevation of continent; Ottawa River; effect of glacier on river; on lakes. (*c*) *Erosion:* absence of sediment; effect on valley form. (*d*) *Niagara:* near Buffalo; Grand Island; Goat Island; rapids; two falls; gorge; upper plain; rocks in gorge wall; escarpment; condition below escarpment. (*e*) *Recession of falls:* cause of retreat; condition in American Fall; rate in Horseshoe Fall; future of falls. (*f*) *History of Niagara:* birth of falls; cause of gorge; proofs of this; cause of whirlpool. (*g*) *Age of gorge:* facts known; causes for variation; probable age.

QUESTIONS. Section 210. What is the situation of the Columbia? Its length and drainage area? What are the two great branches? What is the condition in the upper part? In the lower part?

211. Describe the Sacramento Valley: its situation; lower portion: size; large branches; small tributaries; uses of water.

212. State the general features of the Colorado: source of water; size; canyons; lower portion. Describe the Grand Canyon. Why are there few tributaries? What is the condition between them?

213. What are the surface features of the Great Basin? What is the climate? What effects has this on the region?

214. Compare the Rio Grande with the Colorado. How do they differ? Why is there so much irrigation? How does the volume vary? What is the condition in the lower course?

215. What is the size of the Mississippi and its largest tributaries? What is the origin and form of its valley? What is the condition in the headwaters? What are the principal characteristics of the Ohio? What effects have been produced by glaciation? What are the characteristics of the flood plain: area; meanders; floods; swamps; farm land; levees? What is the condition on the delta?

216. What two reasons are there for asking the question: Does the Mississippi River flow uphill? Explain how the level of the surface of the sea is caused and how this affects downhill flow.

217. What is the general condition of the system? What is the condition below Lake Ontario? What was the preglacial condition? Why is there little erosion? Describe Niagara River. Account for the rapids above the falls. What is the rock structure of the gorge walls? How, and at what rate, is the cataract caused to recede? What will happen as the fall recedes farther? What proofs

are there that the gorge was formed by the river?   Explain the whirlpool.   What is known of the length of postglacial time?

Reference Books.   SALISBURY, BARROWS, and TOWER, *Elements of Geography*, Henry Holt & Company, New York, 1912; WHITBECK, *High School Geography*, The Macmillan Company, New York, 1922; *Central Black Hills, Folio*, No. 219, United States Geological Survey, Washington, D. C.; *Niagara Folio*, No. 190, United States Geological Survey, Washington, D. C.   (Send also for a list of other Folios published to date, one of which may cover the locality of the school); GILBERT, *Niagara Falls, National Geographic Monographs*, American Book Company, New York, 1895.

CHAPTER XVII

DISTRIBUTION OF PLANTS

INTRODUCTORY

218. The organic world. In the preceding chapters attention has been directed almost entirely to the forms of the land, and to the composition and physical qualities of the oceans of water and of air. Inanimate nature was considered and described. Valleys and divides; rivers, lakes, and glaciers; ocean currents and winds; were the subjects of our studies. But the world has another aspect. A cloak of vegetation mantles and in some places so completely hides (Fig. 463) the forms of the rocks and the soil as to make it difficult to see what these inanimate forms really are. Further this plant cover is inhabited by a great variety of animal species. Animal forms, indeed, extend to regions where the cover of vegetation is very thin, or where it has a different make-up, as in the waters of the seas. Of this organic, or living world, plant and animal, only incidental mention has been made in previous chapters. But as the organic world is just as much a feature of the landscape as is a river and its valley, its description too must be included in physical geography if the account is to be complete.

To be sure the plant world is the subject of a special study, botany; the animal world is considered in books of zoology; and together these are studied as biology. But it may as truly be said that the rocks and their forms are studied in geology. Yet, as we have seen, there remains much of inanimate nature to be studied under physical geography. So also with botany, zoology, and biology; the organic world has a geographic significance that is properly a part of physical geography.

Summary. *What we see as we look over the surface of the earth is not only mountain and plain made up of inanimate rock and soil, but, also, a cloak of organic nature in places completely masking the forms of the land. The geographical aspects of the plant and animal cover of the earth are properly topics for study in physical geography.*

Fig. 463. — The jungle forest of the tropics. View in Jamaica, West Indies. Here the cover of vegetation completely hides the forms of the land.

219. Adaptation. In general it may be said that plants and animals are suited to the places in which they live. This adaptation is found to be especially well marked in those areas that have the most extreme physical conditions (Figs. 464, 465). Hence plant and animal assemblages, as well as particular species, show peculiar characteristics that mark them as belonging together. The plant or the animal has not only to be suited to the physical conditions of its surroundings; it must also be fitted to exist in company with its organic neighbors.

That such common suitability exists is a fact; how it has come about is not a completely solved problem. Whether each plant or animal was created in its present form, or has developed from simpler

Photo by Macey

Fig. 464. — The needles of evergreen trees enable them to withstand the cold of winter. Evergreen trees in the Alps covered with hoar frost.

forms through a long series of changes extending through many generations, is a question that has aroused much discussion. Two facts have been considered by modern science as important in connection with this question: 1. It has been found that no two plants and animals of the same kind are exactly alike. We are well acquainted with changes in the forms of plants and animals in the course of a few generations. 2. Remains and traces, *fossils*, of plants and animals anciently entombed in the rocks show some simpler forms of life from which many scientists believe present more complete forms have been developed. We do not know the end towards which life forms are moving, or how or why these changes take place, but we are slowly learning. To understand what is known it is first necessary to gain an appreciation of the conditions of life, beginning with plants.

Summary. *Life is fitted or suited to its surroundings, physical and organic. Appar-*

ently through countless past generations there have been many changes which seem to be directed to an unknown end. We are learning, slowly, how the changes are brought about.

CONDITIONS INFLUENCING PLANT LIFE

220. Moisture the basic requirement of life. The one basic need of both plants and animals for active existence and growth is water. Water combined with other substances fills the cells and circulates through the organism as cell sap or blood. In consequence of this plant life dies or becomes dormant when and where temperatures are so low that sap freezes, or when and where the temperature is so high, or the air is so dry, that it evaporates. But the degree and duration of cold, heat, and drought that certain varieties of plant life can survive in a dormant condition is remarkable. Many species of warm-blooded animals continue an active existence in the polar regions of excessive cold because they use food for fuel in developing interior bodily heat by oxidation (p. 395). But in areas where water is unavailable over long periods most animals perish, though many varieties of plants survive (p. 543).

The power of resistance to drying that some life forms show is remarkable indeed. Lichens may dry up or freeze up completely and show no life processes for years. Yet when water again becomes available they resume their growth as normally as if there had been no interruption. In the animal world this phenomenon seems even more curious. The bear-animalcules (*Tardigrada*) live in water. If the water dries up the animalcules become shapeless dry lumps. Thus they may remain for years. But on being immersed after so long a period the body of the animalcule swells, the skin becomes smooth, legs appear again, and, after perhaps an hour in water, the animalcule begins to move and crawl. Lung-fishes, capable of breathing both in and out of water, bury themselves in the bottom muds of dried up rivers in tropical lands and, completely inanimate, await the renewal of the water flow which comes many months later. In the Australian deserts certain varieties of toads (*Cystignathoid*) survive for several years in the dry-baked clays of desert hollows, remaining quite dormant until a chance shower brings about another temporary flooding. It is facts such as these that give rise to stories of frogs, and reptiles generally, coming to life after being for years entombed in rock beds.

Summary. *Availability of water is the basic condition of active life and growth of both plants and animals. But in a dormant condition organisms, plants especially, may survive a long period during which water is not available.*

221. Other requirements of plant life.   All organisms must have air.   But as air is universally available on the surface of the earth, and, in limited quantities, even at the bottom of the deep seas (p. 337), life is nowhere precluded because air is lacking.   On the other hand, though animals can and do exist (p. 352) on the deep-sea bottom, plants do not, because there sunlight is lacking and green plants live and grow by collecting and utilizing the energy of sunlight.   It is true that certain species of plants which lack chlorophyll grow in darkness.   But these are parasitic or saprophytic forms.   They get their energy by consuming (as do all animals also) organic material originally manufactured by green plants.   The green plants take carbon dioxide from the atmosphere and separate it into carbon and oxygen; the carbon, with hydrogen from the water, and salts from the soil or water, combining then to form plant tissues.

Air temperature is by some emphasized as the factor that particularly governs plant life.   But, as has been pointed out, air temperature makes itself effective in a limiting way only by causing the water in the cell sap to freeze up or dry up.   On the other hand genial temperatures, neither burning hot nor cold to near freezing, quicken the life activities of plant growth, hence tend to make it luxurious.   In that sense air temperature does in a very great degree govern the development of plants.

Many of the fungi, molds, and rusts are *parasitic* or *saprophytic*, that is they get their food from living or dead organic matter, respectively; matter manufactured by green plants originally, some of which has been further elaborated by animals.   Such forms may grow in total darkness and be altogether colorless.   Then there are green plants, mostly of varieties growing in bogs, the pitcher plants are one example, that supplement the carbohydrates they themselves manufacture by catching and digesting animal forms, insects chiefly.

Summary.   *After water, sunlight is the next most essential factor for most plants as it is their source of energy for growth.   Air conditions, temperature and degree of moisture, govern plant growth only as they affect the water of the cell sap.*

222. Functions of the soil.   Soil is not necessary to some forms of plant life.   Water plants, both fresh and salt, may secure all necessary substances from the surrounding water.   Thus many float freely about, while others have roots solely for the purpose of anchoring themselves in place.   Some land plants, called *epiphytes*, are also able to live without roots, securing all necessary substances from the air.   The great majority of land plants, however, depend on the soil for most of their water, part of their food, and for anchorage.

The plant food in the soil is of such great importance that, where it is almost absent, as in sand, the soil is called sterile, and most species of plants do not flourish.   Plants remove much mineral and organic matter from the soil and, where crops are raised year after year, it is necessary to use a fertilizer to replenish the plant food.

Plants are adapted to different kinds of soils, some thriving best in

Photo by Martin

Fig. 465. — A view in Greenland, showing the prevailing rock surface which has lichens clinging to it.   Small areas of soil are present in the depressions between the ledges.   An Eskimo turf house is seen in the middle of the picture.

loose, open soil, others in compact, clayey soil; some requiring one kind of plant food, others another.   A very little study of wild flowers or crops shows that plant life varies with the soil.

Summary. *Most land plants depend on soil for water, mineral food, and anchorage; but some land and most water plants do not need soil.   Land plants differ greatly according to the soil.*

223.   Importance of gravity.   Plants send their roots into the ground, seeking water which gravity has drawn into the earth.   Seeking sunlight, they send their stems straight up from the ground. This is the easiest way for them to resist the pull of gravity: if they were inclined, for example, they would fall far more easily. To aid in withstanding the pull of gravity and the force of the wind, large plants build strong, woody trunks and branches. Water plants, on the other hand, are usually weak, loose-textured, and flabby, as they live in a denser medium, which buoys them up so that they do not need great strength to resist gravity. Such plants as seaweeds, which are exposed to waves, have a tougher texture.

Summary. *The influence of gravity causes plants to send roots downward, and strong, woody stems straight upward.*

DISTRIBUTION OF PLANTS

From what has been said, it is evident that the distribution of plants is influenced by surrounding conditions; and as there is much difference in the climate and soil of the earth, there are great differences in plant life.

224. Influence of climate. Climate is the greatest factor in determining the distribution of plants. Some species, especially

Fig. 466. — Sugar cane cutters and field of sugar cane in Jamaica, West Indies. Stalks of the cane with the leaves trimmed off are seen in the foreground. The tops and leaves are used for donkey fodder.

the more lowly, have a wide distribution and are adapted to many climates; but most plants of higher orders are fitted for only one set of surroundings. For example, among cultivated plants, sugar cane (Fig. 466) requires a warm, damp climate beyond the reach of frost; cotton grows best in a slightly cooler, though still warm, sunny climate; corn, though requiring a long, warm summer, grows much farther north than cotton; and wheat may be raised in a climate too cold for corn. Wild plants are limited in distribution in similar ways.

There are, therefore, zones of plant life similar to the zones of temperature. An arctic plant will die amid tropical heat as certainly as a tropical plant will perish when exposed to the frosts of a temperate winter. The plant life, or *flora*, of moist climates also differs from that of arid climates. These differences may be best understood by studying the plant life in several climatic zones.

Summary. *There are zones of plant life, similar to those of climate; for, while some lowly plants are adapted to several zones, higher plants are usually fitted for life in only one.*

225. Arctic flora. In the Arctic, plants spring up as soon as the frost melts, and quickly flower and bear fruit, for the season is short. Lichens in great variety cling to the rocks (Fig. 465), and many mosses and water-loving plants live in the swampy soil. There are grasses, numerous flowering plants, and species with woody tissue, including dwarf willows and birches — true trees in all respects but size. They cling close to the ground, not rising high because it is important that the first snows shall cover and protect them from the cold blasts of winter.

For more than two thirds of the year, while the temperature is below the freezing point, plant life is dormant; but in the brief summer season the sap flows, the plants grow, and the tundra (Fig. 116) is covered with a mat of green, dotted with bits of color. Yet only the surface soil is free from ice, for at depths greater than two or three feet frost is ever present (p. 128).

Summary. *In the short arctic summer, when frost melts from the upper layers of soil, plants grow rapidly; all flower and fruit at the same time; and none grows tall.*

226. Temperate flora. Near the cold margin of the temperate zone in both hemispheres is a timber line of low, scraggy trees maintaining their existence amid unfavorable surroundings (Fig. 155). The trees are all of hardy varieties, some *evergreen*, others *deciduous*, that is, shedding their leaves in autumn. The evergreens have tough, needlelike leaves that withstand the cold of

Photo by von E.

Fig. 467. — The deciduous forest of the warmer parts of the temperate zone. The broad leaves are shed in autumn. View in central New York State.

winter (Fig. 464), falling only in spring, when new ones take their place. Among the common evergreens are spruce, hemlock, balsam, fir, and pine.

In the warmer part of the temperate zone deciduous trees increase in number and variety, including the beech, birch, maple, oak, elm, chestnut, hickory, ash, walnut, and many other species (Fig. 467). Here also many fruit trees, such as apple, pear, peach, and cherry, may be cultivated. These trees, which spring into leaf and blossom in spring and bear fruit in summer and fall, are checked by the autumn frosts. Their sap then ceases to flow, the leaves assume brilliant colors, then fall; and during the winter season the trees are dormant.

Other plants, called *perennials*, die down when droughts or the frosts come, growing up again in spring from roots or bulbs in which nourishment has been stored during the active season. Still others, called *annuals*, die completely in the fall, leaving only seeds to reproduce their species when growth is again possible.

The flora of the temperate zone varies according to temperature, exposure, humidity, and soil. There are places where trees do not grow, for example on dry plains, and on prairies (p. 131), on which, however, grasses and many flowering plants grow luxuriantly. In other places tree growth is scrubby and of few kinds, as in sandy soils which support only pines and oaks. On the other hand, there are places where the climate and soil favor a luxuriant forest growth. Most parts of the land are occupied as fully as possible by plants fitted to live there.

One of the most remarkable instances of plant growth is in the region of "big trees" on the west coast of the United States. There, a fertile soil, a damp, equable climate, and absence of strong winds encourage the growth of enormous trees. Only in southeastern Australia, where similar conditions exist, are there trees rivaling these in size. Some of the California trees are 300 feet high, 40 feet in diameter, and more than 2000 years old.

Summary. *Near the polar zones, tree growth ceases, the timber line being marked by scraggy trees, both evergreen and deciduous. Deciduous trees increase in number and variety in the warmer parts of the temperate zone. Plants are adapted to the winter season in several ways: by suspending activity, by dying down to the ground, and by dying completely, leaving seeds to continue the species. There are many differences in flora according to temperature, exposure, humidity, and soil.*

227. Tropical flora. There are two distinct types of tropical flora, that of the rain forest, best developed under the equator in the Amazon and Congo basins; and that of the jungle lands (sometimes called monsoon forest and also commonly included in the savanna lands, p. 463), which border the rain-forest areas on both

the north and south (Fig. 468).   This difference is due to the fact
that the rain-forest regions are hot and rainy throughout the year
but the border zones are drier during that part of the year when

Fig. 468. — A clump of bamboo, a typical tropical jungle plant.   When the breeze
sways them their stems click.   Smaller varieties provide us with fishing poles, but these
are a giant species.   Note the figure of the man.   At Colombo, Ceylon.

the sun is either far to the north or to the south (pp. 610–612).
Accordingly the tall tree growth of the jungle lands is much
less imposing and luxuriant than that of the rain-forest areas.

However, the flora of both the jungle lands and the rain-forest regions of the tropical zone differs from that of the temperate zones in having a much greater number of different kinds of plants within a small area (Fig. 469). Forests of one kind, or of only a few varieties of trees, are the exception in the tropics; in the temperate zones such uniformity is the rule.

When tropical plant life is mentioned the rain forest is ordinarily thought of. And, truly, the rain forest is an impressive phenomenon. We can get at its edge only where it fringes a river (Fig. 463). There one encounters an impenetrable wall of luxuriant herbage, mainly shrubs and creepers. To enter the rain forest, one must slash open a path through this tangle of growth. When thus the real forest interior is penetrated, it is found to be a gloomy, stuffy, steamy, hot place. The trees themselves are tall straight stems only branching out high overhead, and their high tops form an almost perfectly complete, interlacing, leafy canopy, that lets very little sunlight filter through. In forming this canopy, the tree tops are aided by the verdure of great vines, *lianas*, the stems of which climb, twine and twist, and loop down from the tree trunks and branches like great coils of thick rope in snarls. In places

Fig. 469. — A coconut palm. Grows everywhere along the seashore in the tropical zone. Its giant leaves are wonderfully strong, yet light in structure.

a liana is found to have strangled its supporting tree by its tight embrace. Then, after the tree has rotted away, the liana, anchored in the ground, ascends straight through the air to the level of the surrounding tree tops and there holds itself in place by its lateral branches which creep for hundreds of feet through the boughs of the trees. Jack the Giant Killer might well have climbed such a vine.

The underside of the leafy canopy is dark; so also is the forest floor. There is no undergrowth of flowers, green plants, or grass because there is so little sunlight. A thick cover of rotting leaves and twigs is all turning into a steaming mold. Where there is a break in the overhead canopy, where a tree has crashed down, a net-work of lesser climbers covers the

adjoining trees. This matting of foliage and stems also catches mold. In such aerial "fields" various ferns and epi-phytes, of which the or-chids are one sort, establish themselves. One is im-pressed by the fact that the kinds of plant-growth in the rain forest are al-most endlessly various.

Because there are al-ways moisture and heat there is no dormant period; blossoms and fruit (Figs. 470, 471, 472) appear at any and every time of

Fig. 470. — A collection of tropical fruits. How many of them do you know by name? Which ones have you tasted?

the year; there is no season when all the leaves fall. The trees have forced the tall growth on each other, for if one kind grew high and the others did not, the lower ones would get no sun-light. Plants of varieties that do not grow tall, when encountered in the rain forest, are found to have developed into vines. Thus they are enabled to climb up to the sunlight on their stronger neigh-bors. It is in the rain forests that mahogany, ebony, rosewood, and rubber trees grow. There also many kinds of palms grow, among which is the important oil palm.

Summary. *Tropical forest vegetation is of two types, the rain-forest and the jungle. The rain-forest grows where moisture and heat are continuous the*

Fig. 471. — A field of pineapples in Jamaica, West Indies.

year round. It is composed of tall trees, entangled by great vines, and its interior is dark, still, hot, and steamy under an almost unbroken canopy of green, high above. The jungle regions have a dry season and the forest growth is less luxuriant and less continuous. Both types of tropical forest growth have extremely numerous varieties of plants within narrow areas.

228. Flora of savannas and steppes (pp. 463, 128). In regions where there is a pronounced season of drought, as in the savannas and steppes, trees cannot grow except along the streams. Many grasses and flowering plants bridge over the period of drought by means of roots, bulbs, and seeds; springing into life when the rains come, as plants of the cool temperate zone do at the close of winter. Therefore, such regions are excellent pasture lands. In Africa, bordering the Congo rain forest on all sides are savannas varying from jungle forests to grass lands. This is the greatest big game country of the world. Here are found elephants, hippopotami, rhinoceroses, giraffes, lions, zebras, and almost one hundred different

Fig. 472. — Picking tea leaves in Ceylon, India. The tea shrub requires a well-drained soil; note the hill slope site of this plantation.

kinds of antelopes. Note that most of these animals subsist on vegetation, and the lions then prey on the plant-eaters.

Summary. *Regions having a marked period of drought are treeless; but annuals and perennials thrive, making these good pasture lands. Grass-land steppes grade through savannas, having a park-like aspect, into jungle forest.*

229. Desert flora. In deserts there is too little moisture for a great number of individuals. Therefore, instead of having a complete cover of vegetation, the desert is scantily clothed with a scattered flora (Figs. 139, 473). Every possible effort is made by the plants to secure and retain enough moisture for life. Some plants have enormous roots, extending deep into the ground and spreading far about in search of water; the mesquite, for example, has several times as much woody matter below ground as above it. Water is stored in these roots for use during the long droughts.

Photo by Raffius

Fig. 473. — Sage brush and cacti in the desert areas of the southwestern United States. Notice that the vegetation grows in clumps, with bare spots between. Suggest a reason. View near Tombstone, Arizona.

Desert plants have many devices for existence in their dry environment. In order that the surface for evaporation may be reduced to a minimum, no more leaves are produced than are absolutely necessary; and in many cases the leaves are small and tough, or are even reduced to spines. In the cacti (Figs. 139, 473), which are especially well fitted for desert life, water is stored in the tissues; there are no true leaves; the green stem performs the same services that the green leaves of other plants do; and the plant has a hard, shiny, varnished surface, through which evaporation is almost impossible. Some species are globular in form, thus exposing the least possible surface to evaporation; and the sharp, irritating spines protect them from many kinds of animals, which might otherwise devour them. Many desert plants repel plant-eating animals, as the common sage brush does, whose tough, pale green leaves have a disagreeable odor and taste.

Sunlight, temperature, and much of the desert soil are favorable to abundant plant life; but water is lacking (Fig. 474). It is remarkable that any plants should have been developed adapted to life where rain comes at intervals of months or even years. Within a few days after a rain following an absolute drought that lasted thirteen months, a barren and desolate stretch of desert in northern Mexico was transformed into a green prairie dotted with blooming bulb-plants. That lack of water is the only unfavorable condition is also proved where oases exist in the desert, or where irrigation is introduced. Then the watered desert supports plant life in great variety and luxuriance (Fig. 134).

Summary. *Because of lack of water, the desert flora is scattered and plants show many devices for storing enough water to last through the periods of drought. The luxuriance of growth on oases and irrigated sections proves that the lack of water accounts for the general absence of plant life in deserts.*

230. Mountain flora. In every zone the flora varies with altitude. A temperate flora is found on mountain slopes in the tropical zone; and an arctic flora on mountain tops in temperate zones. Thus, species growing in Labrador and Greenland are also found on the top of Mt. Washington.

Fig. 474. — Part of a grove of date palms in the sands of an oasis of the desert in Egypt. Each tree is separately owned and tended; the land has no value. A date palm is said to grow best "with its feet in water and its head in the sun." Explain that statement.

Even in the tropical zone there is a line, the *timber line* (p. 167), above which it is too cold for trees to grow. This line, marked by stunted, scrubby trees, is not regular, but extends highest on those slopes which furnish most protection from winds or longer exposure to the sun (Figs. 155, 199). Above the timber line, wherever there is soil, the surface is covered with low bushes and flowering plants (Fig. 180), forming the mountain or *alpine flora*, famed for the variety and beauty of its flowers. The cool summer air, damp soil, and long, cold winters resemble conditions in the Arctic; but there is more sun heat.

Mountains and high plateaus rising from desert lands may have rainfall enough for forest growth. On the lower slopes the trees are stunted,

Photo by Macey

Fig. 475. — Plant life in the water; a lake in the Alps. Describe the vegetation in this picture.

scrawny, and scattered, showing the difficulty with drought; but higher up the forest becomes dense. If the mountains are high, tree growth may be checked above by cold, as well as by drought below.

Summary. *Because of changes in temperature, the flora varies with altitude. On high mountain slopes the forest disappears, and in the upper portion is replaced by the alpine flora.*

231. Water plants. Wherever conditions favor, both in salt (p. 351) and fresh water (Fig. 475), there is a varied flora, some species floating on the surface, others anchored, and still others having true roots. Lower forms, such as algae and mosses, are especially adapted to life in water; but higher forms, even trees, are not absent. Rushes, reeds, mosses, and lilies are among the common fresh-water and swamp plants; and among trees the cypress, black gum, willow, and mangrove are common, the latter living in salt water (Fig. 364).

Most trees die if their roots are submerged, because air is cut off; but water-loving trees have special provision for securing the necessary air. For example, mangrove roots start from above the water surface, and even from the lower limbs; and knobs, or knees, grow upward from cypress roots till they project above the water surface.

Summary. *Plant life is abundant both in fresh and salt water, the lower forms being especially common, though even some trees are adapted to life in water.*

232. Means of distribution. Since the land is so well occupied that it is difficult for a new plant in the wild state to gain a foothold, it is necessary, if a given variety is to survive and spread after the parent individual dies, that adequate provision be made to insure the establishment of new young plants of the same kind. Seeds are the principal means of insuring this spread. It is necessary to produce far more seeds than can possibly find a chance to grow, for some are eaten, some decay, some fall where they cannot sprout, and some that sprout find conditions so unfavorable that they die.

In order that they may have every chance for a start in life, seeds have developed with many ingenious devices to aid in their spread. Some are so light that they are drifted about by the slightest breeze; some, like the maple, have wing-like projections that catch the wind; some, like dandelion seeds, have a light feathery float (*pappus*); some, like the many burs, have hooks that catch upon the fur of animals; and some, like the apple or peach, are covered with an edible coat. Animals eat these fruits, often depositing the hard, protected seeds far away from the parent plant.

Winds and animals are the two agencies most important in spreading plants. Because light seeds are so easily carried by the wind, light-seeded plants are most readily distributed. Rivers also float seeds and plants from one place to another, and ocean currents may drift them even to oceanic islands. Man has become an important agent in distributing plants over the earth. He carries cultivated plants from one region to another, and also distributes many weeds. In this way the Canada thistle and the white field daisy, now common weeds, were brought to the United States.

It was formerly considered that the distribution of plants by seeding, starting from a given center, went forward very rapidly. In the case of weeds introduced on cultivated areas such is the case. But where a new plant must get a start in competition with established native varieties the spread may be very slow. On this basis Willis has proposed the theory that the most widespread types of plants are the oldest and that plants with only a very narrow distribution, territorially, are new varieties just making a start. Opposed to this is the earlier theory still generally accepted, that the plants of which only a few occur in a limited area are *survivals*, that is kinds of an ancient type once much more widespread. These are now failing to maintain themselves in competition with more successful modern types. Possibly, also, such survivals indicate a change in the climatic or other conditions.

Summary. *Plants are distributed mainly by seeds. As many seeds are destroyed, far more must be produced than could possibly grow. Seeds of many species are distributed by wind and by animals, with the aid of many interesting devices; other varieties are spread by rivers, ocean currents, and by man. Light-seeded plants are most readily distributed. The present general distribution of plant varieties may be due to age, to more successful types modernly developed, or perhaps to the fact that climatic and other conditions change.*

233. Barriers to the spread of plants. If seeds from land plants fall upon water, they do not grow unless drifted ashore. In other words, water is a barrier to the spread; it is, in fact, the greatest barrier to the distribution of land plants, especially if it is a large body like the ocean. It would be under very rare conditions, for example, that even a single seed could be carried from South America to Africa by winds, currents, or birds.

Yet even the ocean is not an absolute barrier, and plants from the mainland are found on all oceanic islands. However, only the seeds of certain plants find their way there, and island floras are, therefore, far less varied than those of the mainland.

Deserts are barriers because no plants, except those adapted to desert conditions, can spread across them, unless carried entirely over. A tropical forest is an equally good barrier for plants that are adapted to desert life. Mountain chains are also barriers (Fig. 476), because plants at their base will not spread into the cold climates above, but gaps or passes often are pathways for the spread of plants across mountains. The wind, although an aid to distribution in one direction, is a very important barrier to spread in the opposite direction. For this reason European plants are not likely to reach America against the west winds; but these winds aid American plants in their spread to Europe. Ocean currents and birds also aid in the same direction.

Summary. *The ocean is the greatest barrier to the spread of land plants; but even this is not an absolute barrier, for plants whose seeds can be carried by*

Photo by Wheew.

Fig. 476. — Mountains as barriers to the spread of plants and animals. View in the Selkirks of British Columbia. Explain the kind of difficulties plants and animals would have in making a crossing of this area. Rogers Pass in the foreground. How would this facilitate spread?

winds, birds, and ocean currents are found even on remote oceanic islands. Deserts and mountains are also barriers; and wind checks the spread of plants against its movement.

234. Variation in plants. Among plants there is an unconscious competition for air, food, light, water, and opportunity to reproduce their kind. This competition is going on everywhere. It may be noted in a neglected flower garden, where weeds, commonly native plants, spring up from chance seeds, and, being better fitted to the conditions than carefully nourished, cultivated plants, take complete possession of the garden. They tower above the cultivated plants, shutting out light and robbing the roots of water and mineral food.

Plants are and have been steadily changing; and those that change to fit themselves best for the conditions have the best chance of surviving and spreading. This has been called the survival of the fittest. Thus plants have changed to survive the cold of winter; to live amid the unfavorable surroundings of the desert; in fact, to grow among most conditions on the earth's surface (Fig. 477).

The following will serve as illustrations of how plants vary with environment. A mountain, rising above the timber line and bearing an alpine flora, is slowly worn down to the low, hilly condition of maturity. If the plants cannot adapt themselves to the changes in climate, slope, and soil, they must give place to forms better fitted.

The effect of the ice sheet of the Glacial Period offers another illustration. As it advanced over the land, it either drove southward or destroyed all life. When the glacier melted away a new soil was uncovered, and the best suited plants got possession of it. This accounts in part for the fact of uniform forests and few varieties of trees in the regions affected by the glaciation in comparison with the great number of species in narrow areas, typical of the tropics. The history of plant life during past ages has been a succession of changes by which plants have become better adapted to their surroundings.

Plants have undergone many changes as a result of their relation to animals. As these animals also depend on plants for food, some means must be provided to prevent complete destruction. For this purpose hard woods, thorns, bitter taste, and other variations have developed. Many plants make use of animals, for example, in spreading seeds and in distributing pollen. Honey, odor, color, and many interesting forms of flowers attract insects and secure from them the service of carrying the pollen.

Whether, however, the plants change in *response* to the conditions, or develop variations, wholly by chance, from within themselves—variations which happen to fit the conditions and are, therefore, successful and spread—is a question in dispute. In some instances, the adjustment of the plant to its surroundings is so perfect that it is difficult to conceive how it could have come about by chance. On the other hand it is no easier to think that because animals grazed on a plant it developed thorns from within to protect itself. Still, our hands become callous when we do hard labor and our faces tan as a protection against the intense light of summer. It is also difficult to say whether the changes take place by small variations or by great changes all at once, *mutations*. If the changes are slow and small, it is hard to see how the thorny bush was protected while it was getting thorny; if sudden and from within, it is equally difficult to understand why the change to thorniness took place in just the plant and the place where protection was needed. Again, many plants have peculiar characteristics that do not seem to serve any useful purpose. Much that we take for granted because we see it every day is as yet little understood. It is true that the fittest *survive* but that does not explain how they *arrive*.

Fig. 477. — The olive tree, Greece. A tree that thrives in regions having a long summer dry season, typical of the Mediterranean lands. Olive trees grow and bear fruit for a hundred years and longer.

Man is now one of the most important agents in changing plants. By giving them better care, with plenty of light and food, and removing weeds, thus relieving them from the competition with other plants, he is able to secure far larger seeds and fruits than grow naturally. For example, a good apple tree, left to itself, soon has to struggle with weeds and bushes, and its fruit becomes sour or bitter. By much care and many devices, men are constantly producing new varieties of flowers and fruit. In this way changes may be caused in a few years which, by natural processes, might require centuries, or never occur.

Summary. *Plants are adapted to their surroundings. Weaker forms die out and the fittest survive. Slow changes in climate or in land form result in variation in plants. Changes are also brought about for the purpose of protection from, or for making use of, animals; and man is now causing changes at a far more rapid rate than adaptation naturally works. How or why the changes are brought about is a complicated problem.*

235. Plants of value to man. Man, like other members of the animal kingdom, depends upon plants for food. Although he may feed on meat, the animal from which the meat came receives nourishment, directly or indirectly, from plants. In a warm climate so great an abundance of plant food may be easily obtained at all seasons, that there is little need of special provision. But in climates with a dry or cold season it is highly important to provide a store of food for use during the unfavorable season. This need has led to the cultivation of food plants.

The portions of plants most useful for food are those in which nourishment has been stored to aid in the propagation of the species. Among these are seeds, like wheat; fruits, like bananas; bulbs, like onions; and tubers, like potatoes. Some of the food plants, such as dates, coconuts, breadfruit, and bananas, used extensively in warm climates, have been changed very little from their original wild forms.

Others, especially those cultivated in the temperate zones, have been so improved that they are now quite unlike the original plants which savage man first ate. The most important of these, including the orange, apple, pear, peach, cherry, grape, wheat, barley, oats, and rye, have been carried to many parts of the world. In the case of many, the original home is not now known; but most of our food plants apparently came from Asia, where they had been cultivated for thousands of years. America has added the potato, tomato, pumpkin, and Indian corn, or maize.

Plants also supply us with materials for shelter, clothing, medicine, and other purposes. Cotton is the most valuable of the several plant fibers used for clothing. In all lands wood is used both for shelter and for ornamental purposes. Sugar (Fig. 466), coffee, tea (Fig. 472), cocoa, vanilla, tobacco, quinine, and many other plant substances, not of vital importance, are much used by man. The list of valuable plants is a very long one.

For food and clothing, plants are carefully cultivated; but for shelter it has been customary to depend upon the forest, which grows without care. In parts of Europe, however, so much of the forest has been removed that it has become necessary to cultivate even the forests, planting the trees, weeding out the poor ones, and carrying on lumbering with great care. The time has now arrived in America when the forest needs to be cultivated. Accordingly, both the national and state governments have set aside large tracts as forest reservations. A division of the National Government is known as the Bureau of Forestry, and a number of states have forestry bureaus. There are also schools of forestry at many universities, where men are scientifically trained to be foresters.

Summary. *Man and all animals rely for their food, either directly or indirectly, on the vegetable kingdom. In regions with a cold or dry season, it is necessary to provide food for the unfavorable season, and this has led to the cultivation and improvement of a number of plants for their seeds, fruits, bulbs, or tubers. Many plants are also used to supply materials for clothing and shelter; and now even forests are cared for by methods of scientific forestry.*

TOPICAL OUTLINE, REVIEW QUESTIONS, AND SUGGESTIONS

TOPICAL OUTLINE. 218. **The organic world.** How organic world is part of physical geography. Special studies of the organic world.

219. **Adaptation.** Plant and animal organisms suited to their surroundings. Evidences of adaptation.

220. **Moisture the basic requirement of life.** Function of water in plant and animal life. Degree and manner in which drought is resisted, instances.

221. **Other requirements of plant life.** Need of air. Where present in least quantity. Difference between plants and animals in need for sunlight, effects of this difference. How air temperatures affect plants. How fungi, molds, and rusts live; bog plants.

222. **Functions of the soil.** Water plants; epiphytes; dependence of most land plants on soil; plant food; effect of differences in soil.

223. **Importance of gravity.** Roots; stems; wood; water plants.

224. **Influence of climate.** Lowly plants; higher plants; illustrations; effect of temperature, or moisture.

225. **Arctic flora.** Rapid growth; kinds of plants; clinging to ground; winter; summer.

226. **Temperate flora.** Timber line near Arctic; evergreen trees; kinds; deciduous trees; kinds; dormant condition in winter; perennial plants; annuals; treeless regions; sandy soils; "big trees."

227. **Tropical flora.** Difference between rain-forest and jungle lands; between tropical and temperate zone forests. Nature of the rain forest: trees, vines, darkness, orchids, changes in form of plants, kinds of trees.

228. **Flora of savannas and steppes.** Drought; plant growth. Big game region.

229. **Desert flora.** Scattered growth; large roots; nature of leaves; cacti; plants with disagreeable taste; proof that water alone is lacking.

230. **Mountain flora.** Tropical zone; temperate zone; timber line; alpine flora; flora of desert highlands.

231. **Water plants.** Position; kinds; adaptation of trees.

232. **Means of distribution.** Abundance of seeds; devices for their spread; distribution — wind, animals, rivers, ocean currents, man. Rate of distribution; new varieties; survivals.

233. **Barriers to the spread of plants.** The ocean barrier; ocean-island flora; desert barrier; mountain barrier; wind barrier.

234. **Variation in plants.** Cause of competition; illustration; changes resulting; survival of the fittest; illustrations of causes for change and survival; variation in past; securing protection from animals; making use of animals; how changes are effected; changes brought about by man.

235. **Plants of value to man.** Dependence on plants; plant food in warm climates; in places with an unfavorable season; parts of plants used; improvement; important food plants; source of food plants; American food plants; plants used for other purposes; care of the forest.

QUESTIONS. Section 218. Explain how the organic world is part of the landscape.

219. What is meant by adaptation of plants and animals? What are the evidences of such adaptation?

220. Why do drought and freezing affect plants in the same way? How do organisms survive drought and cold? Give examples. How does air temperature affect plants?

221. Why are plants not found on the deep-sea bottom? State peculiar ways in which some plants get their food.

222. What plants are not dependent on soil? Of what importance is soil to land plants? Why is fertilizer used?

223. State the effects of gravity on land plants. On water plants.

224. How are plants influenced by climate? Give illustrations.

225. State the peculiarities of plant life in the Arctic.

226. What are the conditions of tree growth near the polar zone? In the warmer temperate zone? In what ways are plants adapted to winter conditions? How does the flora of the temperate zone vary? What conditions favor the "big trees"?

227. What is the nature of the rain forest? Of the jungle? How do tropical forests differ from temperate zone forests? Describe the rain forest in detail. Name some of the rain-forest trees.

228. What are the characteristics of the flora of savannas and steppes? What big game is found on the African savannas and jungle lands and why?

229. How are desert plants fitted to survive periods of drought? How are they protected from animals? What do the oases prove?

230. What changes occur in the flora of mountains? Compare alpine and arctic floras. What are the conditions on highlands in deserts?

231. What kinds of plants thrive in water? How are trees adapted to water life?

232. Why are so many seeds produced? What devices are there to aid in the spread of seeds? By what agencies are plants spread? What conditions govern the rate of spread? Explain survivals.

233. Why is water a barrier? How is it certain that the ocean is not an absolute barrier? What other barriers are there?

234. For what are plants competing? Give an illustration. What is the result of the competition? What do fossils prove? Give two illustrations of how changes on the earth may influence variation. What is the effect of the relation between plants and animals? How is man influencing variation? How does variation take place?

235. How is man dependent on plants? What is the condition in warm climates? In regions with cold or dry seasons? What parts of plants are used for food? What effect has cultivation had? Where have the cultivated plants come from? For what other purposes are plants used? What is now being done with the forest?

SUGGESTIONS. (1) Place a hardy plant, such as moss, in boiling water for a few minutes, and plant it to note whether it will grow again. (2) Freeze the same plant for a night and note whether it will grow. Freeze a delicate plant, for example a geranium, and note whether it will continue to grow. (3) Place a plant, say a geranium, in the cellar and let it grow for a few weeks, and note the change. (4) Leave a plant in its pot without water and note whether it grows. Keep water up to the top of the earth (a swamp) and note whether it kills the plant. Get a cactus and note whether it will live in dry soil. Study the cactus. (5) Using the same kind of seed, try growing plants in several different kinds of soil, sandy, fertile loam, etc., and observe which thrives best. (6) Try to burn ash. Perhaps the teacher of chemistry can suggest an experiment to prove that there is mineral matter in ash. (7) Put a plant in a pot, inclining it at an angle to the surface. Does it keep on growing in that direction? (8) Collect and study seeds to find out what devices they use for distribution. (9) Plant a bean in a flowerpot in absolutely dry earth (a desert). Does it sprout? Place one in a jar of water? Does it grow after it has used up the nourishment in the seed? This illustrates why deserts and water are barriers. (10) Study the flora of your vicinity to note whether the plants vary in kind from one soil, or exposure, to another. If there is a swamp, find how the swamp plants are different from those on dry slopes. (11) What crops are raised in your vicinity? What crops cannot be raised? Why? Is there a difference in crops according to the soil? (12) Make a list of plants valuable to man, their principal uses, and the localities from which they come. Let each student make a list, then combine them for the use of the whole class.

Laboratory Exercise. Exercise LVI in TARR and VON ENGELN's *Laboratory Manual for Physical and Commercial Geography*, The Macmillan Company, New York, correlates with this and the following chapter.

Reference Books. CAMPBELL, *Outline of Plant Geography*, The Macmillan Company, New York, 1926; GADOW, *Wanderings of Animals*, Cambridge University Press, Cambridge, England, 1913; MERRIAM, *Life Zones and Crop Zones of United States*, Biological Survey Division, Bull. 10, Department of Agriculture, Washington, D. C., 1898; COWLES, *Text Book of Botany*, Vol. II, *Ecology*, American Book Company, New York, 1911; WILLIS, *Age and Area*, Cambridge University Press, Cambridge, England, 1922.

CHAPTER XVIII

DISTRIBUTION OF ANIMALS

236. Influence of surroundings. Plants and animals are alike in being dependent for life on their surroundings. Like plants, all animals, even those on the sea bottom, need air to breathe; all require water for their blood and tissues; and for all it is necessary that the temperature shall be neither too high nor too low. Temperatures near the boiling point, or long continued below the freezing point, are fatal to animal tissues. Many, especially the lower animals, are able to survive a period of freezing; others protect themselves by a coat of fur, feathers, or fat; and some, such as bears, lie dormant in a protected place during the cold season.

Most water and many land animals are cold-blooded; that is, their temperature changes with their surroundings. Most water animals require so little air that they obtain all they need from the water. The birds and mammals are warm-blooded, the warmth being due to slow combustion caused within their bodies by the oxygen they breathe (p. 395). Such animals require much oxygen and, even if they live in water, as the whales do, must rise to the air to obtain it. Those that live in water, or in cold climates, need to protect themselves by a warm covering in order to keep the warmth in their blood.

Animals differ from plants in the way in which they secure food. While some remain fixed in one place, depending on supplies brought to them, as plants do, most animals seek their food. They need carbon and mineral substances, but are unable to secure them directly from air and earth. They depend upon plants to perform this work, and the basis of animal food is, therefore, plant life. Even the food of flesh-eating animals may be traced back to the plant kingdom. Thus plants are of vital importance to animals.

Unlike green plants, animals do not absolutely require sunlight, as they do not need it to transform air, water, and mineral matter to food, as plants do. Consequently, animals are able to live even in the darkness of the deep sea and of caves.

Summary. *All animals must have air for breathing, water for blood and tissues, and a temperature neither too high nor too low. There are both warm- and cold-blooded animals, and all are dependent on the plant kingdom for food.*

237. Animal life, or fauna,[1] of the Arctic. No animals live in the ice-covered interior of Greenland; but in and near the Arctic Ocean there is much life, especially in summer. There are many kinds of fishes and other sea animals, and a great variety of sea birds feeding on them. Other birds migrate to and from the Arctic; wild geese, for instance, which spend the summer on the tundras of northern America, fly as far south as Mexico. The golden plover makes its nests along the arctic coast from Hudson Bay to Alaska in summer and then flies to Argentina in southern South

Photo by Sanborn, N. Y. Zoological Society

Fig. 478. — The musk-ox (ovibos) of the land fringe of the arctic islands and Greenland. He endures the bitter cold of the arctic night and subsists on mosses and lichens that he obtains by pawing through the snow.

America to spend the winter! Other species go no farther south than Labrador and Newfoundland. During the summer, such birds congregate in great numbers in their arctic breeding places.

On the land, hares, foxes, reindeer (including the American caribou), and musk oxen (*Ovibos*) are found (Fig. 478). There are practically no reptiles, but there are numerous insects, of which the mosquito is especially abundant.

A number of mammals live part or all of the time in the sea.

[1] A fauna is the assemblage of animals occupying a region. Thus we may speak of a Greenland fauna, an Alaskan fauna, etc.

The polar bear (Fig. 479) spends most of his time on the sea ice, seeking the seal for food. There are walruses (Fig. 480) and a number of species of seal, — warm-blooded, air-breathing mammals, which now and then leave the sea for a short time and take to the ice or shore. Whales also live in the Arctic, but, though air-breathing, they never leave the water.

The warm-blooded animals are well adapted to life in the severe arctic climate. They are well protected, the birds with feathers and down,

Photo by Sanborn, N. Y. Zoological Society

Fig. 479. — The polar bear of the Arctic. He lives on the ice floes and catches the seal as it climbs out on the ice to breathe and sleep.

which keep out wind and water, and enable them to retain their body heat; the mammals with fur or fat, or both. In winter, when most needed, the fur is thickest. Eider down and the fur of the fur seal of the Bering Sea are highly valued by man for their warmth and beauty.

Many arctic animals, such as the fox, hare, and polar bear, being white like the snow and ice around them, escape notice, both of their foes and their prey. The ptarmigan becomes white in winter; but its summer plumage resembles the vegetation amid which it feeds. The baby seal, which spends its first days on the ice, is also white; but as it grows older, and takes to the water, its color changes more nearly to resemble the water.

Summary. *In the arctic region there are many sea birds and migratory land birds which move southward in winter when the freezing of sea and land* *cuts off their food supply. On the land there are a few birds and mammals, numerous insects, but practically no reptiles. A number of mammals live part or all of the time in the sea. Warm-blooded arctic animals are protected from the cold by fur, feathers, and fat, and are commonly white like the surrounding snow and ice.*

238. Temperate fauna. In the temperate zones animal life is more varied, and differs greatly from place to place. Certain species, like the bison (Fig. 481) and antelope, have become especially adapted to life on open plains; others, like the moose and

Photo by Sanborn, N. Y. Zoological Society

Fig. 480. — The walrus. His home is the arctic seas and he lives on shellfish. This is a young animal that has not yet grown tusks.

squirrel, to the forest; others, like the mountain sheep and chamois, to high mountains; others, like the jack rabbit and coyote, to arid lands. Some, like the blindfish, live in caves, losing their eyes because they are not needed in the darkness. Still others, like the earthworm, woodchuck, prairie dog (Fig. 481), and mole, burrow in the soil, spending part or all of their lives underground. Some, like the owl and wild cat, sleep by day and hunt by night; but the majority rest when it is dark.

Many animals of the temperate zone are protected by a coat of fur, highly prized by man (Fig. 482a, b, c, d). Animals bearing fur of value, including mink, otter, sable, and beaver (Figs. 483, 484), are found especially in the cold north, where they are still hunted.

Summary. *Animal life in the temperate zone is abundant and varied, different species being adapted to life on the prairies, in the forest, on mountains, in arid lands, in caves, and underground. Many mammals have fur of value to man.*

239. Tropical fauna. Since plants are the basis for animal food, animal life thrives where plants abound. Hence, animals are abundant in the tropical regions. But in the rain forest much of the animal life exists in the leafy canopy of the tree tops, on the roof of the area as it were. There innumerable insects, feeding on pollen, honey, fruit, leaves, bark, wood, or decaying vegetation, furnish food for countless birds. The insects include many beautiful

Photos by Sanborn, N. Y. Zoological Society

Fig. 481. — A group of three characteristic animals of western North America, prairie dogs (top), the grizzly bear (middle), and the bison (bottom).

Photos by Sanborn, N. Y. Zoological Society

Fig. 482*a, b, c, d.* — A group of fur-bearing animals of the cold temperate regions of North America: *a*, mink; *b*, the weasel or North American ermine; *c*, lynx; *d*, otter.

butterflies. The birds, including parrots, parrakeets, humming birds, and birds of paradise, number thousands of species. Monkeys,

Photo by Sanborn, N. Y. Zoological Society

Fig. 483.

Photo by Pack

Figs. 483 and 484. — The beaver and the dam he builds, creating shallow lakes in stream courses. This lake is in the Uinta Mountains, Wyoming.

subsisting mostly on fruit, are also present. Reptiles too are very numerous; lizards preying on the insects, and tree snakes big enough to capture and devour birds and monkeys. One of these is the huge boa constrictor, which, hanging from a treetop, resembles a thick vine. One of the lizards, the iguana, attains a length of several feet. In the more open jungle and savanna lands are found such mammals (Figs. 485, 486) as the lion, tiger, hippopotamus, rhinoceros, giraffe, and elephant of the Old World (Figs. 487, 488).

Summary. *The abundance of plants in the tropical zone permits the existence of a great variety of insects, birds, reptiles, and mammals.*

240. Desert fauna. A complete list of the desert animals would be much shorter than one enumerating those of a humid forest region. There is a great contrast between the abundance and variety of life in the

Photos by Sanborn, N. Y. Zoological Society

Fig. 485. — A group of three characteristic southern Asiatic animals; pelicans (top), rhinoceros (middle), tiger (bottom).

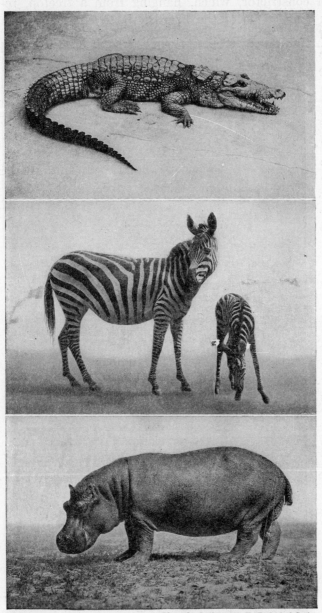

Photos by Sanborn, N. Y. Zoological Society

Fig. 486. — A group of three characteristic African animals; the crocodile (top), the zebra (middle), and the hippopotamus (bottom).

African forest and savanna lands and its paucity in the barren Sahara. There is also a decided contrast between the abundant and varied life in an Arkansas forest and the limited fauna of the desert portion of southwestern United States. There the chief animals are the antelope, puma, coyote, jack rabbit, cottontail rabbit, rattlesnake, horned toad, and a limited number of birds and insects.

Animals need to be peculiarly adapted for life on a desert; and their number and variety are limited by the small amount of water and plant food. Some, like the snakes, require little water, aside from what

Photo by Sanborn, N. Y. Zoological Society

Fig. 487. — The Asiatic (Indian) elephant. Compare with Figs. 488 and 489.

Photo by Sanborn, N. Y. Zoological Society

Fig. 488. — The African elephant. Study Figs. 487, 488, and 489 to see how the Asiatic and African elephants differ in form and descent.

they secure from the animals they eat; others are supplied with water from the roots or stems of the desert plants upon which they feed; and still others live near springs, or go long distances to them. The camel (Fig. 135) is wonderfully adapted to desert life. It is able to make long journeys on the desert because of the store of water which it carries in its water pouch; its broad, flat feet are admirably suited for travel over sandy surfaces; and its nostrils may be closed to keep out sand which the wind blows about.

Summary. *The dryness of the climate, and the scarcity of plant food, limit animal life in the desert; but some species, like the camel, are peculiarly adapted to existence in such an environment.*

241. Fresh-water fauna. Rivers and lakes have varied faunas, including especially fishes, insects, and lower invertebrates, or animals without a backbone. Many insects and amphibia (toads, frogs, salamanders, etc.) breed in water, coming to dry land during a later stage. Numerous reptiles, including crocodiles, alligators, turtles, and some snakes, live in fresh water.

There are many differences in fresh-water life. For example, the faunas of muddy water, sandy bottoms, swampy ponds, quiet water, and flowing rivers are quite different. Salt lakes have very few animals. The Dead Sea receives its name because of the general absence of life, contrasting strikingly with the fauna of the neighboring fresh-water Sea of Galilee.

Summary. *Lower invertebrates, insects, fishes, birds, mammals, amphibia, and reptiles are adapted to life in fresh water; and faunas vary with surrounding conditions.*

242. Spread of animals. As in the case of plants, there is a tendency for animals to spread. The fact that more young are born than can possibly live, promotes this and insures the survival of the species. Some of the young die for lack of food, others are killed by enemies. It is during the young stage that animals are least able to protect themselves, and animals such as fishes, which do not protect their young, lay thousands of eggs for every one of their offspring that reaches maturity. When the young are protected and fed by the parents fewer offspring are necessary. Those animals that take the best care of their offspring are the highest.

The tendency to spread has taken animals to all parts of the earth; and the tendency to change so as to become better adapted to surroundings, has brought about their variation. It is because of this adaptation that the European reindeer and American caribou, of the same ancestral form, are slightly different. The African elephant is a different species from that of Asia, though from similar ancestral forms; and the extinct mammoth and mastodon, living in a cold climate, had hairy coats, quite unlike the elephants of warm regions (Fig. 489).

It does not follow that the variations that occur in the form of species are induced by the surroundings, or, if they are, that they are necessarily such as will enable the new type to succeed better in the environment. Indeed many changes are apparently of little significance as aids or hindrances to existence, as far as we can tell, and may occur in what is seemingly an environment of singular uniformity of conditions. Thus it is reported by Professor Crampton of Barnard College that on the isolated tropical island of Moorea of the Society Islands in the Pacific Ocean, new species of the family of land snails, called Partula, have developed since 1888. In and preceding that year another scientist, Andrew Garrett, had made very complete collections of all the varieties of these snails then existing. When Crampton visited the island in 1919 he found that each of the varieties previously described had spread over wider areas, and that, in addition, new forms had appeared. Instead of three species only, seven were found. Instead of all having shell spirals twisting to the right, the new varieties had in some instances shells twisting to the left. Others had altogether different bandings and colorings from those of the original species. These results were confirmed by further studies in 1923 and 1924. These new species could hardly have been missed in the earlier surveys and as they do not occur elsewhere could not have been brought in. Thus variation of the Partula is now in active progress.

Ocean dwellers (p. 351) are among the most widespread of animals. They swim, or are drifted, here and there; and their surroundings are so uniform that there is little reason for change. Because they can fly, insects, birds, and bats are among the most widely distributed of land animals. Those animals that walk or crawl move more slowly, meet more enemies, and find more barriers to overcome, such as rivers, mountains, deserts, and sea. For these reasons particular species of large mammals and running birds are usually confined to limited areas. Yet some, especially the fierce carnivorous animals, cover a wide range; in India the tiger (Fig. 485), for example, lives in the hot jungle, on open plains, and on cool mountain slopes.

Summary. *Many animals make provision for the survival and spread of the species by the production of numerous offspring; but higher animals* *protect their young so that fewer offspring are necessary. Animals have migrated to all parts of the earth, and the forms have become fitted by adaptation to their surroundings. Ocean and flying animals are most widely distributed, while land dwellers move more slowly and are often confined to very limited areas.*

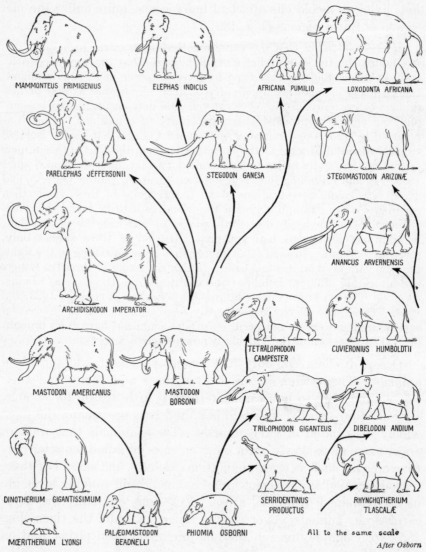

Fig. 489.—The development of the elephant through the geological ages from similar ancestral forms. Notice that the one series ascends to the modern Asiatic (*Indicus*) elephant, the other to the modern African (*Africana*) elephant, and that these two species are quite different. See Figs. 487 and 488.

243. Barriers to the spread of animals. The spread of animals is interfered with by the same barriers as in the case of plants. Water is the greatest barrier, but it is overcome by flying animals and by those small forms that may be drifted, clinging to logs. The tropical forest is a barrier to a desert animal, and the desert to one that needs water every day. Nor can animals accustomed to a warm climate or to life on plains easily cross to the other side of a cold, rugged mountain range. Thus very different faunas may exist on opposite sides of such barriers, though some species, especially those that fly, will be the same on both sides.

Summary. *The same barriers — water, desert, and mountain — affect both animals and plants; they are most easily overcome by flying animals.*

244. Australian fauna. The fauna and flora of Australia are both peculiar. Among the birds are the emu and cassowary, two running birds; also parrots, lyre birds, and other peculiar kinds. The mammals include several species of *marsupials*, the very peculiar *monotremes*, and a few other species. The monotremes, the lowest order of mammals, are represented by the remarkable duck-billed platypus (Fig. 490), which is one of the mammals, but lays eggs. The marsupials, another low order of mammals, to which the opossum belongs, include the kangaroo. These animals carry their young in a pouch, and, instead of walking, hop about by means of their long hind legs and stout tail. Although higher forms of mammals inhabit southern Asia and the East Indies, they have not found their way to Australia.

The explanation of this peculiar life is as follows. Fossils in the rocks prove that, far back in time, momotremes and marsupials were widespread. Australia was then so connected with other continents that the ancestral forms of these animals were able to migrate there. Fiercer animals developed in the other continents and killed off the monotremes and most of the marsupials; and their place has been taken by new types that were successful in resisting the attacks of the beasts of prey. But the new devouring beasts were prevented from reaching Australia because sinking of the land cut off its connection with other continents. Therefore, animals that belong to the geological yesterday are to-day living in Australia, though unfit to survive in other lands.

Summary. *The Australian fauna is peculiar, because the ocean barrier has prevented stronger species, developed on other continents, from entering and destroying the defenseless animals that came long ago, before these stronger species had developed, and when Australia was united with other lands.*

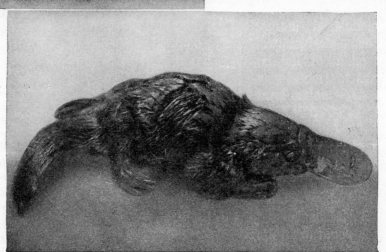

Fig. 490. — The primitive animals of Australia, the brush-tailed wallaby (top left), the koala (top right), and the platypus (bottom). These and many others of the Australian animals have traits that were general in the animal world of earlier geological times but are not found elsewhere now.

Photos by Sanborn, N. Y. Zoological Society

Fig. 491. — Three typical South American animals, the armadillo (top), the ant-eater (middle), and the llama (bottom). These forms are also primitive, but not to the same degree that many Australian animals are.

245. South American fauna. South American animals are also peculiar, though less so than those of Australia (Fig. 491). The huge condor, second largest of flying birds, lives there; also the rhea, a running bird, by some called the American ostrich; the llama and its allies; various species of monkey; the sloth; the anteater; the armadillo; the tapir; and other strange forms. The fact that these peculiar animals exist in South America, while only some of them extend up into southern North America, leads to the conviction that South America has also been cut off from other lands, though not for so long a time, nor so continuously, as Australia. According to this general idea the more primitive forms are always to be found in the areas most remote and isolated from the locality in which the type originated.

Summary. *The peculiar fauna of South America also indicates a former separation from other lands, but not so long or so continuous as in the case of Australia.*

246. Faunas of other continents. There is much closer resemblance between the life on other continents. In the north temperate zone there is such resemblance as to lead to the belief that there has been even better connection in the past than at present. For example, hairy elephants (mammoths and mastodons), now extinct, lived in Siberia, Europe, and North America; and, among living animals, there are close resemblances throughout the whole region. The faunas of Africa and southern Asia are also quite alike indicating close connection.

Summary. *There is close resemblance between the faunas of northern Asia, Europe, and America; also between Africa and southern Asia, indicating former land connection.*

247. Realms and regions of animal life. The distribution of animals as described has led to the division of the earth into several faunal *realms and regions* (Fig. 492), each differing in important respects from the others. The differences between these areas are due to two principal facts: (1) that barriers — mountain, desert, and ocean — have checked the spread of animals; and (2) that variation and adaptation have led to the development of animals of different kinds on opposite sides of a barrier. The boundaries of these areas are not sharply marked, nor are the areas absolutely unlike; for some species will find their way across even the most difficult barriers.

Summary. *Barriers, variations, and adaptation have caused such differences among animals that several realms and regions of animal life are recognized.*

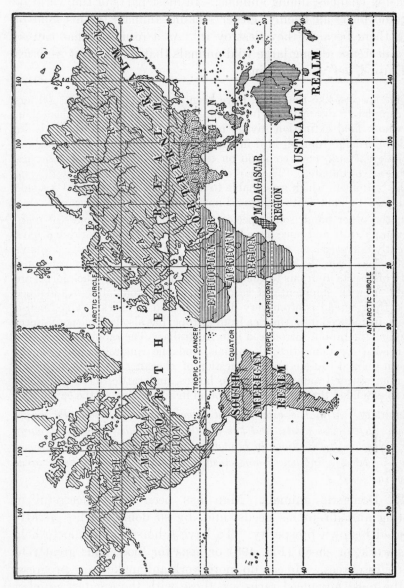

Fig. 492. — Map showing the three *realms* of animal life and the main subdivisions, or *regions* (see Figs. 490 and 491). Notice that the most distinctive and primitive forms of animal life come from the two more remote realms which seem to have been cut off at an early time from the development proceeding in the Northern Realm.

248. Influence of man. Man has been a very important agent in causing changes among animals. In most parts of the world he has come in as an enemy, either seeking animals for his food or killing them because they destroy it. As a result, he has caused such a decrease among large wild animals that, in parts of America and Europe, very few remain.

Some species, like the bison, have been almost exterminated. Others have completely disappeared; for example, the mammoth and mastodon, with whose final extinction savage man probably had something to do. The dodo, a large running bird in the islands of Mauritius and Bourbon and the great auk, once common on the northeastern coast of America, have been exterminated. The eggs of the auk were eaten in large numbers, and the bird itself, which was unable to fly, was easily captured. A single specimen of the auk or its egg would now bring a very high price.

On the other hand, some species thrive under the influence of man. For example, rats and mice have been carried all over the world and have so greatly increased as to become a pest. The worst result of man's activities has been the unintentional introduction into new regions of a variety of insects injurious to cultivated and other plants. Such forms are brought in with shipments of seeds and plants from abroad and once started their spread is often very difficult indeed to check. The English sparrow, introduced into America from Europe, has also become a nuisance; and so has the rabbit, introduced into Australia. The rabbit destroys the food needed for domesticated animals, and the Australian government has been obliged to take up the question of checking its further spread. Such domesticated animals as sheep, horses, and cattle, have had their range so extended that they are now found in all quarters of the earth.

Summary. *Man has exterminated some species, especially the larger and more defenseless kinds, and has greatly reduced the numbers of many others. He has unintentionally brought about the spread of many animal pests. Under his influence, domesticated animals have had their range greatly increased.*

249. Domestic animals. Man has been very successful in adapting animals to his needs; and, by so doing, he has greatly increased his own prosperity. To have a horse or buffalo to help in his work, or sheep (Fig. 493) or hens for food, adds greatly to a man's resources. He can do more work and make more progress; and the most advanced races are those with the greatest number and variety of domestic animals.

Some animals resist efforts at domestication; it seems scarcely possible, for example, to domesticate the lion. Yet it is remarkable how large a number of animals man uses. The reindeer of northern Europe is used as a draft animal and for food supply. Eskimo dogs (Fig. 494), which are little better than half-tamed wolves, are of great service in hunting and in drawing sledges over the ice. In the highlands of central Asia the yak is domesticated; the buffalo and elephant in southern Asia, and the camel in the arid belts of

Fig. 493. — Sheep in the Scottish Highlands. A thick coat of wool enables these animals to endure the cold of a northern winter.

Africa and Asia. Cats, dogs, donkeys (Fig. 495), horses, cattle, sheep, goats, and pigs are domesticated all over the world. Among domesticated birds are hens, turkeys, ducks, geese, and doves.

As in the case of plants, the origin of many of these is not known; they date back thousands of years, long before the first records of history. It is a striking fact that the New World has supplied only two domesticated animals, the llama (Fig. 491) of South America and the turkey.

Photo by Johnson

Fig. 494. — Eskimo dogs. Their heavy coat of hair enables them to withstand the rigors of the arctic cold. They are depended on for transportation over much of the North. This picture shows the country of the "little sticks" south of the tundra lands.

Fig. 495. — Donkeys used as beasts of burden in Jamaica, West Indies. As the dog is used as a draft animal in the Arctic of North America, so the donkey is used in wide areas of the Tropics.

Summary. *While some animals resist domestication, man has succeeded in adapting many mammals and birds to his use, either for food or as work animals. Of these, the New World has supplied only two, the llama and turkey.*

TOPICAL OUTLINE AND REVIEW QUESTIONS

TOPICAL OUTLINE. 236. **Influence of surroundings.** Air; water; heat; cold; cold-blooded animals; warm-blooded animals; cause of warmth; protection; dependence on plants; sunlight.

237. **Animal life, or fauna, of the Arctic.** Animals in and near the sea; sea birds; southward migration; land birds; mammals; reptiles; insects; mammals in the sea; protection from cold; white color.

238. **Temperate fauna.** Mode of life: open plains; forest; mountains; arid regions; caverns; underground; nocturnal animals; fur-bearing animals.

239. **Tropical fauna.** Plants; insects; birds; reptiles; mammals.

240. **Desert fauna.** Contrast with humid regions; fauna of southwestern United States; limit of food; source of water; the camel.

241. **Fresh-water faunas.** Kinds; illustrations; difference in surroundings; temperature; salt lakes.

242. **Spread of animals.** Reason for large number of young; unprotected young; protection of young; adaptation; reindeer; elephants; Partula; distribution of ocean animals; of air dwellers; of land animals.

243. **Barriers to the spread of animals.** Water; forest; desert; mountain. Animals that easily pass barriers.

244. **Australian fauna.** (*a*) The animals: birds; monotremes; marsupials. (*b*) Explanation: former distribution; development of fierce enemies; separation of Australia.

245. **South American fauna.** Peculiar animals; explanation.

246. **Faunas of other continents.** Resemblance in northern lands; in Africa and southern Asia; explanation.

247. **Realms and regions of animal life.** The divisions; names; cause; boundaries.

248. **Influence of man.** (*a*) Man as an enemy; cause for destruction; general result; bison; mammoth and mastodon; dodo; auk. (*b*) Influence in spreading animals: rats and mice; English sparrow; rabbit; insects; domestic animals.

249. **Domestic animals.** Importance; instances of domesticated mammals; birds; New World animals.

QUESTIONS. Section 236. What is the dependence of animals on air, water, and temperature? By what means is cold endured? What is the difference in the blood of animals? Why are animals dependent on plants for food? Why are they not dependent on sunlight?

237. What is the nature of arctic bird life? What is the condition of life on land? What warm-blooded animals live in the sea? How are arctic animals protected from the cold? What about their color?

238. Under what different conditions do temperate animals live?

239. Why are animals so abundant in the tropical zone? What is the condition of insect life there? Bird? Reptile? Mammal?

240. Contrast desert and tropical-forest faunas. What animals are found in the desert of southwestern United States? Why are there so few? How do they secure water? How is the camel adapted to desert life?

241. What kinds of animals live in fresh water? How do the faunas differ?

242. In what way is the spread of animals made certain? Give illustrations of adaptation. What kinds of animals are most widespread? Why? What about land animals?

243. What barriers are there to the spread of animals? What kinds of animals most easily overcome them?

244. What are the peculiarities of animal life in Australia? Explain this.

245. What does the South American fauna indicate?

246. What is indicated by the faunas of other continents?

247. What are the reasons for the different faunal areas? Name the realms. Name the regions of the northern realm (Fig. 492).

248. Why is man an enemy of many animals? Give illustrations of his influence in extermination. In increasing the range of animals.

249. Of what advantage are domestic animals? Give instances of domestic animals in various parts of the world. What domestic animals has the New World supplied?

SUGGESTIONS. No special suggestions are made for this chapter, largely because of the difficulty of offering general suggestions adapted to widely separated schools. Yet a teacher especially interested in this phase of the subject will find opportunty for illustrative work, — with books, pictures, specimens, and museums, if in a city; in the field, if in the country.

Reference Books. GADOW, *The Wanderings of Animals*, Cambridge University Press, Cambridge, England, 1913; JORDAN and KELLOGG, *Animal Life*, D. Appleton & Company, New York, 1902; NEWBIGIN, *Animal Geography*, Oxford University Press, Oxford, England, 1913; BORRADAILE, *The Animal and its Environment*, Henry Frowde, London, England, 1923; WALLACE, *Island Life*, The Macmillan Company, New York, 1892; LYDEKKER, *Geographical History of Mammals*, The Macmillan Company, New York, 1896.

CHAPTER XIX

MAN AND NATURE

DEVELOPMENT OF MANKIND

250. Early man. What sort of life man lived before any people were sufficiently enlightened to leave written accounts of their activities, we can judge only by the records of accomplishments as shown in mounds, monuments, drawings, utensils, weapons, and other relics, and by comparison with the life of uncivilized tribes of the present day. Written records tell us much about our ancestry during the last two or three thousand years. For example, when the Roman Empire was developing, the Germans and British were rude barbarians; and still earlier, the inhabitants of the Italian Peninsula had a similarly primitive culture. To-day, both in the Old and the New World, there are tribes of men that have not yet risen above savagery. But through the centuries various groups of mankind have in turn and, on the whole, steadily and progressively acquired useful knowledge from experience. As a result of effort, modern civilization enjoys many advantages, comforts, and conveniences over savage and semi-civilized people.

Summary. *Through labor and thought man has made wonderful progress in civilization since the dawn of history.*

251. Dependence of man on nature. Man differs from the other animals in his power to take thought and to work intelligently and purposefully for the accomplishment of a task. But even the most civilized men are dependent on nature, as animals and plants are. Man must have air to breathe, water to drink, and food to eat. Furthermore, his sight depends on sunlight, and his speech and hearing on sound waves, transmitted through the air. If his home is in a cool climate, he must have clothing and shelter; and he obtains materials for these from nature.

In these respects both savages and civilized men are in the same degree dependent on nature; but to live as civilized men do, other resources must

Fig. 496. — Planting rice in Japan. In places of dense population the land must be cultivated intensively and arduously, as here, in order that even a meager livelihood may be got by all. The greater part of the Japanese population lives on the narrow coastal plain belts of the islands. A portion of one such belt is shown here.

also be utilized. The materials and energies of all the world are drawn upon by civilized man, and his powers have so developed that he has learned to adapt to his needs many of the products and forces of nature. Each year his ability to do this increases. In this respect man has risen immeasurably above all other forms of life.

Summary. *All men depend on nature for air, water, and food; and civilized man secures many other things. Each year he is learning better how to make use of nature.*

252. Food supply. Man began his conquest of nature because of the need of food. Steam and gas engines, great manufacturing plants, the airplane, and the radio are the climax of a series of inventions which began when, instead of depending solely on teeth and claws to secure food, as animals do, man made simple implements to aid his hands.

By using stone implements, such as spear and arrow points, hammers, and hatchets; by fashioning wood for handles and for bows; and by making simple hooks for fishing, early man greatly increased his ability to obtain

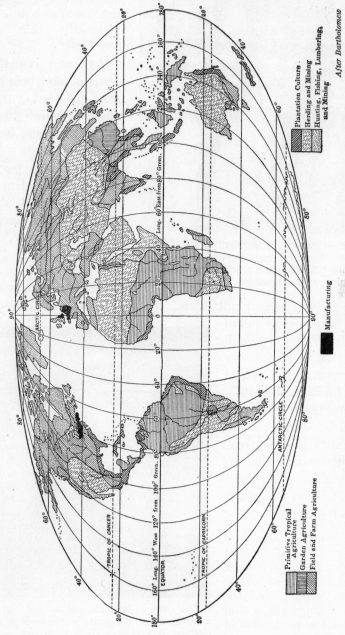

Fig. 497. — The chief dependence of peoples in different parts of the world for earning a livelihood. The map shows the most important occupation in each region. State why Japanese and Chinese cultivation is designated "garden" agriculture. (See Fig. 496.)

Fig. 498. — Natives of southern India showing how little clothing is necessary in such a hot climate. How can one tell that the sun was nearly overhead when this picture was taken?

animal food. Savage races make use of such primitive implements (Fig. 515) even to-day.

As an important source of food, primitive man collected various plant materials, especially the seeds, fruits, bulbs, and roots. The sweet potato, potato, yam, cassava, plantain, banana, coconut, date, and the grains, including wheat, barley, rye, corn, rice (Fig. 496), and millet, were used at a very early date and continue to be leading plant foods. To gather these, scattered as they are in nature, required much effort for a small return, and man accordingly found it profitable to plant and care for them (Fig. 497). Simple spades and hoes, at first made of stone or wood, aided greatly in this work. By domesticating plants (p. 550) and animals (p. 572) a great addition was made to man's resources.

To-day nearly all the world depends on the farmer and herder for food. Wherever conditions favor, the land is cleared for farming, and the majority of mankind is still engaged in the production of food. The plow, the reaper, and the threshing machine

Fig. 499. — Japanese coolie, or laborer, carrying water. In parts of the tropical lands clothing is necessary as a protection against moisture, if not against heat. This coolie is wearing a raincoat made of grass.

have taken the place of the primitive spade and hoe. More recently the gasoline tractor and the motor truck are displacing the horse as a work animal. Thousands of railway cars and vessels are constantly engaged in moving products of the farms to places where men are engaged in other pursuits, or where the population is too dense to permit the production of all the food needed. Agriculture, although modernized, continues to be the most important of industries.

Summary. *The devising of simple implements for securing plant and animal food is the basis of modern invention. All the world depends on the*

Photo by Libbey

Fig. 500. — Eskimo at Cape York, Greenland, wearing tight-fitting fur garments — somewhat the worse for a winter's wear. The stone and turf igloo, half underground, is their winter home.

farmer and herder for food, and agriculture continues to be the fundamental and most important of industries.

253. Clothing. In a hot climate man has little need of clothing (Fig. 498); but in a cool or cold climate some protection is necessary (Fig. 504). Without clothing man could not occupy the cold temperate zone. Various natural products, including skins, wool, and plant fibers, have been used to protect the body. Early Germans and Britons were clothed in skins, as the Eskimo are to-day (Fig. 500).

In cold climates one of the objects of hunting has always been to secure materials for clothing; and one of the objects of herding is the production of wool and leather; and of farming, the production of fibers for cloth. The principal vegetable fibers used for making cloth, rope, etc., are cotton, flax, hemp, and jute. Wool, silk, furs, and leather are animal products, at present widely used by civilized people for clothing. Since the most civilized races live in the cool temperate zones, the production and manufacture of clothing are among the most important of industries.

Summary. *Clothing is needed by all dwellers in cool climates, and for it various animal and plant products are used.*

254. Shelter. Man has adopted many devices for securing shelter from the elements. The summer home of the Eskimo

Fig. 501. — Tents made of blankets used for shelter by nomads of the Sahara. The desert lands are often quite cold at night, and the woolen blankets serve to keep in the heat of the day.

is a skin topek; his winter home a turf and stone hut (Fig. 500), or an igloo of snow or ice. Indian wigwams were made of skins. The nomad of the deserts uses skins and blankets (Fig. 501) made of the wool of his domestic animals. Sod houses are still built in many regions. Grass huts and branches woven into a simple shelter (Fig. 502) are common in the tropical zone; and some savages live there with hardly any shelter. In parts of Europe

Fig. 502. — Huts of grass thatch, the homes of negroes in Africa.

Fig. 503. — Swiss house near the timber line in the Alps. The abundance of wood leads to the building of wooden houses; the strong winds make it necessary to weight down the roofs with large stones. Rough-hewn boards are used in these houses. In parts of Europe where wood is scarce, as in Ireland (see Fig. 505), wooden houses are very rare.

and southwestern America, caves and overhanging ledges furnished shelter to primitive man.

Long before the historical period, clay and wood were used, at first very crudely, as materials for building permanent homes. The use of wood began in forest regions (Fig. 503), at first doubtless by the use of boughs, branches, and logs; then of rough-hewn boards.

Stone houses were probably first made by merely piling stones together (Fig. 504), as is done to-day by the Cape York Eskimo.

Fig. 504. — Ruins of an Inca palace, Bolivia. The stones were laid without cement or mortar but were very closely fitted although these people of ancient American civilization had no iron tools to work with. The Indian in the foreground is a descendant of the Inca tribes.

Then mud was used to fill the cracks, and later, mortar was employed (Fig. 505). The first use of clay was in making sun-dried bricks, or adobe, still employed in arid countries, as in Egypt, Spain, and Mexico. Adobe is too easily affected by dampness for use in moist climates; but the discovery of how to bake bricks by fire has made the use of clay possible there.

Summary. *Many primitive means have been employed for securing shelter; for example, skins, turf, snow, blankets, grass, branches, and caves. The use of wood, stone, and clay doubtless started in a very primitive way: wood from the use of boughs and logs; stone from mere piles; and clay in the form of sun-dried brick.*

255. Selection of homes. Early man probably had no fixed home, but wandered about in search of food, as many primitive tribes do to-day. When for any reason a home became desirable, two considerations led to the selection of a location: (1) nearness

Fig. 505. — A primitive stone hut with a turf and thatch roof in Ireland. The family has just been evicted, expelled, from this rude home for non-payment of the rent, and they are about to move with their few belongings.

of food supply; (2) protection from enemies. Homes are still located by large numbers of people with the first idea in mind: for example, fishermen (Fig. 342), and hunters; but, fortunately, civilized men are no longer obliged to take account of the second.

There are many illustrations of the location of houses on sites that give protection from enemies. Some savages build houses in trees (Fig. 506), and some on piles in water, as the ancient lake dwellers of Switzerland did. The Pueblo Indians lived on top of steep-sided buttes and mesas (Fig. 507); others lived in caves and under overhanging ledges on cliff sides. Castles in Europe were often built on hills, and other places difficult of access (Fig. 508); and, for further protection, strong walls were built around them.

Summary. *Primitive man in the past chose, as do savage and barbarian tribes to-day, home sites near the food supply where some degree of protection from enemies was available. For the sake of protection, homes have been located in trees, in the water, on cliff sides, and on hills.*

Fig. 506. — Native grass and palm-thatch houses in the trees, New Guinea. These huts give protection from the rain and from the dampness of the ground. They also afford a refuge from attack by hostile tribes and harmful animals. Note further that the houses are in trees growing on a hilltop.

256. Location and growth of cities. When and where men depend on collecting natural products, on hunting and fishing for subsistence, it is easier to secure sufficient food if few rather than many live in one place. But as dependence is more and more placed on agriculture and as commerce develops, man tends to gather into communities, villages, towns, cities. Even savages establish semi-permanent villages for purposes of defense. From their villages, these primitive people go out to hunt or fish and yet, being near together, are ready to resist attack. They are also ready for an expedition to attack a neighbor for revenge or profit.

Many European towns grew up because of the need of defense. One man, more capable than the rest, built a strong stone castle, perhaps on a hill, and protected the area about it by a wall (Fig. 508). Farmers, soldiers, and others, under the protection of the castle owner, worked for him, lived in houses within the walls, and helped defend the castle when it was attacked. In Europe, hundreds of places like this are still to be seen, but they are now useless for purposes of defense. However, around some that have otherwise favorable situations, large cities have developed. But modern cities are primarily commercial and manufacturing centers. Of defense sites that have survived to become great cities, the capitals of Europe: London, Paris. Berlin, Vienna, and Rome, are the best examples.

The flourishing cities of the modern world, whether great or small, owe their prosperity, in large part, to geographic conditions favoring commerce and manufacturing. Some, like Milan in Italy, and Vienna in Austria, are situated where routes of overland travel converge or cross. They had their beginning long before the days of railways; but the railway, making them centers of modern traffic, has greatly increased their prosperity. Many cities, like Cincinnati, St. Louis, Vienna, and Paris, are on rivers; and others, like Buffalo and Chicago, are on large lakes. Still others, like Genoa, Liverpool, San Francisco, and New York, are seaports. Such seaports as London, New York, Philadelphia, Baltimore, and

Photo by Raffius

Fig. 507. — An Indian pueblo in Arizona, on the top of a mesa, and overlooking the surrounding country. The steep face makes access difficult.

New Orleans, which are at the mouths of rivers that open pathways into the interior, have especially favorable situations. With one exception (Cairo in Africa) the greatest city of every continent is a seaport.

Many cities, like Lowell, Lawrence, Spokane, Niagara Falls, and Rochester, owe their growth to water power, which has encouraged manufacturing. Others, like Scranton, Wilkes-Barre, Pittsburgh, Butte, and Denver, owe their development mainly to near by mines.

Summary. *The tendency of people to congregate in centers had its origin in the need of defense. Some large European towns grew around fortified castles; but the largest have prospered either because they are capitals of great nations or are manufacturing and commercial centers. Flourishing modern cities are mainly located on one of the following sites: on the sea at harbor sites; at the crossing of overland trade routes; on rivers, especially at their mouths; on lake shores; near water power; near mines.*

Fig. 508. — An old castle on the Rhine built in a position fairly safe from attack. The modern town is built along the river side.

257. Development of commerce. Even primitive men desire articles which they cannot produce. For example, Eskimo tribes will gladly exchange skins for pieces of wood; and central African negroes will trade ivory for simple trinkets. From such simple exchanges our vast world commerce has developed.

Objects of trade were early carried overland, at first on foot, later by the aid of animals, even across deserts and mountains. The first commerce by sea was carried on in small, open boats, propelled by oars; later, sails were used. Even before Bible times, and before Europeans became civilized, caravans crossed the deserts of Asia Minor, bringing treasures from Asia. The enclosed Mediterranean offered opportunity for the extension of this com-

Fig. 509. — The Suez Canal. The neck of land which separates the Mediterranean and Red Seas forced those who sought a water route to India, four or five centuries ago, to undertake the explorations which led to such important discoveries. The demands of modern commerce for a shorter water route between Europe and Asia led to the construction of the Suez Canal.

merce by sea and for the introduction of Egyptian and Asiatic civilization along its shores.

The ancient Phoenicians and Greeks carried their commerce to all parts of the Mediterranean, establishing colonies which later developed into powerful independent cities. As the boats were made larger, the commerce which developed among Mediterranean nations was gradually extended into the open ocean, and even up the European coast to the British Isles. The Mediterranean has been called the cradle of early navigation. It shares this dis-tinction with the calm sea behind the islands of the Norwegian coast. From thence the Vikings sailed forth on their bold voyages.

When the Mohammedans interfered with trade between Europe and Asia, a sea route to India was sought (Fig. 509). The Portu-guese found one around Africa; and Columbus, in searching for one toward the west, discovered America. For the development of these new lands, and the valuable commerce with them, ships were made still larger and stronger. Then came the use of steam; and now huge steel ships carry the increasing commerce of the world over all oceans. The next step in this development will be the use of great airships and this has already begun.

Commerce has aided greatly in the spread of civilization, for it has brought people into closer communication and sympathy with one another, and has made it possible for people in one section to learn from those in another. As a means of communication, writing has developed, and, like other features of our civilization, this has been evolved from simple be-ginnings. For example, picture writing, or recording events by symbols carved on wood or stone, has been used by many primitive peoples. From this the alphabet developed, then printing, which has proved so important an aid in spreading knowledge. The telegraph, ocean cable, and telephone, made possible by the use of electricity, have now brought all parts of the civilized world in close touch with one another. Wireless telegraphy and telephony and the transmission of pictures by radio mark the latest great advances in communication. Easy and swift communi-cation is part of the progress of the human race toward higher and higher civilization, in which commerce has had so great an influence.

Summary. *Commerce has developed from simple exchange carried on among primitive people, at first overland, either on foot or by the aid of animals, and on sea by the use of boats propelled by oars. Early commerce between Asia and Europe, overland across Asia Minor, and thence in the enclosed waters of the Mediterranean, made the Mediterranean a cradle of navigation. The discovery of a water route to Asia and to the New World, resulting from the closing of routes to Asia by the Mohammedans, has led to the development of larger ships and to the great advances of modern commerce. The extension of civilization, the development of writing and printing, and communication by electricity are among the important outcomes of the development of commerce.*

258. Influence of man on nature. In his progress, man has in many ways profoundly influenced his surroundings. He has modified, extended, and destroyed plants (pp. 550, 551) and animals (pp. 572, 573). By removing the forest he has made it possible for water to run off more rapidly (p. 72), washing soil into the streams and causing great variations in river volume. As a result some areas, as parts of Italy, France, and of the State of Mississippi, have had their soil stripped off, leaving either bare rock or a surface too badly gullied for farming (p. 73).

On densely settled flood plains and deltas, the river courses have been controlled and annual floods prevented. Stream courses have been straightened and deepened for navigation, and canals dug around rapids, and from ocean to ocean. For use in irrigation, river water has been led over arid lands; and lakes and ponds have been formed to secure steady water supply for irrigation and for other purposes. Each of these acts of man interferes with natural conditions.

Along the seacoast, walls are built to check the work of the waves. To better fit them for shipping, harbors and channels are dredged; jetties and

Fig. 510. — A primitive but ambitious type of bridge. It spans the Jhelum River in the Vale of Kashmir, India.

sea walls are built to prevent currents from closing harbor mouths with sand bars; and, by building breakwaters, harbors are actually made by artificial means.

Much change is made on the dry land also. The ground is pierced with wells for water, oil, and gas, and these substances are led to the surface. In the removal of coal, iron, and other mineral products, the rocks are honeycombed with shafts and tunnels; and in quarrying, and in removing clay and sand, hills are lowered and deep pits made. Tunnels are dug through mountains (Fig. 183) and deep cuts made in hillsides, while great embankments are built of the rock removed. Earth and rock are removed in making roads and in digging cellars; and, over great areas, the soil, by being loosened and overturned in plowing, is exposed to the weather.

Thus over a very considerable portion of the land areas of the world the aspect of the earth, those features which principally compose the scene, are the result of human effort.   Fields and fences, farm homes and cities, roads, railroads, bridges (Figs. 510, 511), and canals, are all there because of the activities of the human being.   Civilized man is everywhere at work modifying nature to serve his needs; and he is utilizing his surroundings, and the forces of nature, to help in his onward march toward higher civilization.   In this respect man stands apart from all other forms of life.

Summary.   *In a multitude of ways man is influencing nature: destroying, modifying, or extending the range of animals and plants; removing the forest, thus allowing the rain to run off rapidly and carry away the soil; changing or controlling streams; improving or making waterways; forming lakes; interfering with the natural action of oceanic agencies; boring into the earth and re-*

Fig. 511. — Bridge across the Firth of Forth, near Edinburgh, Scotland.   This bridge, like many others, was built to accommodate the increasing modern commerce.

moving materials; and exposing soil and rock to the weather.   Over wide areas the face of nature is given its expression chiefly by the works of man.

DISTRIBUTION OF MANKIND

259. The spread of man.   During the development of man, as outlined above, he has migrated to almost all lands.   Starting apparently either from a center in central western Asia or one in western Europe he spread slowly, guided by the same laws as animals, and influenced by the same barriers.   But man's superior intelligence has permitted him to spread farther than any species of animal, and to adapt himself to all climates.   Even as a savage he reached every continent and most oceanic islands.   The use of boats aided him in crossing the ocean barrier; and, by means of clothing and shelter, he has equipped himself to live in cold climates.

The spread of man has been in part a slow, steady advance outward in all directions, as in the case of animals, and in part successive rapid migrations of large numbers. It was such rapid spread that led to the building of the great Chinese wall (Fig. 512) as a barrier to the hordes that moved outward from central Asia.

© *E. M. Newman*

Fig. 512. — A part of the great Chinese wall, built to prevent invasion by hordes of Mongolians, spreading outward from central Asia.

Similar hordes from Asia overran Europe, and still others crossed the Alps and advanced to Rome. The spread of man has often been a part of warfare and conquest. This is illustrated by the Roman Empire which, by conquest, caused the diffusion of Romans and Roman civilization, not only along the Mediterranean shores, but throughout western Europe, even as far as the British Isles.

The discovery of new lands, especially in the New World, has had a great influence on the spread of man. By the time of Columbus there had been such advance in knowledge of sailing, including the invention of the compass, that even the ocean could be crossed at will. The much higher civilization of Europeans enabled them to displace the savage occupants, not only of America, but of Australia and the more attractive parts of Africa.

Summary. *The spread of primitive man was influenced by the same laws and barriers that affect animals; but man's superior intelligence, and especially the use of boats, clothing, and shelter, have made it possible for him to spread much farther. Man's spread has been in part slow migration, in part rapid movement in large numbers, often as a part of warfare and conquest. Where, as in the New World, lands previously occupied by primitive tribes are invaded by a more advanced people, the natives are rapidly displaced.*

260. Origin of races. Although mankind now exhibits great diversity in physical and mental characteristics it is probable that all peoples came from the same stock in western Europe or Asia. The first dispersals of primitive men from the source area to the remoter parts of the earth must have taken an exceedingly long time. The spread, further, appears to have been in all directions away from the common center of origin. Thousands of generations must have been born while the first dispersal was taking place. Following that came even longer periods of geographical isolation of any one group (from groups that migrated in other directions) when a large region like Africa or Australia was once completely peopled. These vast lapses of time with generation following generation in unlike environments made possible great modifications and diversity in mankind.

Why or how these modifications were brought about is as yet an unsolved question. There are several possible explanations each of which may be in part true. As the original type of man moved into a region with different climatic or other conditions than those of the source area of the common stock, these new conditions may have directly affected his being and caused it to change. That this is not impossible is indicated by the fact that the physical characteristics of the children of South European immigrants to America have been found to differ from those of their parents. The further fact that the change is in all cases in the same direction indicates that some condition of the new home brings it about.

Another possibility is that the changes from the original type of man were not influenced by the surroundings but developed independently within man himself. Any new, helpful trait, thus originated, would

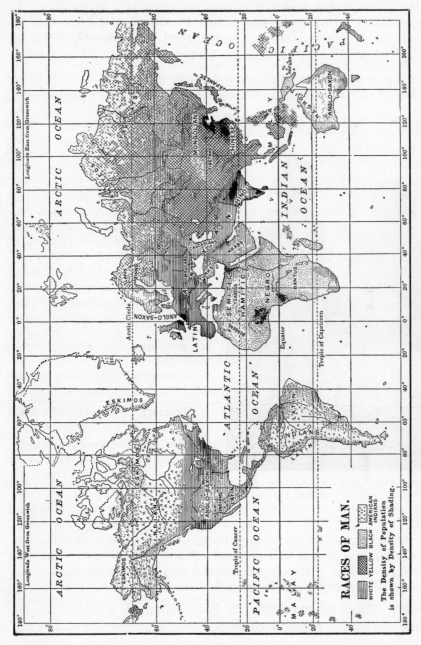

Fig. 513. — Sketch map, showing the general distribution of the races of man.

make the man who possessed it more successful in a given place. In consequence, such persons would tend to survive and leave children inheriting that trait. Persons who developed injurious traits would on the contrary tend to die out.

The difficulty with these two ideas is that, considering the long time that has been available for such changes to make themselves effective, native peoples all over the world ought to have developed characteristics quite completely suited to the places in which they live. Also, peoples living in the same kind of places ought to have like characteristics. As a general rule such is indeed the case, but there are exceptions. The exceptions require that consideration be given to two further possibilities. One is that the natives of a given region may be there because of a geologically recent migration and have displaced an earlier, better adapted, but culturally less advanced group. The other is that the native group came into the region after having so far developed one set of special traits that it was impossible for their beings to develop an opposite set.

Fig. 514. — Negroes from the Sudan, Africa. Compare with Fig. 515 and note how greatly racial characteristics may vary aside from skin color.

Summary. *All mankind is probably descended from a single original stock but, owing to slow dispersal over all the earth and long isolation in unlike environments, has developed into numerous varieties, physically and mentally different. These variations may in part have been caused by the environment, in part through changes arising in man himself, which, in either case, if helpful were preserved. Where native man is not the type suited for the kind of place he occupies, this may be due to too recent arrival there, or to too firmly fixed characteristics developed elsewhere.*

261. Races of mankind. A large group of mankind having quite distinctive physical characteristics in common and differing greatly from other large groups, similarly distinguishable, is called a *race.* It is customary to recognize four, and sometimes five, races on the basis chiefly of differences in color of the skin. Thus we have (1) the black, or negro (*Ethiopian*) race; (2) the yellow (*Mongolian*) race; (3) the red, or Indian (*American*) race; and (4) the white (*Caucasian*) race. A fifth division, the brown (*Malay*) race is often recognized. Other students include the red race with the brown race and so have only four divisions.

Fig. 515. — Zulu warrior, a negro from the south of Africa. Compare with Fig. 514.

Fig. 516. — Portrait of a Bedouin sheik. On the basis of skin color he, as well as the Cossack of Fig. 517, belongs to the Caucasian or "white" race.

Variation in skin color in all races is due simply to the relative abundance or paucity of brownish granules in the deeper parts of the outer layer of the skin. Darker coloring gives protection against the actinic rays of the sun, which are most effective near the equator, and white coloring serves best to preserve the heat of the body from escape to the air. We have in these facts a general reason why tropical peoples should be darker in color than those of the higher latitudes. But this effect did not result in the New World, nor in the southern hemisphere. Neither do dark-skinned peoples have all their other characteristics alike.

Because there has been a mixture of blood wherever they have come in contact, the boundaries between races are not distinct (Fig. 513). Moreover, the members of one race have often migrated into the territory of another. Thus the Finns and Hungarians, though surrounded by Caucasians, are Mongolian in origin.

The red men after migrating there apparently developed distinctive characteristics on the American continents. As a new type the American Indian did not, however, extend his occupation to further regions. But other races have spread widely. In modern times the Mongolians have spread very little, and the negroes of Africa have spread mainly through the influence of white men, who carried them to other lands as slaves, and especially to the New World. The white race has migrated extensively, taking possession of the territories of weaker and less well-fitted peoples. This is illustrated in North America, where the Indians have been ousted by the aggressive, civilized Caucasians.

Fig. 517. — Portrait of a Cossack chief. One type of white man. See Fig. 516.

It should be understood that skin color does not of itself afford a complete basis for a scientific classification of races, although it is a convenient means of indicating general differences between varieties of mankind. Other factors that need to be taken into account are form of the head, color and nature of the hair, stature, form of the nose, and geographical location (Figs. 514, 515). It will be evident that no simple division of men into races is possible when so many factors need to be correlated. Such correlation is the subject matter of the study of ethnology (Figs. 516, 517).

Summary. *Mankind may be divided, for convenience, into four main races: (1) the black, or Ethiopian; (2) the yellow, or Mongolian; (3) the red, or American; and (4) the white, or Caucasian, on the basis of skin color. Another classification includes the American Indians and the Malays in a single brown race. Because of intermixture and migration, the boundaries between these races are by no means distinct. A scientific classification of* *races is not readily made. The white race has rapidly extended its range and influence, has ousted the Indian from North America, and has taken possession of much of the rest of the earth.*

INFLUENCE OF SURROUNDINGS

262. Man in the Arctic. Agriculture is impossible in the Arctic, and there is too little plant food to support human life (Fig. 116). Under such difficult conditions, the inhabitants of the North must look to animals for food; and, as these are most abundant in the sea, the shores of the Arctic are inhabited by a sparse population. On the tundras of Europe and Asia the reindeer is domesticated, making it possible for more people to live there than otherwise could. The caribou is not used by the Eskimo; but Siberian reindeer have recently been introduced into Alaska.

Life in the Arctic is well illustrated by the Eskimo (Figs. 465, 500) who live along the coast, depending for food chiefly on the hair seal, birds, fish, walrus, and polar bear. The extent to which these interesting people depend on animals is shown by the following: they obtain from them most of their food; skins for their clothing and summer tents, or topeks, bone for their spears; and bone framework and skins for their boats, or kayaks. Wood, occasionally drifted to their shores, is one of their most highly prized possessions.

To live amid such surroundings requires great hardiness and constant effort; and death by starvation is not uncommon. The Eskimo has to work hard in order to obtain the barest necessities, and there are no luxuries. Such surroundings offer little opportunity for cultural advance.

Summary. *The Arctic is sparsely populated, mainly along the coast where there is most animal food; but in the Old World the reindeer is domesticated, increasing man's chance of living. The Eskimo depends on animals for food and materials for shelter, clothing, and boats. Life in the Arctic is so hard that there is little chance for advance; all the energies are needed for obtaining the barest necessities.*

263. Man in the tropical zone. Conditions in the tropical zone are opposite to those in the Arctic. There man, except in the rain-forest regions, is surrounded by an abundance of food, both plant and animal, and he requires little clothing (Fig. 498) or shelter (Figs. 502, 506). All his needs are met with slight effort. Under such conditions man resembles animals in being content with bare necessities. Being so easily satisfied, he cannot advance far in civilization.

It is for these reasons that some of the least civilized peoples of the world to-day are found in hot climates. The Indians of Central and South America, the negroes of central Africa, the Australian natives, and the Negritos of the Philippines are examples. By some of these people, as among animals, the eating of one another, or cannibalism, is still prac- ti ed. They live in the most primitive way, — lazy, unintelligent, superstitious, human animals. Yet they talk, they think a little, and they know the use of simple implements. When brought under the influence of civilization they show themselves capable of some degree of advancement, indicating that it is only surrounding conditions that have kept them so low.

Summary. *In the tropical zone the ease of obtaining food, and the small amount of clothing and shelter necessary, call for little work. It is for these reasons chiefly that the least civilized peoples are found in the tropical zone.*

264. Man in the temperate zone. This zone has been the scene of the development of our modern commercial and industrial civilization, mainly for the following reasons: (1) While there is an abundance of food in summer, there is little in winter. It has, therefore, been necessary to secure food in summer and store it for winter use. This requires energy, intelligence, and foresight; yet the amount of work necessary is not great enough to discourage or to prevent advance. (2) Both clothing and shelter are needed, and to provide these also requires intelligence, ingenuity, and energy. (3) The lands of the temperate zone are irregular, and the climate varied. This has led to the growth of different crops in different sections; and the people of one section, desiring the products of another, have opened communication with them. From this has arisen commerce, leading people of one region to learn from those of another.

Summary. *The need of providing food, clothing, and shelter for winter has caused people of the temperate zone to advance; and the varied products of different sections have given rise to commerce.*

265. Man in the desert. Living on a desert resembles life in the Arctic in the fact that there is so little food that men often die of starvation. But the nomads of the desert (p. 157) have domestic animals, — cattle, horses, and camels especially, — which help them greatly. Their mode of life makes these wanderers intelligent and brave, otherwise they could not live amid such surroundings; but they do not hesitate to seize from others the goods they need.

Desert conditions are so unfavorable that people more civilized have not entered to crowd the nomads out; and the desert barrier prevents the inhabitants from learning from others. For this reason, customs of the time of Christ are to-day preserved among the inhabitants of the Old World deserts.

On oases conditions are very different, for there agriculture is possible. Large oases, such as the valleys of the Euphrates and Nile, have been cradles of ancient civilization. Civilization early developed in such situations because it was necessary to work in order to store up food for the season when crops will not grow; and the surrounding desert served to protect the stores of food from invaders.

Both in the Euphrates and Nile valleys there developed a wonderful ancient civilization, which spread along the shores of the Mediterranean. This ancient culture was based on the development of the practice of irrigation and the social organization its extensive employment made necessary. This ancient culture is at the foundation of our modern civilization. The oases were favorable to the beginning, and the Mediterranean to the spread of civilization (p. 589). But as modern civilization has an industrial and commercial basis while the ancient cultures rested wholly on agriculture, these early centers of civilization have not kept up and are now really backward regions. The temperate lands afforded and compelled the use of a wider variety of resources. Accordingly modern civilization is much more comprehensive and complicated than those of ancient Egypt and Mesopotamia were.

The most advanced of the American Indians were those that lived in situations similar to those of Egypt and Mesopotamia. The Pueblo Indians of New Mexico, the Mayas and Aztecs of Mexico, and the Incas of South America lived in positions where agriculture with practice of irrigation was possible, and where deserts or mountains afforded partial protection from invasion. When discovered, these red men were barbarians, far higher in culture than the other Indians, who were savages.

Summary. *Because of lack of food and water, desert conditions are unfavorable. The inhabitants are scattered and nomadic; they are greatly aided by their domestic animals. The desert barrier prevents desert peoples from learning from others, and hence they preserve many ancient customs. The oases, however, were cradles of ancient civilization, because (1) agriculture was possible; (2) it was necessary to provide food for the unfavorable seasons; and (3) the desert in some degree protected the inhabitants from invasion.*

266. Influence of mountains. There is no part of the world where, in so short a distance, there are found races as different as those on the north and south sides of the Himalayas. It seems that all dark-skinned peoples are now confined to localities south of this mountain axis or are descendants of groups that migrated from thence into other regions. The American Indians accordingly are thought to have their origin in the country south of the Himalayas. Perhaps early man in the first dispersal crossed this region before the mountains had been raised as high as they are now. But later these mountains served as great walls (p. 194), hindering the migration of man as well as of animals; and it was partly because of their protection that the people of India became so civilized in very ancient times. Much the same is true of the Alps, whose protection helped to make the powerful Roman Empire possible.

When a country is invaded, its inhabitants often retreat to mountains; for there is little about mountains to attract invaders, and forcible entrance is difficult. The passes and valleys are easily defended. For these reasons the Welsh and Scotch, who occupied the more mountainous parts of Great Britain, were far less affected by the inroads of invaders than the inhabitants of other sections of the island. Even now their ancient languages are spoken, and sermons are even preached in them. In the Pyrenees there is a small group of people, called the Basques, who still retain an ancient language no longer spoken by others. In the single, small, mountainous country of Switzerland four languages are now spoken, — German, French, Italian, and Raeto-Romanic dialect.

Among mountain people ancient customs, as well as languages, are preserved. For example, until very recently, homespun was still used in the mountains of eastern Kentucky; and peculiar, old-style costumes are worn by Swiss mountaineers and inhabitants of the Black Forest mountains of Germany. Such places, like deserts, are among the last to be reached by new customs.

Mountain people are brave and hardy, for their life is one of hardship, and there are many dangers. The open-air life, with plenty of space and freedom, develops a love of freedom. They desire to be left alone, and resist attempts at conquest.

Summary. *Mountains are barriers, protecting people from invasion; they are places of retreat before invaders; in them ancient languages and customs linger; in them brave, hardy, freedom-loving people develop.*

267. Influence of coast line. Closed seas and irregular coasts, having quiet water, encourage fishing and commerce. It is along such coasts, therefore, that navigation has developed. The Mediterranean and the irregular Grecian coast illustrate this; also the irregular Scandinavian coast, with its many narrow, quiet fiords (p. 364). Here developed the brave, hardy Norsemen, who ravaged the coast of western Europe, and even visited America, before the time of Columbus.

The British nation became "mistress of the seas" because it had a so favorable position and coast. No part of the British Isles is far from the sea; there are innumerable bays and harbors; and many of the inhabitants have engaged in fishing. The separation from the mainland has been of the highest importance, for it has prevented invasion by land and has made commerce by water necessary. Furthermore, these small islands are unable to supply food enough for the large manufacturing population that has developed there. To bring food and to carry away manufactured products call for ships; and to protect these and the coast from attack demands a navy.

Colonies were established as a source of food and raw products for manufacture; they also served as a market for manufactured articles, and commerce with them became great and mutually beneficial. As a result of these facts, and the presence of coal and iron for manufacturing, the British nation has become the greatest sea power in the world, and has come into possession of the largest amount of territory that any nation has ever controlled.

Summary. *Protected seas, like the Mediterranean, and irregular coasts, like those of Greece and Scandinavia, encourage the development of navigation. The British nation has become the greatest sea power, and the possessor of the largest amount of territory, of all nations. Because Great Britain is an island it has been necessary to import needed food, and raw products for manufactures by water, and such transportation is greatly facilitated by the irregular coast.*

268. The United States. The situation of the United States in the temperate zone, with several different climates, is favorable to advance. There are great natural resources of nearly every kind, and the wisdom and love of freedom of our ancestors led them to establish a government that has encouraged the full use of these resources. The coast line is favorable to navigation, and the Atlantic Ocean, which separates us from other highly civilized nations, is so narrow that communication and commerce with them are easily possible. Yet the Atlantic is wide enough to afford some protection from attack and invasion.

Early settlements were naturally first made along the coast, because this was the first place reached. Although the natives were finally pushed aside, for a while, aided by the mountain and forest barrier, they held back the westward advance of the pioneers.

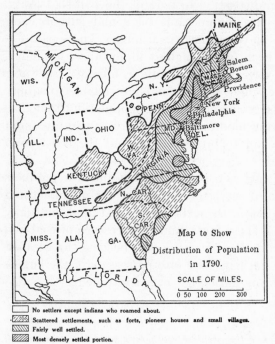

No settlers except indians who roamed about.
Scattered settlements, such as forts, pioneer houses and small villages.
Fairly well settled.
Most densely settled portion.

Fig. 518. — Distribution of white men in the United States, 1790.

Thus the settlers continued to live along the coast; and in 1790, (Fig. 518), when the West was a vast wilderness crossed only by Indian trails, it was possible to travel by stage from Portland, Maine, to Virginia, stopping each night in a good-sized village.

The Spanish and French settlements were far more scattered; the Spanish had two coasts along which to travel, and the French, the great interior waterways. Therefore, when the French and Indian war came, the English, being closer together and able to unite, had a great advantage. The success of the Revolution was also in large part due to the fact that the Colonists were concentrated along the coast.

The mountains were finally crossed along the water gaps, through Cumberland Gap to Tennessee and Kentucky, and along the Mohawk Gap to the Great Lakes. When the way to the interior was well opened, migration was rapid, because the soil was good, the climate favorable, the surface over wide areas clear of forest, and the land free or very cheap to all. Soon the central plains developed into a great agricultural, mining, and manufacturing section. The water gaps and water ways are still the leading routes to this interior.

West of the prairies was another great barrier, in the form of arid plains and plateaus, extensive deserts, and lofty mountain ranges. How great a barrier this was may be appreciated from the fact that when gold was discovered in California many gold-seekers preferred to go entirely around South America rather than to suffer the danger and hardship of a wagon trip across the continent. Now many lines of railways cross the western mountains; there are mining cities in the mountain valleys; and irrigated farms dot even the desert.

Our country has developed greatly, and in a short time has changed from a weak nation, struggling for existence, to perhaps the greatest of the world powers. This growth is not the result of a mere accident; nor is it due to a single cause. The invigorating climate encourages work, and in fact requires it; and intelligent effort secures great reward. In a new country there are wide opportunities for those who work hard, and this fact has helped make the American people energetic. Mineral, farm, and forest products may be obtained in great variety; and physiographic conditions, as well as the wise government under which we live, are favorable to their development. It is no wonder that the United States has advanced so rapidly; and the present century should see still more wonderful progress.

Summary. *The climate, resources, government, and coast line of the United States are favorable to progress. The early settlements along the coast, and the interference by Indians and by mountain barrier with westward advance, helped make the English colonies successful in war with France, and the Colonists in the Revolution against the mother country. The mountain barrier was first crossed along the water gaps, and the fertile, open prairie was then quickly developed; but the great western barrier of desert and mountain held back further progress until after the discovery of gold in California. Our rapid development has depended on the energetic people, wise government, and vast resources; and since the foundation is solid, our prosperity promises to continue.*

TOPICAL OUTLINE AND REVIEW QUESTIONS

Topical Outline. 250. **Early man.** Knowledge of early development. Progress through effort and experience.

251. **Dependence of man on nature.** How man differs from animals; de-

pendence of all mankind on nature; further dependence of civilized man; use of nature by civilized man.

252. **Food supply.** Basis of invention; primitive implements; present use; parts of plants eaten; instances; reasons for cultivation; importance of domestication; farming at present; dependence on farmer.

253. **Clothing.** Need of clothing; materials used; use of skins; vegetable products; animal products; reason for importance.

254. **Shelter.** (*a*) Primitive shelters: Eskimo; Indians; nomads; sod houses; tropical shelter; caves. (*b*) Building materials: first use; wood; stone; mortar; sun-dried brick; baked brick.

255. **Selection of homes.** Two objects in selecting sites; condition of civilized man; instances of sites selected for protection.

256. **Location and growth of cities.** (*a*) Primitive man: reasons for communities; savages; advantages of villages. (*b*) European towns: castles; gathering of people about them; present condition. (*c*) Modern cities: capitals; industries; cities at junction of trade routes; on rivers; lake ports; seaports; seaports at mouths of rivers; effect of water power; of mining.

257. **Development of commerce.** (*a*) Exchange: desires of primitive people; methods of gratifying them; early commerce. (*b*) Greeks: favorable location; colonies; extension beyond Mediterranean. (*c*) Discovery of new lands: reason for exploration; results. (*d*) Effects of commerce: exchange; spread of civilization; early writing; alphabet; electricity.

258. **Influence of man on nature.** Life; forest removal, — effect on rivers, on soil; changes in stream courses; irrigation; lakes; work along seacoast; borings; mines; quarrying; tunnels; roads; plowing; effect of activities of man; use of surroundings.

259. **The spread of man.** Resemblance to animals; superior intelligence; use of boats; of clothing and shelter; slow spread; rapid spread; conquest; discovery of new lands; aid of commerce.

260. **Origin of races.** Original home of man; dispersal; isolation; modifications. Reasons for diversity. Reasons for exceptions to rule of adaptation.

261. **Races of mankind.** Nature of races; the races; significance of skin color; boundaries; spread of the red race; the black race; the yellow race; the white race. Difficulty of classification.

262. **Man in the Arctic.** Plant food; animal food in sea; reindeer; Eskimo, — food, dependence on animals, wood, effect of surroundings.

263. **Man in the tropical zone.** Food; ease of meeting needs; effect of climate on civilization; instances of uncivilized people; their condition; possibility of advance.

264. **Man in the temperate zone.** Reasons for civilization: abundant food; need of storing food for winter; need of clothing and shelter; varied climate and land form.

265. **Man in the desert.** (*a*) The desert itself: comparison with Arctic; domestic animals; nomadic characteristics; effect of desert barrier. (*b*) On oases: agriculture; cradles of civilization; reasons for development of civilization. (*c*) Euphrates and Nile: early civilization; its spread; present condition. (*d*) American Indians.

266. **Influence of mountains.** (*a*) Barriers: races on two sides of Himalayas; protection to India; Alps. (*b*) Retreats: reasons; Welsh and Scotch; Basques; Switzerland; ancient customs. (*c*) Mountain people: character; love of freedom.

267. **Influence of coast line.** (*a*) Closed seas: Mediterranean. (*b*) Irregular coasts: Greece; Scandinavia. (*c*) British nation: nearness to sea; irregular coast; fishing; island condition; food supply; colonies; commerce; coal and iron; great importance.

268. **The United States.** (*a*) Favorable conditions: climate; resources; government; coast line; ocean. (*b*) Mountain barrier: first settlements; natives; barrier to westward movement; condition in 1790; Spanish; French; French and Indian war; Revolution. (*c*) Interior: crossing barrier; development of interior; present routes to interior. (*d*) Western barrier: nature; difficulty of crossing; present condition. (*e*) Growth of country: climate; energetic people; resources; government; future.

QUESTIONS. Section 250. What is known of the early development of man? Why has he made advances?

251. How does man differ from animals? Upon what conditions are all men dependent? In what other ways are civilized men dependent on nature?

252. What simple implements were early used? Why? Why were plants cultivated? What parts are used? Give examples. Of what importance is domestication? Of what present importance is agriculture?

253. What materials are used for clothing? Why are the production and manufacture of materials for clothing so important?

254. What primitive means were employed for securing shelter? How has the use of wood developed? Stone? Clay?

255. What considerations have led to the selection of sites for homes? What influences civilized man? Give illustrations of protected sites.

256. Why do men gather in centers? Illustrate. What was the condition in Europe? What great European cities are capitals? What else accounts for their growth? What situations especially favor the growth of cities? Give instances. In what several connections is London mentioned?

257. What is the nature of commerce among primitive peoples? How was early commerce carried on? What was the nature of ancient commerce between Asia and Europe? What influence had the Mediterranean? What effect had the Mohammedans? State other effects of commerce.

258. State some of the ways in which man influences nature: (*a*) life; (*b*) rivers; (*c*) seacoast; (*d*) the land.

259. Compare and contrast man's spread with that of animals. In what ways has his spread been accomplished? Give illustrations.

260. What places may have been the original home of man? How did diversity in mankind come about? Explain exceptions to the rule of adaptation to surroundings.

261. What are the difficulties in classifying races? Name the four races. Where is each found (Fig. 513)? Why are the boundaries not sharp? What about the spread of the different races? What is the significance of skin color?

262. What are the sources of food for the inhabitants of the Arctic? How do the Eskimo live? Why may they not advance?

263. What conditions in the tropical zone are unfavorable to civilization? What is the condition of the inhabitants? Can they be civilized?

264. What three conditions have favored advance to civilization in the temperate zone? How have they aided?

265. What is the condition of man in the desert? Why are primitive customs preserved? Why were oases favorable to the development of early civilization?

Of what importance was this in the Old World? What was the condition in the New World?

266. What are the effects of mountains as barriers? Why are they places of retreat? Give illustrations of the influence of this on language. On customs. What effect have mountains on character?

267. Give instances of the influence of closed seas and irregular coasts. What facts account for the importance of the British nation?

268. What conditions are favorable to the advance of the United States? What were the nature and effects of the barrier west of the coast? Where was this barrier crossed? What was the result? What barrier was found farther west? How has it been overcome? Upon what has our progress as a nation depended?

Reference Books. HADDON, *Races of Man*, The Macmillan Company, New York, 1925; VON ENGELN, *Inheriting the Earth*, The Macmillan Company, New York, 1922; DENIKER, *Races of Man*, Chas. Scribner's Sons, New York, 1900; STEFANSSON, *The Friendly Arctic*, 1922, and *My Life with the Eskimo*, 1913, The Macmillan Company, New York; CONKLIN, *Heredity and Environment*, Princeton University Press, Princeton, 1915; THOMAS, *The Environmental Basis of Society*, Century Company, New York, 1925; FAIRGRIEVE, *Geography and World Power*, E. P. Dutton & Company, New York, 1917; BRUNHES, *Human Geography*, Rand McNally Company, Chicago, 1920; SMITH, *North America*, Harcourt, Brace & Company, New York, 1925; NEWBIGIN, *The Mediterranean Lands*, Christophers, London, 1924; SHALER, *Nature and Man in America*, Chas. Scribner's Sons, New York, 1891; RIPLEY, *Races of Europe*, 2 vols., D. Appleton & Company, New York, 1899; VIDAL-LABLACHE, *Principles of Human Geography*, Henry Holt & Company, New York, 1926; COMAN, *Industrial History of the United States*, The Macmillan Company, New York, 1910; JONES and BRYAN, *North America*, Dial Press, New York, 1924.

APPENDICES

APPENDIX A

REVOLUTION OF THE EARTH

1. Apparent movements of the sun. In addition to the daily rising and setting of the sun there is a slower change in its position which can be detected by noting the point of sunrise or sunset for a week or two. In the north temperate zone, the sun rises exactly in the east and sets due west on March 21 and September 22. From March to September sunrise and sunset are north of true east and west, and the days are longer than the nights. But from September to March the sun rises and sets south of due east and west, and the nights are then longer than the days. The midday sun also changes in position. It is higher in summer than in winter, but is always in the southern half of the heavens (Fig. 519). In the temperate zone of the southern hemisphere the same changes occur in the opposite season; but there the midday sun is always in the northern half of the heavens.

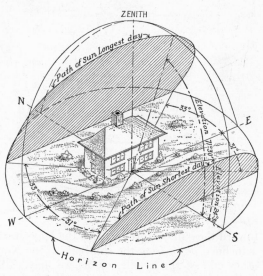

Fig. 519. — Diagram of a house at 42° N. Lat. and facing south in its relation to the sun's course. With the assistance of the teacher of mathematics make a similar diagram for the latitude of your school. Try placing the house in different positions, or try a differently designed house with the idea of having sunlight in the dining room at breakfast in winter, etc.

2. Experiment to illustrate revolution. One or two simple experiments will aid in a better understanding of the way in which revolution (p. 8) causes these apparent movements of the sun. Place two balls that will float half submerged in a tub of water (Fig. 520), one in the center to represent the sun, the other off to one side to represent the earth. The

609

water surface represents the *plane of the ecliptic,* or the plane in which the earth moves in its revolution around the sun.   If the earth ball is moved around the central ball, its path will represent the orbit of the earth in its revolution.

A knitting needle passed through the center of the earth ball will represent the position of the earth's axis.   When the ball is so floated that one end of the needle projects straight up into the air, the axis of the ball is perpendicular to the water surface; if the axis of the earth were in a similar position, it would be perpendicular to the plane of the ecliptic.   Now weight the earth ball so that it floats with the needle inclined as in Figure 520, which is the same angle as that at which the earth's axis is inclined. The axis of the earth is inclined $66\frac{1}{2}°$ to the plane of the ecliptic, or $23\frac{1}{2}°$ to a perpendicular from that plane.

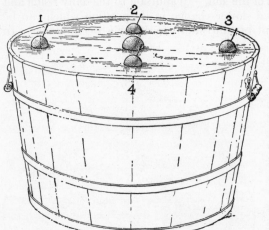

Float the earth ball around the central ball, always keeping the needle axis inclined at the same angle and parallel in direction at each position with the direction at every other position, and you will see quite clearly how the earth moves around the sun.

Position 1 (Fig. 520), with the needle pointing *toward* the central ball, may represent the earth's position in summer when the North Pole points toward the sun.   In the ball on the opposite side of the tub (3), the needle

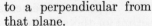

Fig. 520. — To illustrate revolution of the earth.

is inclined *away from* the sun ball, as the North Pole is in winter; but the other end of the needle, or, as we may call it, the South Pole, is then inclined toward the sun ball.   Halfway between these summer and winter positions (2 and 4), the axis is inclined neither toward nor away from the sun.   These points represent spring and autumn.

3. Rotation and revolution.   The manner in which revolution causes the sun's position in the heavens to change may be understood by another simple experiment.   Let a globe or ball represent the earth, and a lamp or candle the sun.   Have only the single light in a dark or nearly dark room.   Carry the globe in a circular path around the light, being careful to keep the axis always inclined at the same angle, and in each position parallel to every other position in the circuit as explained in the preceding section (2).

When the position is that of summer, the full rays of the lamp illuminate the northern half of the globe and reach beyond the pole. So in the case of the earth, when it has reached the summer position in its orbit, the sun's rays reach beyond the North Pole and illuminate all the space within the Arctic Circle (Fig. 521).

This circle is located $23\frac{1}{2}°$ from the pole because the sun's rays of midsummer (June 21) reach that distance beyond the North Pole. They reach that far because this is the amount that the earth's axis is inclined.

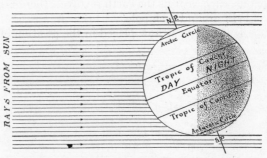

Fig. 521. — Position of the earth June 21

Now rotate the globe, and you will see that all points within $23\frac{1}{2}°$ of the pole are lighted throughout the entire rotation. The same is also true of the earth. This makes it clear why, on the longest day, June 21, every point within the Arctic Circle has sunlight for the full 24 hours (Fig. 522). Notice also that at latitudes intermediate between the Arctic Circle and the equator more than one half the circumference is illuminated; and that at the equator the illumination is just one half the circumference. How, therefore, does the length of daylight vary between the Arctic Circle and the equator on June 21?

Photo by Tarr

Fig. 522. — The sun at 9.30 P.M. in August on the Yukon River at the Arctic Circle. The river flows west, left, the sun is setting in the far northwest. Where in the picture, will it rise next morning. At what time? Trace, on the picture, the sun's course between 9 P.M. and 3 A.M., at this point on June 21.

Still holding the globe in this position, observe the conditions at the opposite end of the axis, or the South Pole. Even when the globe is rotated, no light reaches that portion. This is also true of the earth in the northern hemisphere summer, for then the midday sun barely appears on the Antarctic Circle, $23\frac{1}{2}°$ from the South Pole. All within that circle is dark, even at midday.

Moving the globe to the opposite, or winter, position (3, Fig. 520), with the North Pole inclined away from the lamp, conditions are reversed. All is darkness within the Arctic Circle, while all within the Antarctic Circle is bathed in light (Fig. 523). This is the earth's condition in winter. Thus, each year as the earth revolves, there is a season of darkness and one of light around each pole.

If the globe is now placed in the position of spring or autumn (2 and 4, Fig. 520), the light will

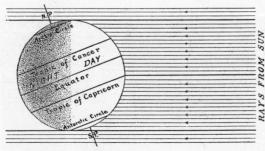

Fig. 523. — Position of the earth December 21.

exactly reach each pole. The half of the polar region that faces the lamp is lighted, the half away from it is in darkness; but by rotating the globe the dark side is turned toward the light. When the earth reaches a corresponding position in its orbit, it is divided into a dark and a light half by a plane passing from pole to pole (Fig. 524). At these times come the *equinoxes* (equal nights); all over the earth day and night are each twelve hours long. One period is called *vernal* (spring) *equinox*, the other *autumnal* (autumn) *equinox*.

During the equinoxes, when the sunlight just reaches each pole, the midday sun is directly above the equator. After December 21, in all parts of the earth, the sun appears to be slowly moving northward, and the sunlight slowly creeps over the curvature of the earth into the Arctic.

After the earth has passed its summer position, the sun seems, from all points on the globe, to be slowly moving southward, and the sunlight is gradually withdrawn from the Arctic (Fig. 525).

If the earth's axis were perpendicular to the plane of the ecliptic, there would be no such changes; but, since it is inclined, revolu-

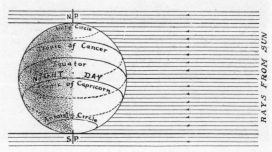

Fig. 524. — Position of the earth September 23.

tion turns one hemisphere toward the sun for a time, then away from it. These annual changes recur so regularly that, in all the time of human history, there has been no noticeable change.

SUGGESTIONS. (1) Study Sections 2 and 3 at the same time that you are yourself performing the experiments described. (2) Make careful observations of the change in the sun from day to day. On a platform, or table, placed where the sun reaches it from morning till night, draw a north-south (p. 642) line intersecting an east-west line drawn at right angles to the north-south line. Where the lines cross drive a long knitting needle into the table. Once a week at noon (when the shadow is shortest) mark on the north-south line the point to which the needle's shadow reaches. Also mark the point reached by the shadow just after sunrise or just before sunset. What movements of the sun cause these changes? Observe also the exact place where the sun sets each week. Deduce from your observations where it will set during summer when school is not in session.

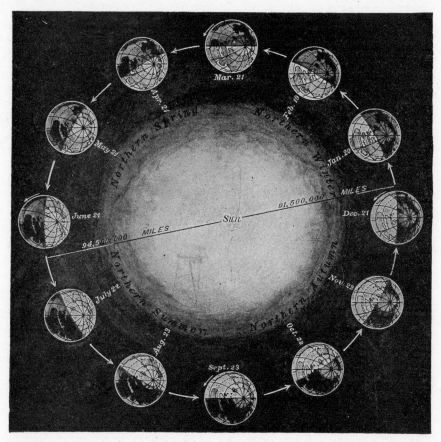

Fig. 525. — To illustrate the revolution of the earth around the sun. The north pole is turned toward us.

(3) In what direction does your shadow point at solar noon? In what direction would it point in South Africa? At each tropic, in the middle of March, June, September, and January? At the equator? What is the direction of a shadow at solar noon in summer in the Arctic? At midnight? Are such shadows longer or shorter than in the temperate zone?

Laboratory Exercises. If not previously performed, Exercises VI and VII in TARR and VON ENGELN's *Laboratory Manual for Physical and Commercial Geog-*

raphy, The Macmillan Company, New York, should be done by the class in connection with the study of Appendix A.

Reference Books. JOHNSON, *Mathematical Geography*, American Book Company, New York, 1907.

APPENDIX B

LATITUDE, LONGITUDE, AND TIME

1. Latitude. The intersection of two lines fixes the location of a point. On a nearly spherical earth the most convenient method of locating points is by imaginary circles extending in opposite directions. Any point can then be definitely located by the intersection of such circles. These are called circles of *latitude* and *longitude*, names given when the extent of the lands of the world was not known, and one direction, east and west (longitude) was considered to be the long direction, the other, north and south (latitude) the broad direction.

For measurement of latitude imaginary circles are extended in an east-west direction. The largest circle (about 25,000 miles), the *equator*, extends around the earth midway between the poles. Other circles parallel to this, and called *parallels of latitude*, are located at intervals between the equator and either pole. The plane of each parallel of latitude, like that of the equator, is perpendicular to the axis of the earth. As their distance from the equator increases, these circles diminish in diameter (Fig. 526) until at the poles a circle of latitude is reduced to a point. (Note that although the circles of latitude extend in the east-west direction they do not measure the east-west direction.)

For convenience in use the parallels are numbered. From the equator to the north pole there are 90 parallels, numbered as *degrees* (indicated by the sign °); there are also 90 from the equator to the south pole. The equator is called 0° latitude; the north pole, 90° north latitude (abbreviated N. Lat.); the south pole, 90° south latitude (S. Lat.). The Tropic of Cancer is $23\frac{1}{2}$° N. Lat.; the Arctic Circle, $66\frac{1}{2}$° N. Lat.; the Tropic of Capricorn, $23\frac{1}{2}$° S. Lat.; the Antarctic Circle, $66\frac{1}{2}$° S. Lat. Which parallel of latitude is nearest your home?

Since there are 180° from pole to pole there are twice that number, or 360°, in a complete circle extending around the earth across the poles. It is customary to divide circles into 360°. This is a convenient number because it is exactly divisible by so many numbers. No geographic condition compels a division of the circle into 360°; if 100° had been a more convenient number it could have been chosen.

The length of a degree of latitude, that is the distance in miles between two successive parallels of latitude, varies slightly because the earth is not a perfect sphere (p. 4). Where the curve of the earth's surface is flattened most, that is in the polar regions, the degrees of latitude are longest, because each is $\frac{1}{360}$ of a larger circle than that which would be formed by the curve of surface in the equatorial belt. At the equator a degree is about 68.7 miles, at the poles about 69.4 miles, in the latitudes of the United States 69 miles.

On a small map of a large area, as a continent, it is impossible to draw a

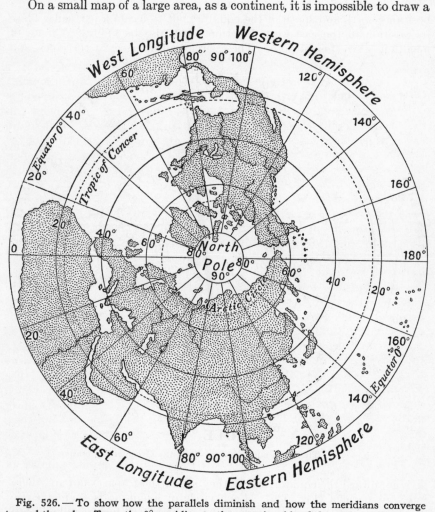

Fig. 526. — To show how the parallels diminish and how the meridians converge toward the pole. Trace the 0° meridian to the opposite side of the globe. What is it numbered there?

parallel for each degree, for the lines would be too close together. Accordingly, every fifth or tenth circle is placed on such a map. But for a map of a small section (Plate VIII) the parallels for single degrees are too far apart, and additional circles marking distances less than a degree are necessary. For this purpose degrees are subdivided into minutes (indicated '), and minutes into seconds (indicated "). There are 60 seconds in a minute of latitude, and 60 minutes in a degree. What is the latitude of your town in degrees, minutes, and seconds?

2. Longitude. Circles of latitude serve to fix accurately *lines* of positions north and south of the equator; but to locate a particular place its position in the east-west direction must also be known. Circles of longitude serve this purpose. These circles all intersect at the poles, and

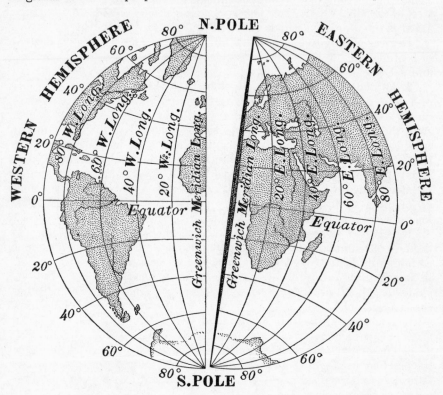

Fig. 527. — The earth cut in halves along the Greenwich meridian.

diverge toward the equator, where they are farthest apart, and are, therefore, not parallel (Fig. 526). Each circle of longitude is a great circle; its plane passes through the center of the earth. (Which parallel of latitude is a great circle?) To circles of longitude the name *meridian* is applied.

At the equator a degree of longitude is about equal to a degree of latitude (69 miles), being $\frac{1}{360}$ of the earth's circumference. In latitude 40°, which is a much smaller circle than the equator (Fig. 526), a degree of longitude, $\frac{1}{360}$ of that circle of latitude, is only about 53 miles. In latitude

60° a degree of longitude is about 34.7 miles; and at the poles, where all the meridians come together, a degree of longitude has no length.

Each circle of longitude is arbitrarily divided into 360 degrees. Since there is no such natural starting point as the equator, there is no general agreement as to where the numbering of meridians shall begin. Most nations, however, have adopted as the 0°, or *prime meridian*, the circle that passes through the Greenwich Observatory, at London, England. From this meridian the circles are numbered up to 180° both east and west (Fig. 527). New York is 74° W. Long. Jerusalem is 35° E. Long. What is the nearest meridian to your town?

Degrees of longitude are divided into minutes and seconds, as degrees of latitude are. What is the longitude of your home in degrees, minutes, and seconds?

3. Latitude and longitude. If, now, both the latitude and longitude of a place are given exactly in degrees, minutes, and seconds, its position on the earth's surface is indicated very exactly, as the two sets of figures show the point at which a certain divisional circle of latitude is intersected by a certain divisional circle of longitude, and their crossing marks one point only. As degrees of latitude and longitude at the equator are both about 69 miles apart, it is readily calculated that a minute of longitude or latitude there will be only a little over a mile long, and that a second of longitude or latitude will be only a little over 100 feet long. How long is a second of longitude at 40° N. Lat.?

It is worth while to memorize the latitude and longitude (in whole degrees) of ten important places in different parts of the world. Then if a certain latitude and longitude are mentioned it is easy to place the region, in imagination, at quite its proper position on the globe. Indeed, students should practice learning positions on the earth by referring the latitude and longitude given back to the starting points of the counts — the equator and the 0° of longitude at Greenwich. Thus in what part of what continent is 20° N. Lat. and 20° E. Long.? A good game like a spelling-match may be developed on this basis. There should also be practice in learning the distance between places, by noting their latitudes and longitudes on a map, and calculating the distance into miles.[1]

4. Longitude and time. Rotation causes the sun to appear to pass completely around the earth in 24 hours. That is, it passes over 360° in 24 hours; and, dividing 360 by 24, we find that it passes over 15° in an hour. From this it is evident that places 15° apart will have just one hour's difference in time. As the sun appears to move from east to west, this means that the noon, or highest position of the sun during the day, will come one hour later every 15 degrees that one goes toward the west.

---

[1] In western states where the township, section, quarter-section, etc., system of land survey is used and constantly referred to, the teacher should secure a copy of JOHNSON, *Mathematical Geography*, American Book Co., 1907, and devote a lesson or two to the subject matter of Chapter XI: "The United States Government Land Survey."

Formerly, places in United States kept local or solar time, that is, they measured their hours from the time when it was noon, or sun highest, crossing their meridian; and even neighboring cities would have different times. This caused so much inconvenience that it was agreed to adopt a *Standard Time,* by which the time changes one hour for every 15° of longitude. Now in traveling across the continent one need change his watch only three times (Fig. 528).

If longitude may be used to determine time, it is evident that time may be used to determine longitude. Ships crossing the ocean are able in this way to determine their east-west position. They start with an accurate clock, or *chronometer,* set to Greenwich time. By means of an

Fig. 528. — Map to illustrate Standard Time in the United States. The meridians 75°, 90°, 105°, and 120°, are near the centers of the four time belts. The map is only approximately correct because changes are frequently made along the boundary lines to suit the convenience of railway schedules and for other reasons.

instrument, the *sextant,* an officer observes the sun to determine the local noon, that is, the time when the sun has reached its highest position. Comparing this local time with that of the chronometer, it is easy to tell just how many minutes' difference there is between Greenwich time and that where the ship is. Knowing that one hour's difference means 15° of longitude, the longitude of the ship is readily determined.

5. Daylight Saving. As summer days in the higher latitudes (Appendix A) are much longer than 12 hours and the sun rises an hour or more before six o'clock in the morning, it has become the custom in certain places, cities especially, to push the hands of the clock an hour ahead at the beginning of the summer season. This is known as Daylight Saving, or

Daylight Saving Time. Its purpose is easily seen, but it may not be fully appreciated why it is desirable to change clock time to accomplish this — why not simply get up an hour earlier? The answer is (*a*) that human habit is strong, persons accustomed to getting up at 7 o'clock will get up at 7 o'clock if the clock shows it to be that time, but they will not get up at 6 o'clock. Also (*b*) by pushing the clock hands ahead *all* human activities are started an hour earlier, trains, business, meals, etc. In consequence an extra *daylight* hour of *leisure* is gained for the evening after working activities are done and when the hour will be most enjoyed. Country people object to this scheme, for they usually get up at daylight anyhow, and daylight saving compels them to hurry up all their work in order that they may deliver milk in time for city breakfasts, etc. In other words, country folk ordinarily work by solar time, they use a watch or clock as a convenience, whereas city people are governed by clocks!

6. International Date Line. If a person could travel westward as fast as the sun seems to move, about 1000 miles per hour, he would always be in daylight. For him day would never end. If he started March 21 at noon at New York City it would be noon all the way and noon still when he returned to New York City. Nevertheless 24 hours would have elapsed and he would find that people in New York City were using the date March 22. The traveler accordingly would need to make up his mind that like other people he was entitled to only 12 hours of day on

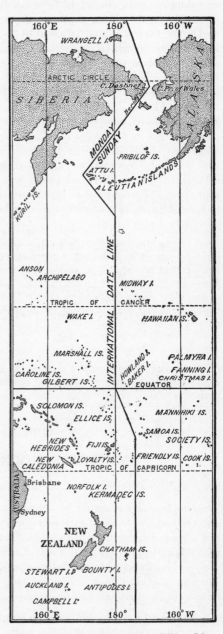

Fig. 529. — The International Date Line.

any one *date* even though he did have noon sunlight over the whole trip.   It will also be clear that even if one travels more slowly one will gain an hour of sunlight, day, for each 15° of longitude one moves westward.   Accordingly, somewhere, if the trip is continued completely around the earth, the traveler must be content to give up one *date* to make up for the longer days he will be enjoying.   Then comes the question where shall the *date* be skipped by the traveler, or, for the world at large, where shall a *new date* be considered to begin *first?*   All places east of the meridian of longitude chosen will have March 21 as the date, while all places west will have March 22.   Quite evidently it would not do to choose a meridian that anywhere passed through a densely settled region.   That would result in no end of confusion.   Therefore the 180° meridian has been chosen as the basis for the International *Date* Line (Fig. 529), the actual line being shifted east or west to avoid having the line pass through any settled islands.   There in the lonely Pacific only passengers on ships (who probably will have leisure to think it out) are subject to the confusion in mind this matter of *dates* causes when not understood.

SUGGESTIONS.   (1) To understand the need of circles of latitude and longitude, try to state exactly the location of New York City without these.   Do the same by use of latitude and longitude.   (2) If the earth were flat, what would be the effect on time?   To answer this, imagine a table top to represent the earth. Raise a lighted candle up to the edge to represent the rising sun.   How much of the table do the rays reach at once?   Is any more of the table reached as the candle is raised higher?   Now, to represent part of the globular earth, place a curved object on the table top; for example, a large sheet of cardboard or blotting paper, resting on books or dishes.   How much of this curved surface is lighted when the candle is raised?   Is more lighted as the candle is raised higher?

Laboratory Exercises.   Exercises V and VI in TARR and VON ENGELN'S *Laboratory Manual for Physical and Commercial Geography*, The Macmillan Company, New York, should be done in connection with the study of this Appendix B.

APPENDIX C

MINERALS, ROCKS, AND SOILS

MINERALS

This appendix should be studied with an accompanying use of mineral specimens.   Systematic direction for such study will be found in Tarr and von Engeln's Laboratory Manual for Physical and Commercial Geography, The Macmillan Company, New York, Exercises X, XI, XII, XIII, and XIV. Each mineral should be carefully examined to note its color, hardness, cleavage, luster, and crystal form.   The text may be referred to, but each student should have a set of specimens and be expected to observe and determine the properties.

A mineral may be defined as a single element, or two or more elements chemically combined, forming a part of the earth's crust.   Some, like sulphur, consist of one element; but most minerals are formed by a combination of several. For example, quartz is made of silicon and oxygen; one of the feldspars contains silicon, oxygen, aluminum, and potassium. Rocks are made up of minerals, some rocks of only one mineral, but a rock ordinarily does not have a definite chemical composition. A *mineral does*. This is the great distinction between a mineral and a rock.

There are about 2000 known minerals, of which only one or two hundred are abundant, while less than a dozen are common in most rocks. The more important of the rock-forming minerals are described below.

Common rock-forming minerals. *Quartz.* This, the most common of minerals, is present in many rocks and soils. It is made of silicon and oxygen, forming silica (SiO_2). These elements are so firmly united that quartz does not decay; but it is slightly soluble in underground water. Mechanical, fine fragments of this mineral form the bulk of most *sands*. Quartz has a glassy appearance, or *luster*, and varies in color from clear glassy to milky white, blue, rose-color, red, or variegated. Agate, opal, jasper, and chalcedony are other mineral varieties of silica. Quartz is so hard that it will scratch glass, but is brittle and easily broken, having a shelly or *conchoidal fracture*. When it crystallizes it takes the form of a six-sided (hexagonal) prism terminated by a six-sided pyramid.

The feldspars. There are a number of kinds of feldspar, each formed by the union of several elements, and all nearly as hard as quartz. Crystals are not common. *Cleavage planes*, directions in the mineral along which the force of cohesion is less than in others, extending through feldspar, cause it to break along smooth faces. Unlike quartz, feldspar is not soluble. When exposed to air and water, however, it decays, becoming dull and whitish; and, if exposed long enough, the hard mineral crumbles to a whitish clay, or *kaolin*. In fact the bulk of clays, though only seldom pure kaolin, were derived originally from the decay of feldspar. Many soils contain decayed feldspar, and some of the best pottery clays are kaolin. Thus, though insoluble and nearly as hard as quartz, its decay makes feldspar less durable than quartz, when both are subject to weathering in humid climates.

Calcite (calcium carbonate), like quartz, varies greatly in color. It often has a perfect crystal outline; and since it has cleavage in three directions, it is apt when broken to take the form of a rhomb. It has a pearly luster. Unlike quartz and feldspar, calcite is so soft that a knife readily scratches it. Moreover, it is one of the most soluble of common minerals; and the cleavage planes afford opportunity for water to enter and dissolve the mineral. For these reasons a calcite rock is far less durable than one made of feldspar or quartz.

The mineral *dolomite* resembles calcite; but it is less soluble, and has a different chemical composition. Calcite contains calcium, carbon, and oxygen, and is, therefore, carbonate of lime ($CaCO_3$); dolomite has magnesium in addition, and is, therefore, magnesian carbonate of lime [$CaMg(CO_3)_2$].

The micas. There are a number of different minerals belonging to this group, all having a complex chemical composition. Some are black, some colored, and some so colorless that they are used in stove doors as "isinglass." Two of the most common forms are *biotite* and *muscovite*, the former dark colored, the latter light. All are easily scratched with a knife, and all have so remarkable a cleavage that they readily split into thin sheets. Some micas decay readily; but others so resist decay that they occur as shiny flakes in soils and some rocks, such as sandstones and shales.

Hornblende is a black mineral of complex chemical composition, common in some granites and lavas. It is hard, has a bright luster, is often crystalline, and has well-defined cleavage in two directions. When exposed to air and water it decays, one of the products being an iron compound which stains the rock. Iron is one of the elements in this mineral.

Augite, found in many lavas, resembles hornblende in several respects. In small grains it is difficult to distinguish between them. The chemical composition is very like that of hornblende; but the crystal form, and the angle at which the cleavage faces meet are different, and the color of augite is dark green instead of black. Like hornblende, augite decays readily.

Magnetite, a compound of iron and oxygen (Fe_3O_4), is black, hard, heavy, usually crystalline, and has a metallic luster. A magnet will attract the grains. *Iron pyrite*, or pyrites, the sulphide of iron (FeS_2), is a hard, heavy, golden yellow mineral, sometimes mistaken for gold, and hence called "fool's gold." It often occurs in perfect cubical crystals and decays readily.

ROCKS

Classification of the common rocks. Rocks are made up of a mineral or mixtures of minerals, and if composed of a mixture of minerals are not of definite chemical composition. They may be classified in three great groups:—

(1) *Sedimentary rocks*, most of which were deposited in water; (2) *Igneous rocks*, which were once molten; and (3) *Metamorphic rocks*, which have been altered from some previous state by heat, pressure, and water. A few of the most common are described below.

1. Sedimentary rocks. *Fragmental or clastic rocks.* By the disintegration of rocks, fragments of all sizes, from clay to bowlders, are detached. When assorted by water these are deposited in layers (p. 46), the pebbles forming *gravel beds*, the sand, *sand beds*, and clay, *clay beds*. Rock fragments may also be brought by glaciers, by wind, and by volcanic explosions, which supply ash and pumice. These fragmental, or clastic, materials may be cemented into solid rock by the deposit of mineral substances carried by underground water (p. 55).

Consolidated gravel beds, called *conglomerates*, are composed of pebbles, often with a matrix of sand, cemented together. The pebbles may be nearly all of one kind or quite varied. Consolidated sand beds, or *sandstones*, usually consist of small quartz grains, quartz being the most indestructible of common minerals. Some sandstones are well cemented and firm, others friable; and iron oxide cement often gives to them red, yellow, or brown colors.

A well-cemented sandstone or conglomerate, with much quartz in it, is one of the most durable of rocks, resisting denudation so well that it forms peaks and ridges, as in the Appalachians. Since quartz does not decay and furnish mineral plant food, as feldspar and many other minerals do, sandstones make poor soils.

Shale, the most common clay rock, varies in color from black to blue, red, or light gray. Because of the presence of large numbers of flattened particles, often small mica flakes, it splits readily along the bedding planes. Shales split so easily, and are so soft that they readily disintegrate, and among mountains are, therefore, usually found in the valleys. Soils produced by the decay of shale are much more fertile than sandstone soils.

Chemically formed rocks. The decay of minerals produces many substances which underground water dissolves. After being carried for a while, some may be deposited. For example, carbonate of lime is being deposited as *stalactites* in caverns (p. 98) and as *tufa* around the Hot Springs of Yellowstone Park (Fig. 224). On the coast of Florida and in Great Salt Lake it is also being collected or precipitated in small water-rounded, sometimes *oölitic grains* (p. 308). *Salt* is being deposited on marshes bordering Great Salt Lake and the Caspian Sea; and, by the drying up of salt lakes, as in western United States.

SEDIMENTARY ROCKS

Origin	Name	Composition
Fragmental or clastic rocks	Gravel beds Conglomerates Sand beds Sandstones Clay beds Shale	Made of pebbles derived from other rocks Consolidated masses of pebbles Finer fragments, usually quartz grains Consolidated sand beds Decomposed feldspar, hornblende, etc. Consolidated clay beds, splitting readily
Chemically formed rocks	Stalactite, oölite, tufa Salt Gypsum	Carbonate of lime, deposited in water Sodium chloride Hydrous sulphate of lime
Organic rocks	Most limestones Coal (bituminous, lignite, peat)	Carbonate of lime, made of shells, etc. Called dolomitic limestone if they contain also magnesium carbonate. Made of plant remains.

Organic rocks. Carbonate of lime, secured from lime compounds in water, supplies many animals with materials for shells, or limy framework. Where such animals are abundant, as in coral reefs (p. 381), their limy remains often accumulate as thick beds of *limestone.* Many such beds have been raised to form part of the land. Limestone, being both soft and soluble, is worn away to form lowlands; and, since it is rich in plant food, it forms a fertile soil. This is illustrated in the broad, fertile limestone valleys which extend among the mountains of New England and New Jersey, and thence through the Shenandoah valley of Virginia to Tennessee.

Remains of plants accumulate in swamps, as in *peat* bogs (p. 316), where the water retards decay. When such swamp deposits have been covered with beds of other rocks, they gradually lose their water and gases, and change to *coal* (p. 320). The early stages of this change form *lignite*, later stages *bituminous* coal, and a still more advanced stage is *anthracite.*

2. Igneous rocks. These rocks, which have risen in a melted condition from within the earth, have cooled either on the surface, near volcanoes, or below the surface as *intruded* masses in the crust (p. 227). In the latter case, the overlying blanket of rock has allowed the lava to cool so slowly that the minerals have had opportunity to grow to fair size, giving these intruded rocks a crystalline structure. In many places denudation has worn the surface down to these intruded, sometimes fine-, sometimes coarse-grained, igneous rocks.

Granite (Fig. 39). Granite is the most common intruded igneous rock. Of what minerals is it composed (see table, p. 625)? The structure is so coarse that the different mineral grains are plainly seen and easily distinguished. The color of granite varies mostly according to the color of the feldspar, being commonly light and either gray, grayish green, red, or pink. It is a valuable building stone, and is one of the hardest and most durable of rocks, resisting destruction so well that, in the wearing down of mountains, it is commonly left standing as peaks. *Syenite,* a coarse-grained rock, resembles granite, but has no quartz.

Diorite and *Diabase* are dark-colored igneous rocks without quartz, the color being due to dark-colored minerals, especially hornblende, augite, and mica. Diabase, also called *trap,* is often so fine grained that the minerals cannot be distinguished without a microscope. The Palisades of the Hudson and the trap hills of New Jersey and the Connecticut valley are diabase.

Rhyolite and *basalt* (see table) are among the most common lavas erupted from volcanoes. The first of the two is light-, the other dark-colored. In most cases, erupted lavas have cooled too rapidly for the mineral grains to grow large enough to be distinguished by the eye alone. *Trachyte,* like basalt, lacks quartz, but has orthoclase feldspar.

A porous structure may be given lavas by the expansion of steam, creating a *vesicular* condition, which forms cavities; and rapid expansion of the steam blows the lava into bits, forming *pumice* (Fig. 39) and *volcanic ash* (p. 217).

The ash from the Martinique eruption (p. 201) was lava blown to pieces by steam; the lava of the Hawaiian volcanoes is basalt. Much of the country west of the Rocky Mountains is covered with basalt, and other lava rocks erupted from ancient volcanoes and fissures. These lavas, having many cavities for water to enter, and being made of minerals that decay readily, are soon covered with a fertile soil, for the minerals of lava are rich in plant food.

IGNEOUS ROCKS

TEXTURE	NAME	CHIEF MINERAL COMPONENTS
	Granite	Quartz, feldspar (orthoclase), and hornblende or mica or both
Coarse grained	Syenite	Feldspar (orthoclase) and either mica or hornblende or both
	Diorite	Feldspar (plagioclase) and either hornblende or mica or both
Both coarse and fine grained	Diabase	Feldspar (plagioclase) and augite
	Rhyolite	Quartz, feldspar (orthoclase), and hornblende or mica or both
Fine grained to glassy	Trachyte	Feldspar (orthoclase), and either hornblende or mica or both
	Basalt	Feldspar (plagioclase), and augite (often olivine)

3. Metamorphic rocks. Any rock subjected to great pressure, as in mountain folding, and to the action of heated water, is certain to suffer change or *metamorphism*. In sandstone, for example, silica may be deposited around the grains until the rock becomes almost one solid mass of quartz, called *quartzite*. Shale, when altered by metamorphism, changes to *slate*. New minerals are then developed, particularly micas, and these, together with the original minerals, so arrange themselves under pressure that their cleavages extend in the same direction. Thus the slate itself is caused to split, or cleave readily. By metamorphism limestone is changed to crystalline calcite, as in the case of white *marble*. In the Appalachian Mountains (p. 198), coal has been metamorphosed to anthracite.

When subjected to metamorphism so intense that the minerals have recrystallized, some rocks are altered to *gneiss*. Gneiss resembles granite; but there is a slight banding of the minerals (Fig. 39), due to the fact that they have developed along lines of least resistance — that is, at right angles to the pressure. Where the banding is so distinct that the rock readily cleaves, it is a *schist*. Gneisses and schists are durable crystalline rocks, found in regions of intense mountain folding.

METAMORPHIC ROCKS

NAME	SOURCE	MINERAL COMPOSITION
Quartzite	Altered sandstones	Quartz
Slate	Altered clay rocks	Partially crystallized micaceous minerals developed out of the clay particles
Marble	Altered carbonate of lime	Calcite
Anthracite	Altered coal	Mainly carbon and carbon compounds
Schist	Altered from various rocks, *e.g.* shale, diorite, etc.	Variable — usually two or more of the following: feldspar, quartz, hornblende, or mica
Gneiss	Altered from various rocks, *e.g.* sandstone, conglomerate, granite, diorite, etc.	Variable — usually two or more of the following: feldspar, quartz, hornblende, or mica

SOILS

Soil is that portion of the mantle rock (Fig. 57) which supports plant growth, both chemically and mechanically. From the point of view of the farmer that would be only the few inches (less than one foot) of the top layer in which cultivated plants are grown. This upper layer is however to be distinguished as the *topsoil*. Under it occurs the *subsoil* penetrated to considerable depths by the roots of trees and of shrubby plants.

1. Origin of soils. As has been explained elsewhere (p. 62) the mantle rock consists of mineral and rock particles spread as a sheet of unconsolidated material over most of the land area of the world, and varying in thickness from place to place. The upper part of the mantle rock comprises the soil, and 90 to 99 per cent of the dry substance of the average soil is inorganic mineral matter.

On the basis of how they came to be where they are, soils may be divided into two broad classes: (1) sedentary soils, (2) transported soils. The sedentary soils were derived and developed in the place where they occur by the chemical or mechanical breaking down or both of the bed rock that formerly outcropped there, or are accumulations of organic material at a given place, *muck* soils or *peat* soils. Transported soils consist of mineral and organic particles that have been shifted from the place where they were formed to a new site.

The sedentary soils are either residual or cumulose. The *residual* soils (p. 62), as the name implies, are remainders of bed rock that has been broken down by weathering. Accordingly residual soils vary in characteristics as the bed rock from which they are derived varies or the weathering processes have been different. In a region covered by residual soil the nature of the soil will therefore be quite uniform over a large area if one kind of rock occurred, and weathered similarly there over a wide tract. On the other hand the residual soil will vary in type quite markedly if different kinds of bed rock came to the surface in bands or patches. *Cumulose* soils are masses of plant remains partially decayed and accumulated chiefly in swampy areas. These are popularly termed *muck* soils.

The transported soils may be divided into colluvial, alluvial, marine, lacustrine, glacial, and aeolian subclasses according to the transporting agency and the conditions of deposit. Thus *colluvial* soils are "base of the mountain" soils due to gravity action building up talus and landslide masses. *Alluvial, marine,* and *lacustrine* soils are respectively soils deposited in rivers, the sea, and in lakes, by water action. Of these subclasses the colluvial and the glacial will tend to be coarse in texture and unassorted, the others to be made up of fine particles quite uniformly assorted.

2. Soil classification. Although the classification given above helps toward an understanding of soils, it is not sufficiently detailed for distinguishing between soils in agricultural practice, nor is it based on the factor found to be of the most significance in that connection. That factor is *texture,* the variation in soils that comes from differences in size of the soil particles. On that basis seven gradations are recognized: fine gravel, coarse sand, medium sand, fine sand, very fine sand, silt, and clay. But as soils are seldom composed of one size particles it is necessary in *soil classification* to use in addition a number of terms indicating mixtures. Accordingly soils are regularly named as belonging in one of the following classes: 1, Gravel; 2, Coarse sand; 3, Medium sand; 4, Fine sand; 5, Very fine sand; 6, Coarse sandy loam; 7, Sandy loam; 8, Fine sandy loam; 9, Very fine sandy loam; 10, Loam; 11, Silt loam; 12, Silty clay loam; 13, Clay loam; 14, Clay; 15, Heavy clay; 16, Sandy clay.

These standardized terms will be immediately understood, except perhaps silt and loam. *Silt,* as is indicated by its place in the table of seven sizes of soil particles, consists of grains too fine to be sand and too coarse to be clay. If a sample of soil containing silt is shaken up in a glass of water, then the coarser silt particles will be just visible to the naked eye as separate grains suspended in the liquid. The finer clay particles will color the water, but the separate grains of clay can not be seen. *Loam* is a mixture of sand, silt, and clay particles in the proportion 50 per cent of sand, and silt and clay together the other 50 per cent. Most of the better soils are loams, since loams have the good properties of both sandy and clayey soils without having the bad qualities of either. Sandy soils usually dry out too quickly, and clayey soils are sticky wet, cold, and late (warm up too slowly in spring).

To the classification on the basis of texture a geographical *type* name is added in designating a particular soil as it occurs in nature. This is because two soils in different places and of different origins, though alike in texture, may be made up of particles of different minerals, be of different color, have different quantities of organic matter, and so on. Accordingly the full name of a soil will be "Norfolk sandy loam," "Dunkirk clay," etc.

All the organic matter in the soil is popularly referred to as *humus,* but more strictly that term includes only such part of the organic matter as has been partially or completely decomposed from its original state. In the topsoil this organic material is largely derived from the above-surface growth of plants. But there is also some organic matter in the subsoil, derived from the root extension and later decay of the roots of the larger plants, shrubs, and trees. Similarly the roots of the lower plants contribute much to the organic content of the topsoil. Further it is a mistake to consider that all organic matter is made up of residues of the higher plants. Bacterial growth in the soil itself, for one thing, adds a considerable quantity of organic material to the soil.

SUGGESTIONS. (1) Collect minerals from your neighborhood and study them. DANA's *Minerals and How to Study Them* is a good book of reference. (2) Collect rocks from the ledges, bowlders, quarries, and stone yards. If you live in a part of the country reached by the ice sheet (Fig. 272), you will find a varied store of rock specimens in the gravel banks. See how many kinds you can collect. Study their characteristics; place them in one of the three groups and, if possible, give them their proper names. The teacher can systematize this work and make it of great disciplinary value. PIRRSON and KNOPF's, *Rocks and Rock Minerals* is a book of reference. (3) To which of the three groups do the rocks of your neighborhood belong? What kind or kinds do you find? Of what are they made? Are they hard or soft? Do they make rich or poor soil? If your home is in a valley, see if the rocks on the hills are different. What are the differences? Do they help account for the hills and valleys? (4) Collect samples of various classes of soils occurring in the locality. Dry them and put them in wide-mouthed bottles of the 16-oz. size. Get facts about the relative fertility of the different soil classes collected. Shake a sample of soil in a glass of water and let it stand to settle. Note the different sizes of soil particles that are separated by this process. If conditions permit, attempt the collection and preservation of prisms of the natural soil about eight to ten inches square at the top and about eighteen inches deep. It will be necessary to dig a trench all around the prism to be collected, then to fit a box over it, then to cut it loose across the bottom. If transferred later to a tight-fitting glass case like an aquarium and sealed top and bottom, the prism may be preserved indefinitely with its natural moisture. A series of three such samples from the forest floor, from a field, and from a meadow will be found very instructive.

Reference Books. DANA, *Minerals and How to Study Them*, John Wiley & Sons, New York, 1895; PIRRSON and KNOPF, *Rocks and Rock Minerals*, John Wiley & Sons, New York, 1926; MERRILL, *Rocks, Rock Weathering, and Soils*, The Macmillan Company, New York, 1906; LYON and BUCKMAN, *The Nature and Properties of Soils*, The Macmillan Company, New York, 1922.

APPENDIX D

GEOLOGICAL AGES

While it is impossible to tell the age of the earth in years, exactly (p. 66), geologists have divided the rocks into stages, or periods, and have determined their *relative* age. This is made possible by the fossils the strata contain. For example, there was a time when no animals higher than fishes lived on the earth; and if strata contain remains of birds, it is certain that they were not deposited in those ancient times. In the table the important divisions as they apply to North America are given. It is suggested that the *bed rock* (not loose bowlders) of strata near the school be examined for fossils and collections made of the varieties (if any) that are found. A general idea of the age of the rocks near the school can then be got from the table, but for identification and exact determination of age specimens should be sent to the U. S. Geological Survey, Washington, D. C., or to the State Geologist at the capital city of the state. Ask at the same time for geologic literature and reports relating to the school locality. Usually such papers and books will be sent free of charge to schools.

GEOLOGICAL TABLE FOR NORTH AMERICA

ERAS	EPOCHS		LIFE CONDITIONS
PSYCHOZOIC ERA (Age of mind)	Recent or Post Glacial		Man assumes importance, but existed in the Glacial epoch and perhaps much earlier
	Pleistocene or Glacial		Periodic glaciation. Great mammals such as the mastodon become extinct.
CENOZOIC ERA (Age of Mammals and Flowering Plants)	Pliocene		Anthropoid apes appear
	Miocene		Period of greatest mammals
	Oligocene		Modern mammals and birds develop
	Eocene		Ancient mammal types fade and new ones come in
MESOZOIC ERA (Age of Reptiles)	Upper Cretaceous		Reptiles of great size and great variety
	Lower Cretaceous		Flowering plants appear
	Jurassic		Time of toothed birds and flying reptiles
	Triassic		Time of dinosaurs
PALEOZOIC ERA (Age of Invertebrates)	Permian		Time of amphibians
	Carboniferous	Pennsylvanian	Rise of primitive reptiles and amphibians Ancient coal-swamp floras
		Mississippian	Period of ancient sharks and crinoids
	Devonian		Dominance of fishes, corals, and shelled animals
	Silurian		Rise of lung fishes and scorpions
	Ordovician (Champlainian)		Rise of shelled animals
	Cambrian		Dominance of trilobites
PROTEROZOIC ERA (Age of Primitive Life)	Algonkian		Time of first invertebrates
	Timiskamian		
ARCHEOZOIC ERA (Age of Larval Life)	Archean		Larval life
EOZOIC ERA (Age of Beginnings of Life)			Dawn of unicellular life
AZOIC ERA (Age of No Life)			Time of the formation of the outer Lithosphere shell of the earth

APPENDIX E
TIDES*

Difficulty of the subject. The subject of the tides causes even the earnest and intelligent student misgivings.   Yet the chief facts concerning the tides are not really difficult of comprehension and ought to be learned, because the phenomenon is one of great significance and of considerable interest.   This is especially true for those students whose homes are at or near the seashore.

It should, however, be appreciated that particular complexities of the tides are not understood even by those who have made a special study of them and who are qualified to analyze the tides mathematically.   The reasons for this failure to comprehend the tidal movements completely are (1) that observations and records are lacking from many places and (2) that calculation of the importance and effect of each of a great number of conditions which must be taken into account in developing a complete theory of the tides, is a very complicated and involved problem. But concerning the main causes, the nature, and the variations of the tidal phenomenon, an understanding sufficient for all practical purposes and for an intelligent appreciation of the subject may be gained if the student makes sure he has mastered each point as it is presented.

Summary. *Referred to the actual earth as a whole the problem of the tides is one of great complexity.   But the general reasons for the occurrence of the phenomenon, and for its variations, are known, and are not difficult to understand if studied systematically.*

The basic conditions. The student will recall from earlier studies that: (1) Land, water, and air are held on the earth by the force of surface gravity that attracts all matter to the center of the mass of the earth ball.   (2) Each particle of land, water, and air is also subject to the force of attraction of the moon and the sun, and of the planets and the stars, and to other forces so slight that they have no relation to the problem of the tides.   In fact only the attractive force of the moon and the attractive force of the sun are of sufficient magnitude to be significant in the causing of the tides.   The strengths of these two forces vary appreciably in their action on particles on the surface of the earth and those at its center. It is this differential attraction that gives rise to tides.   Water is far more mobile than the rock and other solid materials of the earth.   Consequently a force may act to move water particles on the surface of the earth which is not great enough to overcome the rigidity of the solid earth.   The solid earth then responds to the force, not particle by particle as does the water, but as a unit mass collected at the center of the earth.   (3) Each

*The author is deeply indebted to Dr. S. L. Boothroyd, Professor of Astronomy in Cornell University, for constructive help in the preparation of the Appendix on Tides.

member of the solar system and of the universe is subject to the attraction of all the rest. Each member also has its own energy of motion in a certain direction. The adjustment or interaction between the force of inertia (the directed motion of the body) and the forces of attraction determines the path that the body follows. Thus the planets are caused to revolve about the sun, the moon about the earth. In this adjustment of forces each body acts as though all its mass was collected at a point at its center.

Summary. *The force of attraction of the moon and the force of attraction of the sun are great enough to act differentially on the solid and the water particles of the earth. The solid earth is rigid and responds to these forces as if it were a single particle located at the center of the earth. The water is mobile and its particles respond independently of each other and of the solid earth.*

The tide-raising forces. Gravity and gravitation are slightly different terms for what is really the same kind of force, the attraction (independent of magnetism) that masses of material have for each other. Gravity attracts particles on the earth toward the earth's center; to the sun the earth is a particle that the sun is attracting toward its center by gravitation. Every particle in the universe is attracted by every other particle. This attraction acts in accordance with two laws. One is, that the greater the mass the greater, in direct proportion, is the attraction it exerts. A mass twice as great as another mass exerts twice the force of attraction. The other is, that the attraction becomes less as the distance between the objects is increased in proportion to the square of the distance. This is concisely stated by saying that the attraction varies inversely with the square of the distance. Thus if the attraction between two objects is equal to 1 when they are 1 unit of distance apart, then if they are 2 units of distance apart the attraction will be only $\frac{1}{4}$ as great. This puts a distant body, even if large, at a great disadvantage compared to a near body in exerting attraction.

Consider, now, that instead of having the moon and the sun comparatively near the earth these bodies were as far away as the stars. The earth might be in adjustment with all the heavenly bodies but would be very little affected by the attraction of *any one* of them because they would all be so distant that no one would, by itself, have any appreciable effect. Under those circumstances tides would be so slight on the earth that their existence could not be detected. The adjustment of forces would be exceedingly nice and perfect over all the surface as well as at the center of the earth. But the *moon is so near* and the *sun is so large* that they both exert a very pronounced attraction on the earth, an attraction that is so far in excess of that exerted by other celestial bodies as to put them in a class by themselves.

Thus far the subject is not particularly difficult to understand. But now it is necessary to grasp just how this superior attraction of the moon and sun causes tides, a more intricate study. First it is well to keep in mind that the adjustment of forces acting occurs at the center of the earth. Then it may be perceived at once that as the surface of the earth is approximately 4000 miles distant from the center, and as the effect of distance on gravitative attraction is measured by the square of the amount, the surface of the earth must experience a force that is *greater or less* than the average at the center by a considerable magnitude. This, then, is the chief fact in the development of the tides.

Summary. *The attraction of gravitation varies directly with the size of the masses acting, and inversely with the square of the distance between them. The stars are so distant, and the planets are so small and distant, that the moon, which is so near, and the sun, which is so large, exert preponderating attractions on the earth. Because distance is effective in the order of the square of its amount and the adjustment of forces is effective at the center of the earth, the surface of the earth is subject to a differential attraction by the sun and the moon.*

Development of the tides. The solid earth consists of the outer rock shell which we know about, and an interior core (p. 24). This solid earth mass is very coherent, the interior part is even more rigid than steel. If acted on by a force not great enough to overcome the strength indicated by such rigidity the solid earth responds as a unit. That is, it acts as a whole. Further the solid earth as a whole responds exactly in the measure that a particle at its center would.

On the other hand the water of the ocean is a liquid and very mobile. It yields by change of form to every force affecting it, even if the force is quite small. This difference in behavior of the solid earth and the liquid ocean may be appreciated by considering the effect of a pulling force on two balls. One ball is made of very soft rubber. The other is a solid wooden ball. If a slight pull is exerted at one point on the surface of the very soft rubber ball, the surface material at that point will be made to bulge out, but the ball itself will not move. The same pull acting on the wooden ball will not change its surface shape but will move it as a whole, cause it to shift in position. Therefore the solid earth, from surface to center, keeps on a course in its orbit that is fixed by the adjustment of forces acting at its center.

Accordingly the direct pull of the sun and moon on the mass of the ocean on the side of the earth facing them lifts the water up in a mound. This mound of water is the initial development of the *near-side*, or *direct* high tide. Directly opposite, on the far side of the earth, a similar mound develops (Figs. 530, 533), the *far-side*, or *indirect* high tide. This indirect high tide presents a seeming contradiction to the beginning student, and therefore confuses him.

He should remember that the solid earth as a whole is governed by the adjustment of forces acting as its center.   Hence the surface of the solid earth on the side toward the moon is prevented from projecting toward the moon as it would if the solid earth were not so rigid.   But the water is not rigid, therefore heaps up in response to the greater (than that which it exerts at the center of the earth) attractive force of the moon at the earth's near-side surface.   Now the opposite side of the solid earth is 4000 miles more distant (Fig. 531) from the moon than is the center of the earth.   So it is subject to an attraction much less than that felt at the center.   But the solid material there is bound to the center, hence is pulled toward the moon more than it should be on the basis of the amount of attraction to which it is subjected.   Therefore the surface of the solid earth on the far side is actually *pulled away* from the water which covers it.   The water thus left behind makes this apparent by its heaping up, protuberance, there in a tidal mound.   In other words, the balancing at its center of all the forces acting on the solid earth permits the water to pull away from the surface on the near side, and the surface of the solid earth to pull away from the water on the far side.   The manner of

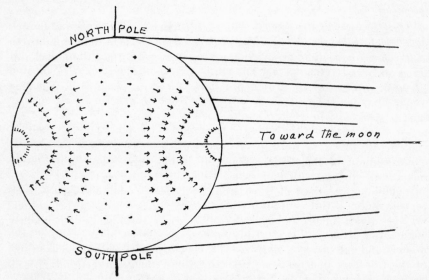

Fig. 530.   Action of the tide-raising forces with moon over the equator.   The arrows illustrate the direction and degree of movement of the waters in bringing about the heaping up of the tidal mounds on opposite sides of the earth.   It is to be noted that the direct, vertical pull immediately under the moon is not effective in causing the tides. There the water has to be lifted up directly against the earth's gravity and the attractive force of the moon is only one ten millionth as great as the downward pull of the earth's mass.   But at other points the attraction of the moon is partly vertical, partly horizontal.   Because of the great mobility of the water a very slight force can cause it to move horizontally.   Thus the water is pulled from all sides toward the center and heaps up there.   At the line from pole to pole the horizontal pull is equal in both directions, accordingly the tide there is low.

the heaping up on the two sides is illustrated diagrammatically in Fig. 530.

Because distance is so important a factor (actually the magnitude of the tide-raising force varies inversely with the *cube* of the distance) a much greater tide-raising effect acts on the near side than on the far side of the earth. Otherwise stated, the far side of the solid earth is not pulled away from the water there as much as the water is pulled away from the solid earth on the near side. Hence, theoretically, the near-side high tide should be greater than that of the far side. The difference however is lost in the action of other factors which are even more effective in causing variations in the magnitude of the tides.

Summary. *The solid earth acts as a unit in response to the gravitative forces, the attraction of the moon and the sun, to which it is subjected. It responds in the measure that it would if all its mass could be collected at the point of its center. The water of the oceans is, however, mobile. Therefore the ocean surface may be deformed by forces of different magnitudes and different directions acting on its parts. On the side toward the moon (or sun) the ocean water is heaped up by the excess of attractive force on the surface of the earth as compared to that acting at the center. This excess of force is due to the fact that the surface of the earth on the near side is 4000 miles nearer to the attracting body than is the center of the earth. On the opposite side the ocean water is not pulled toward the moon as much as is the surface of the solid earth there because the solid surface is governed by the greater force acting at the center of the earth. Consequently the earth is pulled away from the ocean water. This condition makes itself apparent in a heaping up of the water, the far-side high tide.*

Movement of the tides. Thus far it has been assumed that the moon and sun are both facing the same side of the earth, in the same straight line, and that all three stand still after having caused the tidal protuberances. But actually the earth rotates on its axis, and the moon revolves about the center of gravity of the earth and moon independently of the sun's position, and the three bodies actually act in conjunction only at new and full moon. Further, the visible phenomena and variations of the tides are due principally to these movements and differences in position. Hence they need to be considered next.

As the tide-raising force of the moon is over two (11:5) times as great as that of the sun, and the sun acts therefore only to increase or decrease the far greater moon tides, it will be well to give attention first to the conditions resulting from the earth and moon relations.

Assume that the moon stands still while the earth rotates on its axis, once in 24 hours. This rotation is from west to east. Then the tidal bulges would remain directly under the moon, while the rest of the earth rotated beneath them. On an earth all covered with water of sufficient depth that is exactly what would happen. Any given place would have a **direct** high tide at a certain time and twelve hours later an indirect high tide with a low tide condition between the two high tides (Fig. 533).

But the moon does not stand still. The moon goes around the center of the earth-moon revolution in the same direction that the earth rotates on its own axis, that is, from west to east. Hence, while the earth is rotating on its axis, the moon is moving forward in its orbit. A given place on the earth's surface must, accordingly, make more than a complete rotation to come again directly under the moon. It takes that spot on the earth 52 minutes to catch up. Therefore at any given place two direct high tides should be 24 hours and 52 minutes apart, and a direct high tide is followed by an indirect high tide in 12 hours and 26 minutes.

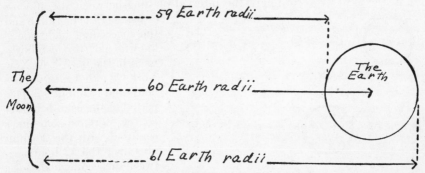

Fig. 531. — Diagram to illustrate the differences in distance (between the near and far sides of the surface of the earth, and the earth's center) from the moon expressed in terms of earth radii, each 4000 miles. The fact of the rigidity of the solid earth (causing it to act as a unit, responding to the attractive force of the moon as though all the earth mass were concentrated at its center) permits deformation of the mobile ocean water, forming tides.

As a matter of fact at only very few places is a given tide the tide caused by the last crossing of the meridian of that place by the moon (moon highest in the sky). It has therefore been argued that tides started in the Southern Ocean become a series of waves of translation moving through the other oceans; thus from south to north through the Atlantic. The waves come at the proper intervals for the successive tides. This explanation is called the progressive wave theory.

The progressive wave theory does not, however, fit all the observed facts. According to the stationary wave theory the true effect of the tide-raising forces is to cause the ocean waters to rock back and forth in the manner of the two ends of a see-saw. The center, over the pivot, of a see-saw does not change in level. Only the two ends go up and down corresponding to high and low tide. There are certain areas in the oceans that correspond to the pivot points. In those regions there is very little change in level due to tides. Imagine a number of see-saws so placed that their ends are close together, and so arranged that they follow the pattern of the oceans on the earth. Think of these see-saws in action so that the ends of any two that are adjacent will go up and down together. Picture next the whole system of see-saws working thus in unison. Then one has a notion of the ocean waters heaving up and down to form the tides. This stationary wave theory is not contradictory to the explanation given of the nature and effect of the tide-raising forces. It does make clear how the waters in the actual ocean basins behave when subjected to the attraction of the sun and moon. The oscillating waves tend, however, to run up openings along a coast line in the manner of the progressive wave theory.

It follows from this that high tide at a given place will only by chance occur at the time when the moon crosses the meridian at that place (is highest in the sky). Accordingly the interval of time between the moon's crossing of the meridian and the succeeding high tide is known as "the establishment of the port." At New York City that interval is 8 hours and 13 minutes. This period of the establishment of the port is sometimes confused with the 26 minutes over the 12 hours between succeeding high tides, already accounted for, or with the "lag" of the tides to be described in a following paragraph. The establishment of the port has no connection with either of these phenomena.

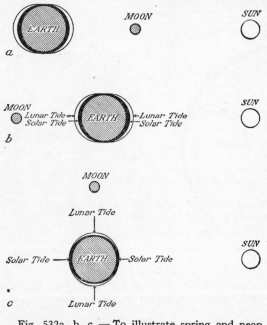

Fig. 532a, b, c. — To illustrate spring and neap tides. All figures greatly distorted as to size and distances. In (a) new moon position, and (b) full moon position the spring tides are illustrated; in (c) first quarter position, one neap tide is illustrated. Make a drawing to show the last quarter position and explain it. The circle representing the earth is the equator. Note that at the neap tides the trough of the solar tide has to be filled by the lunar tide.

Summary. *Because the moon revolves about a center within the earth in the same direction that the earth rotates on its axis, the earth must make more than a complete turn to bring a given point under the moon again; hence two successive direct tides are 24 hours and 52 minutes apart. The actual tide probably consists of a number of oscillating waves. The period of time that elapses between the crossing of the meridian by the moon and the occurrence of high tide at a given place is termed the establishment of the port.*

Variations of the tides. In the open oceans the *tidal range,* that is the difference in level between high tide and low tide, is very slight — one or two feet on the coasts of oceanic islands. But various conditions along coast lines may bring about much greater tidal ranges (p. 341).

When the sun and moon are in line (Fig. 532) as at the full moon (b) and new moon (a) positions, the tidal range at a given place is greater than the average; such high, high tides and low, low tides are called *spring tides.* This term has nothing to do with the seasons. When the sun and moon are at right angles, at first quarter and last quarter of the moon's phases, the solar tide is subtracted (Fig. 532c) from the lunar tide. The range of the tide (*neap tides*) in those periods is less than the average.

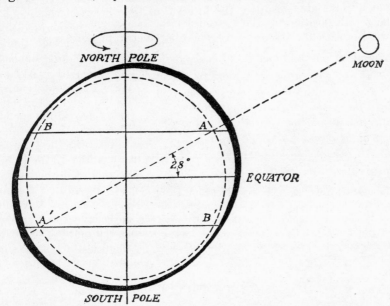

Fig. 533. — To illustrate the possible inequality of succeeding direct and indirect tides. When the moon is overhead at 28° (N. Lat.) there is a high, direct, high tide at A, as illustrated; 12 hours and 26 minutes later, however, A will experience the low, indirect, high tide as here shown at B. Why will this inequality not develop when the moon is overhead at the equator? Make a diagram to show this and explain it.

In the period *after* the spring tides the tides first *prime* and then *lag,* that is, come in earlier or later than the normal interval of 12 hours and 26 minutes. This is because at those times the crests of the lunar and solar tides nearly, but not quite coincide, and the highest level of the water lies between them. Hence high tide also lies between them. High tide then is due to the *partial* combination of the two waves. If now the solar tide is ahead (west) of the lunar tide, the high tide stage will develop earlier than the normal interval of 12 hours and 26 minutes and the tides are said to prime. This priming occurs just after the new and full moon positions.   About a week later when the crest of the solar tide is behind, that is east of, the lunar tide there is a corresponding lag of the high tide.

If the moon and sun are directly overhead (zenith position) at the equator, the two succeeding high tides, 12 hours and 26 minutes apart, the direct and indirect high tides, will be nearly equal everywhere (Fig. 533). But if the moon is in the zenith position at some latitude (28 degrees is the maximum) north or south of the equator the succeeding high tides at a given place may be quite unequal (especially true of the north Pacific) as will readily be perceived on inspection of Fig. 533.

The highest high tides will occur (a) at the spring tide positions of the moon and sun, (b) when the moon and sun are nearest the earth, (c) when the moon's and sun's zenith positions are in, or as near as they approach to the zenith position of, the latitude of the place considered, (d) when the wind is with the tide, and (e) when barometric pressure is low.

Summary.   *Tidal range in the open ocean is low.   Spring tides are those with more than average range of tide level at a given place and come at new and full moon; neap tides are less than average range of tide level and come in the first and third quarter positions of the moon.   The tides first prime and then lag after the spring tide period.   Successive high tides about 12 hours apart may be quite unequal in height, depending on the latitude of the moon's zenith position.   The highest tides at any given place result from the coincidence of a number of favoring conditions.*

Laboratory Exercise.   Exercise XLI in TARR and VON ENGELN's *Laboratory Manual for Physical and Commercial Geography*, The Macmillan Company, New York, should be done in connection with the study of this appendix devoted to tides. The student will get from the laboratory study specific and detailed knowledge of the intervals and variations of the tides.

APPENDIX F

MAGNETISM

In the United States, and in other regions, a bar or needle of magnetized steel, so suspended that it freely swings horizontally, will point north and south.   An instrument having such a needle is a *compass*.   Throughout most of the country the compass needle points a little to one side of a true north and south line.   In southwestern Greenland the needle points westward, in northern Greenland, southwestward.   The place toward which the compass needle points is known as the *north magnetic pole*, and is located north of Hudson Bay and west of Baffin Land.   Within the Antarctic Continent, between East Australia and the South Pole, there is a similar region known as the *south magnetic pole*.

It is because of these centers of magnetism that the compass is so valuable.   Sailors depend upon it for determining the course of their ships.

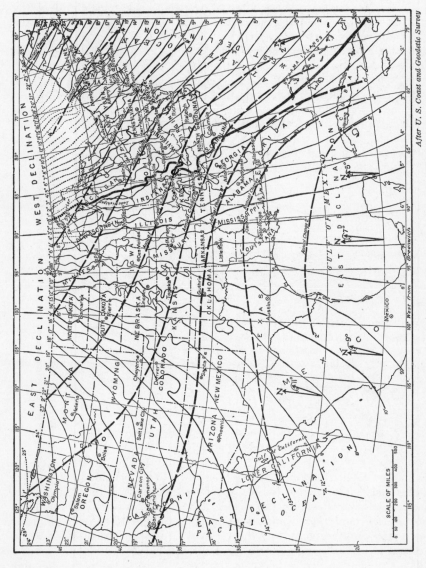

Fig. 534. — Isogonic map of the United States, showing the amount of declination for 1920 and the lines of annual change. With this map figure the declination for your locality in the present year.

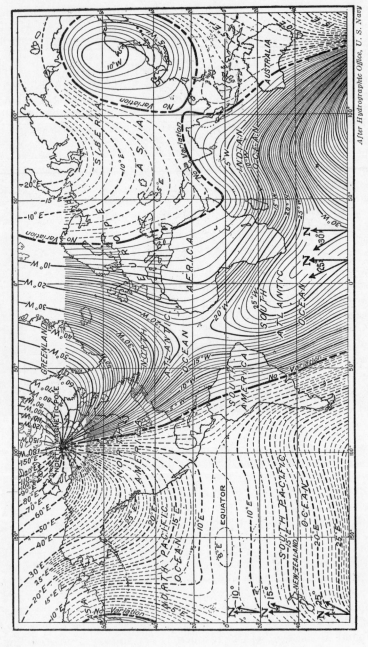

Fig. 535. — Isogonic chart of the World for 1925. Compare with Fig. 534. Note the position of the North Magnetic Pole. How would a magnetic compass act traveling across the Arctic Ocean from Greenland to Alaska over the North Pole?

The steersman always has one in plain sight. In the Arctic the compass is much less useful, for, though nearer the magnetic pole, the needle is less sensitive and more easily deflected by outside influences, such as the presence of iron.

The reason for this fact is that the cause for the attraction of the needle lies beneath the earth's surface. This is proved by so suspending a needle that it will freely swing, or dip, vertically. At the magnetic pole, the needle of such a *dip compass* points directly downward; near the equator it swings horizontally; part way between the pole and equator it points toward the earth at an angle. From this it is evident that, the nearer one goes to the magnetic pole, the stronger becomes the downward attraction and the weaker the horizontal pull, and, therefore, the less useful the compass.

Along a line extending from South Carolina to Lake Superior, *magnetic north*, or north by the compass, is the same as true north; that is, the compass points toward the north pole. East of this line the compass points to the west of true north, northern Maine showing a difference between magnetic and true north, or a *declination*, of 21°. West of the line of no variation, or no declination, the *agonic line*, the needle points to the east of true north, in northern Washington reaching an east declination of 23°.

Fig. 536. — The aurora borealis, photographed in Alaska along the Yukon River.

A map showing lines of equal magnetic declination is an *isogonic map* (Figs. 534, 535).

The amount of declination slowly changes, so that a map made for one year is not strictly accurate for the next year; but the change is so slow that a long time is necessary to produce a marked difference. The cause for these changes, and even the cause for the magnetism of the earth, are unknown. It is a condition within the earth, far from the surface, possibly in some way connected with the probability of a nickle-iron interior mass (p. 24). All that is positively known is that the earth acts as a great magnet.

The *aurora borealis*, or northern lights (Fig. 536), is probably an effect resulting from this magnetism. A similar phenomenon, the *aurora australis*, is found in the southern hemisphere. The aurora is not common in the United States, though sometimes it becomes visible, and even vivid. The northern sky is then aglow with an arch of strange light, with streamers darting to and fro.   Between 65° and 80° N. latitude the aurora becomes much more vivid, and occurs most often.   The nature of the aurora is unknown, though it seems to be caused by faint electrical discharges in the upper air.   Such discharges acting upon mixtures of oxygen and helium gas at low pressure appear to be responsible for the green line which is the puzzling feature of the auroral spectrum.

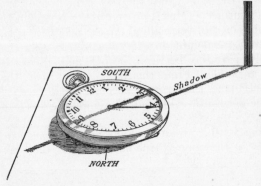

Fig. 537. — A method for determining direction by use of a watch at any time of the day when the sun is shining.   Point the hour hand of the watch toward the sun (line of the shadow) then half way between that line and a line from the figure 12 (noon) on the dial to the center of the dial, will be *south*.   Measure back in the afternoon, forward in the forenoon, toward 12.

SUGGESTIONS.   (1) Learn to read a compass (a small one is quite inexpensive).   A pamphlet entitled *Compass Surveys*, giving instructions how to use a compass, may be had free of charge by any one on application to the "Director, Coast and Geodetic Survey, Washington, D. C."   Determine the true north and south line.   This can be done by setting up two poles in line with the north star when it has the position shown in Fig. 14.   (See also Fig. 537).   With a compass, observe the difference between true and magnetic north.   (2) Place a bar of iron near a compass. Is the needle disturbed?   (3) If you have ever seen an aurora describe it. Have you ever read a description of one in a book of Arctic travel?

Laboratory Exercise.   Exercise V in TARR and VON ENGELN's *Laboratory Manual for Physical and Commercial Geography*, The Macmillan Company, New York, will supplement the study of Appendix F.

APPENDIX G

METEOROLOGICAL INSTRUMENTS

1. Thermometers.   The ordinary thermometer is a sealed glass tube with a cavity of small (capillary) diameter ending below in an expansion, or bulb, in which there is mercury.   The mercury can rise and fall freely in the tube because there is no air in it.   The principle of the thermometer is that liquids, such as mercury, expand and require more space when warmed, but, when cooled, contract and take up less space.   As the temperature changes, therefore, the mercury in the bulb causes a tiny thread of mercury to rise and fall in the tube.   Other liquids may be used; in fact, alcohol is used when thermometers are to be exposed to cold greater than the freezing point of mercury (−40° F.).

Thermometers are graduated in degrees; the division commonly used in America and England is the Fahrenheit (Fahr. or F.) scale. In this, the boiling point of water is placed at 212° and its freezing point at 32°. This is not nearly so simple a scale as the Centigrade (Cent. or C.) which is commonly used on the continent of Europe. In this, the freezing point is placed at 0° and the boiling point at 100°. To convert Centigrade to Fahrenheit, multiply by 1.8 and add 32°. Thus 10° Cent. equals 50° Fahr. (10° × 1.8 = 18° + 32° = 50°.)

Metals also expand when warmed and contract when cooled. Because of this fact, thermometers may be made of metal strips connected with a hand that moves over a graduated dial. A metal thermometer may also be connected with an arm, bearing a pen, which is moved as the temperature changes. This pen may be so placed as to press against a piece of paper on a cylinder, revolved by clockwork. As the pen rises and falls, while the cylinder regularly revolves, it writes a record of temperature changes for every minute of the day. Such a self-recording thermometer is called a *thermograph*.

2. Barometers. The weight, or pressure, of air will push liquid up into a tube having a vacuum in the top. The top of the tube must be closed and the air above the surface of the liquid exhausted to create the vacuum. It will push the liquid up until a column is formed that equals the weight of the air column pressing on it. It is because of this air pressure that water is pushed up from a well into the tube of a pump. The stroke of the pump exhausts air from the tube, thus tending to make a vacuum, into which the water may be pushed by the air pressure. Since a column of water about 30 feet high balances the air pressure, an ordinary pump could not possibly raise water from a fifty-foot well.

Years ago water, in tubes over 30 feet long, was used to measure air pressure. Mercury is now employed because it is so heavy that a column only thirty inches high balances the air pressure. An instrument containing such a mercury column is called a *barometer* (Fig. 538).

Any one can make a rough barometer with a glass tube 35 inches long, sealed at one end. Fill the tube with mercury, and then, holding the finger over the

Fig. 538.—Reading the barometer in a U. S. Weather Bureau station.

open end, invert it, and place the open end below the surface of a pool of mercury nearly filling a small dish. Then remove the finger. The mercury will fall a few inches, and air pressure will keep it there.   As the mercury had previously filled the tube completely the open space above the mercury column must now be a vacuum for there was no way through which air could enter it.   By fastening the tube to a standard to keep it upright, one may watch the mercury rise and fall from day to day. A scale of inches and tenths of inches may be marked on the piece of wood to which the tube is fastened.   By comparison with a standard graduated barometer the scale may be made exact.

Ordinary mercury barometers are graduated in inches and tenths of inches, and a scale, called a *vernier*, enables readings to hundredths of inches.   As storms come and go the air pressure varies, and with these changes the height of the mercury column changes.   When the air is heavy, dense, the barometer column is high, and there is a *high barometer;* when the air is light the barometer column is low, and there is a *low barometer*.   For example, 30.1 inches is a high barometer; 29.3 is a low barometer.

Fig. 539.—Aneroid barometer, graduated in feet (outside) and inches of mercury (inside).

Since there is less air (and therefore less pressure) above highlands than lowlands, the barometer is low on highlands and high on lowlands.   As this difference in pressure varies quite regularly, a barometer may be used to measure elevation; for a change of an inch in the mercury column represents a difference in elevation of a certain number of feet.

A mercurial barometer is too cumbersome, and too easily injured, to be carried about; therefore, for measuring elevations, an *aneroid barometer* is commonly used.   An aneroid, which is so small that it may be carried in the pocket, consists of a sealed metal box from which the air has been exhausted.   The sides of the box are prevented from collapsing by a strong spring.   Differences in air pressure cause the spring to stretch or be compressed slightly, and this movement is communicated to a hand which moves over a dial (Fig. 539).   When the dial is graduated in feet, one can tell at a glance how high he has climbed.

One serious disadvantage in the use of the aneroid in determining elevations is that it is affected by *all* changes in air pressure.   Thus, if a storm passes while the aneroid is being used to measure an elevation, the change in air pressure causes the hand to move, making an error in the observation. This can be corrected, however, by comparing its readings with those of another barometer kept at a fixed place.

As in the case of thermometers, there are self-recording barometers, or *barographs*. In these, as in thermographs, a pen point pressed against a roll of paper on a cylinder, revolved by clockwork, gives a continuous record of changes in pressure.

3. Anemometers. Wind *direction* is determined by the ordinary *weather vane*, and the *rate* at which the air is moving by the *anemometer* (Fig. 540). The latter instrument consists of four metal cups on crossbars, revolved by the wind striking the hollow sides of the cups. Each revolu-

tion is communicated to a cog-wheel, which causes a hand to move on a dial, recording the velocity.

Wind velocity is measured in miles per hour, and the dial is so graduated that the hand indicates the number of miles the wind has moved. An anemometer may be connected by electric wire to a self-recording apparatus.

Estimates of wind velocity may be made by an observer without using instruments and the wind correctly named in accordance with the following conditions. When there is no perceptible movement of anything a *calm* prevails, the wind velocity is 0 miles per hour.

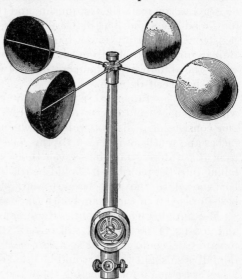

Fig. 540. — An anemometer.

When the leaves of a tree just move but the branches do not move or sway a *very light breeze* is moving, the velocity is up to 4 miles per hour. When the wind velocity is 4 to 12 miles per hour the branches of trees move, papers and dry leaves are blown up from the ground; this is a *gentle* to *fresh breeze*. At 12 to 22 miles per hour a *strong wind* is blowing; branches of trees swing, dust clouds form, leaves and papers scurry. From 22 to 32 miles per hour whole trees sway and walking is hindered; it is a *high wind*. Over 32 and up to 72 miles per hour *gales* from ordinary to *strong gale* and *violent gale* are encountered; these break small branches, loosen bricks in chimneys and offer decided resistance to walking. Above 72 miles per hour the wind is blowing a *hurricane* and causes all sorts of destruction.

4. Measurement of vapor. There are several instruments for determining the humidity of the air. One of these is the *hair hygrometer*, which consists of a long human hair robbed of its oil. Such hair will absorb vapor, changing in length as the amount of absorbed vapor varies. It is because of this fact that the hair of many people becomes straight in damp weather. In the hair hygrometer a hand is moved over a graduated scale, in one direction if the humidity is high, in the other if it is low.

Another instrument, the *sling psychrometer*, consists of two thermometers attached to a board, one having a piece of wet muslin around its bulb. Its use depends upon two facts: (1) That evaporation is more rapid in dry than in humid air; (2) that evaporation lowers the temperature.

Since the evaporation will take place more freely and uniformly if fresh air is continually supplied to the wet bulb the sling psychrometer is whirled around for a minute or two. If the air is saturated, there will be no evaporation from the wet muslin, and the two thermometers will, therefore, read the same; but if the air is dry, the wet bulb thermometer will register a perceptibly lower temperature. The United States Weather Bureau furnishes tables from which the relative humidity can be calculated when the difference in temperature between the *dry* and *wet bulb thermometers* has been determined.

Various instruments are used for determining the *rate of evaporation*, which changes from day to day and from place to place. An *evaporating pan* consists of a dish of water in which is placed a ruler graduated in inches and tenths of inches. By this, one can tell how much is evaporated from the water surface in a given time. Rain should be prevented from falling into the pan, but it should be freely open to the air. It should not be exposed to the sun, because warming increases evaporation. It is best to place it in the ground with the top level with the surface.

5. Rainfall measurement. Rainfall is recorded in number of inches and tenths of inches that fall on a given surface. Any cylinder, as a tomato can, could be used as a *rain gauge*, or measurer; but an ordinary rainfall is so slight that it would be difficult to measure it unless some provision were made for collecting the water in a smaller space than the surface on which it fell.

Any tinsmith can make a rain gauge, with two cylinders, one inside of the other, about 20 inches high; the inside cylinder having a diameter of 2.53 inches, the outside one 8 inches (Fig. 541). This gives an area of 50 square inches to the opening of the outside cylinder and of 5 square inches to the bottom of the inside cylinder. A funnel fits over the outside cylinder, and a hole in it leads into the inside cylinder. The rain that falls on the funnel collects in the bottom of the inner cylinder to a depth ten times that of the actual rainfall. Measuring this with a ruler, and dividing by ten, gives the actual rainfall, even though it is slight. There are also self-recording rain gauges.

Instruments are sometimes used for measuring snowfall; but usually this can be fairly well done by measuring its depth in some place where it is not drifted. The average snowfall is about ten times the amount that would have fallen as rain. In weather records it is customary to record snowfall in inches of rain. Place snow in a cylinder, filling it to a depth of a foot, and melt it to see how much water it produces. Do not pack the snow down.

6. An instrument shelter. In order to get good results, meteorological instruments must be placed where they are not influenced by local conditions. For example, two thermometers, one in the shade, the other exposed to the sun, will give very different readings. A simple *instrument shelter*, made of inclined, overlapping slabs, far enough apart to let the

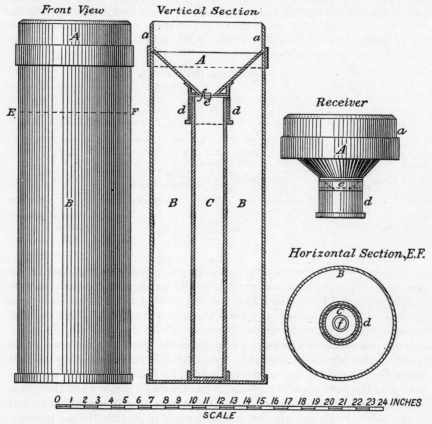

Fig. 541. — Rain gauge. *B*, outer cylinder; *C*, inner cylinder; *a, a,* (and small right-hand figures), the funnel.

air circulate freely, and yet near enough together to keep the sun out, is easily made. It should be placed either on open ground or on the roof.

The barometer may be kept in the schoolroom, the rain gauge on open ground away from a building, and the anemometer on the roof; but the other instruments are best kept in an instrument shelter.

SUGGESTIONS. For purchase of meteorological instruments, see p. 659. As indicated above, it is possible to make several of the common instruments, especially the barometer, psychrometer, evaporating pan, and rain gauge. This might easily be done in the manual training department. With these instruments daily records may be kept, and laboratory work of value done, especially for comparison with the study of weather maps and storms. Daily and seasonal temperature curves may also be made. If this work is carried along with the study of the atmosphere, the teacher will find many opportunities for connecting observations with facts in the book. For example, observe the humidity of the air near the ground when dew is forming and when it is not. When frost is forming, take the temperature of the ground and of the air 10 feet above it to see if radiation cools the ground. After the barometer begins to fall, does it rain? What change in wind direction then takes place? In temperature, etc.?

SUGGESTED RECORD

	JANUARY 1, 1927			JANUARY 2, 1927			JANUARY 3, 1927		
	8 A.M.	1 P.M.	8 P.M.	8 A.M.	1 P.M.	8 P.M.	8 A.M.	1 P.M.	8 P.M
Temperature	5°	10°	2°	−1°	20°	18°	17°	30°	31°
Barometer	30.0	30.0	30.1	30.1	30.0	29.9	29.8	29.7	29.6
Wind	West	West	Calm	Calm	S. W.	S. W.	South	S. E.	East
Wind Force	F. Breeze	Strong	Calm	Calm	Light Breeze	F. Breeze	Light Breeze	Strong	Gale
Sky . . .	Clear	Cumulus	Clear	Clear	Clear	Cirrus	Cirrus	Cirro stratus	Stratus
Rainfall .	0	0	0	0	0	0	0	.1 light snow	.3 heavy snow
Humidity .	80	60	82	85	55	85	90	100	100

The following experiment convincingly demonstrates the fact of air pressure. Take a metal can with a single small opening that may be tightly capped. Pour water into the can so that the bottom is covered to the depth of one inch or so. Place the can over a Bunsen flame or other heater and *boil* water for some minutes. Then, immediately before removing can from over heater, put cap on the opening and screw down tightly. Put the can under cold water; it will be collapsed by the air pressure. The water vapor (steam) formed by boiling the water displaces the air in the can. But this steam is condensed to water when the can is put under cold water. Accordingly a vacuum is formed inside the can and as the sides of the can are not strong enough to sustain the air pressure the can is crushed. A calculation of the area of the surface of the can will show how great this pressure really is (p. 398) on a given surface.

APPENDIX H

WEATHER MAPS

The U. S. Weather Bureau issues daily maps showing weather conditions throughout the country. These can be secured for the school by sending a money order subscription in advance to the Superintendent of Documents, Washington, D. C., at the rate of 30 cents per month, or $3.00 per year, and asking that the Daily Weather Map, Form C, second edition, be mailed to the school. Another smaller map issued from each of 65 stations scattered over the United States should be applied for by schools remote from Washington, D. C. Send subscription also to Superintendent of Documents, Washington, D. C., and ask for Daily Weather Map DD from your nearest station, 20 cents per month, or $2.00 per year.

The weather maps are based upon reports telegraphed from Weather Bureau Stations in all sections of the country; and the facts regarding temperature, rainfall, and wind are placed in a table at the bottom of the map. On the basis of these reports, predictions for the next day are made at a central office.

On the map, which is an outline map of United States, the direction of the wind is indicated by arrows. At the ends of some of the arrows is the letter R, meaning rain, or S, meaning snow. Arrows that terminate in blank circles (⊘) mean clear weather; when half black (◑), partly cloudy; and when all black (●), cloudy. The centers of high and low pressure areas are indicated by the words *High* and *Low*. Dotted or red lines (*isothermal lines*) pass through places having equal temperatures, and continuous black lines (*isobaric lines*) pass through places with equal air pressure. The barometric readings (29.8, 30.1, etc.) are all reduced to sea level; that is, made to read as they would if the station were at sea level. Temperature readings are also shown in figures.

Thus the weather maps, besides describing the weather conditions and predicting for the next day, contain a large amount of information concerning the weather of different sections. A study of the maps on several successive days will make their meaning plain, and will illustrate many points discussed in the book. Sets suitable for the work suggested below are easily obtained by keeping the maps for a year or two.

SUGGESTIONS. (1) Study a weather map to understand its meaning. Which isotherm passes nearest your home? What other places have the same temperature? What is the air pressure? What other places are on the same isobar? Is the weather at your home clear, cloudy, or rainy? What is the wind direction? How do these facts compare with your own observations the previous day? Study the weather maps for the next two days. What differences are noticed? Do you find any explanation? (2) Select weather maps to illustrate a typical storm. Let each student make a copy on a blank map of the United States. Such blank maps may be had at the rate of 25 cents per hundred (only 100 at a time) by sending a money order to and payable to "Chief, U. S. Weather Bureau," and asking for blank Map DD. As many different orders for 100 as may be necessary may be sent by the same school but only 100 can be mailed on one order. Determine in what parts the pressure is low, and where high. Shade between the isobars. Shade on the map the rainy or snowy sections. With another colored pencil mark the cloudy areas. What is the direction of the winds in the different areas? What part of the storm area is warmest? What part coolest? What is the direction of the wind in each case? Can you find

an explanation of any of the facts observed?   (3) In the same way, study the
weather maps for the next three days.   Write a statement of the changes that
have occurred.   On an outline map draw the path followed by the storm center.
Select some place on the map, and for that place describe the weather changes
— pressure, temperature, wind, and rain — for the four days.   (4) In the same
way study a set of maps in which a typical high pressure area, or anticyclone,
passes across the country.   (5) On an outline map plot around the same central
point the winds of three well-defined storms.   Also three anticyclones.   What
about their direction?   (6) Give to each student a map with a well-defined storm,
and have him tell what he thinks the weather conditions were the day before,
and what they were the next day.   First remove the predictions from the map.
After the predictions have been written down, show the actual maps.   This practice may be continued until the class becomes fairly proficient in predictions.
Toward the end of these exercises have the students sketch their predictions on
outline maps; that is, upon the basis of their study of a map for a given day let
them make a weather map of the previous and succeeding days.   Care should be
taken to select well-defined storms that move regularly, otherwise the results may
be poor.   (7) Give out problems; many will be suggested by a study of a series
of weather maps.   For example, given a well-defined low at Chicago, temperature
34.5°: is it clear or rainy?   Is the temperature probably higher or lower at Minneapolis?   At Indianapolis?   On a sketch map of United States ask that the area
of probable snow be indicated.   Of rain.   Ask what will the weather probably be
next day at Chicago?   At Cleveland?   (8) Upon the basis of observations with
instruments in the school make weather predictions.   (9) Each day give the
weather map to one of the students and let him report the facts of barometer,
temperature, position of Highs and Lows, etc.; or, better, sketch them on an
outline map for the class to see.   Then call for predictions from the class and
have them give their reasons.   Then read the prediction on the map.   Next day
call for a statement of how nearly correct the prediction was.

APPENDIX I

MAPS AND MAP PROJECTIONS

Various methods are employed to represent the surface of the earth
by maps.   Among these are relief maps, hachure maps, and contour
maps, all of much value in a study of physical geography.

1. Relief maps or models.   Ordinary maps are flat; and on a political
map little attempt is made to represent relief.   Yet by shading, or by
color, some are made to indicate the general distribution of highlands
and lowlands.   A far better means of representing a country is by relief
map, or model, in which the surface is actually raised to represent irregularities of the land.

Owing to the small size of such maps, it is usually necessary to exag-
gerate the vertical, that is, make the scale of elevation, or vertical scale, different from the horizontal scale.   Thus one inch vertically may represent
1000 feet, while in the horizontal scale an inch represents 10,000 or even
20,000 feet.   To avoid wrong impressions from the use of such maps, care

should be used to understand and make allowance for this exaggeration.

If funds are available each school in which physical geography is taught should have at least a few relief models as part of its equipment. It is just as important that equipment be available for the teaching of the science of physical geography as for the teaching of physics or chemistry. On page 655 suggestions are made as to what should be obtained in relief models and where these may be had.

2. Hachure maps. The United States Coast Survey and the surveys of many European countries make use of *hachures* to represent irregularities of the surface of small sections. A hachure map is one in which the relief is brought out by shading, through the use of lines drawn more or less closely together, and all pointing in the direction of the slope (Fig. 196). Such a map is very graphic, and exceedingly useful in a study of the general form of the land. For some purposes its usefulness is lessened by the fact that, though it clearly brings out *differences* in elevation between adjoining areas, it does not show the *actual* elevations.

3. Contour maps. The fact last mentioned has led other surveys, for example the U. S. Geological Survey, to adopt *contour lines*, or lines passing through places of equal elevation.

Imagine a rather irregular beach at low tide when there are no waves. The water level marks a contour line, and extends up the depressions, or valleys, in the sand. This may be called the 0 contour; if the tide rises five feet, a new contour is marked five feet above the other. This would be called the five-foot contour.

In making contour maps, sea level is reckoned as 0, and each contour passes through all places on the map that are at the same level above the sea; that is, places which the sea would touch if it rose that high. Every place through which the 100-foot contour passes is just 100 feet above sea level. On such maps, therefore, it is possible to tell the elevation of every place. Contour maps do not express relief so graphically as hachure maps, but, with a little study, one learns to interpret quickly from them the forms of the land.

Some of the more recent issues of contour maps by the U. S. Geological Survey are *shaded relief maps*. On these the topography is indicated in addition to the contours by shading and the forms of the country show very clearly indeed. By using a contour map without shading and one with shading of the same area, the pupil can be led very easily and quickly to get an understanding and appreciation of contour maps. Suggestions regarding the procuring of such comparable and other contour maps are made on page 657. See also Plate III.

Plains have few contours, far apart; gorges have many, close together; rounded hills have contours of different shape from those on steep-sided hills, etc. On the U. S. Geological Survey maps the horizontal scale is usually nearly one inch to the mile. The vertical scale, or *contour interval*, is usually 20 feet; that is, a contour is drawn for every 20 feet of elevation. Therefore, the vertical distance, or interval, between two contours is 20 feet.   In sparsely settled or mountainous regions a contour interval of 100 feet is often used.

SUGGESTIONS.   (1) Find out if the U. S. Geological Survey has issued a contour map of your vicinity. (Write to "Director U. S. Geological Survey, Washington, D. C.," and ask for an "Index Map of topographic sheets" for your state, This will be sent free of charge.) If so get a copy (cost 10 cents, 50 for $3.00), mount it (p. 659), and carry it on walks or rides.   It will prove to be very instructive. (2) Let the class have practice in making simple contour sketches; for example, have students make contours to show a round hill, a long hill, a hill steep on one end, two hills and a valley, a broad valley, a gorge, etc.   Also draw simple contour sketches on the board (for example, a round hill), and have the class make cross sections of them; that is, sections to show the profile as if the hill were sliced through.   Keep the class at this work until pupils understand how to do quickly what is given. (3) Have the class sketch a contour map of a selected portion of a relief model. (4) Obtain a series of contour maps, and have the class make cross sections along lines drawn on the map by the teacher.   Detailed suggestions on how to make accurate cross-section profiles are contained in *A Guide for Laboratory Geography Teaching* by von Engeln, a pamphlet which may be obtained from The Macmillan Company, New York. (5) After some practice in cross-sectioning, select a series of maps and assign to each student part of the task of defining in words the topography of part or all of a map.   This may well be followed by other maps. (6) The teacher may, possibly, deem it worth while to have the class make a map of a small area.   With a tape line, an aneroid barometer, a level, and a compass, a rough map may easily be made. (7) If the teacher would each year have a model made by the class, the school would soon accumulate a valuable equipment.   It is not very difficult to make a model. For the first one start with a simple region — say the Marion, Iowa, sheet.   Find the lowest contour on the sheet and transfer it to tracing paper, then to a thin cardboard sheet the size of the map.   Then cut the cardboard along the line. Tack it to a board, or thick cardboard, the size of the map.   Do the same for the next higher contour, and tack this to the first.   Continue until there is a pile of cardboards, one for each contour.   Divided among many, this is not a very difficult task.   With molding wax, smooth the surface so that no cardboard edges appear.   After one or two trials a very satisfactory model will be made.   On more complex sheets it is not necessary to trace every contour.   An interesting model may be made by starting with a large number of sheets of the same map and, instead of tracing the contours, cut the map itself, and paste sheet on sheet until each contour is represented.   To cut the sheets with an even edge, lay the map on a sheet of glass or zinc and cut it with a sharp knife.

4. Map projections.   Contoured and hachured topographic sheets are usually large scale representations of a small area.   On them the lines of latitude and longitude are nearly at right angles, the areas are so small that the maps apparently do not need to give consideration to the fact that the earth is a sphere and has a curved surface.   But if the contoured topographic sheets of the United States Geological Survey are examined closely it will be noted that the meridians of longitude converge toward the north.   This indicates that some scheme has been devised to represent as accurately as possible the curved surface of the earth on a flat map.

Such a scheme for map drawing is known as a *map projection*. When flat maps of wide areas or of the world as a whole are to be attempted, the problem of representing the curved surface of the earth on a plane with some degree of accuracy in regard to relative distances between points and comparative areas is of first importance. It is obvious that a curved surface cannot be represented on a plane surface with complete accuracy.

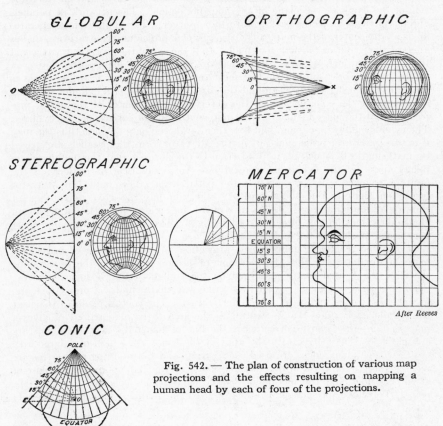

Fig. 542. — The plan of construction of various map projections and the effects resulting on mapping a human head by each of four of the projections.

In Fig. 542 four of these schemes are shown by diagrams. Paired with each diagram is a map of a human head made by that projection. It will immediately be noted that the distortion is more or less grotesque in each instance. Yet the same head was mapped in each of the diagrams with latitudinal and longitudinal positions corresponding for each feature. This will make clear how difficult the adequate and accurate representation of a spherical surface on a plane map is.

In the *globular* projection the map is made by imagining that an observer's eye is placed at a point in space at a calculated distance from one side of the earth and at the level of the equator. The map sheet stands upright on the opposite side of the earth and touches the earth at the equator. Then the network of the parallels of latitude and the meridians of longitude, as the observer would see it by looking through the earth to the far side, is *projected*, that is, extended and pushed away from the observer so that it makes a trace on the plane of the paper. The globular projection has the least distortion of those shown in Fig. 542.

In the *orthographic* projection it will be noted that the eye of the observer is assumed to be at a very great distance away from the earth and on the same side of the earth as the plane of the map projection. The network of parallels and meridians is projected back toward the observer. This projection exaggerates areas at the center of the map. The *stereographic* projection, contrariwise, makes areas at the center of the map too small. In it the eye of the observer is conceived to be at the surface of the earth and viewing the opposite hemisphere.

In the *Mercator* projection the sheet on which the map is to be made is thought of as being wrapped around the earth in the form of a cylinder touching all around at the equator. Then the observer, at the center of the earth, projects the latitudinal and longitudinal net on the inside surface of the cylinder. The cylinder, unwrapped, and laid flat, then forms the map. Made thus the map is a true *cylindrical* projection, but in the Mercator form the parallels are spaced by mathematical calculation in proportion to the distance that the meridians are pulled apart by the cylindrical projection. Any cylindrical projection has the fault of tremendously exaggerating the polar areas. This fault the Mercator projection shares. But the Mercator projection has the great advantage of showing all meridians and parallels as straight lines and at proportional distances. Hence directions on this map are straight lines. This makes the Mercator chart very useful in plotting the course of a ship at sea.

Conic and *polyconic* (many cones) projections are commonly used in making maps of small areas. Thus the polyconic projection is used for the topographic sheets of the United States published by the United States Geological Survey. Such projections are made in much the same way that cylindrical projections are, except that a cone instead of a cylinder is used. The cone is made to touch at the parallel of latitude that is central to the area to be mapped. This gives a map that is quite nearly correct near the line of touching. The meridians are straight lines that converge to the apex of the cone. If a map of a large area is to be made, many cones are used successively, and the resulting map strips are put together. The effect of this method is to keep the map approximately correct at all latitudes and the meridians become curved lines bending in toward the poles. Polyconic projection is usually used in making wall maps of continents.

Laboratory Exercises. Exercises II, III, IV, XV, XVI, XVII, and XVIII in TARR and VON ENGELN's *Laboratory Manual for Physical and Commercial Geography*, The Macmillan Company, New York, are designed to afford pupils systematic instruction and training in the construction, comprehension, and interpretation of map projections and contoured topographic maps.

Reference Books. JOHNSON, *Mathematical Geography*, American Book Company, New York, 1907; FINCH, *Topographic Maps and Sketch Mapping*, John Wiley & Sons, New York, 1920; DAKE and BROWN, *Interpretation of Topographic and Geologic Maps*, McGraw-Hill Publishing Company, New York, 1925; LOBECK, *Block Diagrams*. John Wiley & Sons, New York, 1924.

APPENDIX J

EQUIPMENT

1. Models. If only limited funds are available for the purchase of equipment secure, in relief models, the *Harvard Geographical Models*, a set of three, sold by Ginn and Co., Boston, for $20 a set. A manual describing them and their use is issued by the same publishers. If more money is available, an attempt should be made to get a relief model of the home state or of the region about the school. Apply to the Central Scientific Company, Chicago, Illinois, Ward's Natural Science Establishment, Rochester, N. Y., and to Denoyer-Geppert Co., 5235 Ravenswood Ave., Chicago, Illinois, for catalogs of what they have available, and for further information. For construction of models from topographic maps, see page 652. The Wisconsin Geographical Press, 1635 Madison St., Madison, Wis., supplies Lobeck's inexpensive *Physiographic Diagrams of the United States and of Europe* in both large and small scale editions for the United States, and in a small scale edition for Europe. These will serve to give students a regional concept of many of the phenomena described in this text. Their *Panorama of Physiographic Types* issued in 1926, will be found very useful in correlating between characteristic topographic forms and the expression given such forms by contoured maps. Single copies are sent postpaid for 35 cents.

2. Maps. It is difficult to make a general statement applicable to all schools and all classes in physical geography as to the most desirable equipment of wall maps showing relief and physical features of continents and parts of continents. As no two teachers will use such maps in quite the same way and for exactly the same purpose, a recommendation that would be suitable in one case would not apply so well in another. A second difficulty is that there is such a variety of material available that no few selected items can properly be termed the best available. Accordingly the suggestion is made that teachers secure the catalogs of the following map makers and dealers and choose, from the material offered in these, maps in certain series that are best suited to their needs.

Map makers and dealers. A. J. Nystrom and Co., 2249 Calumet Ave., Chicago, Ill.; Denoyer-Geppert Co., 5235 Ravenswood Ave., Chicago, Ill.; Rand McNally Co., Chicago, Ill.; C. S. Hammond and Co., Hudson Terminal Building, New York, N. Y.

Map series. The *Sydow-Habenicht* physical maps (Nystrom and Denoyer catalogs) published in Germany are probably the most effective in showing relief and physical features by color and shading. The *Haack* physical series, also published in Germany, has relief in color and shading, is of very large size easily visible at classroom distance, and has, in addition, some further shading to show political features. The Johnston *Bathy-Orographical* series (Nystrom catalog), an English publication, is not so large, is lower in price, and relief is shown by the layer system of color shading. This series includes maps of the Oceans with currents and depths shown. The Philips *Large Comparative Wall Atlas Physical Map* series (Denoyer catalog) is another English publication similar to the Johnston Bathy-Orographic maps. The Philips map publications include also very good series on temperature, climate, and vegetation. The Kuhnert *Relief-Like* maps (Denoyer catalog) are a series giving a semi-pictorial expression to the larger features of the relief that is very convincing and realistic for beginning students. These maps are also large size and relatively inexpensive. Through Hammond and Company a variety of governmental relief maps of large size can be obtained; the 12-sheet India Survey map of India and Adjacent Countries showing the Himalaya Mountains and the central Asiatic plateau in contrast with the Ganges and Indus plains; the Kummerly and Frey Swiss Government, Physical and Political Map of Switzerland, perhaps the finest and most effective single wall map ever produced; the Dutch Colonial Government map of Java, showing the line of volcanic cones extending along the axis of that island, being especially noteworthy items. Of American publications the *Goode Physical Maps* (Rand McNally) deserve commendation; they show much detail quite accurately, have many novel features, and are relatively inexpensive. The South America map is especially good in this series.

Perhaps as good a plan as any for most teachers will be to get a single map from several of these series and then fill out sets later. Even if not used systematically in recitation work, large wall maps of the continents and countries, kept on display and available in the classroom for ready and immediate reference, will be found to promote effective teaching of physical geography. Possession of a few will create the desire for many wall maps.

It is worth while to write to practically every Federal and State Government department for a list of maps that it publishes. Many such maps, wall maps and others of smaller scale, may be had free of charge. Some may be secured on application to the local congressman, others from the Superintendent of Documents, Washington, D. C., at small cost. Apply to him also for a catalog of maps issued by the government.

The entire United States coast is charted by the U. S. Coast Survey, and many parts of the country are mapped by the U. S. Geological Survey. The Geological Survey topographic sheets may be ordered for $0.10 each, or at the rate of $0.06 a sheet if 50 or more are ordered. Money must be sent by money order *in advance*. The Geological Survey also issues special maps, for example a series of different scale maps of the United States; also geological folios, — perhaps of your district.

3. Use of topographic maps. The use made of topographic sheets will vary with the teacher, the time available, and the number and variety of sheets at hand (Fig. 543).

If the Tarr and von Engeln's *Laboratory Manual of Physical and Commercial Geography* is systematically used, as suggested in connection with the different chapters and sections in this book, the topographic sheets indicated for the exercises in the *Manual* will provide wide acquaintance with physiographic phenomena as represented on such maps. If systematic work is not carried on, a number of especially instructive sheets should be secured and used to illustrate and supplement instruction with the text. And even if the laboratory exercises are done, some additional sheets will prove very helpful and will promote understanding and appreciation of particular phenomena. As a minimum requirement in ability to read contour maps, students should be able to recognize outstanding and typical physiographic phenomena as expressed in the relief of the land.

Fig. 543. — Part of a laboratory for physical geography. Large table, made by grouping small tables, in foreground. Students are seated around this for map work. It is possible to assemble around this table a large assortment of models, maps, and photographs for use during a laboratory period.

The author of this book has noted throughout his long experience in teaching geography that the concepts of "relief" and "topography" of the land are among the most difficult for students to grasp. Adequate and painstaking instruction on the meaning of these words will be effort well spent.

The United States Geological Survey, Washington, D. C., issues circulars numbered 16808, 9-323y, and 9-323z, describing and listing respectively, sets of 25, 50, and 100 different sheets of its topographic maps that illustrate physiographic phenomena especially well. In general a map that is listed in the 25 set is not repeated in the 50 or 100 set, so that in all some 175 different authenticated maps are made available through these lists which are free on application to the Director. In some places congressmen can supply the 25 set free of charge to schools in their districts; where not, these sets can be had at a cost of $1.00 for the set, by sending cash or money order to the Survey. The 50 set costs $3.00, the 100 set, $6.00.

In addition there are listed below certain maps that are particularly worth while. In some instances those listed duplicate items included in the 25, 50, and 100 sets, but most of them are different.

A few of the maps issued by the Survey have descriptions and pictures of the features they show printed on the back. These are special editions, and it should be indicated on the order that the edition with the text and pictures is wanted. Delaware Water Gap, Pa.-N. J.; Bright Angel, Ariz. (Colorado Canyon); Mt. Ranier National Park, Wash., (these first three are included in the 25 set); Niagara River and Vicinity Special, N. Y.; Crater Lake Special, Ore.; Yosemite Valley Special, Calif., (the last three included in the 100 set), are such maps.

The following maps illustrate special features as indicated before each map name or series of names:

Sink Holes: Mammoth Cave, Ky.; Natural Bridge; Natural Bridge Special, Va.; *Escarpment:* Pocono, Pa.; (three following are shaded relief maps) Altoona, Pa.; Philipsburg, Pa.; Lock Haven, Pa.; *Rock Terraces:* Port Leyden, N. Y.; *Headwater Erosion:* Saypo, Mont.; *Stream Piracy:* Harpers Ferry, Va.–W. Va.–Md.; *Stream Diversion:* Cordova, Iowa–Ill.; Elmira, N. Y.; *Water Gap:* Mt. Union, Pa.; *Entrenched Meanders:* Lockport, Ky.; *Alluvial Fan:* Sultana, Calif.; *River Terraces:* Marseilles, Ill.; *Aggrading Stream:* Gothenburg, Neb.; Herndon, Calif.; *Ox-Bow Lake:* Bayou Sara, La.; *Natural and Artificial Levee:* Hainville, La.; *Sand Dunes:* Lakin, Kans.; Moses Lake, Wash.

Stream Erosion, youth: Parmele, N. C.; Shirley, S. C.–Ga.; Oak Orchard, N. Y.; *Stream Erosion, maturity:* Charleston, W. Va.; *Stream Erosion, old age:* Princeton, Ind.–Ill.; Butler, Mo.; *Plain in youth:* Lehigh, Iowa; *Plain in late youth:* Melcher, Iowa; *Plain in old age:* Eldorado, Ill.; Braymer, Mo.; *Dissected Plateau:* Cameron, W. Va.–Pa.–Ohio; Andes, N. Y.; *Butte:* Lebanon, Ore.

Cirques: Hayden Peak, Utah–Wyo.; *Glacially Oversteepened Slope:* Pawlet, Vt.; *Till Sheet:* Durant, Iowa; Lansing, Mich.; *Morainic Topography:* Milford, Mich.; Farmington, Me.; *Terminal Moraine and Outwash Gravel:* Randolph, N. Y.; *Drumlins:* Sun Prairie, Wis.; *Esker:* Passadumkeag, Me.; *Disorganized Drainage:* Minneapolis, Minn.

Offshore Bar: Ocean City, Md.–Del.; Rehoboth, Del.; *Low Marshy Coast:* Dennisville, N. J.; *Drowned Coast:* Bath, Me.; Great Wass Island, Me.; *Fault Scarp:* Mt. Trumbull, Ariz.; *Fault Rift Valley:* Priest Valley, Calif.

4. Mounting maps. It is real economy to have all maps backed with cloth. This can be done by many bookbinders. The firm of C. S. Wertsner and Son, 211 N. 13th St., Philadelphia, Pa., specializes in map mounting and will do this work very well and inexpensively. It can be done in the school, using a thin, bleached, white cotton cloth of ordinary width for single sheets; extra width for grouped sheets. Use ordinary flour paste, which costs very little if purchased from a paper hanger. For successful map mounting have a smooth surface (a large drawing board or table top) on which to tack the cloth. Stretch the cloth and tack it firmly on all sides, then thoroughly wet it. Apply paste to the back of the map and allow it to lie until thoroughly limp, then put it on the cloth, which must not be too wet. Carefully press the map to the cloth with a piece of clean cloth or a photographic roller. Leave until thoroughly dry (at least 24 hours).

Combined topographic sheets must first be trimmed, leaving on alternate sheets a margin of 1 inch for adjoining sheets to overlap. For trimming, to secure an even cut, place the map on a sheet of zinc (tacked to a board), and, with a sharp knife, cut along a metal straightedge placed on the map. If a map is not complete, blank spaces may be filled with white paper. It will be found very desirable to have a combined map of all the available sheets of the region surrounding the school, about four or five north and south and an equal number in the east and west direction. Mounting such a number had best be done by a firm specializing in this work, see reference above.

Large maps should be rolled, and a wood turner will supply rollers at small cost; also strips for the top of the map. Curtain rings may be screwed into the wooden strip for hanging the map, which, for class use, may be hung on brass rods ($\frac{3}{8}$ inch in diameter) along the sides of the room. A curtain hanger will make hooks to hang over the rods or Dennison card holders may be used. If single sheets are hung, Dennison gummed-cloth suspension rings may be used.

Single sheets are best kept in a case of shallow drawers, using care not to put too many in a drawer, for they are then difficult to handle. Rolled maps are best preserved when kept in a case with shallow partitions, allowing the rolled map to lie horizontal. A cabinet-maker will build a combined case for rolled and flat maps.

5. Minerals and rocks. Ward's Natural Science Establishment, Rochester, N. Y., offers cheap sets of minerals and rocks suitable for laboratory use in connection with Physical Geography.

6. Meteorological maps, etc. Directions for securing weather maps are given in Appendix H, p. 648. Meteorological instruments (see p. 642) may be purchased from Taylor Instrument Companies, Rochester, N. Y., or H. J. Green, 1191 Bedford Ave., Brooklyn, N. Y.

7. Lantern slides. Various firms now supply good stereopticons for use in schools. It is altogether inadvisable to spend money for anything except the regular standard projection lantern models using standard size lantern slides. Opaque projection, film-strip projection, daylight projection, or any similar device or modification may not give satisfaction. Use mazda bulb illumination; 600 watt in a large room, 400 watt in a small room. Buy a standard opaque screen. Such screens are inexpensive and are really better than specially prepared metallic screens. Advise the stereopticon makers what distance the lantern will be from the screen and the size picture desired; do not have it too big.

Lantern slides illustrating physical geography phenomena are now included as part of the supply equipment of city school systems. Several states have central borrowing stations as part of the State Department of Education. New York State is especially well served by the Visual Education Division at Albany; New Jersey, Pennsylvania, Ohio, Nebraska, and other states have similar slide libraries at the capital cities from which schools may borrow at no expense.

If an appropriation can be had it is, however, well to secure an adequate set of slides as part of the permanent equipment of the school. To facilitate the purchase of instructive slides there are listed below, topically, numbers from the catalogs of the Geography Supply Bureau, College Ave., Ithaca, New York, that provide authoritative illustrations of the phenomena indicated. The catalogs from which these numbers are taken will be sent free of charge on application of any teacher using this book. A few of these slides duplicate illustrations in this book, most of them are different.

Lantern slides should not be used picture show fashion. Not over ten different ones should be shown in one recitation period except for some special purpose. Let the slides be used regularly to give the students opportunity to identify phenomena that they have learned about in the text. Find out how well the concepts they have gained through study of the printed descriptions fit the phenomena as found in nature. Lantern slides are the best substitutes for field trips; a class can be led to observe, and discuss, and make deductions about features in widely remote regions almost as well as if actually at the scene.

Before ordering the slides listed below the teacher should have the catalogs at hand in order to use the descriptions as a guide in making choices. Then also it will be possible to note other numbers that have a special local significance or are considered more desirable because of the teacher's personal acquaintance with certain areas. A typical description as taken from the catalog is as follows:

"475.— MONUMENT ROCK, GROVE COUNTY, KANSAS. An isolated butte on a very level plain.

"What is striking about the position of this butte? How are buttes formed? What resemblances and differences are there between buttes and mountain peaks?"

In ordering only the numbers need be given. The complete set of 455 slides listed below may be purchased at the special price of $200.00 by referring to this book; selections of 100 or more at 45 cents each, less than 100 at 50 cents each. Address: Geography Supply Bureau, College Avenue, Ithaca, New York.

Stratification, 1, 1372; Ripple marks, 8; Joints, 30, 32, 34; Unconformity 38, 1348; Rock texture, 41; Rain prints, 1371; Land slides, 103, 104, x1364; Earth pillars, x1516, 134, 135, 136; Talus, 95, 1352; Weathering processes and results, 46, 49, 50, 55, 58, 65, 77, 92, 93, 199; Residual soil, 113, 114, 117; Exfoliation, 123; Bad lands, 126, 128; Wind erosion, 176, 177; Sink hole, 392; Caverns, 394, 401, 406; Alluvial fan, 379, 384, 1359, x 1541; Stream erosion, 109, 195, 201; Potholes, 203, 236; 238; Plunge pool, 1362, 1431; Waterfalls, 229, 234, 245, 248, 1361, 1426; Rapids, 277, 279; Drowned river, x 1271; River and delta lands, 371, 374, 422, x 636, x 710, x 1783; Stream guidance, 211, 1355, 1370; Young river, 302, 303, 305, 1395; Late youth valley 316, 322; Mature valley, 324, 326, 330, 335; Old valley, 1364; Hanging delta, 1435; Stream terrace, 387, 388, 1528; Accordant stream junction, 332, 885; Overburdened stream, 354; Meanders, 358.

x 235; Floods, 217, m 121, m 139, m 143, m 144, m 150, m 155, m 159, m 163, m 174, m 182; Plains, 413, 414, 424, 432, x 535, x 580, N 11; Rejuvenation, 304; Dissected plateau, 447, 453, x 1793; Plateau upland, 1425; Peneplain, 455, 457; Escarpments, 477; Buttes and mesas, 86, 1487, 475; Deserts, 179, x 28, x 30, x 879, x 903; Sand dunes, 143, 146, 149, 162, 172, 174, x 26, m 59; Oases, 185, x 15; Mountain peaks, 490, 492, x 1162; Mountain ranges, 482; Hog backs, 487; Mountain parks, 525; Mountain barriers, 537; Mountain pass, 505, 506, 516; Water gap, 337, 339, 340, 1427; Anticline, 478, x 1592; Timber line, 544; Mature mountains, 549, 550, 556, 558; Monadnocks, 553, 554; Laccolith, 691; Mountain road, 509, x 241, x 1455; Mountain industry, x 1175, 532, 535; Mountain city, 528, x 226, x 1459; Faulting, 28, 1253, 1255, x 880; Earthquake effects, 697, 699, 705, 717, 718, 723, x 1763; Volcanic eruptions, 586, 595, 612, 614, 630, 639, 661; Volcanic eruptive material, 588, 640, 644, 665; Volcanic cones, 585, 592, 604, 628, 629, 653, 657, 659, 664, 1389, 1409, 1413, 1475, x 612; Craters, 584, 611, 672; Solfatara, 1404; Volcanic destruction, 573, 574; Pompeii, 616, 619, 620; Lava flows, 678, 680, 685; 686; Mud flow, 590; Crater lakes, 667, 668, 670, 1472; Volcanic necks, 675, 677; Lava palisades, 346; Volcanic island, x 1351; Geysers, 728, 731, 733, 737, 741; Hot springs, 747, 748, x 807; Mud volcanoes, 744; Snowfields, 753, 804; Névé, 759, 786, 787; Crevasses, 771, 1436, x 1171; Tidal glacier, 814, 818, 837, 1286; Icebergs, 860, 865; Piedmont glacier, 821, 822, 823, 826, 829, 833; Glacier table, 778; Débris cones, 775, 776; Ice cave, 792; Marginal lake, 1398; Glacial stream, 796, 830, 833, 957, 958, 1385; Glacier advance, 828; Glacier recession, 797; Glacial erosion, 875, 880, x 745, x 1219; Striated pebbles, 867, 868; Glacial striations, 870, 872, 1381; Roches moutonnées, 878, 879; Fiord, 1230; Glacial bowlders, 882, 884, 888, 889; Moraines, 762, 768, 770, 791, 812, 913, 920, 921, 925, 1367, 1397; Till, 891; Drumlins, 934, 935, 943, 945, 1383; Continental glaciation, 910, 911; Hanging valleys, 895, 898, 906; Kettle pond, 928, 930; Pitted plain, 959; Kames, 947; Eskers, 949, 953, 955; Sand plain, 965; Stream diversion, 963; Loess, 968, 1520; Lake basins, 973, 985, 987, 998, 1001; Lake overflow channel, 1050, 1369; Lake filling, 1011, 1013, 1016, 1019, 1037, x 1178; Swamps, 1024, 1028, 1029, 1032, 1391; Tides, 1089, 1091; Sinking coast, 1202, 1203, 1210, 1219; Harbors, 1212, 1214, 1222; Rising coast, 1233, 1236, 1240, 1249; Coral reefs, 1190, 1193, 1194, x 1578; Coast erosion, 1102, 1105, 1108, 1111, 1115, 1121, 1375, x 1797; Stack, 1155; Littoral deposits, 1128, 1141, 1142, x 1588; Bars, 1147, 1151, 1161, 1166, 1168, 1366, 1406; Salt marsh, 1176, 1183; Sunshine table, m 4; Isotherms, m 12; Temperature distribution, m 15, m 16, m 17, m 228; Cloudiness, m 61; Fog, m 82; Dew, m 69 a; Frost, m 79 a; x 1180; Clouds, x 1351, m 83, m 83 a, m 85, m 92, m 96, m 99 a, m 103, m 108; Sun drawing water, m 112; Midnight sun, m 116; Twilight, m 117; Lightning, m 119; Aurora, m 120; Planetary winds, m 23; Lows, m 32, m 33, m 36; Highs, m 37, m 38; Storm tracks, m 40, m 43; Rainfall, m 66, m 69; Snow, m 70 a, m 71, m 72, m 75; Thunderstorms, m 53; Tornadoes, m 50; m 51; Tropical cyclones, m 44, m 48; Foehn, m 56; Meteorological instruments, m 195, m 199; Weather districts, m 202; Climate, m 212, m 216, m 220, m 221, m 222, m 223, m 224, x 271, x 273, x 625, x 985, x 1049, x 1700: Sea ice, 1098, 1087; Niagara, n 5, n 62, n 70, n 76, n 77, 252, 254, 263, 269, 270, 271; Yellowstone, 280, 284; Yosemite, 288, 498, 499; Grand Canyon, 289, 300.

Valuable slides may also be had from other dealers. The subjects are not, however, ordinarily listed for physical geography classes. This makes selection more difficult.

APPENDIX K

FIELD WORK

Field work is so valuable that it should be included in every course in physical geography. No laboratory or textbook work can take the place of well-conducted field work; it is worth undertaking even if Saturday is the only time available for it. But a progressive school should provide regular periods for out-of-door work.

Directions of sufficient explicitness to be useful as a guide for field work cannot be given without taking up far more space than is available in this book. The kind of work to give is a question which can be settled only by local conditions; therefore the teacher must develop his own outline. There is no region without some good physiographic phenomena within easy reach. See Appendix L for detailed suggestions as to how the teacher may become informed as to the resources of the local region as indicated by published studies conducted by the national and state governments and other investigators.

To make proper use of these field opportunities, the teacher needs a personal knowledge of methods. There are, of course, many teachers of physical geography who have not had the training necessary for this work. Most summer schools in large universities offer instruction in this direction, and any teacher who desires to give field work, but lacks the necessary training, can secure it easily and at slight expense. Knowing how field work is conducted in one region, any real teacher can adapt the same methods to his own needs.

The introduction of laboratory work, indoors and out, places physical geography on a par with other science courses in the secondary school curriculum. Many of the better secondary schools provide for it and have specially equipped laboratories. The normal school or university course that does not include such work is now considered weak and unsatisfactory. A course in chemistry and physics that is solely a textbook course is now considered ridiculous; the same should be true of physical geography.

The following are some of the phenomena that are likely to be found within easy reach of a school. The great thing to make sure of on such excursions is that each student sees, observes, and recognizes that a phenomenon seen in the field is the same thing as that described in the text and in how many details it fits to the text description. Thus the text is made to serve its real purpose, that of being a guide to the understanding of the actual occurrences. If after that any safe deductions can be made as to the significance of the feature in the interpretation of the general physiography of the region a very great deal will have been gained from the excursion. (1) *Illustrations of weathering:* cliffs, ledges, bowlders, old stone or brick buildings. (2) *Nature of country rock:* in river valleys, railway cuts, quarries. In such places stratification, joint planes, folding and faulting, and fossils may possibly be found.

(3) *The soil:* for characteristics and depth, look in cuts, as in (2). Is it a soil of rock decay or transported? If the former, study its origin in the cut. If the latter, how transported? (4) *River transportation:* road gutters, plowed fields, small wet-weather streams, — nature of action, load carried, disposition of load, result of removal. Fine examples of young stream valleys, alluvial fans, deltas, and waterfalls (over pebbles) are very often found in a road, field, or railway cut. (5) *River action and valley formation:* source of water; variation in volume; sediment load; variation; source of sediment; temporary disposal of it, — on stream bed, in bars, in flood plains, etc.; place of final deposit of sediment; effect of removal of sediment on valley form. The entire subject of river action and life history of valleys may be built up around one or two field excursions to a near by stream. It is not necessary to have grand waterfalls or broad flood plains. A meadow brook has its full lesson. In some places it will be possible to build a dam across a small stream and so divert the flow of the water. Then on a visit to the site·made some time later the changes effected by the stream processes may be noted, and the fact of the occurrence of such changes convincingly realized by the pupils. (6) *Shore lines:* a lake shore or the sea shore; even a river bank or the shore of a pond may serve. What are the waves doing? What changes have they wrought? Why are the pebbles round? Where has the ground-off material gone? What is the source of the pebbles or sand? Which way are they moving? Are there bars, wave-cut cliffs, small stream deltas, shore swamps? Perhaps there are all, possibly only one; in the latter case study that, even though it may seem very insignificant. (7) *Glacial phenomena:* striæ; till banks, — in railway or other cuts; nature of material; scratched stones, etc. Are the pebbles or bowlders foreign, *i.e.,* unlike the country rock? Is the till unstratified? Why? Find cuts of stratified drift — evidence of water action. There may be moraines, kames, eskers, or drumlins.

Besides these there may be plains, or mountains, or plateaus, or volcanic phenomena. If so, so much the better; but profitable field work does not necessarily demand grand features. It will be well to have most of the excursions devoted to details and the study of principles; hence a seemingly small illustration may be of the very highest value. At the same time, the field work should not entirely ignore the broad, general features. A very profitable excursion may be conducted in a high tower, or on a high hill overlooking the surrounding country.

Field excursions should be made for the purpose of showing the relationship between physiographic phenomena and human interests. They may often be combined with the other excursions suggested above. For example, an excursion might well consider the reason for the location and the nature of work in a quarry; the location and the difficulties in the way of laying a railway, *i.e.,* the cuts, tunnels, etc., necessary; the differences in the soil and their relation to plant life, and especially to crops; the location of mills, etc. Here again the broad influences of physiographic conditions should not be overlooked. By all means the field work should show clearly the significance of the location and development of the home town and its industries.

APPENDIX L

REFERENCE BOOKS

The first thing that a teacher of physical geography should do when beginning work at a given school is to write to a number of sources from which publications or references in regard to the physical geography of the *local region* may be obtained. On application the "Director, U. S. Geological Survey, Washington, D. C." will send a list of the Survey publications relating to the region with directions as to how they may be obtained. Some of these publications to which a price is attached may be had free of charge for the school by applying to the local congressman, the representative for the district, and advising him what publications are wanted. Next write to the State Library at the Capital of the State and get such publications as may be published by it or by the State Geological or Natural History Survey. Many state libraries, for example that of New York State at Albany, will loan a book or magazine containing a paper of interest, or will make photostat copies of it at low cost. For a list of publications in geographic and other magazines privately published relating to the local physiography, a request sent to the Library of Congress, Division of Geography, Washington, D. C., or to the National Research Council, Division of Geography and Geology, Washington, D. C., will probably be fruitful. The Library of Congress will loan publications from its very complete collection to any local public library on request of the local librarian. By these means a teacher ought to be able to inform himself in regard to special studies that may have been made in the locality of the school.

The reference books listed at the end of each chapter deal in part, if not entirely, with the topic treated in that chapter. But as these are fairly numerous and of different degrees of pertinence and difficulty there follows a list which should be useful as a guide in building up collections. For no subject is it possible to obtain so wide a list of useful and interesting books at low cost as it is for physical geography, yet no subject is so poorly represented in the average school library. This situation ought to be corrected. There will be a great increase in the interest of the class if the textbook study can be supplemented by more extended readings in books of a readily accessible reference library.

This list is intended to be a suggestion as to the books that should be secured first in building up a classroom or school library in physical geography. More extended lists covering the different topics of the subject are placed at the ends of the appropriate chapters.

The letters P and T placed before each title indicate whether the book is more suitable for Pupil or Teacher reading. However, all of them may be used to advantage by pupils for investigation of special topics. The order of listing follows, in general, the chapter succession.

P. JOHNSON, *Mathematical Geography*, American Book Company, New York, 1907.

P. TODD, *New Astronomy*, American Book Company, New York, 1897.

P. GRONDAL, *The Music of the Spheres*, The Macmillan Company, New York, 1926.

T. JONES, *General Astronomy*, Longmans Green & Company, New York, 1922.

T. McCABE, *The Wonders of the Stars*, G. P. Putnam's Sons, New York, 1923.

P. MERRILL, *Rocks, Rock Weathering and Soils*, The Macmillan Company, New York, 1906.

T.P. PIRRSON and SCHUCHERT, *Textbook of Geology*, 2 vols., John Wiley & Sons, New York, 1924.

P. LYON and BUCKMAN, *Nature and Properties of Soils*, The Macmillan Company, New York, 1922.

T. PIRRSON, *Rocks and Rock Minerals*, John Wiley & Sons, New York, 1908.

P. HOBBS, *Earth Features and their Meaning*, The Macmillan Company, New York, 1912.

T. JOHNSON, *Shore Processes and Shoreline Development*, John Wiley & Sons, New York, 1919.

T. JOHNSON, *The New England-Acadian Shoreline*, John Wiley & Sons, New York, 1925.

T. DALY, *Igneous Rocks and their Origin*, McGraw-Hill Company, New York, 1914.

P. HOBBS, *Characteristics of Existing Glaciers*, The Macmillan Company, New York, 1911.

P. COLEMAN, *Ice Ages*, The Macmillan Company, New York, 1926.

T. WRIGHT, *The Quaternary Ice Age*, The Macmillan Company, New York, 1914.

P. SCOTT, *Scott's Last Expedition*, 2 vols., Smith, Elder & Company, London, 1914.

P. STEFANSSON, *The Friendly Arctic*, The Macmillan Company, New York, 1921.

P. JOHNSTONE, *An Introduction to Oceanography*, Hodder & Stoughton, London, 1923.

T. MARMER, *The Tides*, D. Appleton & Company, New York, 1926.

P. MILHAM, *Meteorology*, The Macmillan Company, New York, 1912.

P. TALMAN, *Meteorology, The Science of the Atmosphere*, P. F. Collier & Sons Company, New York, 1922.

T. KENDREW, *The Climates of the Continents*, Oxford University Press, Oxford, 1922.

P. WARD, *The Climates of the United States*, Ginn and Company, Boston, 1925.

T. HUNTINGTON, *Civilization and Climate*, Yale University Press, New Haven, 1923.

T. VON ENGELN, *Inheriting the Earth*, The Macmillan Company, New York, 1922.

P. SMITH, *North America*, Harcourt, Brace & Company, New York, 1925.

T. BOWMAN, *Forest Physiography*, John Wiley & Sons, New York, 1911.

P. CAMPBELL, *Plant Geography*, The Macmillan Company, New York, 1926.

P. GADOW, *Wanderings of Animals*, Cambridge University Press, Cambridge, 1913.

T. PEARSE, *Animal Ecology*, McGraw-Hill Company, New York, 1926.

T. HADDON, *Races of Man*, The Macmillan Company, New York, 1925.

T. RIPLEY, *Races of Europe*, 2 vols., D. Appleton & Company, New York, 1899.

T. LOBECK, *Block Diagrams*, John Wiley & Sons, New York, 1924.

APPENDIX M

TEACHING SUGGESTIONS

It is customary for the author, usually in the Preface, to offer suggestions on methods of teaching. These suggestions are then accompanied by some words of apology to the effect that competent teachers are of course free to follow their own devices and by so doing will unquestionably achieve good results. The author of this revision is of the settled conviction from experience with many secondary-school teachers that such apologies are uncalled for; that, on the contrary, most teachers welcome and are grateful for specific instructions on what to do and how to do it. The few who do find the inclusion of such advice irritating will be spurred on to better teaching according to their own methods, partly in order to prove the superiority of these. Accordingly only good can result from the insertion of these Teaching Suggestions.

For a half year or a junior high-school course in Physical Geography it is suggested that pupils be expected to master only the paragraphs and sections in coarse print. The fine print matter should be read and commented upon in such classes but not be emphasized in recitations nor should examination questions be based on it. But if a full high-school year is given to the study of Physical Geography (and the subject deserves a full year's course) all the content of the book should be well studied. In this connection the attention of teachers is called to the treatment given in this book to "tides" and to the complete discussion of "rotational deflection," the latter sometimes referred to as Ferrel's Law. The account of the tides and other topics of similar import are included as appendices. But this heading Appendix does not mean that the matter there presented may be disregarded. Instead the subject matter appendices as used in this book are simply a convenience of organization. Really they are chapters containing material that would too much interrupt the narrative flow of the regular succession of chapters. The appendices should be studied appropriately at that point in the course where their content first becomes necessary to satisfactory understanding of other topics. The appendix form therefore should suggest to the teacher and the class the necessity for special application to a particular study task.

Although the practice is universally condemned by educators the fact remains that in many classes the textbook is used principally to learn answers to examination questions. There is no intention here of commending the practice but it should be recognized that in making a beginning in a new branch of knowledge, scientific or philosophical, the pupil is confronted with the task of learning a new alphabet and a new vocabulary. Part of the study must therefore be mnemonic. In part the great success achieved by the original edition of *New Physical Geography* was owing to the fact that its organization facilitated the mastery of these fundamentals. That organization and arrangement has been retained in the new issue. Specifically, it may be suggested that if students learn to give definitions of italicized words and terms, and to repeat the matter of the Summaries they will have a memory basis for passing examinations. But — and this is a very important but — in recitations the purpose should be to lead the students to an understanding of the phrases they repeat and an ability to express in their own language the ideas, concepts, and relations the definitions and Summaries present.

If the teacher is called upon to urge the inclusion of Physical Geography in the curriculum, or to defend its place there, he needs only to point out that this is the only introduction the average student will ever get to the natural world in which the rest of life is spent. Also that opposition to such study comes mainly because of the lamentable ignorance of what is involved on the part of the opponents, due to the defects of their own training. In this contention is found the immediate justification of the astronomical chapter at the beginning of the book. That is probably the single contact through systematic study that the great majority will ever have with the vast and fascinating science of the universe outside the earth. Some comprehension of this universe is essential to an understanding of the relative significance of our own world and its phenomena.

Study of the remainder of the book may to advantage be topically arranged with reference to the regional environment of the school. Thus in a small town or rural high school the chapters may quite appropriately be taken up in succession in the order of the book, those on lands first, then water, then the atmosphere. In an urban or metropolitan high school the chapters on the atmosphere and climate may well be studied first. By making a beginning with a topic that has a marked and significant reality in the school environment the observational basis of the study can be immediately established.

The chapter on glaciers is especially rich and full because so much of the United States, and in fact much of the world of western civilization, experienced a great glacial episode in the immediate physiographic past. The consequence of this visitation is that over all the areas affected there is striking evidence of the action of continental glaciers in what are now temperate lands. Also the early life and development of European man was undoubtedly very greatly influenced by the advance and retreat of these prehistoric ice sheets. Comprehension of the nature and phenomena, of the Ice Age would appear to be an essential in the mental equipment of those who wish to be informed.

Practically every point made in the book is illustrated in some way, by photographs, by drawings, by maps. Each illustration is supplied with a complete explanatory legend. Hence the pictures as well as the text should be systematically studied. Tests on how well the pictures are understood may readily be conducted through the use of lantern slides as described in Appendix J.

Another feature is the inclusion of cross references all through the text. In this way both the correlating text passages and the illustrations in other parts of the book are constantly called to the attention of the student. Pedagogical experts proclaim against teachers depending solely on a text-book in presenting a subject. Their objections are met completely by this cross reference plan. Through regular use of the cross references the subject is developed as a coherent whole, and the student gains power to analyze and to interpret complex phenomena as they present themselves in the field. Project problems may readily be developed through use of the cross references and the index at the back of the book.

Excursions may to advantage be made first into the photographic illustrations of the text. If students learn to recognize phenomena as presented in these pictures and in supplementary lantern slides the way is paved for profitable field work. On a field excursion let the purpose be double, first to recognize various phenomena and see processes in operation, then to learn their significance and consequences. If a small stream is observed to be cutting into its bank, the next step will be to reason what the effect of such action will be eventually, then what is the significance of the phenomenon as applied to a larger stream, to all streams. All this should be brought out by question and answer, and by directing the attention and observations of the students to the subject of study. Do not lecture in the field. Excursion work is admittedly the most difficult phase of physical geography teaching. Any teacher who is confident that he does that well may be equally sure that the rest of his teaching of the subject is likewise effective.

INDEX